W9-BBF-663

Date Issued

WITHDRAWN
NDSU

A PUBLICATION ISSUED ON THE OCCASION OF
YALE'S 250TH ANNIVERSARY

A CATALOGUE OF MANUSCRIPTS
IN THE COLLECTION OF
WESTERN AMERICANA
IN THE
YALE UNIVERSITY LIBRARY

William Robertson Coe

A

CATALOGUE OF MANUSCRIPTS

IN THE COLLECTION OF

WESTERN AMERICANA

FOUNDED BY

WILLIAM ROBERTSON COE

YALE UNIVERSITY LIBRARY

COMPILED

by

MARY C. WITHINGTON

NEW HAVEN · YALE UNIVERSITY PRESS

LONDON · GEOFFREY CUMBERLEGE · OXFORD UNIVERSITY PRESS

1952

103819

Copyright, 1952, by Yale University Press

Printed in the United States of America

All rights reserved. This book may not be
reproduced, in whole or in part, in any form
(except by reviewers for the public press),
without written permission from the publishers.

LIBRARY OF CONGRESS CATALOG CARD NUMBER: 52-5370

Z
1251
W5
Y3

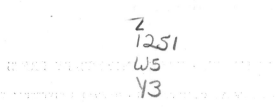

INTRODUCTION

FUTURE generations of scholars will praise the foresight and tenacity of Mr. William Robertson Coe in forming his magnificent collection of books, manuscripts, maps, newspapers, and pamphlets on the history of the United States west of the Mississippi River, as well as his generosity in placing this collection in a large research library and providing funds for its care and growth.

Mr. Coe believes that through the study of our past we can best get a proper understanding of the true values in the development of this country. His interest in the West was intensified by his purchase in 1910 from Colonel Cody (Buffalo Bill) of his ranch in Wyoming. The Rt. Rev. Nathaniel S. Thomas, Bishop of Wyoming, became a close friend and in working with him for the betterment of Wyoming Mr. Coe's interest in Western history became one of his major avocations. He early called in the services of Edward Eberstadt, the leading dealer in Western Americana, to advise and help him, and this association continues and is responsible for the strength of the collection. Since Mr. Coe takes every opportunity to add important material to the collection, this catalogue becomes immediately out of date on publication.

In his collecting he has covered a wide area, but it should be said that he has not specialized in material on the Southwest. However, the scholar interested in that area should not neglect the collection.

This catalogue is of the manuscripts in Mr. Coe's collection and all other comparable manuscripts already in the Yale University Library. The major portion of the latter come from the Pacific Northwest Collection of Winlock W. Miller, Jr., a distinguished member of the Class of 1928 at Yale and Yale Law School 1931, and the youngest trustee of the Yale Library Associates at the time. Mr. Miller was the third generation of a family important in the history of the Pacific Northwest and was fast becoming a valuable citizen of Seattle when his career was cut off in 1939 by death. He very early in life became interested in the history of the Pacific Northwest and avidly searched out original material. His success can be attested by the collection of books, pamphlets, maps, and manuscripts which was given to Yale by Winlock W. Miller, Yale, 1894, in fulfillment of his son's wish.

Not included in this catalogue are the manuscripts on the West among the papers of Othniel C. Marsh, Professor of Paleontology at Yale, 1866–1899. They are housed in the Peabody Museum of Natural History. Nor are some 900 manuscripts on Texas and the Southwest included, which were acquired by the University Library from Henry R. Wagner, Yale 1884, in 1919. They can be described briefly as follows:

1690–1756. Nine manuscripts, the most notable being the 200-page "Relacion" of the discovery of the "New Kingdom of Leon," dealing with the early exploration and settlement of the Spaniards and ending with a description of a French town which they found already there in 1689.

1784–1804. 40 manuscripts, including a group of letters of Spanish governors on aspects and details of trade with the Indians and Americans; and another group describing natural conditions and settlements in various districts.

1801–   140 manuscripts bearing on Philip Nolan's disastrous expedition, around which is built Edward Everett Hale's well-known story, *Philip Nolan's Friends*. These documents include accounts of the trial by the Spaniards of the American survivors, with many depositions, and, of particular interest, the diary of the leader of the Spanish expeditionary force that captured the American party.

1805–1816. 15 documents bearing on Wilkinson's dealings, as governor of Louisiana, with the Spanish officials of Texas, including several Wilkinson letters.

1812. 18 documents bearing on disturbances incidental to the War of 1812.

1822, January–September. Over 300 letters and incidental documents exchanged between Antoneo Martinez, the governor, and Gaspar Lopez, the military commander of Texas, all dealing more or less with the earliest stages of the permanent American colonization, which began in December 1821, under Austin's leadership. This group has fullness and unity and throws interesting light on American "peaceful penetration" and its effect on the penetrated.

1825–1840. About 250 additional letters and documents, among them a number of letters to Stephen F. Austin, and a group from 1834 to 1835 of over 100 letters and documents of Mexican officials and American leaders, illustrating the inception and growth of the movement for Texan independence.

1825–1846. A considerable number of manuscripts of the Swiss naturalist Berlandier, supplementing the Berlandier manuscripts in the Library of Congress.

The Wagner manuscripts, while not as a rule of great importance individually, as a whole give a vivid picture of the political manners, methods, ideas, and actions of the time, a knowledge of which cannot be found in books and is essential to a thorough understanding of the period. Additional Mexican manuscripts have been acquired in recent years.

Some of the more extensive groups of manuscripts in this catalogue are those on the Mormons; on the Pacific Northwest, with records of the early missions; on the Hudson's Bay Company; the Governor Isaac I. Stevens and Elwood Evans papers; the papers of Granville Stuart of Montana, H. Miles Moore and John W. Geary of Kansas; and the overland diaries and journals of 1849 and the early 'fifties. There are a number of important maps, particularly those drawn by William Clark on the Lewis and Clark Expedition, and early pictorial representations of many places and individuals by such artists as Paul Kane and Alfred J. Miller.

All manuscripts in the Yale University Library, except those with restrictions placed on them by donors, are available to qualified scholars for study. The manuscript rooms in the Library are open usually from 8:30 A.M. to 5 P.M. Monday through Friday. Advance notification of the visit by a scholar will often expedite his work. Permission to publish or quote from any manuscript owned by the Yale University Library must be secured from the librarian. The Library has complete photographic equipment for the reproduction of manuscripts.

JAMES T. BABB
LIBRARIAN.

EDITOR'S NOTE

THE chief purpose of this catalogue is to make available to scholars information on the extent of source material not only in the Coe Collection but in the Yale University Library as a whole. When, in 1942, William Robertson Coe gave to the Yale Library the first instalment of his collection on Western American History, which consisted entirely of manuscript material, inquiries and questions about the contents of the collection began to pour in to the Library. During the years that I have been preparing this catalogue, I have seen the type of question that has been received, and I have tried in the descriptions of the manuscripts and through the index to answer as many such questions as possible.

The general plan of the catalogue is an alphabetical arrangement by author, or, in some cases, by the subject or collector of a group of manuscripts. The arrangement within each group varies with the nature of the manuscripts. In the case of papers of a single person, diaries or journals are followed by letters by the writer, letters to him, and, finally, other manuscripts. Manuscripts on a special topic are arranged either chronologically or alphabetically by the writer, whichever seemed more logical.

Each entry consists of the full name of the writer when it could be determined, the subject of the manuscript, or a group heading; a title, quoted, if the manuscript itself has a title; the number of volumes or/and pages, and the size; a brief biographical note about the writer; a description of the subject and scope of the manuscript or manuscripts; the contents, if a group of letters, documents, or other papers; a note of the provenance and publication if known, but no attempt has been made to search newspaper files; and, at the end, a reference to the collection to which the manuscript belongs.

The manuscripts and books in the Coe Collection have been given to the Library in several sections, and with each section has come a typewritten catalogue prepared for Mr. Coe by Edward Eberstadt. As scholars have been and are using the manuscripts continuously and have referred to them in their publications by the numbers in the Eberstadt catalogues, that number has been added in the final note (e.g., Coe No. 295, or Coe No. IV, 430). The most recent accessions have had no individual numbers.

Limitations of space have made it impossible to list in detail all deeds, documents, business letters, bills, receipts, etc., in the individual collections of manuscripts, but the names of the signers of such deeds or documents are included in the index. In listing correspondence if a letter is not in the signer's hand "Signature only" is added.

In preparing the index no attempt has been made to cover every detail as one would in editing a single manuscript. The index includes the full name and dates (when they can be determined) of the authors of the manuscripts; the writers and recipients of letters; signers of documents, except petitions and other long lists; the names of people frequently mentioned, especially if their names appear in several different manuscripts; the names of leaders of expeditions if a manuscript is an account or journal by a member of the expedition, even if the leader is not mentioned by name; the names of places if they are described at some length; the routes followed by overland emigrants or expeditions; the names of ships; and events or subjects discussed in detail. Original drawings, paintings, and maps are also listed in the index under those headings.

The index does not include the names of relatives, friends, and places in the East, even if frequently mentioned in letters or journals; or the names of editors or titles of publications based on the manuscripts, or names of periodicals unless printed copies accompany the manuscripts.

If a manuscript has been edited and published in full, with an extensive index, it has not been as fully indexed in this catalogue as have the unpublished manuscripts.

I wish to express to Mr. Babb my deep appreciation and thanks for the privilege of preparing this catalogue, and of devoting the last few years of my long association with the Yale University Library to such an interesting and congenial task.

I also thank Mr. Kenefick and his assistants in the Circulation Department, Miss Wynne and Miss Stuart of the Rare Book Room, Mrs. Powers of the Historical Manuscripts Collection, Miss Hill of Yale Memorabilia, the members of the Reference Department, Mrs. Dejon of the Catalogue Department, and Mr. Winkler, Mr. Hanna, and Mrs. Taylor of the Coe Collection of Western Americana for their patience and helpfulness; and especially Mr. James R. Tanis, Mrs. Winfield Shiras, and Miss Dorothy W. Bridgwater, whose assistance and advice have been most valuable.

I wish, too, to express my appreciation and thanks to Charles E. von Rhein for his help in securing information for me in Portland, Ore.

MARY C. WITHINGTON

☞ MAP OF THE UNITED STATES WEST OF THE MISSISSIPPI, PP. 168–169

A CATALOGUE OF MANUSCRIPTS

OF WESTERN AMERICANA

---

1 ABERNETHY, ALEXANDER S.

Letter to H. A. Goldsborough. Oak Point, W.T., November 28, 1860.

4 pp. 25 cm.

A. S. Abernethy, brother of George, arrived in Oregon in 1850. He was a member of the second legislative assembly of Washington Territory and of the Constitutional Convention of 1878.

The letter is about a candidate for the next election of a delegate to Congress and discusses at length the qualifications of George Gibbs.

[Miller Collection.]

2 ACKLEY, RICHARD THOMAS, 1832–1881

"A trip across the plains in 1858 by Richard Thomas Ackley of Camden, N.J. Born 1832. Died 1881. A young man of 26 years of age." [Title in pencil in a later hand.]

48 pp. 41 cm. With typewritten transcript.

Journal of a journey from Sidney, Fremont County, Iowa, June 21, 1858, with Thomas A. Atkins, Jim S. Packard, and Oliver Scoggins, who left the party July 20 for the Pikes Peak gold field, by Nebraska City, Platte River, Fort Kearney, Fort Laramie, Fort Bridger, Echo Cañon, to Salt Lake City, and an account of his stay in Salt Lake City, Camp Floyd, and Millersville, to July 1859.

The journal was written at some later date, probably in 1865, because the writer has frequently written 1865 and altered it to 1858; the entries are not always in chronological order and some events are repeated. This has been corrected in the transcript. Some place names, dates, and annotations have been added in the manuscript in a later hand.

The journal occupies 48 pages of a daybook used to record sales of lumber and other building materials at Camden, N.J., by Ackley and Wharton, January 1855 to September 1856. Two entries, May 23, 1855 and September 1, 1856, are signed by R. T. Ackley, and some of the entries appear to be in his hand.

The journal is followed by the records of the Perseverance Fire Co. No. 1, 1848–1860, with some notes of its transactions, 1819–1850, and lists of members.

The journal is printed in full with title: "Across the Plains in 1858. By Richard Thomas Ackley of Camden, New Jersey. Born 1832. Died 1881." *Utah Historical Quarterly*, 1941, IX, 190–228.

[Coe No. 1.]

3 ALBION (Ship)

Twenty-five documents and letters relating to the seizure of the British ship *Albion* in Puget Sound, April 22, 1850, for cutting spars on the American side of the Strait of Juan de Fuca in violation of the revenue laws, 1849–1850.

47 pp. 23–33 cm.

The collection consists of copies of the Certificate of Registry of the *Albion*, 1831, "charter-party" agreements, invoices and inventories, insurance policies, and a letter from J. Dundas to E. Swinton, Admiralty, April 23, 1844, with prices agreed on for spars and enclosing a sketch of the hold; and of the following letters and documents relating to the seizure of the *Albion* with a "List of papers left with Mr. Rockwell":

BARCLAY, ARCHIBALD. Letter to James Douglas at Fort Victoria. Hudson's Bay House, London, March 23, 1849. 2 pp.

LIDGETT, JOHN. Letter of instructions to Captain Brotchie. London, March 22, 1849. 3 pp.

—— Letter of instructions to Captain Hinderwell. London, March 23, 1849. 4 pp.

—— Letter to the Secretary of the Hudson's Bay Company [A. Barclay]. London, October 15, 1849; and, on the same sheet, a letter of instructions to Captain Brotchie at Vancouver's Island, October 18, 1849. 2 pp.

—— Remarks on the letters from Captain Hindewell [*sic*] and Brotchie, also Mr. Dorr's letter on seizure. 3 pp.

—— Letter to Sir Henry Lytton Bulwer, K.C.B. Washington, D.C., March 13, 1851. Signed by his attorney, John J. Lidgett. 2 pp.

HINDERWELL, RICHARD O. Copy of the Petition to the Honorable William Strong, Judge of the District Court of the United States for the District of Oregon, for the remission of the for-feiture of the *Albion*, with his affidavit of the truth of the statements, sworn before James C. Strong, Clerk, November 2, 1850; accompanied by the "Objections to Petition" by Amory Holbrook, U.S. District Attorney, and a letter from R. O. Hinderwell to John Lidgett, Port Vancouver, Columbia, November 10, 1850. 7 pp.

[BULWER, *Sir* HENRY LYTTON] Draft or copy of an unsigned letter to Thomas Corwin, Secretary of the Treasury, calling attention again to the case of the *Albion*. Washington, March 14, 1851. 3 pp.

"Case of Jno. Lidgett, Esq. for remission of forfeiture, &c. in relation to Ship 'Albion.'" Memorandum of acts and laws applicable to the case. Unsigned but may be in the same hand as the preceding letter. 1 p.

The manuscripts are accompanied by the *Message of the President of the United States, Communicating . . . the correspondence in relation to the Seizure of the British Ship Albion, in Oregon, for a Violation of the Revenue Laws*, with marginal notes in manuscript (31st Congress, 2d Session, Senate Ex. Doc. No. 30, February 15, 1851).

Sir Henry Lytton Bulwer was at the time British Ambassador at Washington. Mr. Rockwell, to whom the papers were sent, was probably Julius Rockwell, Member of Congress for Massachusetts and a member of the Committee on Territories.

The first three letters listed are printed in the Senate Ex. Doc. No. 30, pp. 20–22.

[Coe No. III, 5.]

4 ALTON, HIRAM, 1838?–

Journal of an overland journey from Ohio to California, a year's stay in California, and the return journey by the Isthmus of Panama, April 6, 1864 to November 22, 1865.

172 pp. 15 cm. Original binding. With typewritten transcript.

The journal describes the route from Columbus, Ohio, to St. Louis, Leavenworth, Fort Kearney, the South Platte River, Cache La Poudre, Fort Laramie, Fort Bridger, Salt Lake City, the old Mormon Route to the Humboldt and Truckee Rivers, to Sacramento. Alton worked as a bullwhacker on a freight train to the Idaho gold fields from Leavenworth to Cache La Poudre, where the expedition broke up, then joined a horse train for California, arriving September 28; after a winter in San Pablo and a stay in San Francisco, he sailed October 30, 1865 for Panama.

[Coe No. 2.]

5 ANDERSON, ALEXANDER CAULFIELD, 1814–1884

"Historical notes on the commerce of the Columbia River, 1824 to 1848." Victoria, B.C., September 14, 1880. Signed: "A.C.A."

6 pp. 34 cm.

A. C. Anderson was a clerk for the Hudson's Bay Company when he arrived in Fort Vancouver in 1832. He served the company in the New Caledonia district, at Fort Nisqually and Colville, and Fort Vancouver again until 1854, when he retired and settled at Cathlamet. In 1858 he moved to Vancouver Island.

The notes have no title but are endorsed in Elwood Evans' hand: "Hon. Alex C. Anderson. Sept. 14, 1880," with the title quoted above. The notes are accompanied by a newspaper clipping, "Pioneer Ships," with passages numbered to correspond with Anderson's comments.

[Miller Collection.]

6 ANDERSON, THOMAS McARTHUR, 1836–1917

"Army episodes and anecdotes; or Life at Vancouver Barracks. The romance and the reality of the frontier." 1853–1893.

200 pp. 27 cm. With typewritten transcript.

General Anderson was colonel of the 14th Infantry and in command at Vancouver Barracks for a number of years.

The manuscript includes a list of chapters, a summary of 18 chapters and an appendix, and the complete text of Chapters 4, 6, 8, 10, 14, 17 and Appendices 1–3, 5. These chapters deal with the history of Vancouver Barracks, the Indian wars, the San Juan Islands boundary dispute, and the death of General Canby; the appen-

dices contain copies of letters from Dr. William C. McKay; a letter from Ranald Macdonald; General C. C. Augur's account of the wars in southern Oregon; and a list of deceased officers who served at Vancouver Barracks, 1849–1893.

Chapter 11, which is not included in the manuscript but is in the list of chapters with the title: "The Mission of St. James" and summarized in the synopsis of the contents, was probably used by Colonel

Anderson for his article, "The Vancouver Reservation Case. A Legal Romance," in the *Quarterly* of the Oregon Historical Society, 1907, VIII, 219–230.

[Coe No. 3.]

7 ANDREWS, D. B.

Journal of an overland journey from Indiana to California, March 30 to August 16, 1852.

84 pp. 29½ cm. Original binding. With typewritten transcript.

The journal describes the route from Perry, Ind., to St. Louis, St. Joseph, the Platte and Sweetwater Rivers, Kinney's Cut-off, Raft River, and the Humboldt and Truckee route to the American Valley and Nelson Creek, Calif., the country, animal life, camping places, and alternate routes; and is followed by a list of the amount of gold washed each day from August 24 to September 16, 1852, accounts, and memoranda.

[Coe No. 4.]

8 ANGELL, JOHN CARPENTER, 1818–1904

Ten letters to his mother, Mrs. Mary Angell, of Clyde, Wayne County, New York, and two to his brother. January 1, 1848 to December 1, 1850.

12 letters. 58 pp. 25–27½ cm.

John Carpenter Angell graduated from Yale College in 1847, spent a year traveling in the interests of the *American Journal of Science* for Professor Silliman, and in 1849 sailed for California by way of Cape Horn.

The first three letters were written in 1848 while Angell was traveling in the South. On January 15, 1849, he wrote from New York giving his reasons for going to California and his plan to sail on the *Pacific;* the next three letters were mailed from Rio de Janeiro, February 23–March 26, and Callao, Peru, May 12–June 8; and five were from San Francisco, August 10, 1849–December 1, 1850.

The letters describe the voyage, the delay in Rio when the U.S. consul arranged a change of captains, the arrival in San Francisco in August, a visit to Sacramento, and two months in Oregon.

Gift of Stephen H. Angell.
[Yale Memorabilia, Class of 1847.]

9 APPLEGATE, GEORGE W.

Twenty-three letters from George W. Applegate and two from his father, Lisbon Applegate, about events on their journey to California by Panama in 1849, and life in California and at the mines, December 9, 1849 to May 24, 1891.

82 pp. 20–31½ cm. With typewritten transcript of the letters written from 1849 to 1854.

Lisbon Applegate, brother of Jesse Applegate, and his sons, George W. and John, left Keytesville, Mo., for California in 1849. After failing in the mines they were employed on the construction of the Bear River Canal. Lisbon, in 1854, returned to his family and home in Keytesville; George visited St. Louis and his home in the winter of 1852–1853, but returned to Placer County, Calif., and became a farmer at Applegate.

Besides describing events and living conditions in California the letters discuss financial problems of Lisbon Applegate and family affairs.

APPLEGATE, GEORGE W. 21 letters to his brother, Lewis M. Applegate. December 9, 1849–May 24, 1891. 67 pp.

—— Letter to his father. October 20, 21, 1854. 4 pp.

—— Letter to his brother, James L. Applegate. January 15, 1878. 4 pp.

APPLEGATE, LISBON. Two letters to his son, Lewis M. Applegate. January 7, 1850, February 25, 1852. 7 pp.
[Coe Collection.]

10 APPLEGATE, JESSE, 1811–1888

Six letters to his brother, Lisbon Applegate, of Missouri. September 9, 1830 to October 11, 1847.

16 pp. 25½–33 cm. With typewritten transcript.

Jesse Applegate joined the 1843 emigration to Oregon from Missouri, in 1845 was the leader of the party that opened the southern road, or "Applegate Trail," into Oregon by the Rogue and Humboldt Rivers, and was a member of the committee that established the Provisional Government in Oregon in 1845.

The letters discuss family affairs, land transactions, literature and politics, the organization of the Provisional Government for Oregon Territory, his exploration for a new route from Fort Hall to the Willamette, and his life in Oregon.

Four of these letters are published in part in Maude A. Rucker, *The Oregon Trail and Some of Its Blazers*, New York, 1930, pp. 219–221, 221–225, 230–239, 242–247.

[Coe No. 5.]

11 APPLEGATE, JESSE, 1811–1888

Three letters to Archibald McKinlay, Yoncalla, Umpqua Co., O. T., May 3, 1850 to October 30, 1857; and a letter to Allan and McKinlay, Yoncalla, Umpqua Valley, January 16, 1857.

17 pp. 24½–31½ cm.

The letters discuss personal affairs, the mines in southern Oregon and the development of the Umpqua Valley, his suggestion that Allan & McKinlay open a branch of their business in southern Oregon, and his relations with John B. Preston, Surveyor General of Oregon.

—— Letter to William H. Farrar, April 20, 1862. 1 p.

The letter is in answer to one asking for Applegate's reminiscences for Mr. Evans for use in compiling his history of the Pacific Northwest.

[Miller Collection.]

12 ARTEAGA, IGNACIO

"Relacion del viaje echo ala alaska pr. las fragatas de su Magd. la princesa y la favorita—mandada aquelta pr. el comandante de la expedicion y theniente de navio de la Real armada Dn. Ignacio Artheaga; siendo su segundo dela misma clase el Sr. Dn. Fernando Quiros y Miranda, y capitan de la favorita el oficial del mismo grado el [word crossed out] Dn. Jun. Francisco de la Bodega y Quadra . . ." 1779.

5 pp. 29½ cm.

Account of Arteaga's expedition from San Blas, February 11, 1779, to continue and complete the discoveries made by Quadra in 1775. He explored Bucareli Sound and the Northwest Coast as far as Mt. St. Elias, set sail July 28 on the return journey, stopping at Cape Mendocino and San Francisco, and sailed again, October 30 for San Blas.

The manuscript is endorsed: "Diario de la expedicion, que se hizo por Mandaño de 1779, hasta la altura de 54 grados, y fundacion de la Mission de Sn. Gabriel. Car. 5 Leg. 6 n. 12."

Arteaga's original diary is in the Archivo General de la Nacion in Mexico, and a copy is in the Archivo General in Spain. This manuscript is endorsed as belonging to some library [Archive 5, Bundle 6, No. 12] and probably belonged to the Library of the College of San Fernando at San Blas, from which the chaplains were sent to serve on the expeditions. That library was dispersed at the time of the reform in Mexico and many of the documents passed into the hands of José María Agreda, after whose death, about 1920, his library was sold. (Cf. H. R. Wagner, "Diary of Fray Benito Sierra," *California Historical Quarterly*, 1930, IX, 206, and Nos. 52, 53, 378 *infra*.)

[Coe No. 6.]

13 ASTOR, JOHN JACOB, 1763–1848

Eleven letters to James Monroe, Secretary of State, James Madison, President, and William Jones, Secretary of the Navy, concerning Astor's efforts to secure protection from the Government for his Pacific Fur Company post at Fort Astoria, 1813, with a wrapper addressed "To the Secretary of the Navy" and endorsed: "1813–1817. Astoria. John Jacob Astor relative to his settlement on Columbia River."

63 pp. 25 cm. With typewritten transcripts.

GALLATIN, ALBERT. Letter to William Jones, Secretary of the Navy, introducing Mr. Astor. January 10, 1813. 1 p.

ASTOR, JOHN JACOB. Letter to James Monroe, Secretary of State. February 1813, enclosing copies of letters and documents relating to the fur trade in the Northwest from Duncan McDougall and David and Robert Stuart to Astor, Fort Astoria, July 22, 1811; from David Thompson to McDougall, Stuart, and Stuart, Columbia River, July 15, 1811; McDougall, Stuart and Stuart to Thompson, Fort Astoria, July 16, 1811; extract from a letter to William McGillivray from the partners of the North West Fur Company [n.d.]; and a report on the *Isaac Todd*. 14 pp.

—— Eight letters to William Jones. April 6–August 23, 1813. 34 pp.

—— Letter to James Madison. July 27, 1813, giving an account of the founding of the American Fur Company, and enclosing a copy of a letter from Thomas Jefferson to Astor, May 24, 1812. 14 pp.

These letters have been edited by Dorothy W. Bridgwater and published in the *Yale University Library Gazette*, 1949, XXIV, 47–69, with the title: "John Jacob Astor relative to His Settlement on Columbia River."

[Coe No. 7.]

14 ASTOR, JOHN JACOB, 1763–1848

Letter to George Clinton, V.P. Newyork, March 9, 1808. Endorsed: "From Mr. Astor in relation to Indian trade &c. &c. &c."

2 pp. 25 cm.

The letter was written in answer to a letter of March 5, from Vice President Clinton, with regard to the founding of the American Fur Company.

[Coe No. 8.]

15 ATKINSON, HENRY, 1782–1842

Journal of the advance corps of the military branch of the Yellowstone Expedition, August 30, 1818 to July 10, 1820.

77 pp., including 2 plans in color. 33½ cm. Original binding. With typewritten transcript.

In 1818 Colonel Atkinson was put in command of the military branch of an expedition to explore the Upper Missouri to the mouth of the Yellowstone, and to establish military posts to protect the growing American fur trade and to control the Indians. On August 30, 1818, the 1st Battalion of the Rifle Regiment, under the command of Colonel Talbot Chambers, left its encampment at Belle Fontaine, proceeded up the river and reached Isle des Vaches October 18, where the winter was spent, with Captain Martin in command. By the spring of 1819 the original plan was abandoned, and Major Stephen H. Long, in command of the scientific branch of the expedition, was ordered to explore the Missouri and its principal branches. His party arrived at Isle des Vaches on the steamboat *Western Engineer* August 15 and proceeded to Council Bluffs. The military detachment, increased by the arrival of Colonel Atkinson, the 2d Battalion of the Rifles, and part of the 6th Infantry, resumed its journey up the river and encamped near Major Long, building Cantonment Missouri where the winter was spent.

The journal, mainly written by Lieutenant Thomas Kavanaugh, describes the journey, the hunting expeditions for food, the various travelers on the river, councils with the Indians, and life in the cantonments during the winters. It includes two drawings and copies of letters from the post surgeon about the serious epidemic of scurvy among the men at Cantonment Missouri in the winter and spring of 1820. The drawings and letters are:

"Plan of Martin's Cantonment on the Missouri" October 31, 1818. 20 x 33 cm.

"Cantonment Missouri" November 23, 1819. 40 x 33 cm.

GALE, JOHN. Letter to gentlemen [of the board of war, Major Humphreys, Major Foster, and Captain Magee]. February 25, 1820.

—— Three letters to Captain Magee. January 23–February 23, 1820.

—— Seven letters to Lieutenant Colonel Morgan. February 5–April 28, 1820.

The letter of February 5 is signed also by Wm. Mower, Surgeon, 6th Infantry.

The journal is followed by a three-page inventory of bedding in the hospital at Jefferson Barracks, September 5, 1830.

[Coe Collection.]

16 AUDUBON, JOHN WOODHOUSE, 1812–1862

"Memorandum of an agreement made and entered into this 27 day of January in the year of our Lord one thousand eight hundred and forty-nine." Between Henry L. Webb, John W. Audubon and Henry C. Mallory of the first part and Edward W. Whittlesey of the second part, signed by Henry L. Webb, J. W. Audubon, Henry C. Mallory, E. W. Whittlesey, with seals, in the presence of Egbert Beuser [?]. [n.p.] 1849.

Broadside. 20½ x 43½ cm.

Printed agreement and terms of employment, with names and date in manuscript.

John W. Audubon, son of John James Audubon, with Colonel Henry L. Webb, organized and commanded an overland company for California, which left New York February 7, 1849. The agreement was probably printed in New York.

[Coe No. II, 766.]

17 AUSTIN, STEPHEN FULLER, 1793–1836

Letter, in Spanish, to Sen. D. Lucas Alamán. [n.p.] March 5, 1835.

1 p. 25 cm.

During the first six months of 1835 Austin was detained in Mexico City under bond, after having been imprisoned for a year for his efforts to have Texas separated from Coahuila with its own state government.

The letter, written to Lucas Alamán, the Mexican historian and statesman, says that he is sending him a map of Texas, the second edition published by Tanner in 1834, and pointing out some errors in that edition that were not in the first.

18 AYER, EDWARD EVERETT, 1841–1927

"Early reminiscences of Edward E. Ayer's first trip from home in 1860, journey across the Plains"; of later trips west, to Mexico, Europe, and around the world; with transcripts of his journals of a trip east in the fall of 1916 and a trip to San Diego and the West in 1918; and copies of two letters to the Directors of the Field Columbian Museum (later the Field Museum of Natural History), Chicago, January 14, 1899. Compiled in 1924.

Typewritten manuscript (carbon). 180 pp. 28½ cm.

Inscribed "To Mr. W. R. Coe compliments of Edward E. Ayer. Nov. 7, 1924." Extracts from these reminiscences are quoted by F. C. Lockwood in his biography of Mr. Ayer published in Chicago in 1929.

[Coe No. IV, 1042.]

19 BACKUS, GURDON, 1820–

Diary of a journey from Burlington, Vermont, to St. Louis, Missouri, and across the Plains to Sacramento; and of his stay in California, March 14, 1849 to May 1, 1851.

164 pp. 15½ cm. Original binding.

Gurdon Backus engaged in the clothing business in New York and Burlington until his departure for the West, leaving his wife and two children behind. After some time in the mines he tried hotel keeping in San Francisco but returned to Sacramento and later was prominent in California politics.

The diary, written almost daily through August 18, 1850 and then occasionally to May 1, 1851, describes the route from Burlington to St. Louis, Fort Kearney, the Platte and Sweetwater Rivers, Sublette's Cut-off, Fort Hall, and the Humboldt River to Sacramento, with descriptions of the country, observations by the way, and notes on life in the mines and in Sacramento. [Coe No. 9.]

20 BADMAN, PHILIP

Diary of a journey from Warren, Pennsylvania, to California, April 14 to October 2, 1849.

2 vols. [i.e., 165 pp.] 12½–17½ cm. Original bindings.

The diary describes the route to St. Louis, Independence, Bellevue, the Platte and Sweetwater Rivers, Sublette's Cut-off, Hudspeth's Cut-off, the Humboldt, and Lassen Route to the Feather River, with a "Waybill of the distances" giving routes and camping places from Great Salt Lake City to the gold mines. Although the writer was a man of little education, he describes the country, the birds, flowers, etc., and the trains he meets or travels with. The volumes contain in addition 150 pages of recipes, addresses, memoranda, and accounts dated from 1845 to 1857.

[Coe No. 10.]

21 BAKELESS, JOHN EDWIN, 1894–

"Lewis & Clark, Partners in Discovery."

1,012 pp. 27½ cm.

The original typewritten manuscript, with many alterations and insertions in manuscript, and including a number of passages omitted in the published work. There are also a few notes on Lewis and Clark made by Mr. Bakeless but not used in his book.

Published in New York, 1947, by William Morrow & Company.

Gift of the author.

22 BALDWIN, ROGER SHERMAN, JR., 1826–1856

Letters to his mother and father and other members of his family, and other correspondence, during his journey from New York to California by Nicaragua, and his stay in California, March 20, 1849 to August 18, 1856; and letters from his companions after his accident and death, November 2, 1856 to April 2, 1857.

94 letters. 411 pp. 17–28½ cm.

Roger Sherman Baldwin, son of the Hon. Roger S. Baldwin, graduated from Yale in 1847, studied law, and in 1849 sailed on the brig *Mary* from New York, February 21, for Nicaragua and California. He was employed as a clerk in the Customs Office under Collector T. Butler King. After losing his law library in one of the San Francisco fires he joined his friends in the mines near Folsom and engaged in express forwarding and mining in association with Charles T. H. Palmer. In 1856 he was thrown from his horse, and died as the result of an injury to his head.

The letters describe the journey of a group of recent Yale graduates, Baldwin, Charlie Blake, Ned Tyler and William J. Powell, on the brig *Mary*, Gordon's Passenger Line, to San Juan de Nicaragua, the long wait on the Isthmus for passage from Realejo to California on the *Laura Ann*, arriving about October 1; his work in San Francisco and, later, in the mines, and life and conditions in California.

A few of the letters are copies made by members of the family, others are accompanied by copies or extracts made for circulation among the family and friends. The manuscripts include:

BALDWIN, ROGER SHERMAN, JR. 44 letters to his mother, Emily Perkins Baldwin. March 20 [1849]–August 18, 1856. 175 pp.

—— 12 letters to his father. October 13, 1849–June 28, 1854. 37 pp.

—— 18 letters to his sister, Elizabeth Wooster Baldwin Whitney. May 14, 1849–March 31, 1853. 88 pp.

—— Two letters to his sister, Henrietta Perkins Baldwin Foster. May 20–July 13, 1849; July 29, 1851. 28 pp.

—— Four letters to his cousin, Ellen Perkins. April 27, 1850–January 30, 1853. Not complete. Copies. 17 pp.

—— Letter to Emily Perkins [?]. March 28, 1849. Not complete. Copy. 4 pp.

GORDON, GEORGE. Two letters to Messrs. Beecher, Blake, Tyler, Taylor, and Baldwin. June 5, July 2, 1849. The letter of June 5 is a true copy, certified by C. T. Blake, Roger S. Baldwin, Edwin Tyler, George Beecher, C. L.

Taylor, Leon, June 11. In Baldwin's hand. 4 pp.

DUDLEY, WILLIAM L. Letter to Messrs. Tyler, Blake, Baldwin, Powell, Taylor, Beecher, and others. June 7, 1849. Signed also by B. S. Haight, H. C. Logan, John F. Evans, Seymour, and B. McKeage. 2 pp.

BALDWIN, ROGER S. Letter to Messrs. McKeage, Dudley, Doolittle. June 23, 1849. Signed also by C. T. Blake, Ed Tyler, C. L. Taylor, C. L. Drury, George Beecher, Wm. Farnum, G. Stillwell, Wm. J. Powell. Copy in Baldwin's hand. 1 p.

BALDWIN, MRS. EMILY PERKINS. Letter to her daughter, Elizabeth Whitney, with a copy of Roger's letter of August 31. October 7, 1851. 4 pp.

BLAKE, CHARLES THOMPSON. Letter to his father and mother, describing the voyage from the Isthmus and arrival at the mines. February 3, 1850. With a note on the last page from Edwin Tyler to "Sister Hettie." 12 pp.

—— Copy of part of a letter "to fill in Roger's." April 14 [1850]. 4 pp.

—— Letter to his brother George. May 29, 1850. 11 pp.

—— Two letters to the Hon. Roger S. Baldwin about Roger's accident and death. November 2, 14, 1856. 11 pp.

PALMER, CHARLES THEODORE HART. Letter to H. T. Blake. November 11, 1856, about Roger's death and funeral. Copy by R. S. Baldwin, Sr. 1 p. With added note on same sheet, November 18, 1856. 2 pp.

—— Two letters to Mrs. Baldwin. November 18, 1856, April 2, 1857. 7 pp.

Two of Roger Baldwin's letters are written on paper with lithographic views, and one, August 31, 1851, on the second leaf of a sheet with the *San Francisco*

News-Letter, Saturday, August 30, 1851, Vol. I, No. 3 [2 pp.]. The lithographs are a heading on the letter of May 30, 1851, "Ye Kinge & ye Commones, or ye manners & customes of California. A newe Farce, lately enacted May 28th 1851" [23 x 28 cm.]; and the first page of the letter of July 14, 1851, "James Stuart hung by the Vigilance Committee . . . 11th of July 1851 . . ." [28 x 23 cm.]

The collection also contains a copy, in an unidentified hand, of the letters of May 20 to July 13, 1849, with some slight variations, describing the stay in Nicaragua. This manuscript and the letters of October 4 and 22 from California were printed in *The Century Illustrated Monthly Magazine*, 1891, XLII, 911–931, with title: "Tarrying in Nicaragua. Pleasures and Perils of the California Trip of 1849."

[Baldwin Papers, Historical Manuscripts Collection.]

23 BALLARD, DAVID W.

Letter to Mr. Drew in Washington, D.C. Executive Office, Boise City, I.T., June 30, 1866.

3 pp. 25 cm.

David W. Ballard, Governor of Idaho Territory (1866–1870) and ex officio Superintendent of Indian affairs, to George Drew, Collector of Customs, Puget Sound District, on the political situation in Idaho and Oregon, the illegality of Howlett's appointment by former Governor Lyon to succeed Secretary Gilson, who had absconded, and Nesmith's candidacy for senator from Oregon.

[Coe No. 11.]

24 BARANOV, ALEXANDER ANDREEVICH, 1746–1819

Letter to Mr. Abram Johns, in Boston. New Archangel, October 4/16, 1816.

3 pp. 20½ cm. With part of wrapper showing the address, and a translation in a contemporary hand.

Baranov was head of the Russian American Company in Alaska from 1790 to 1818. The letter to a former tutor to his children gives news of his family, life in New Archangel [now Sitka], and the settlement at Fort Ross, New Albion [California] during the preceding nine years.

[Coe No. 12.]

25 BABBÉ-MARBOIS, FRANÇOIS, *marquis* DE, 1745–1837

Letter to Monsieur Livingston, Ministre plénipotentiaire des États Unis. Paris, le 14 frimaire, an 12 de la Répque. [December 5, 1803.]

2 pp. 31½ cm.

A copy made for the Secretary of State with a note at the end: "Déposée aux minutes du Secretaire d'État, le quinze frimaire, an douze. Hugues B. Maret."

The marquis de Barbé-Marbois was Minister of the Treasury in 1803, and the letter deals with the payment for Louisiana under the terms of the Treaty of Paris.

[Coe Collection.]

26 BARD, ISAAC N., 1842–1919

Diaries, account books, and memoranda of Isaac N. Bard, 1862 to 1917; with a diary of a journey into the Black Hills during the gold rush, April 5 to July 6, 1877, kept by William Price; two diaries kept intermittently by Henry D. Huff in 1878, 1882, 1887, 1888; and a diary kept by George A. Danforth, January to March, 1882.

40 vols. and a leather wallet containing 6 small notebooks and miscellaneous papers. 12½–38 cm.

Isaac N. Bard was born in 1842 near Booneville, N.Y. He served in the Civil War in Co. C 26th New York Volunteers and Co. H 18th U.S. Infantry; on January 1, 1868, he was in Dakota Territory working on the railroad, and later lived in Cheyenne, Wyoming Territory.

These records cover the years 1862–1917. Some of the volumes contain his business accounts, stock book, memoranda and brief entries of events, others are journals of life as a freighter and in Wyoming from 1868–1875, and 1888–1917. Account books, with some notes, cover the years 1876 to 1888. The diaries describe the life of a trader in the early days, his early attempts at farming, trips to Omaha with cattle, and to Denver, Chicago and the World's Fair, to California and Texas, and life on his Chugwater and Little Bear ranches.

PRICE, WILLIAM. Diary, April–July, 1877. 35 pp. 15 cm.

Price left his home in Somerville, N.J., on April 5, 1877 for the Black Hills. He returned to Cheyenne, June 3, disillusioned and without money, and on June 7 started working for Bard at Little Bear.

HUFF, HENRY DRAPER. Diary, January 1878–1888, and accounts. 2 vols. 15–16 cm.

Huff left his home in Brockport, N.Y., in 1833 for Buffalo, by steamer to Detroit, and on foot to Chicago. The diaries record world events and Huff's activities in connection with his smelting works and hardware business.

DANFORTH, GEORGE A. Diary, 1881–February, 1882. 12½ cm.

Danforth's diary is a daily record of his life in New Haven Mills, Vt., employed by Mr. Chapman, and later at Sutherland Mills. A note in the back, possibly in Bard's hand, says "G. A. Danforth's Book. Charlie found it last summer on the road . . ."

[Coe No. IV, 425.]

27 BARRIER, EUG.

Letter to [James W.] Wiley. Seattle, July 11, 1856.

6 pp. 25 cm.

Mr. Barrier was a Frenchman who wished to write for the Olympia *Pioneer* *and Democrat* of which Wiley was editor.

[Miller Collection.]

28 BARRY, EDWARD

Letter to Mr. Fleet of North Fork, Pualup [Puyallup]. Fort Steilacoom, February 5, 1863.

1 p. 25 cm.

Edward Barry, Captain in the 1st Washington Territory Infantry, writes about a prisoner who is awaiting court martial. The letter was probably intended for John Flett.

[Miller Collection.]

29 BASKERVILLE, WILLIAM

Diaries of William Baskerville, 1852–1853 and 1861–1864.

Typewritten manuscript. 54 pp. 21½ cm.

William Baskerville kept books and a diary for F. X. Aubry whose "office" man he was. Aubry was a French-Canadian explorer and trader, trading between Independence, Mo., and Santa Fé, becoming famous for the speed with which he made the journeys. Growing weary of this trading, he made two trips driving sheep from Santa Fé to California in 1852–1854. According to Aubry, Baskerville was wounded by the Indians, August 14, 1853.

The diaries record a journey from the Rio Grande to California by the southern route, December 12, 1852–April 22, 1853, with F. X. Aubry, and back by Tejón Pass and Mohave Desert toward Albuquerque, July 10–September 10, 1853. The diary breaks off August 14 when he was wounded by the Indians. Then follow seven pages of scattered entries about the weather, crops, and farming conditions, between April 7, 1861 and July 20, 1864; and an account of a journey from Peralta, via Albuquerque, Las Vegas, Pawnee Rock, Council Grove, to Warrensburg, Mo., August 28–October 24, 1864.

The copy of the diaries was obtained from Baskerville's daughter.

The records of the first journey to California and return were probably made for Aubry, who kept a brief diary of his travels. The account of the return journey from Tejón Pass to Albuquerque was first printed in the *Santa Fé Weekly Gazette*, September 24, 1853 and reprinted by Bieber in his edition of Cooke's, Whiting's, and Aubry's journals (*Exploring Southwestern Trails*, 1846–1854, by Philip St. George Cooke, William Henry Chase Whiting, François Xavier Aubry, ed. by R. P. Bieber, 1938. Southwest Historical Series, VII). This text follows Baskerville's manuscript almost word for word, but with spelling corrected, up to August 14.

[Coe No. II, 769.]

30 BELDEN, JOSIAH, 1815–1892

Three letters to his sister, Mrs. Eliza M. Bowers, Upper Middletown, Connecticut. December 21, 1841 to June 15, 1845.

11 pp. 24–31 cm. With typewritten transcripts.

Belden, in May 1841, joined the first emigrant wagon train from Missouri to California under the leadership of Captain Bartleson and John Bidwell. He established a ranch on his Sacramento grant and engaged in business in Monterey, San Francisco, and San José until 1881, when he moved to New York.

The letters describe the hardships of the journey from the Fort Hall road southwest, where they left the wagons and packed, finally reaching the Humboldt River and California; his arrival in Monterey and engagement to work for Thomas O. Larkin for a year; his removal to Santa Cruz to take charge of a store for Mr. Larkin; his own business ventures; his part in the revolution against the Mexican governor; his naturalization as a citizen of California; and his grant of land in the Sacramento Valley.

[Coe No. IV, 427.]

31 BELSHAW, GEORGE

"Journey from Indiana to Oregon. March 23 to September 27, 1863."

Typewritten copy. 76 pp. 18½ cm.

Journal of a journey from Lake County, Ind., to the Willamette Valley in Oregon, kept by George Belshaw, commander of a train of ten wagons, which on the way was increased to 26. From Council Bluffs they followed the Mormon Trail along the north bank of the Platte to Fort Laramie, and then the Oregon Trail. Entries are brief and contain little of a personal nature. Belshaw is careful to include all information useful to future travelers along the route; daily mileage, condition of the road, description of the camp sites, and prices for food and grain.

From the collection of the Rt. Rev. Nathaniel Seymour Thomas, Bishop of Wyoming. The original manuscript was in 1931 in the possession of the writer's daughter, Mrs. Annie Belshaw Howell of San Francisco. An account of the trip based on the journal with extracts from it and from letters of the author was published by Mrs. Gwen Castle with the title: "Belshaw Journey, Oregon Trail, 1853," *Oregon Historical Quarterly*, 1931, XXXII, [217]–239.

[Coe No. 13.]

32 BENT, GEORGE, 1843–1918

The Bent papers. Letters, written between February 23, 1904 and May 8, 1918, to George E. Hyde, containing personal reminiscences of life with the Cheyenne Indians, as source material for a book.

260 letters. 717 pp. 20½–28 cm.

George Bent was the son of Colonel William Bent, fur trader and founder of Bent's Fort, and Owl Woman, a Cheyenne, daughter of White Thunder. He was sent to school in St. Louis as a boy and at the time of writing these letters was living in Colony, Okla.

The letters describe in detail his life with the Cheyenne Indians, the customs of the Cheyennes, Arapahoes, Comanches, Kiowas, Sioux, and other tribes of the Arkansas and Platte valleys. They include accounts of the Indian wars, with personal narratives of the Chivington massacre, 1864, the Julesburg raid, 1865, Platte Bridge, Brave Bear's report of the Custer Massacre, and statements of other Indians who took part in these and other battles.

Accompanied by George Bird Grinnell's "Bent's Old Fort and Its Builders," Kansas State Historical Society *Collections*, 1923, XV, 28–91; reproduction of a photograph of George Bent and his wife [7 x 8½ cm.]; lithographs of two views of Bent's Fort with a reproduction of the two on one sheet [10 x 16 cm.]; three manuscript maps, Bitter Lake Region [21½ x 28 cm.], Bent's Fort Region [75 x 21½ cm.], and Dodge City Region [24 x 20 cm.]; and other papers; and a typewritten letter from George E. Hyde to Morris H. Briggs, Omaha, May 14, 1926, certifying that none of these letters has been published in full. 1 p.

The letters were sold by George E. Hyde to Morris H. Briggs, from whom they were purchased. They have not been published in full, and Mr. Hyde has not published the book anticipated by George Bent. He did, however, edit the contents of many of the earlier letters for publication, with the title: "Forty Years with the Cheyennes," Parts 1–6, by George Bent, edited by George Hyde, *The Frontier. A Magazine of the West*, Colorado Springs, Colorado, October 1905–March 1906, Vol. IV. Material in the letters has also been used by George Bird Grinnell in his *The Cheyenne Indians*, New Haven, Yale University Press, 1923, and *The Fighting Cheyennes*, New York, Scribner, 1915.

[Coe No. 14.]

33 BIDWELL, HIRAM HART, 1804–1877

Agreement between Hiram H. Bidwell and Patrick Finn of West Stockbridge, Massachusetts, January 27, 1849, that Bidwell pay and provide for Finn a passage to California with Gordon's California Association, and in return Finn will comply with all rules of the Association and pay to Bidwell one-half of the net proceeds of his labor.

2 pp. 33 cm.

Endorsed: "Hiram H. Bidwell & Patrick Finn Contract, Jany. 27, 1849."

The agreement is signed by Hiram H. Bidwell and Patrick Finn (his mark) in the presence of Victor C. Spencer and John B. Woodruff.

Hiram H. Bidwell was born in West Stockbridge, Mass., the son of Isaac Bidwell, blacksmith, and Lavina Harb.

Gordon's California Association was organized in Philadelphia. A broadside describing its equipment and terms was printed in 1849, and a copy is in the collection of Mr. Thomas W. Streeter.

[Coe Collection.]

34 BLAINE, DAVID EDWARDS, 1824–1900

Sixty-two letters from the Pacific Northwest written by David E. Blaine and his wife, Kate P. Blaine, September 23, 1853 to August 9, 1858.

Typewritten copies. 235 pp. 33½ cm.

David Edwards Blaine was minister of the Methodist Episcopal Church, Seattle, 1853–1856, and his wife, Catherine Palmer Blaine, taught the first school in Seattle. After the Indian uprising in 1856 they went to Portland and in October Mr. Blaine was assigned to the church at Oregon City.

The letters were written to various members of their families and to friends, often with no superscription. The first 3 describe the journey to Seattle from New York State, the second being a diary of the voyage from New York to Panama; 35 letters were written from Seattle and contain information on the early history of that city; 9 were written from Portland and 15 from Oregon City.

Extracts from the letters are quoted in many works on Seattle. Mrs. Watt received permission to use the letters in *The Story of Seattle*, published in 1931, from E. L. Blaine, son of the writers.

[Coe No. 15.]

—— Another transcript of the Blaine letters, 1853–1858. Carbon copy. 247 pp. 28½ cm.

[Miller Collection.]

35 BLAIR, JAMES L.

"Journal of a cruise in U.S. Ship *Vincennes*. Charles Wilkes Esqre. Commander." November 23, 1841 to May 16, 1842.

241 pp. 32½ cm. Original binding.

James L. Blair, Midshipman, U.S.N., was a member of the U.S. Exploring Expedition, 1838–1842, at first on the *Relief*, joined the *Peacock* at Rio, the *Flying Fish* in the Columbia River, and the *Vincennes* at Honolulu.

The journal begins November 23, 1841, in the Harbor of Honolulu, and continues with a daily record of the voyage to Manila Bay, Mangsee Islands, Singapore, Table Bay, James Town, St. Helena, until May 16, 1842.

A letter to Blair from Commander Wilkes, November 22, 1841, refusing his request to return to the United States and ordering him to report for duty on the *Vincennes*, is copied on the page preceding the journal.

[Coe No. IV, 426.]

36 BLAKE, WILLIAM PHIPPS, 1826–1910

Letter to James Dwight Dana. San Francisco, Cal., January 29, 1867, enclosing a letter-press copy of his reply to Wm. H. Brewer.

1 p. 25 cm.

William P. Blake was one of the geologists of the Pacific Railroad Surveys. He was later appointed mineralogist of the California State Board of Agriculture.

—— "The age of gold bearing rocks of the Pacific Coast. Reply to Professor Wm. H. Brewer." Signed: "Wm. P. Blake, San Francisco, California, January 25, 1867." Letter-press copy. 8 pp. 30 cm.

With note attached in Blake's hand: "Duplicate copy. The original sent overland January 26, 1867. 100 copies desired by Wm. Blake . . ."

The manuscript was sent to Mr. Dana for publication in the *American Journal of Science* (cf. 1868, XLV, 264–267).

[Rare Book Room.]

37 BLUE, DANIEL

Letter to Mr. John Wilson. Denver City, Cherry Creek, May 12, 1859. Signed: "Daniel Blue pr. Alexander J. Pullman."

3 pp. 25 cm.

The letter was written by Alexander J. Pullman, at the request of Daniel Blue and in part dictated by Blue after his arrival at Denver but while he was still too weak to write himself. The letter, which is to Blue's brother-in-law, John Wilson, describes briefly his departure, with his brothers Alexander and Charles, from Whiteside County, Ill., for the Pikes Peak gold mines, the journey on foot from Kansas City to Fort Riley and Smoky Hill Fork; their suffering from hunger; the death of a companion, George Soley, followed soon after by the death of Alexander Blue; the necessity of eating the flesh of their brother; the death of Charles; and finally the rescue of Daniel by three Indians.

With the manuscript is a page proof, corrected in pencil, of six pages of a second printing of Blue's *Narrative* but not including the letter to John Wilson. The letter, with some alterations, is printed in Daniel Blue, *Thrilling Narrative of the Adventures, Sufferings and Starvation of*

Pike's Peak Gold Seekers on the Plains of the West in the Winter and Spring of 1859. By one of the survivors, Whiteside County, Ill., 1860. Chicago, Ill., 1860, pp. 19–21.

[Coe No. IV, 428.]

38 BOND, ROBERT, *d.* 1849

Diary of an overland journey to Great Salt Lake City March 1 to July 17, 1849.

12 pp. 15 cm. Original binding. With typewritten transcript.

Narrative of a journey from Newark [?] to Salt Lake City by way of Philadelphia, Baltimore, Cumberland, Pittsburgh, St. Louis, Independence, Mo., and overland to Fort Laramie and Fort Bridger, where the journal ends. Entries are extremely brief with little of a personal nature.

Inscribed on the inside front cover: "Robert Bond. Direct to Wm. S. Bond or Mr. D. Price. Newark, N.J." and on flyleaf: "Diary written by Robert Bond, brother of Mary D. McKirgan, Esther's great-grandmother. He died at Salt Lake City 1849."

[Coe No. 16.]

39 BOND, SAMUEL R.

Journal of the Fisk Expedition to protect the emigrants on the northern route to the gold regions of Oregon and Washington, kept by Samuel R. Bond (Secretary to the Expedition) June 16 to December 21, 1862.

Positive photostat. 240 pp. 28½ cm.

This expedition, under the command of Captain James Liberty Fisk, was authorized by Congress in 1862 to provide an escort for emigrant trains going westward through the Indian country. The journal is much fuller than the official account published by the government with the title: *Expedition from Fort Abercrombie to Fort Benton* (37th Congress, 3d Session, House Ex. Doc. No. 80, Washington, 1863). After Captain Fisk and the military escort arrived at Walla Walla, where

he disposed of the stock and equipment, Bond and several others proceeded by the Columbia River and the coast to San Francisco, then by steamer to Panama and New York.

Original manuscript deposited by the author in the Ipswich Historical Society. A short passage is quoted under "Accessions," *Minnesota History Bulletin*, 1922, IV, 450.

[Coe No. 17.]

40 BOOTH, CALEB, 1825–1850

"En route to California. By Caleb Booth. May 1850" copied from Booth's journal in a contemporary hand.

44 pp. 16 cm. With typewritten transcript.

The party left Farmington, Iowa, May 1, 1850, crossed the Missouri near Kanesville and followed the north bank of the Platte to Fort Laramie. The journal breaks off on June 25, to be resumed on July 28 at Salt Lake City, and describes the journey over the Mormon Route from Salt Lake to Goose Creek and Humboldt River, when it breaks off on September 6. A final note states that "the following day Sabbath, he [the diarist] died of cholera after an illness of about ten hours . . . He was buried by his friend and the companion of his travels, Mr. James Thomas of Farmington, Iowa, beside the river of which he speaks so often, St. Mary's, frequently called the Humboldt."

The entries are very brief with little detail about the route or incidents on the journey. The original journal was probably sent to and copied by a member of his family. The following note appears after the entry for June 25: "Here is a break in the journal, by letter however, we heard of their health & prosperity . . . The next from the Journal is an extract from a Mormon sermon at Salt Lake."

[Coe No. III, 639.]

41 BORÉ, JEAN ÉTIENNE, 1741–1820

Autograph note, signed also by Derbigny, on Laussat's "Arreté. Pour l'établissement de l'Autorité municipale à la Nouvelle-Orléans . . . Nouvelle Orléans, 30 Novembre, 1803."

Broadside. 20½ x 32½ cm.

The note reads: "Vu par nous maire & officiers municipaux séance tenante, Ordonons l'enregistrement du present arreté. 1. Maison Commune le 8 frimaire an 12 (30 Novembre 1803) Boré. Par le Maire —Derbigny, Secre. greffr."

The broadside is endorsed: "8 frimaire an 12me. 30 Novbre. 1803. Nommination d'un conseil municipal, par le Prefet Colonial. Commissaire du gouverment françois, No. 6."

This broadside bears the book label of G. Cusach and was formerly in the library of Mr. Simon J. Schwartz of New Orleans which was sold at the Anderson Galleries in November 1926.

[Coe No. III, 1153.]

42 BOWMAN, JAMES S.

Letter to James B. Carrington, Chicago, Ill., April 28, 1929, with an undated and unsigned draft of Carrington's answer.

4 pp. 27–22½ cm.

The letter, about Fort Philip Kearney and General H. B. Carrington, is accompanied by five photographs [17 x 15–20½ x 15 cm.], forming a panorama of the Big and Little Piney valleys showing the site of the Fort, taken by Mr. Bowman in November 1919.

Gift of Walter H. Cook.

43 BOYD, ROBERT

Two manuscript maps of southern Minnesota and North Dakota.

25 x 19–49½ x 15½ cm.

Map of the route of the army from Fort Snelling to Fort Ridgely, Redwood Ferry and Birch Coulée, and the route taken by the Indians and their captives to the Big Cheyenne River and the Black Hills, and the country of the "Crazy Band," 1862. 49½ x 15½ cm.

Map of the route from Fort Ridgely to Redwood Ferry, Beaver Creek and Birch Coulée. 25 x 19 cm.

The maps are folded and tipped in an autographed and annotated copy of Boyd, *The Battle of Birch Coulée* [Eau Claire, Wis.]. Copyright 1925.

[Coe No. III, 684.]

44 BRACKETT, ALBERT GALLATIN, 1829–1896

"Fort Bridger by Col. Albert G. Brackett."

Typewritten copy. 43 pp. 21 cm.

History and description of Fort Bridger, Wyo., from its foundation in 1843 to 1873, written by the officer then in command of the post. The manuscript includes many references to James Bridger, the trapper and guide who founded the fort.

From the collection of the Rt. Rev. Nathaniel Seymour Thomas, Bishop of Wyoming, with his bookplate. Published in Wyoming State Historian, *Biennial Report*, Laramie, Wyo., 1920, I, [111]–120.
[Coe No. 18.]

45 BRADLEY, HENRY, 1823–

"A daily journal kept by N. J. and H. Bradley on an overland trip to California in the spring and summer of 1852."

92 pp. 32 cm. Original binding.

Henry Bradley, born in Sidney, N.Y., December 26, 1823, came to Elkhorn, Wis., with his parents in 1837; married Nancy J. Mallory in 1847, returned from California in 1855, went again to California in 1859, and returned permanently to Elkhorn in 1860.

Henry and Nancy Jane Bradley left Elkhorn, Wis., March 31, 1852, with a party of friends and neighbors, and arrived at Kanesville May 2, left May 8, followed the route by the north bank of the Platte past Fort Laramie, to the Sweetwater and South Pass, Fort Bridger, Echo

Creek and Salt Lake City; followed the trail east of Great Salt Lake to Bear River Ferry, Blue Springs, Pilot Springs, Goose Creek, and Thousand Springs Valley. The journal ends abruptly on July 8 near the headwaters of the Humboldt River. It describes the country passed through, road conditions, camp sites, flowers and wild life; mentions many Mormons met on the trail, and others; and records in detail the distance between springs and streams, noting when the water is not fit to drink. Total distance 1,804½ miles.
[Coe No. 19.]

46 BRADY, CYRUS TOWNSEND, 1861–1920

"The West Wind. A Story of Red Men and White."

186 pp. [p. 145 missing] 33 cm.

Original typewritten manuscript with many corrections and additions in the author's hand.

Note on page 1: "Original Mss of my Wyoming Novel The West Wind pre-

sented to Bishop Thomas my old and beloved friend—Cyrus Townsend Brady—Signed at St. George's Rectory, Kansas City, Mo., March 11, 1913."

From the collection of the Rt. Rev. Nathaniel Seymour Thomas, Bishop of Wyoming. Published with the title: *The West* *Wind. A Story of Red Men and White*, Chicago, 1912.

[Coe No. 20.]

47 BREWER, WILLIAM HENRY, 1828–1910

Diaries, notebooks, lectures, correspondence, scrapbooks, and other papers. 41 boxes and bundles.

William Henry Brewer, after graduating from the Sheffield Scientific School at Yale in 1852 and a few years' teaching, spent two years abroad studying chemistry, botany, geology, mineralogy, and agriculture. After his return he served for four years, from 1860 to 1864, as first assistant to Professor Josiah D. Whitney, geologist of the geological survey of California; in 1869 he spent the summer camping in the Rocky Mountains with Professor Whitney; and in 1899 accompanied the Harriman Alaska Expedition to Bering Sea. In 1864 he was appointed Professor of Agriculture in the Sheffield Scientific School and served in that position until his retirement in 1903.

The Brewer papers contain much of interest to the student of western history, including especially three diaries, 1860–1871; pocket notebooks; lectures and notes on the forest states, Sierra Nevada, placer mining in California, mountain scenery in California, Lassen's Peak, the destruction of the big trees of California (typewritten), botany of the Pacific states, the Yosemite, California petroleum controversy, missionary labor among the Indians of California and Oregon, the acquisition of Oregon (typewritten), notes from Parker manuscript on Oregon, the Mormons, the Great Basin, the Rocky Mountains, the Harriman Expedition, a trip from South Park, Colo., to Denver, 1869; five notebooks, Rocky Mountain trip in 1869; four volumes of California letters, 1860–1864; and one of Rocky Mountain letters.

Many of these papers have been published in scholarly periodicals. The California letters were edited by Francis P. Farquhar and published by the Yale University Press in 1930 with title: *Up and Down California in 1860–1864. The Journal of William H. Brewer, Professor of Agriculture in the Sheffield Scientific School from 1864 to 1903*, and the Rocky Mountain letters, with notes prepared by the author, were published by the Colorado Mountain Club in 1930, with title: *Rocky Mountain Letters, 1869, "Letters Written to My Wife during a Trip to the Rocky Mountains, July to September, 1869,"* Denver, 1930.

Gift of Arthur and Henry Brewer.

[Historical Manuscripts Collection.]

48 BRINGHURST FAMILY

Seven letters written by a family group of eastern Mormons while on their journey to Great Salt Lake City and after their arrival there, 1848–1856. 20 pp. 24½–31 cm. With typewritten transcripts.

The party included William Bringhurst, his wife Ann Dilworth, her mother Mrs. Caleb Dilworth, her brother John T. Dilworth, and two sisters Elizabeth Dilworth and Harriet M. Brinton, from Chester County, Pa.

The letters, written to relatives in the East, describe life among the Mormons, their prosperity, high cost of necessities, and family affairs.

BRINTON, HARRIET M. DILWORTH (MRS. DAVID). Letter to her father, Caleb Dilworth. January 23, 1848. 2 pp. Appended is a note from Elizabeth Dilworth. 1 p.

BRINGHURST, WILLIAM. Letter to his father, Joseph Bringhurst, Sr. October 14, 1849. 2 pp.

BRINGHURST, ANN DILWORTH (MRS. WILLIAM). Letter to her aunt, Mrs. Olivia Wollerton. April 15, 1850. 3 pp.

DILWORTH, JOHN T. Three letters to his uncle, William Wollerton. April 16, 1850–May 30, 1852. 9 pp.

DILWORTH, ELIZA (MRS. CALEB). Letter to her brother, William Wollerton. July 13, 1856. 3 pp.

The letter from William Bringhurst to his father, October 14, 1849, is cited (p. 14) by R. P. Bieber in "California Gold Mania," *Mississippi Valley Historical Review*, 1948, XXXV, 3–28.

[Coe No. 21.]

49 BROWN, ROBERT, 1842–1895

Original drawings in pencil, ink, and color, of scenes at the Fraser River Mines, 1859–1860.

5 drawings. 29½ x 22–35½ x 25 cm.

Dr. Robert Brown was botanist on the British Columbia Exploring Expedition and commander and government agent of the Vancouver Island Exploring Expedition, 1864.

Indians, Fraser River, 1859. Pen and ink. 30 x 20 cm.

Fort Hope Saw-Mill, Fraser River, 1859. Pencil. 29½ x 22 cm.

Hell's Gate Cañon, Fraser River, British Columbia, 1859. Pencil. 34 x 24½ cm.

Grand Potlach (or distribution of blankets, guns and money) at Fort Hope, Rancherie, Fraser River, 1859. Watercolor. 35½ x 25 cm.

The Town of Fort Hope, Fraser River, 1860. Pencil. 30 x 21 cm.

[Coe No. III, 368.]

50 BRUFF, JOSEPH GOLDSBOROUGH, 1804–1889

Diaries, journals and notebooks of J. Goldsborough Bruff, Captain of the Washington City and California Mining Association, April 2, 1849 to December 14, 1850.

16 vols. [i.e., 1,415 pp.] 14½–22 cm.

J. Goldsborough Bruff, born in Washington in 1804, spent two years at West Point and some years in the Navy. He was a draftsman in the Bureau of Topographical Engineers when he organized the overland expedition to California. After his return to the East he was employed by the Government.

The diaries describe in detail the progress of the expedition from the departure from Washington, April 2, 1849, to St. Jo, Fort Kearney, Fort Laramie, South Pass, Sublette's Cut-off, Bear River, Cantonment Loring, Raft River, Humboldt River, Lassen's Route to Deer Creek, Bruff's camp, October 1849, and life in California to December 14, 1850; and record all graves on the road.

The diaries were evidently written on the road and contain many diagrams and maps of the route and sketches. The journals were written up later from the diaries. The notebooks contain sketches of scenes on the way, trees, equipment and other objects; memoranda of supplies and equipment, routes, remedies for illness and accidents, and original poems written on the journey.

The Bruff diaries and notebooks were formerly the property of Mrs. W. J. Procter of Washington, D.C., Captain Bruff's granddaughter. The Huntington Library owns two other journals, August 28–November 5, 1849, and March 17–October 9, 1850, covering the same periods as the diaries. The Huntington Library owns also an account of Bruff's journey from April 2, 1849 until his return to Washington on July 20, 1851, which he prepared after his return, hoping to have it published.

In 1944 Georgia Willis Read and Ruth Gaines edited all of the Procter journals and diaries, the Huntington journals, and that part of the complete version that is not covered by the diaries and journals. This edition includes also reproductions of the majority of the sketches, diagrams and maps, many of the poems, and, in the Introduction and Appendices, most of the material in the notebooks.

These were published with the title: *Gold Rush. The Journals, Drawings, and Other Papers of J. Goldsborough Bruff, Captain, Washington City and California Association, April 2, 1849–July 20, 1851* . . . New York, Columbia University Press, 1944. 2 vols. Another edition with the same title, edited by Georgia Willis Read and Ruth Gaines, California Centennial Edition, was published by the Columbia University Press in 1949 in one volume. It does not include the Procter-Coe diaries or the material printed in the Appendices of the 1944 edition, but does include the Procter journals 1 and 6 and many of the sketches and diagrams.

[Coe No. V, 5.]

51 BRYANT, JONATHAN WHEELER, *d.* 1853

Letter to his brother, George [Quincy] Adams Bryant, Winchenden, Mass. Diamond Springs, November 18, 19, or 20, 1852.

Photostat. 3 pp. 25 cm.

Three sons of Clement Bryant of Athol, Mass., Jonathan Wheeler, Richard L., and Calvin Tenney Bryant, went to California in the Gold Rush. Jonathan and Richard died of yellow fever immediately after their return in 1853 via Panama. Calvin lived until 1906 in Winchenden, Mass.

The letter describes a typical mine in a ravine, how the mining is done, and the miners' courts that settled questions about claims; domestic arrangements, and social life at the mines.

Gift of Hollon A. Farr, who owns the original.

52 BUCARELI Y URSÚA, *Viceroy* ANTONIO MARÍA, 1717–1779

Letter to R. P. [Rev. Padre] Guardian del Colegio Apostolico de Sn. Fernando, signed with rubric: "Anto. Bucarely Virrey, Mexico 19 de Noviembre de 1774."

3 pp. 29½ cm. With typewritten transcript.

The letter to the Rev. Padre [Fr. Raphael Verger], Guardian of the College of San Fernando, announces the appointment of Fr. Benito Sierra and Fr. Vicente de Santa Maria, chaplains for the exploration of the coast to the north of Monterey; that Fr. Miguel de la Campa is to go with Fr. Benito Sierra on the *Santiago* and Fr. Vicente de Santa Maria and Fr. Ramon de Usson on the *Principe* and *San Carlos;*

and that the Commissary at San Blas, Don Francisco Hijosa, is to provide them with money.

This letter probably belonged in the library of the College of San Fernando. It is endorsed: "Car. 6. Leg. 2. n. 1." (See note under No. 12.)

[Coe No. 22.]

53 BUCARELI Y URSÚA, *Viceroy* ANTONIO MARÍA, 1717–1779

Letter to R. P. Guardian de San Fernando, signed with rubric: "Anto. Bucarely Virrey, Mexico 4 de Diziembre de 1775," with the answer of the R. P. Guardian de Colegio de San Fernando [Fr. Raphael Verger], Dizre. 6 de 1775.

4 pp. 30 cm. With a typewritten translation by Professor Jacques Malakis.

The letter requests chaplains for the packet boats *San Carlos* and *Principe* that are to sail with supplies to California in January, 1776, either the same who went on the recent expedition on the *Santiago* or others. The answer states that Fr. Vicente Santa Maria and Fr. Benito Sierra will be appointed, or, if they cannot go, Fr. Miguel de la Campa.

This letter probably belonged in the library of the College of San Fernando. Endorsed: "Car. 6. Leg. 2. n. 1." (See note under No. 12.)

[Coe No. 23.]

54 BUCHANAN, JOHN C.

Letter to George Hyde, Alcalde of the District of San Francisco, requesting the grant of title to Lot No. 266. San Francisco, July 3, 1847.

1 p. 26 cm.

John C. Buchanan emigrated to California from Kentucky in 1846, joining Edwin Bryant's party. In 1847 he was municipal clerk in San Francisco and in 1848 was engaged in auctioneering. He became the owner of many lots in the city.

The original broadside deed [33 x 41 cm.] is also in the collection. It is dated July 13, 1847, and signed by George Hyde, 1st Alcalde. The names and date have been filled in by Buchanan, who also added the record: "This Title to Lot 266 is Recorded in the Archives of Land Title in San Francisco Book A Page July 13, 47 . . . Jno. C. Buchanan Municipal Clerk." The receipt for the amount due the Municipal Fund for the deed is signed by Pedro T. Sherreback, Collector.

Gift of J. Ward Mailliard, Jr.

55 BURCH, JOHN CHILTON, 1826–1885

"Missouri to California in 1850. The autobiography of Hon. John Chilton Burch. Being his narrative of early struggles: of his early life in Missouri . . . and his later career on the Pacific Coast. Together with his outspoken judgments on public affairs and men of his day. A transcript of the original written for the Association of Territorial Pioneers of California, 1879."

Typewritten manuscript. 60 pp. 28 cm.

The manuscript recounts his ancestry, family history, early life and education, his journey to California in 1850 by the Platte River and South Pass to Sacramento and the site of Weaverville, his mining experiences, his return to the legal profession at Weaverville, his career in public life, and election to Congress from California.

[Coe No. 24.]

56 BUREAU OF MUNICIPAL RESEARCH, NEW YORK CITY

"Report on a survey of the Province of the Northwest of the Protestant Episcopal Church in the United States. Prepared for the Committee on Survey of the Province of the Northwest by the Bureau of Municipal Research —New York City. October 1918." Accompanied by a letter of transmittal to the Rt. Rev. N. S. Thomas, Chairman, Committee on Survey, signed: "Charles A. Beard, Director, October 11, 1918."

169 pp., including folded tables; 1 map, 15 charts (photostats). 29½ cm.

Typewritten document with the original letter of transmittal and some manuscript alterations.

Laid in the back are printed copies of the map and 14 of the charts with some alterations and additions; a typewritten copy of a petition unanimously adopted by the Missionary District of Wyoming assembled in convocation on June 15, 1917, addressed to the General Convention, to create a new province to be known as the Ninth Province, and to transfer the district of Wyoming from the Sixth Province into this Ninth Province, with a blueprint map indicating this division.

The petition is printed in the *Journal* of the 10th annual Convocation of the Missionary District of Wyoming, 1917, pp. 27–28; and reported in the *Journal* of the General Convention, 1919, p. 24.

From the collection of the Rt. Rev. Nathaniel Seymour Thomas, Bishop of Wyoming.

[Coe No. 202.]

57 BUREAU OF MUNICIPAL RESEARCH, NEW YORK CITY

"A report on the acceptance and administration of a home for the aged in Laramie, Wyoming. Prepared for the Rt. Rev. Nathaniel S. Thomas, Missionary Bishop of the Missionary District of Wyoming Protestant Episcopal Church, U.S.A. By the New York Bureau of Municipal Research, July–August, 1917." Accompanied by a letter of transmittal to Bishop Thomas from E. P. Goodrich, Director, August 24, 1917.

Typewritten report (carbon). 42 pp. 7 folded tables. 29 cm.

From the collection of the Rt. Rev. Nathaniel Seymour Thomas, Missionary Bishop of Wyoming, with his bookplate.

[Coe No. 201.]

58 BURRELL, MARY (afterward MRS. WESLEY TONNER), 1835–

"Mary Burrel's Book." Diary of a journey overland from Council Bluffs to Green Valley, California, April 27 to September 1, 1854.

69 pp. 15 cm. Original binding. With typewritten transcript.

Inserted at end: Letter from Wesley Tonner to "Dear Friends," San José City, September 10, 1854. 5 pp. 32 cm.

The diary begins April 27, at Council Bluffs, one month after leaving Plainfield, Ill., describes with youthful enthusiasm the details of the journey from the Missouri River along the Mormon Trail on the north bank of the Platte to Fort Laramie, Sweetwater River, Pacific Springs, Fort Bridger and Great Salt Lake, the Mormon Route by Pilot Springs, the Humboldt and Carson Rivers to Ragtown, Sacramento, and, September 1, the home of C. Burrell in Green Valley.

The party consisted of Mrs. Mary Burrell, widow of George Burrell; her 19-year-old daughter, the diarist; her son Edward, his wife Louisa, and her father and mother, Mr. and Mrs. Hannibal;

Putnam Robson, Mrs. Burrell's nephew; Isaac Harter; and Wesley Tonner, Mary Burrell's fiancé. For part of the journey they traveled with or near the Isaac Foster party, also from Plainfield, Ill. Some entries or parts of entries are in the handwriting of Wesley Tonner.

Some passages of the diary describing events while traveling in company with the Foster party are quoted by Lucy Foster Sexton in her *The Foster Family, California Pioneers* [Santa Barbara, 1925], pp. 180–184.

[Coe No. III, 641.]

59 CAIN, JOHN, 1805–1867

Letter to Colonel B. F. Shaw. Portland, October 25, 1855.

1 p. 25 cm.

In 1855 John Cain, father of Andrew Jackson Cain, was acting superintendent of Indian affairs, Washington Territory.

The letter calls Colonel Shaw's attention to the importance of providing adequate protection for Governor Stevens,

who was returning from his expedition to make treaties with the Indians, and Pearson, probably W. H. Pearson, the express rider, who was bringing letters and the reports of the commissioners.

[Miller Collection.]

60 CALIFORNIA AND OREGON UNITED STATES MAIL LINE

Two waybills, Yreka and Marysville, Thursday, November 22, 1886, and Marysville and Sacramento, Wednesday, May 22, 1867, with lists of passengers and fares received.

Printed forms filled in by hand. 39½–39 cm.

In 1866 the mail contract was with the Oregon Stage Company and the waybill made out by Chas. R. Mayhew, agent. In 1867 the contract was with H. W. Corbett & Co. [Henry W. Corbett of Portland, Ore.], W. H. Rhodehamel, agent.

The California Stage Company contracted with the Postmaster General in

1860 for daily service by stage from Sacramento to Portland and continued until June, 1865, when the company demanded $300,000 a year. The Postmaster General did not accept the bid and made a new contract.

[Coe No. II, 1113.]

61 "THE CALIFORNIAN'S ADDRESS to his family." A poem, unsigned and undated.

3 pp. 24½ cm.

The poem, written probably in 1849 or 1850, is a farewell to the author's family and his New England home, and explains

his reasons for leaving for California.

Gift of Davenport Hooker.

62 CARLIN, WILLIAM PASSMORE

Letter to H. H. Bancroft. Fort Omaha, Neb., November 14, 1884.

Typewritten transcript. 12 pp. 20½ cm.

The letter relates briefly the experiences of Wm. P. Carlin, Colonel, 4th Infantry, Brevet Major General, U.S. Army, from his arrival, as a lieutenant in the 6th Regiment of Infantry, U.S.A., at Fort Laramie, Wyo., in 1855, at the time of the expedition against the Sioux, until 1858, when the 6th Infantry was sent to Fort Bridger to reinforce the army under General Albert Sidney Johnston, and on to California.

From the collection of the Rt. Rev. Nathaniel Seymour Thomas, Bishop of Wyoming, with his bookplate.

[Coe No. 25.]

63 CARRINGTON, HENRY BEEBEE, 1824–1912

"History of Indian operations on the Plains, 1866."

Typewritten manuscript (carbon). 59 pp. 32 cm.

In 1866 General Carrington, then colonel of the 18th U.S. Infantry, commanded an expedition from Fort Kearney, Neb., to open a wagon route around the Big Horn Mountains to Montana, established Fort Philip Kearney, Dakota Territory, and was in command of the Rocky Mountain District.

The manuscript contains a topical abstract of Senate Ex. Doc. No. 33, 1st Session, U.S. 50th Congress, 1887; official report of Colonel Henry B. Carrington of the action with Sioux Indians, December 6, 1866, to Brevet Major Henry G. Litchfield, A.A.A.G. at Omaha; the explanation of congressional delay for 20 years in the publication of General Carrington's full history of the Indian operations in 1866 culminating in the loss of Fetterman's detachment; affidavit procured by J. F. Kinney, of the Special Indian Commission, from Brevet Major James Powell, Fort Philip Kearney, D.T., July 24, 1867; General Carrington's response to a letter from the Secretary of the Interior, Mr. Browning, transmitting a copy of the affidavit of James Powell; report of Captain Ten Eyck as to his part in duties on the day of the massacre, dictated to his daughter, Frances D. Ten Eyck, Chicago [undated, after 1887]; letter to Colonel Carrington from Lieutenant A. H. Wands, Fort Sanders, D.T., November 27, 1867, relating to Captain Powell's affidavit; letter to Colonel Carrington from Captain Ten Eyck, Chicago, November 23, 1903; and letter from Colonel Carrington to E. S. Ricker of Chabron, Neb., Hyde Park, Mass., June 29, 1906. The manuscript is accompanied by a reprint of Appendices I and II of the sixth edition of Mrs. Margaret I. Carrington's *Ab-sa-ra-ka, or Wyoming Opened*, Philadelphia, 1890, with an introductory note dated Hyde Park, Mass., December 21, 1905. 21 pp. and a map of the scene of the Fetterman massacre.

General Carrington's report was finally published in Senate Ex. Doc. No. 33, 50th Congress, 1st Session, pp. 37–38. The map was printed in *My Army Life and the Fort Phil. Kearney Massacre*, by Frances C. Carrington, Philadelphia, 1911, facing p. 142.

Gift of Walter H. Cook.

64 CARTER, WILLIAM ALEXANDER, 1820–1881

Journal of transactions of the post trader at Fort Bridger, Wyoming, August 18 to December 15, 1869.

285 pp. 35 cm. Original binding.

A note on the flyleaf reads: "Quarter Master Property 1st. Mich. Cavalry June 24, 1865. Invoice Book." The first page contains an invoice of stores turned over by Captain Ballard to R. D. Pike, R.Q.M. 1st. Mich. Cav., March 1865, followed by invoices from April to June 1865 and copies of nine letters from Lieutenant Pike to M. C. Meigs, Q.M.G., Fort Bridger, January 27–March 2, 1866. [16 pp.] The volume was next used by Scott Eddy and Company, who dealt largely in the purchase and sale of cattle, May 25, 1867–July 1, 1868 [9 pp.], and finally by the post trader at Fort Bridger [260 pp.].

William A. Carter came to Fort Bridger with Captain Philip St. George Cooke in 1857 as sutler and post trader. He was later also postmaster and probate judge. He built a store and warehouse, established a sawmill and carried on a prosperous trading business until his death.

Carter's name appears frequently in the accounts of Scott Eddy and Company. The accounts of the Fort Bridger trader are with the members of the garrison, the Indian agent Luther Mann, civilian settlers and travelers. Among the names are those of Colonel C. C. Gilbert, Major David S. Gordon, Major S. A. Russel, and "Uncle Jack" Robertson, the old trader and mountaineer.

[Coe Collection.]

65 CARVER, JONATHAN, 1710–1780

Letter to Mr. Banks [later Sir Joseph Banks]. London, August 13, 1778.

2 pp. 22 cm.

The letter, explaining his difficulties in securing the publication of his travels and asking further assistance, is tipped in a copy of the third edition of Carver's *Travels through the Interior Parts of North America*, London, 1781, which is dedicated by the author to his patron, Sir Joseph Banks.

The volume bears a bookplate indicating that it was formerly in the Beckford Collection at Hamilton Palace which was sold at Sotheby's sale in July 1882 to Quaritch. The same copy, with the autograph letter, was sold by Hodgson & Co., February 1923 to Henry Stevens.

[Coe No. III, 1417.]

66 CASCADES MASSACRE

List of killed and wounded, at the Cascades [March 26, 1856], in an unidentified hand.

1 p. 32 cm.

The list gives the names of those killed at Upper Cascades and near the Blockhouse, the wounded and those missing in the attack on the settlement by the Yakimas. (See No. 94.)

[Miller Collection.]

67 CATLIN, GEORGE, 1796–1872

Paintings of North American Indians in oil on cardboard.

3 paintings. 30 x 43½–41 x 61 cm.

George Catlin spent many years in the West, 1829–1838, painting the Indians and their dances and customs and the landscape. He exhibited his paintings in London from 1848 to 1851, and in New York and other cities in the United States. His original collection, some 600 paintings, is now in the U.S. National Museum. There was another collection in the possession of his heirs, known as the "Catlin Cartoon Collection," consisting of copies and original paintings of North and South American Indians.

"His-oo-san-ches. One of the most famous warriors of the Comanchees. Geo. Catlin p. 1848." 30 x 43½ cm.

"Nom-ba-mon-ye (the Double Walker) a celebrated warrior of the Omahas in war dress & war paint. Geo. Catlin p. 1848." 31 x 43½ cm.

Osage Indians. 3 figures. Signed G. Catlin 1864. 41 x 61 cm. "Tchong-tas-sab-bee (the Black Dog), Head war chief of the Osages" (center) ; "Tal-lee a famous warrior and favourite of the war chief" (left) ; "Ko-ha-tunk (the Big Crow), a famous warrior with pipe-tomahawk in his hand" (right).

Only the last of the three paintings is signed, but the titles, as quoted, are on the back of each painting in Catlin's hand.

All of these portraits except that of Nom-ba-mon-ye are reproduced in black and white in the various editions of Catlin's *Letters and Notes*, London, 1841, and in color in his *Illustrations of the Manners, Customs, & Condition of the North American Indians*, London, 1876 (cf. plates 172, 152–154). They are single portraits of all but Ko-ha-tunk, who is in a group with two other Indians and is not holding the pipe-tomahawk. None of the reproductions is as elaborate in detail as the original paintings and the color is much harsher.

[Coe No. IV, 429.]

68 CATLIN, GEORGE, 1796–1872

"O-kee-pa," a religious ceremony, and other customs of the Mandans, by George Catlin.

100 pp. 13 colored plates, and one leaf inserted indicating the size of the illustrations and the type page. 26 cm. Original boards.

Original manuscript in Catlin's hand, signed by him on the title page, at the end of the preface, and at the end of the text. Written on heavy paper, each page surrounded by a single line border. Several passages are deleted by having paper pasted over them. The illustrations are proofs before lettering, the lettering added in manuscript. The coloring in several differs from that in the printed book, and may have been done by hand.

The most important passage deleted describes the Bull Dance, which was later separately printed on two leaves with title: "Folium Reservatum."

Accompanied by proof sheets of the "Folium Reservatum" with Catlin's manuscript corrections, copies of the revised page proofs with manuscript corrections, and the published edition: *O-kee-pa: A Religious Ceremony; and Other Customs of the Mandans*, By George Catlin. With thirteen coloured illustrations. London, Trübner and Co., 1867. vi[2] 52 pp. 13

col. plates. "Folium Reservatum" inserted after p. 24. 3 pp.

This printing of the "Folium Reservatum" is a later impression than the proof sheets.

Published also in Philadelphia by J. B. Lippincott and Company, 1867, but printed in England. The American edition does not contain the publisher's note "To the reader" or the suppressed "Folium Reservatum."

[Coe No. 27.]

69 CATLIN, GEORGE, 1796–1872

"Souvenir of the North American Indians as they were in the middle of the 19th century, a numerous and noble race of human beings fast passing to extinction and leaving no monuments of their own . . ." Signed: "Geo. Catlin, London, 1852 [and added in pencil] '57."

2 vols. 216 drawings. 35½ cm.

The 216 portraits, drawn in pencil [20 x 28½ cm.], are mounted, each mount signed, with captions in ink in Catlin's hand on facing pages.

Binder's title, written and signed by Catlin: "Catlin's N. Amn. Indian portraits" [followed by a list of the tribes, 19 in Volume I, 20 in Volume II], and on the side: "Forever unique."

Most of these portraits are reproduced, with variations, in Catlin's *Letters and Notes on the Manners, Customs, and Conditions of the North American Indians,* London, 1841. 2 vols.

70 CATLIN, SETH, *d.* 1871

Protest against the passage by the Territorial Legislature of a Bill providing for a road from Steilacoom to the county seat of Clark County, to be paid for by counties through which it passes. Written and signed by Seth Catlin.

1 p. 32 cm.

Endorsed: "Protest of Hon. Seth Catlin of Lewis County March 14, 1854. Against passage of House Bill No. 7. . . . Entered upon Journal page 26." In Elwood Evans' hand.

Seth Catlin was a member of the First Territorial Legislature and in 1855 and 1856 president of the Council of Washington.

[Miller Collection.]

71 CHADWICK, STEPHEN FOWLER, 1825–1895

"Oregon Party, 1851–"

2 pp. 25½ cm.

Endorsed: "Salem, Or. April 3, 89. Ed. North Pacific History Co. The within sketch was handed me by Ex. Gov. Chadwick, being the joint effort of Gov. Moody and Chadwick. J. W. Souther, agt."

The "Oregon Party" sailed from New York on the steamer *Empire City*, March 13, 1851 for Oregon by the Isthmus of Panama, and arrived in Oregon April 21.

The manuscript lists the members of the party and tells briefly what happened to them in Oregon.

The manuscript was used by Elwood Evans in compiling his *History of the Pacific Northwest* [1889], and is cited by him, I, 323.

[Miller Collection.]

72 CHAFEE, ZECHARIAH, 1824–1856

"Journal on board ship *Audely* [*sic*] *Clark*," Captain A. W. Dennis, Master, February 15 to September 1, 1849.

76 pp. Drawings. 33 cm. Original binding covered with heavy cotton cloth.

Zechariah Chafee left his wife, Eliza Ann LaCroix, and a young son, in Bristol, R.I., to seek his fortune in the gold fields of California with a company of Rhode Islanders.

A daily record of life on a sailing vessel during a voyage from Newport, R.I., around the Horn to San Francisco on the ship *Audley Clark* in 1849, with six small drawings in the text and on the last leaf of scenes on the way.

The journal records the ship's position every day it was possible to take observations, and includes some verses, one of them to his wife Eliza.

73 CHALMERS, GEORGE, 1742–1825

Letter to the Rt. Hon. Lord Sheffield. Office for Trade, Whitehall, December 22, 1802.

5 pp. 22½ cm.

George Chalmers, Scottish antiquary and historian, was at this time chief clerk of the Committee of the Privy Council for Trade and Foreign Plantations. In the letter to Lord Sheffield he expresses the opinion that England had relinquished all claims to land west of the Mississippi under the treaties of 1763 and 1783.

The letter is inserted in a volume containing the "Report of a Secret Committee of the American Congress on the Policy of Obtaining New Orleans and the Floridas," extracted from *Cobbett's Weekly Political Register*, 1803, IV, Supplement, cols. 1905–1940, and bound with two other pamphlets on the Louisiana question.

[Wagner Texas and Middle West Collection.]

74 CHAMBERS, ALEXANDER, *d.* 1888

Letter to H. H. Bancroft. Fort Bridger, Wyo., January 4, 1885, with the accompanying narrative of the founding and history of Fort Bridger compiled from existing post records.

Typewritten copy. 14 pp. 20½ cm.

Lieutenant Colonel Chambers, 21st Infantry, U.S.A., was in command at Fort Bridger in 1885. The narrative is signed by the Post Adjutant, C. C. Miner, 2d Lieut. 9th Infantry.

From the collection of the Rt. Rev. Nathaniel S. Thomas, Bishop of Wyoming, with his bookplate. Printed in full in *Annals of Wyoming*, Oct. 1927–Jan. 1928, V, 91–95, with note at end: "From files of Dr. Hebard."

[Coe No. 28.]

75 CHAPMAN, JOHN BUTLER

Letter to the Honorable Daniel Webster, Secretary of State. Warsaw, Idaho, September 24, 1852.

Copy in an unidentified hand. 10 pp. 31 cm.

John B. Chapman first settled in Grays Harbor in 1851 but removed to Steilacoom. He was a lawyer from Indiana and was a delegate at the convention that memorialized Congress on the division of Oregon Territory in 1851.

The letter was written to fulfill a promise to the President [Fillmore] to put in writing facts with regard to the land in Oregon Territory claimed by the Hudson's Bay Company and the Puget Sound Agricultural Company.

[Miller Collection.]

76 CHOUTEAU, [RENÉ] AUGUSTE, 1749–1829

Two letters, in French, to William Grant. St. Louis des Illinois, May 8, June 4, 1797. Signatures only.

4 pp. 31–34 cm.

Chouteau, with his stepfather, Pierre Laclede, founded St. Louis in 1764, and with him built up a large trade with the Indians. After the transfer of Louisiana he was appointed one of the three justices of the first territorial court.

The letters give instructions to Grant for the purchase and sale of furs and other business matters, and mention a number of the early traders.

[Coe Collection.]

77 CHURCH OF JESUS CHRIST OF LATTER-DAY SAINTS

Letter to His Excellency, George N. Briggs, Boston, Massachusetts. Nauvoo, Illinois, April 25, 1845, signed by a Committee in behalf of the Church of Jesus Christ of Latter-day Saints, Brigham Young, President, Willard Richards, Clerk of the Quorum of the Twelve, N. K. Whitney and George Miller, Trustees of the Church.

3 pp. 31½ cm. With typewritten transcript.

As early as March 1845 a petition had been drafted by John Taylor appealing to the governors of all the states except Missouri and Illinois for help and protection, and recounting briefly the injustice and persecutions the members of the Church had endured in Missouri and Illinois. This petition, dated April 24, 1845, was addressed to the President of the United States and, with slight variations in the wording, to the governors of the states.

The Coe manuscript is the copy sent to Governor Briggs of Massachusetts.

The petition as addressed to President Polk is printed in full, dated April 24, 1845, in Tullidge, *History of Salt Lake City*, 1886, pp. 9–11, signed by a committee of seven; in Whitney, *History of Utah*, 1892, I, 241–242; and in Tullidge, *Life of Brigham Young*, 1876, pp. 129–133.

[Coe No. 205.]

78 CHURCH OF JESUS CHRIST OF LATTER-DAY SAINTS

Deeds signed by B. W. Nowlin of Ogden City, March 10, 1857, Simon Noall of Great Salt Lake City, April 7, 1857, Stephen Nixon, of the City of Provo, March 3, 1857, and Alfred Nethercott of Provo City, March 16, 1857, conveying their property to Brigham Young, Trustee in Trust for the Church of Jesus Christ of Latter-day Saints.

4 printed broadsides filled in by hand. 30–32 cm.

After the arrival of David H. Burr, Surveyor General, in Salt Lake City, the Church directed its members to convey their land and property to Brigham Young as Trustee in Trust for the Church in the hope that by this means they might secure title to their lands.

[Coe No. I, 1093.]

79 CHURCH OF JESUS CHRIST OF LATTER-DAY SAINTS

"A License Liberty Power & Authority given to John Whitmer signifying & proveing that he is an Elder of this Church of Christ established . . . A.D. 1830 on the 6th day of April . . ." signed by Joseph Smith, Jr., first Elder, Oliver Cowdery, second Elder, with added note in Whitmer's [?] hand: "Given to bearer in conference held in Fayette, Seneca County, N.Y., June 9, 1830."

1 p. 19½ x 18½ cm.

The two signatures appear to be in the same hand, possibly both written by Cowdery.

John Whitmer was a brother of David Whitmer, who was one of the "three witnesses" to the Book of Mormon, and during the month of June the translation of the Book was completed in his father's home in Seneca County, N.Y. John was closely associated with Joseph Smith and helped with the writing of the translation. He was later excommunicated and, after the saints left Far West, he bought land there and remained until his death.

[Coe Collection.]

80 CHURCH OF JESUS CHRIST OF LATTER-DAY SAINTS

Quitclaim signed by Brigham Young, Trustee in Trust for the Church of Jesus Christ of Latter-day Saints, releasing land formerly owned by Alma T. Angell to Sarah D. Crowther, November 21, 1861. Witnesses Albert Carrington, William Clayton, with affidavit signed by John C. Caine, Notary Public, County of Great Salt Lake, November 21, 1861.

2 pp. 32 cm.

This transfer is canceled in red ink, on the face, returning the property to Brigham Young, Trustee in Trust, signed by Alma T. Angell [n.d.]. Endorsed: "Release to Alma T. Angell for Consecrated Property."

[Coe No. 206.]

81 CLARK, BENNETT C., 1819–1890

Diary of a journey from Missouri to California in 1849.

102 pp. 13 cm. Original binding. With reprint from *Missouri Historical Review*, 1928.

Bennett C. Clark was born in Booneville, Mo., in 1819, succeeded his father as clerk of the Circuit Court of Cooper Co., 1841. From 1853 to 1878 he lived on his farm in Cooper County, but returned to Booneville in 1878 when he was elected judge of the Probate Court of the County, an office he held until his death in 1890.

Clark was captain of a party of gold seekers from Cooper County, Mo. The party traveled to Westport, across the Plains to Wakarusa [?] Creek, the Kansas River and northward along the Big and Little Blue to the Platte, along the Platte to South Pass, Fort Hall and southward to the Humboldt. After reaching the Truckee River Clark was taken ill and his diary ends abruptly August 10, when the party had reached a point near the western border of Nevada. Friends assisted Clark to reach San Francisco and shortly afterward he started the return voyage to his home in Missouri by way of the Isthmus, New Orleans, and St. Louis.

In 1928 the diary was the property of Clark's grandson, Dr. Bennett Clark Hyde of Lexington, Mo., whose name appears at the end of a note at the beginning of the diary. Published by Ralph Paul Bieber in the *Missouri Historical Review*, 1928, XXIII, 3–43, and reprinted as a separate, Columbia, Mo., 1928.

[Coe No. 29.]

82 CLARK, FRANK, 1834–1883

Part of a letter written and signed by F. Clark, with the date and superscription missing.

1 p. 15 cm.

Frank Clark, a lawyer, came to Washington in 1852, and took an active part in politics.

The letter advises the addressee how to deal with "Collins" upon whom papers will be served in a day or two, evidently in connection with an estate.

[Miller Collection.]

83 CLARK, JOHN

"The California guide. With distances & notes of travel by Clark & Co. in fifty two from Ohio to the Sacremento Valley . . .''; an account of life at the diggings, 1852–1856; and the return journey to Ohio by the Isthmus of Panama in November, 1856.

206 pp. 21½ cm. Original binding. With typewritten transcript.

After failing in business John Clark of Portsmouth, Ohio, organized a company to go to the gold fields of California. They left Cincinnati by water, April 13, 1852, for the Upper Missouri, and followed the trail from St. Jo to Fort Kearney, Castle Rock, Fort Laramie, the Sweetwater, South Pass, Fort Bridger, Salt Lake City, the Humboldt River, to the Feather River Valley, arriving at the end of August. After four years in the Feather and Yuba River districts Clark sailed from San Francisco, November 5, 1856, to return to the East by the Isthmus route, and reached Portsmouth December 7, 1856.

The journal records the distance traveled each day, camping places, location of water, fuel and grass, topography of the country, graves passed, the stay at Salt Lake City; and describes life at the diggings where he was twice elected recorder, the robberies and murders, and the rule of the Vigilance Committees.

[Coe Collection.]

84 CLARK, MERIWETHER LEWIS, 1809–1881

Letter Book. Missouri Light Artillery. 1834–1847.

145 pp. 38 cm. Original binding.

Meriwether Lewis Clark was the eldest son of General William Clark. He graduated from West Point in 1830, was colonel in the Illinois Volunteers in the Black Hawk War in 1832, and resigned in 1833; served in the Mexican War with the Missouri Volunteers, 1846–1847, and was U.S. surveyor general for Missouri, 1848–1853. He joined the rebellion against the United States, 1861–1866, and resided in Kentucky until his death in 1881.

The letter book contains copies of the official correspondence, orders, and reports of the "Extra Battalion" of Artillery, some of them signed by Major M. L. Clark, Commanding, from the Articles of Agreement, July 26, 1834 to April 4, 1847, when a note in pencil refers to the "file of letters unrecorded."

The record opens with a letter from Major Clark to Brigadier General John Ruland of the Missouri Militia, acknowledging the receipt of the commissions of the officers of the "Extra Battalion," and continues through Clark's efforts to secure the necessary equipment from the War Department through Governor Dunklin, Governor Boggs, and in 1843 through Governor Reynolds. He learned that none of the earlier requests could be found, probably due to the destruction of the State House by fire in 1837, and therefore submitted copies of the official records in relation to the organization and equipment of the Battalion in the files of General Ruland for 1834–1837. In 1846 the Battalion voted to volunteer its services for the expedition to Mexico and accompanied Colonel Doniphan's Expedition to Santa Fé and Chihuahua.

The report of the Battalion of Light Artillery, from Major Clark to Colonel Doniphan, dated "Camp near Chihuahua, March 2, 1847" (pp. 128–133), is printed in the *Report of the Secretary of War*, 1847, pp. 508–513.

[Coe No. III, 297.]

85 CLARK, WILLIAM, 1770–1838

Letter to the Honorable William H. Crawford, Secretary of War. Missouri Territory, St. Louis, October 29, 1816.

1 p. 25½ cm. With typewritten transcript.

Endorsed: "St. Louis, Oct. 29, 1816. Govr. Wm. Clarke Reports the number of persons employed in that Territory in Indn. Dept. with the place of nativity—salary."

William Clark, younger brother of George Rogers Clark, was serving in the army in campaigns against the Indians from 1789 to 1796, when he retired to his home. In 1803 he was asked by Captain Meriwether Lewis to accompany him in leading the expedition to the Pacific Ocean. After the successful completion of this journey he retired from the army, was appointed superintendent of Indian affairs at St. Louis and in 1813 was appointed governor of Missouri Territory.

In compliance with a request from the Secretary of War, William Clark encloses a tabulation: "A list of the Indian agents, Sub Agents, Interpreters and other persons in the Indian Department within the Missouri Territory, specifying the amount of compensation pay & emoluments allowed to each & the state or country in which they were born . . . Missouri Territory, Executive Office. St. Louis, October 29th, 1816. Wm. Clark." 1 p. 39 cm.

[Coe Collection.]

86 CLAY, JOHN, 1824–1904

Letter to Mr. W. Stone Abert, Newport, Kentucky. Kerchesters, Kelso, Scotland, October 21, 1874.

4 pp. 20½ cm. With envelope postmarked Kelso Oct 21–74.

Tipped in his *New World Notes; Being an Account of Journeyings and Sojournings in America and Canada*, Kelso, J. & J. H. Rutherford, 1875.

John Clay came of a long line of Berwickshire farmers and occupied a prominent place in the agricultural life of Scotland.

The letter outlines Clay's journey from Kentucky, where he had evidently been entertained by Mr. Abert, to Chicago and Denver and the Colorado gold mines, where he saw western life in all its glory. He returned by Canada, Niagara, and the Hudson River to New York in the summer of 1874, and arrived home August 21, 1874, after 18 weeks.

[Coe No. I, 18.]

87 CLAYTON, JOSHUA E.

Draft of an address to the president and members of the convention of quartz miners of the State of California at Sacramento in June 1857, at which the Quartz Miners' Association was organized.

5 pp. 32 cm.

Endorsed: "To the Quartz Miners convention at Sacramento, June 18th, 1857."

J. E. Clayton was a mining engineer of long experience in Georgia and California and later in Utah.

Clayton was unable to attend the convention in person and so addressed to the president his appeal in behalf of the working miners for a uniform system of mining, and suggestions for other action that should be taken by the convention.

[Coe Collection.]

88 CLAYTON, JOSHUA E.

Reports on two mining districts in Nevada, 1865–1879.

25 pp. 30½–31½ cm.

——Report on the Live Oak group of veins in the "Mammoth District," Nye County, Nev. Austin, June 24, 1865. Signature only. 9 pp. With a manuscript "Map of the Live Oak Mine, Weston, Mammoth District." 19½ x 31½ cm.

——Report to John Schoenbar on the Vanderbilt series of mines in the Secret Cañon Mining District, Eureka County, Nev. Salt Lake City, Utah, March 2, 1879. Signature only. 16 pp.

[Coe Collection.]

89 CLAYTON, WILLIAM, 1814–1879

Letter press copy book of William Clayton, Notary Public, Auditor of Public Accounts, and Recorder of Marks and Brands of the Territory of Utah, from February 2, 1860 to April 1869.

958 pp. 45½ cm. Original binding.

Laid in the back are 15 loose leaves [34–41 cm.] containing the following:

"To the Speaker of the House of Representatives of the Legislative Assembly. Exhibit of taxes due February 1, 1869." 10 pp.

"Amount of stationery etc. needed for the year 1869. February 6, 1869." 2 pp.

Clayton's accounts on J. R. Robbins' books, December 4, 1866–June 12, 1868. 5 pp.

The letter press book contains documents executed by William Clayton as notary public of Great Salt Lake County, as auditor of public accounts, and as territorial recorder of marks and brands, including letters, powers of attorney, applications for bounty land warrants, deeds, marriage certificates, affidavits, reports to the Legislative Assembly, accounts with the several counties, January 5, 1865, sums appropriated but not provided for in the appropriation bill, etc. Many of these documents were copied after they were fully signed and executed. An index of six pages precedes the letter press copies.

Formerly in the library of the late Herbert S. Auerbach (Parke-Bernet Galleries, Catalogue sale No. 893).

[Coe Collection.]

90 CLEVELAND, RICHARD JEFFRY, 1773–1860

Narrative of the fur trading voyage of the brig *Caroline* from China to the Northwest Coast of America, January 10 to September 13, 1799. Captain Richard J. Cleveland.

16 pp. 31½ cm. With typewritten transcript.

The manuscript, signed R.J.C., is headed: "At Sea, between Sandwich Islands & Macao. Augt. 1779," and gives a detailed account of the winter voyage from China to Norfolk Sound, the monsoon off the China coast, mutiny of some of the crew, and trading with the Indians, and summarizes the return voyage to China.

The account of this voyage is contained in Cleveland's *A Narrative of Voyages and Commercial Enterprizes*, Cambridge, 1842, I, 51–96. In the *North American Review*, 1827, XXV, 458–464, the editor, Jared Sparks, prints an account of the voyage from China to the Northwest Coast abridged from Cleveland's original journal. These narratives follow the Coe manuscript closely in content but vary in phraseology. In *Voyages of a Merchant Navigator . . . Comp. from the Journals and Letters of the Late Richard J. Cleveland*, by his son, H. W. S. Cleveland, New York, 1886, the author states that he has in his possession his father's original journal of the voyage and also a manuscript of 28 pages of letter sheet written at sea, on his return voyage, for the entertainment of his father, giving a full account of his experiences. The passages quoted vary only slightly from the passages in the 16-page manuscript in the Coe Collection. The "Log of the Caroline," January 10–October 2, 1799, is published in the *Pacific Northwest Quarterly*, 1938, XXIX, 61–84, 169–200.

[Coe No. 430.]

91 CLINTON, CHARLES P.

"Charles P. Clinton. His journal Book, 1803." May 24, 1803 to September 26, 1806.

56 pp. 31½ cm.

Charles P. Clinton was stranded on the coast of Patagonia in the brig *Genius* of New York, D. Cornwall, Master, April 17, 1803, and sailed from there May 17 on the *Betsey*. He was evidently later on the *Vancouver* as there is a note on the vellum back: "Charles Clinton Nootka Sound March 14, 1806, on the N.W. Coast of America."

The journal contains: "Remarks on board of the Schooner Betesy [*sic*] Capt. Amariah Williams from the South Seas Bound to New London," June 14–September 12 [1803]; "Abstract of a Journal from Cape St. Augustien [*sic*]" bound to New London, July 23–September 12; "Accompt with the Ship Vancouver," Au-

gust [1804]–August 1806 [by Ebenezer Clinton]; "A slight description of the coast of Pategonia," signed by Charles P. Clinton; "A description of the Pategonian Indians"; and poems and sea-chanties, many of them signed by Charles P. Clinton or Ebenezer Clinton, and dated between September 15, 1804 and September 22, 1806.

Beginning at the back, with the volume reversed, are examples in navigation, tables, weights and measures, etc.—many of the pages signed by Charles P. Clinton —and the "Account of William Woodworth with Schooner *Betsey*," 1802.

[Coe No. 31.]

92 CLINTON, EBENEZER

"Remarks on board the ship *Vancouver*, Capt. Brown commanding. Bound from Boston to the N. West Coast of America and China," from August 4, 1804 to September 8, 1806.

88 pp. 32½ cm.

The account covers the voyage from Boston to the Sandwich Islands, the Northwest Coast, and Queen Charlotte Isles; the arrival, April 2, 1805, of the *Atahualpa;* Clinton's exchange, May 16, with a man on the *Atahualpa;* the massacre of Captain Porter and many of the crew of the *Atahualpa*, June 13; Clinton's return to the *Vancouver*, July 12, 1805; his experiences with the natives, accounts of the massacre of the crew of the *Boston*, and the rescue of the two survivors [December 7, 1805, March 15, 1806]. The remarks end with their departure from the Northwest Coast, September 8, 1806.

Beginning at the back of the volume, Clinton has copied the log of the *Vancouver* from August 9, 1804 to March 26, 1805. The *Vancouver*, Thomas Brown, Master, Thomas Lyman, owner, sailed from Boston to the Northwest Coast to

meet Lewis and Clark, whose orders from President Jefferson were that at least part of the company were to return by sea with a copy of their notes.

On the inside of the back cover there is "A List of the Officers and People of the Ship *Boston* of Boston, taken by the Savages of Nootka Sound and all Murdred except 2," and a brief account of the rescue of the survivors.

Laid in the journal is a single leaf containing a poem in Ebenezer Clinton's hand, entitled "The Bold N. West Man," describing the massacre of the crew of the *Atahualpa*, June 13, 1805. Clinton's poem is similar in form to that of the same name describing the adventures of Captain Kendrick of the *Lady Washington*, 1791, which was printed as a broadside.

[Coe No. 30.]

93 CLOUGH, JOHN P., JR.

Two letters from John P. Clough. May 2, 1849; July 28, 1853.

6 pp. 25–25½ cm.

—— Letter to his brother Horace. St. Joseph, May 2[–6], 1849. 3 pp.

Horace P. Clough married Mary Leibee, daughter of Daniel Leibee. "Friend Vira" may be the Alvira mentioned in Daniel Leibee's letter to his wife, November 24, 1850. (See No. 300.) The letter describes the preparations for the overland journey, the dishonesty of the contractor who was to supply the mules, and mentions Mr. Leibee.

—— Letter to "Friend Vira." Stockton, July 28, 1853. 3 pp.

He writes of family affairs, of her father, and of his life in California attending service and teaching Sabbath School on Sunday, and painting, papering, and building on weekdays.

94 COE, LAWRENCE W.

The Cascade massacre of March 26, 1856. Letter from L. W. Coe to Putnam Bradford. Cascades, W. T., April 6, 1856.

Typewritten copy. 9 pp. 28 cm.

The letter describes the massacre and appends a list of those killed and wounded.

In 1881 the original letter was in the possession of Mr. Bradford, who "gave" it for publication in the *Oregonian*, January 1, 1881. Published in full, with slight variations, by Robert Williams, in his "The Cascade Massacre," *Transactions* of the Oregon Pioneer Association, 1896, pp. 72–82; also in *Oregon Native Son*, 1900, I, 496–501.

[Coe No. 32.]

95 COFFEY AND SHARP

Letter to Colonel J. Patton Anderson, Delegate in Congress. Olympia, W.T., June 7, 1856.

Draft [?] 9 pp. 32 cm.

A. L. Coffey and William Sharp were privates in the Oregon Volunteers.

The letter details developments of the past winter in the Indian War, quotes from reports received from the eastern part of the Territory, and blames General Wool for neglecting to take action against the hostile Indians.

[Miller Collection.]

96 COLEMAN, M.

Letter to Miss Susan R. Stedman. Auburn, January 27, 1851, describing briefly the latter part of his journey overland in 1850, the mines and California.

32 pp. 12½ cm. With typewritten transcript.

Written in a *Miners' & Travellers' Pocket Letter Book*. Printed cover. Coleman gives few details of the journey.

[Coe No. III, 642.]

97 COLGROW, DAVID

Eight letters and papers describing Colgrow's experiences and observations in the newly discovered Rocky Mountain gold diggings. 1859.

21 pp. 8½–31 cm.

David Colgrow's letters describe conditions in the gold diggings in the Rocky Mountains and his illness there.

—— Four letters and a note to his wife, Jane. February 7–August 8[–18], 1859. 14 pp.

—— Marriage certificate of David Colgrow of Edmeston, N.Y., and E. J. Bennit of Burlining, N.Y., August 12, 1849. 2 pp. Printed form in a border of flowers and butterflies with a vignette of a marriage ceremony.

COLEGROW, GEORGE A. Letter to his brother David. June 15, 1853, announcing the death of their father. 4 pp.

HIRARD, RALPH, hospital steward U.S.A. Letter to Norman Bennett. [Fort Kearney, Nebraska Territory, 1860], telling of the death of David Colegrove [sic]. 1 p.

[Coe No. 33.]

98 COLLINS, CASPAR WEVER, 1844–1865

Letters from Caspar Wever Collins and his mother, Mrs. Catherine Willis Wever Collins, September 20, 1862 to April 18, 1865.

Typewritten copies. 38 pp. 19½ cm.

Lieutenant Collins was serving under his father, Lieutenant Colonel William Oliver Collins of the 11th Ohio Volunteer Cavalry stationed at Fort Laramie to protect the emigrant trains from the Indians. In July 1865 he was ordered to go with 25 men from Platte Bridge to bring in a wagon train traveling from the Sweetwater. The Indians soon closed in on them and Lieutenant Collins was killed.

COLLINS, CASPAR WEVER. Two letters to his mother, Mrs. Catherine Willis Wever Collins. September 20, 1862, April 15, 1865, and an extract from a letter, October 8, 1862. 15 pp.

—— Letter to his uncle, Dr. P. Wever. Fort Laramie, September 21, 1864. 5 pp.

—— Letter to his uncle, Carleton C. Sams. Fort Laramie, December 13, 1864. 6 pp.

—— Letter to his aunt [Virginia Wever?]. Sweetwater Bridge, April 18, 1865. 4 pp.

COLLINS, MRS. CATHERINE WILLIS WEVER. Letter to her sister, Virginia Wever. Fort Laramie, November 15, 1863; and an incomplete letter, probably taken from a newspaper, with the caption, "Correspondence of the News, issue Aug. 1, 1865. Letter from the 11th O.V.C. Sweetwater Bridge, D. Ter., Aug. 1, 1865," describing the battle at Platte Bridge, near the present Casper, Wyo., July 25–27, 1865, in which Lieutenant Collins was killed. 8 pp.

From the collection of the Rt. Rev. Nathaniel Seymour Thomas, Bishop of Wyoming. The originals were in the possession of Agnes Wright Spring in 1927. All but the last item in the collection were published in Part II of *Caspar Collins, the Life and Exploits of an Indian Fighter of the Sixties*, by Agnes Wright Spring, New York, Columbia University Press, 1927.

[Coe No. 34.]

99 COLORADO. GOVERNOR'S GUARD

By-laws and minutes of the meetings of the Governor's Guard, Denver City, September 13, 1862 to July 13, 1863.

32 pp. 32 cm. Original binding. With typewritten transcript.

The original manuscript record of the meetings of the Governor's Guard, the election of officers, the adoption of by-laws, ending July 13, 1863, with the report that Governor Evans had accepted the offer of the services of the Guard and had tendered these services to Colonel Chivington, who declined them.

The minutes of the meetings of September 13–27, 1862 were "Copied from T. G. Wildman's report of the meeting. G. L. Moody Sec. Pro tem." On November 3, 1862, Moody was elected secretary pro tem., Thos. G. Wildman having gone to the States, and continued as secretary, signing the minutes through March 1863. June 29, 1863, James Macdonald was elected secretary pro tem. and signed the minutes until July 13.

This original Governor's Guard was mustered into the 3d Colorado Cavalry as Company A, August 20, 1864.

Extracts from the record are printed with title: "Extracts from the Minutes of Meetings of the Governor's Guards, Sep-

tember, 1862, to July, 1863," as Appendix B in J. H. Nankivell, *History of the Military Organizations of the State of Colorado* [Denver, 1935], pp. 437–444, from a typewritten copy in the State Historical and Natural History Society of Colorado made with the permission of the Old Colony Bookstore. A note, p. 437, reads: "The existence of the book in which the minutes were kept appears to have been unknown for many years. It is badly torn, appears to have been submerged in water for a long period of time, and many words are illegible because covered with a paste of sand that cannot be removed. It is believed . . . to have been carried off in the Cherry Creek flood of 1864 and its general appearance lends strong support to this theory. The document was discovered among the law books of the late David Mitchell, a Denver attorney, when the books were purchased after Mr. Mitchell's death by the proprietors of the Old Colony Book Store of Denver."

[Coe No. 37.]

100 COLTON, JOHN B.

A brief biographical sketch of James Bridger, written on the back of a photograph of Bridger, copied by Johnson of Kansas City, "from a photo taken in St. Louis in 1857."

11 x 16½ cm.

The inscription was evidently written after Bridger's death in 1881. The date has been added in another hand and in ink similar to that of a note added at the bottom and signed by Mrs. Virginia K. Wachsman, Bridger's daughter.

A rubber stamp at the top reads: "The

Jayhawkers of '49. Headquarters, Kansas City, Mo."

This same portrait has been reproduced in Robert S. Ellison, *Fort Bridger, Wyoming. A Brief History*, Casper, 1931, and other publications.

[Coe No. II, 196.]

101 COLVOCORESSES, GEORGE MUSALAS, 1816–1872

"Diary of Lt. Colvocoresses on the Wilkes Expedition, May 10, 1840–December 3, 1840. Fiji Group & Hawaiian Islands."

133 pp. 20½ cm.

—— "The People's Book. Or, A Narrative of a cruise in a government expedition to the Islands of Madeira, Cape Verde Islands, Brazil, Coast of Patagonia, Chili, Peru, Paumato Group, Society Islands, Navigator Group, Australia, Antarctic Ocean, Friendly Islands, Feejee group, Sandwich Islands, Northwest Coast of America, Oregon, California, East Indies, St. Helena, &c&c. In one volume. By an officer of the expedition."

346 pp. 33 cm.

—— *Four Years in a Government Exploring Expedition; to the Island of Madeira—Cape Verd Islands—. . . .* New York, Cornish, Lamport & Co., 1852.

371 pp., illus. 19½ cm. Original cloth binding.

George M. Colvocoresses was ransomed from the Turks after the War for Greek Independence, 1821, and brought to America through the Greek Relief. He was sent to Norwich Academy, Vt., and in 1832 appointed midshipman. As passed midshipman he accompanied the Wilkes Expedition in the South Seas and Antarctic, 1838–1842, surveyed Grays Harbor under Eld, and took part in the overland journey from Oregon to California in 1841 under Emmons. He served successively on the *Porpoise*, *Peacock*, *Vincennes*, and *Oregon* during the expedition.

The original manuscript of *Four Years in a Government Exploring Expedition* was, according to the Preface of the published work, "compiled from a Journal, or a diary, which the author kept in obedience to a 'General Order' from the Navy Department."

The printed text follows the manuscript closely through Chapter 21 [p. 315], where two short chapters on California are inserted [pp. 316–342]. The text then follows the manuscript closely to the top of page 358, when the manuscript breaks off abruptly. The last few pages are missing. [Coe No. 38.]

102 COMFORT, AARON IVINS, 1827–1915

"A winter trip to the 'Black Hills,' Trailing on the Prairie with incidents by the way," by Captain Aaron Ivins Comfort, December 1874. Followed by a "Narrative of a visit to an ancient Ree village-site with observations on the state of civilization of the Sioux inhabitants in July 1874"; and "Descriptive narrative of the Sioux Indian Sun Dance as performed near Cheyenne River Agency in July 1874. Witnessed and minutely described by Captain Aaron Ivins Comfort."

46 pp. 31½ cm. With typewritten transcript.

Captain Comfort, Acting Assistant Surgeon at Fort Sully, D.T., in 1874 accompanied Captain Thomas M. Tolman on an expedition into the Black Hills in pursuit of emigrants who, in defiance of the law, were seeking gold in the Black Hills. The first entry in the journal is December 3, but the detachment did not set out until the 6th. The expedition failed to catch up with the emigrant party and turned back, reaching the Agency December 21, 1874.

The manuscript is in the form of a journal but was probably written at a later date; it has paragraph headings in red ink in the margin as if it were prepared for publication in a paper.

The first nine leaves of the second part of the manuscript are in the same hand but not written with such care as the first part. The last three leaves are extensively corrected by hand.

[Coe No. V, 7.]

103 COMSTOCK, NOAH D., 1832?–

Diary of Noah D. Comstock kept during a journey from Ash Hollow, Nebraska, to the mines in Sierra County, California, and a year in the mines. May 31 [1853?] to August 26 [1854?]

142 pp. 15 cm. Original binding.

The diary opens on May 31 [no year] at Ash Hollow, and describes the route in detail by the North Platte to Fort Laramie, Willow Springs, the Sweetwater River [crossed on a bridge, June 20], South Pass, Soda Springs, Raft River, Humboldt River, Truckee River and the Yuba Valley, September 2, noting the camps, the location of water, grass, and fuel, and the weather. The latter part of the diary, to August 26 [1854?] covers in brief entries Comstock's wanderings in California, prospecting and looking for work, and finally working for Charles Heintzen at Forest City.

At the back of the volume there are 13 pages of accounts, those with Heintzen beginning January 17, 1854.

[Coe No. 39.]

104 CONGDON, J. S.

Letter to his brother Joseph. Chinese Camp, Tuolumne County, California, December 9, 1872.

3 pp. 25 cm.

The letter describes events at Chinese Camp on election day in 1872, the election of President Grant, when the writer was one of the "guardians of the palladium of liberty."

Gift of Bradford F. Swan.

105 CONNECTICUT. GOVERNOR, 1858–1866 (WILLIAM ALFRED BUCKINGHAM)

Petition to his Excellency, the Governor of California, to examine the case of Owen Brennan confined in the San Francisco County jail, and stating that if he can be released his father will at once have him removed to Connecticut. New Haven, July 10, 1865. Signed by twelve citizens of New Haven, with a note added and signed by Governor Buckingham, certifying to the character of the signers.

3 pp. 32 cm.

The petition, in an unidentified hand, is endorsed: "Owen Brennan. For Pardon. Petition from New Haven. Refused."

Another endorsement reads: "Respectfully referred to Hon. P. W. Shepheard for information . . . September 18, 1865. F. F. Low, Gov." With added note: "Dist. Atty. Porter reports a bad case, unworthy of executive clemency, F.F.L. October 3, 1865."

Owen M. Brennan later became well known in the hotel business in San Francisco.

The signers of the document were Erastus C. Swanton, Mayor of New Haven; Henry Dutton, ex-Governor of Connecticut; James E. English, ex-Governor; N. D. Sperry, Postmaster; R. I.

Ingersoll (later U.S. Minister to Russia); John Woodruff, Collector of Internal Revenue; James F. Babcock, Collector of Customs; Morris Tyler, ex-Mayor; Theodore D. Woolsey, President of Yale College; C. R. Ingersoll (Governor of Connecticut, 1873–1877); Benjamin Silliman, Professor at Yale College; E. K. Foster, Speaker of the House of Representatives.

The document formerly belonged to James J. Howard, messenger for Governor Markham of California, and was handed down in his family until 1937 when it was sold by his grandson John Howard.

Gift of Harry C. Mabry.

[Rare Book Room.]

106 CONNELL, I.

Letter to William D. Lewis, Esq., Philadelphia. Washington, February 9, 1846. "(Confidential)."

1 p. 25 cm. With address on fourth page of the sheet.

A confidential letter regarding the relations between the United States and Great Britain and his opinion that Congress will not pass any hostile measures in relation to Oregon.

[Coe No. 40.]

107 COOK, JOSEPH WITHERSPOON, 1836–

Diary of Joseph W. Cook, January 14, 1868 to May 9, 1869.

Typewritten copy. 29 pp. 28 cm.

The diary describes his life and work in Cheyenne, Wyo., as a missionary of the Protestant Episcopal Church.

These extracts from Joseph Cook's diary were furnished by his daughter, Charlotte Everett Cook of Minneapolis. The copy belonged to the Rt. Rev. Nathaniel Seymour Thomas and was sold at the Anderson Galleries, January 30, 1929. Published with Cook's letters to Bishop Robert Harper Clarkson and Bishop George Maxwell Randall in *Diary and Letters of Rev. Joseph W. Cook, Arranged by the Rev. N. S. Thomas*, Laramie, 1919.

[Coe No. 41.]

108 COOK, JOSEPH WITHERSPOON, 1836–

Fifteen letters of the Rev. Joseph W. Cook describing his work at Cheyenne as missionary of the Protestant Episcopal Church, to the Rt. Rev. R. H.

Clarkson, D.D., and the Rt. Rev. George M. Randall, D.D. January 17 to December 10, 1868.

96 pp. 19½ cm. With typewritten transcript.

—— Two letters to Robert Harper Clarkson, Bishop of Nebraska. January 17, 20, 1868. 18 pp.

—— 13 letters to George Maxwell Randall, Bishop of Colorado. January 28–December 10, 1868. 78 pp.

The following pieces accompany the letters:

CORNELL, JOHN. Letter to the Rt. Rev. Nathaniel Seymour Thomas, D.D. September 27, 1912. 4 pp.

WEBSTER, S. D. Typewritten note to Charlotte [Everett Cook]. December 29, 1916, containing extracts from his diary referring to his association with the Rev. Joseph W. Cook. 1 p.

—— Typewritten letter to the Rt. Rev. Nathaniel Seymour Thomas. December 30, 1920. 2 pp.

COOK, CHARLOTTE EVERETT. Letter to Bishop Thomas. November 20 [1920]. 2 pp.

Wyoming, the Last of the Frontier, 1918, No. 19. 4 pp.

From the collection of the Rt. Rev. Nathaniel Seymour Thomas. Published with extracts from the diary in *Diary and Letters of Rev. Joseph W. Cook, Missionary to Cheyenne, Arranged by the Rev. N. S. Thomas*, Laramie, 1919.

[Coe No. 42.]

109 COON, HOMER

"The outbreak of Chief Joseph By Homer Coon."

Typewritten manuscript. 6 pp. 34½ cm., and original pen and ink sketch, 30 x 23 cm.

Narrative of the Nez Percé revolt in 1877. The author, a soldier in General Gibbon's command, had been detailed as escort to Colonel Nelson and was in Yellowstone Park when overtaken by a courier with news of the Nez Percé outbreak and orders to return to Fort Ellis. He crossed the Rockies and joined the regiment in Missoula (126 miles) in four days. On August 4 they set out in pursuit of the Indians.

The sketch is a plan of the battlefield.

[Coe No. 43.]

110 COON, HOMER

"Recollections of the Sioux campaign of 1876 as I saw it from the viewpoint of an enlisted man, and from first-hand [information] told to us boys of Gen. A. H. Terry's command by John Martini, the late Gen. Custer's orderly and bugler . . ."

Typewritten manuscript. 11 pp. 34½ cm., and original pen and ink sketch, 8 x 28 cm.

Coon was one of the party of soldiers under General Terry that rescued Reno, Benteen, and the surviving troops of their command, and found the bodies of Custer and his men. The manuscript describes the meeting with Reno and contains an account of the troops on the following days. The narrative is impartial, denies the charge of Custer's suicide and attributes the disaster to his failure to wait for General Terry.

The sketch is a representation of the way the wounded were transferred to the steamer *Far West* at the mouth of the Little Big Horn.

[Coe No. 44.]

111 COOPER, JAMES GRAHAM, 1830–1902

Letter to Dr. G. Suckley. Panama, N.G., December 28, 1855.

1 p. 27 cm.

J. G. Cooper and Dr. George Suckley were naturalists and surgeons with Governor Stevens on the survey of a northern railroad route in 1853.

The letter, written on the journey east, asks Suckley to forward some papers that were left in Rainier.

[Miller Collection.]

112 COPELY, JESSIE SINCLAIR (MRS. ALEXANDER WILTON), 1844–

"The Career of James Sinclair, Being an account of his work from 1840 to 1856 as an explorer in Oregon and the Northwest: Free trapper: Indian fighter: Leader of migrations: and Chief Factor of the Hudson's Bay Company: Together with details of the migrations of 1841 and 1854: the attitude of the American settlers toward the Hudson's Bay Company: the Indian War of 1855–1856: the abandonment and destruction of Fort Walla Walla: and Sinclair's death at the hands of the Indians, at the Cascades, in 1856. As told by his daughter, Mrs. Copeley, of Portland, Oregon."

Typewritten manuscript. 24 pp. 27 cm.

The manuscript contains a brief account of Sinclair's life, with few details.

From the collection of the Rt. Rev. Nathaniel Seymour Thomas, Bishop of Wyoming.

[Coe No. 45.]

113 CORNELL, GEORGE

Journal of a voyage from New York to California, May 4 to July 9, 1852.

20 pp. 19½ cm.

—— Letter to his wife. Sonora, California, January 1 [continued to January 9], 1853.

47 pp. 12½ cm.

George Cornell left New Market, N.J., May 4, 1852; sailed from New York for San Juan May 5 on the *Northern Light*, crossed the Isthmus and arrived in San Francisco on the S.S. *Lewis* July 7; and moved on to Sonora where he obtained work. He later returned to his home and in 1867 was constable at New Market.

The journal describes the voyage, the hardships and delays on the Isthmus, conditions on the ships, his own illness, and the kindness of his fellow passengers, especially William Thrall and his son. The letter tells of his efforts to find work and his life in Sonora.

The letter is written in a "California letter book" in the original printed cover issued for emigrants by Cooke & Le Count of San Francisco.

[Coe Collection.]

114 COWDEN, JOHN

Two letters to Theodore Garretson, Philadelphia, December 24, 1848, Rio de Janeiro, March 9, 1849; and a letter to Miss M. B. Donaldson, Stockton on the San Joaquin, and Upper Bar, Mokelumne River, August 14–26, 1849.

30 pp. 2 prints. 24½–30 cm. With typewritten transcripts.

Cowden and his friends, C. W. Solensky, George W. Hart, and William H. Graham, sailed from Philadelphia, January 16, 1849, on the brig *Osceola*. Together they went to Stockton and to the mines on the Mokelumne River.

The second letter to Garretson was begun at sea off the coast of Brazil before March 4 [the top of the first sheet with date has been cut off] and continued March 4, 5, and 9 after arriving at Rio de Janeiro.

In addition to mentioning personal and family affairs the letters to Garretson describe his plan to go to California and experiences on the voyage to South America; the letter to Miss Donaldson describes life in California and at the mines, and encloses two lithographs:

"The first trail [*sic*] & execution in S. Francisco on the night of 10th of June at 2 o'clock . . ." 24½ x 20 cm.

"A view of the [Elephant]" surrounded by eight scenes in the life of a '49er. 20 x 25½ cm.

Gift of Mary C. Withington.

115 CRAMER, THOMAS J. B.

Diary of a journey from Kansas to California, May 12 to November 9, 1859.

184 pp. 19 cm. Original boards. With typewritten transcript.

A letter transmitting the volume to his father, Major Thomas Cramer, Sacramento City, Cal., November 8, 1859, signed: "Thos.," occupies the front end paper, and the diary is signed at the end: "Thos. J. B. Cramer."

Thomas J. B. Cramer, a man of education, skilful in debate, took an active part in Kansas politics in the 'fifties. He was judge of the elections in 1855, inspector general of the Militia, and territorial treasurer under the Lecompton Constitution. He was the proslavery candidate for treasurer in December 1857 but was defeated by his Free State opponent.

May 12, 1859, with his wife and his brother Samuel, he left his home in Douglas County, Kan., for California, striking the California Trail beyond Topeka, and traveling by Fort Kearney, the Platte and Sweetwater Rivers, Fort Bridger, Salt Lake City, the Mormon Route by Pilot Springs to the Humboldt and Carson Rivers, Hope Valley, Drytown and Sacramento September 22, 1859, and in Sacramento November 5 and 8. The diary describes in detail the route, events of the journey, the country, the Indians encountered, and the conditions in California. In the last entry he is still unable to find employment and writes at length on California politics.

[Coe Collection.]

116 CRAWFORD, MEDOREM, 1819–1891

Journals of the U.S. Emigrant Escort Service, under the command of Captain Maynadier, Captain Crawford, second in command, in 1861; and under Captain Crawford in 1862, 1863, and 1864.

5 journals in 2 vols. [i.e., 138 pp.] 18–32 cm. With typewritten transcript.

Accompanied by the printed report of the expedition of 1862 by the Secretary of War, 1863.

Medorem Crawford first went to Oregon in 1842 with Elijah White, and taught in the Methodist mission school for a year. He later settled on a farm in Yamhill County and took an active part in the affairs of the Territory. In 1861 he was appointed to accompany Captain Maynadier, commanding the first emigrant escort, and was himself in command the following three years.

The first volume contains the "Diary of Medorem Crawford, Oregon pioneer of 1842," from Omaha to Portland, June 3–October 14, 1861; and [Journal II] from Omaha to Willow Spring June 11–July 26, 1862 when the journal breaks off. They are written on alternate pages with the corresponding dates opposite each other. The diary for 1861 is a clean copy in ink, probably by Lieutenant LeRoy Crawford, who wrote the diary for 1862 in pencil on the road.

The second volume contains "Journal [III] of U.S. Emigrant Escort 1862" from Omaha to Walla Walla, June 1–October 14, 1862, by Dr. R. B. Ironside [?]; [Journal IV] expedition from Loup Fork to the Grand Ronde Valley, June 14–October 3 [1863], by S. G. Crawford; and [Journal V] from Saddle Creek to Boise City, June 27–September 30, 1864, in an unidentified hand, written on alternate pages with [Journal III].

Mounted in the front of the volume is an "Itinerary of road from Blackfoot Ferry . . . to Boisie City" with indica-

tions of camps made by Colonel Maury's command in 1863, possibly in S. G. Crawford's hand; and laid in the volume is a photostat of a two-page folio letter from S. G. Crawford to his son, Medorem, Havana [N.Y.], August 2, 1852.

U. S. Secretary of War. *Journal of the Expedition Organized for the Protection of Emigrants to Oregon, &c., under the Command of Medorem Crawford, Captain, Assistant Quartermaster United States Army* (37th Congress, 3d Session, Senate Ex. Doc. No. 17 [Washington, 1863]).

The journals give a daily record of the government escort of the emigrants to Oregon in the summers of 1861, 1862, 1863, and 1864, describing the route taken, condition of the roads, the camps, etc., visits at forts on the way, and meeting the Oregon Volunteers under Maury, September 8, 1862, and August 19, 1863. With Crawford in 1862 were his brother, Lieutenant LeRoy Crawford, principal assistant, his father, Samuel Gillespie Crawford, clerk, and Dr. R. B. Ironside, journalist.

Two brief accounts of the 1862 expedition are in print: The report and journal of Captain Medorem Crawford (Senate Ex. Doc. No. 17) mentioned above, and " 'Arrived: All well.' The Journal of Captain Medorem Crawford . . . Oregon Wagon Train, 1862. War Department Records," ed. by L. Lehrbas, *The Frontier*, 1933, XIII, 226–228. Neither of these is printed from the original journals above.

[Coe No. 46.]

117 CROFT, THOMAS T.

"The gold hunter's diary by Jacobson" overland to California [1850?]. Written by T. T. Croft for "Recorder," January 1, 1889.

5 pp. 37½ cm. Accompanied by a newspaper account of the journey clipped from the Janesville *Recorder*.

Thomas T. Croft came to Janesville, Wis., from England in 1842 with his uncle and aunt, Joseph and Margaret (Ayres) Croft, and their family.

The first three pages of the manuscript are written in ink in a small neat hand. They are corrected in pencil in another hand, in which the last two pages are written. The manuscript breaks off in the midst of a description of an Indian burying ground in Iowa on the route from Dubuque to Council Bluffs. No date for the journey appears in the manuscript, but in the newspaper account it says that "Gold Hunter" (known as Doctor) was in Sacramento at the time of the cholera epidemic, which was in October and November 1850, and some months later he returned to the East by way of Panama.

The newspaper account says that the diary of the "Gold Hunter" had recently been found and is the basis of the printed narrative. It begins with an account of Gold Hunter's family, the Cecils [i.e., Crofts?], and describes incidents of the journey but few details of the route. The author says the youngest of the Cecil family is Gold Hunter, that his own life is closely bound to that of the Gold Hunter. The story "is written in almost the exact language of the 'Gold Hunter' himself . . . through the medium of an intimate friend." The description of the "Cecil" family seems to point to the Croft family, and Gold Hunter may be the youngest son of Joseph Croft.

[Coe No. II, 598.]

118 CUMMINGS, CHARLES J.

"Cummings diary." May 10 to September 14, 1859.

107 pp. 21½ cm. Original binding. With typewritten transcript.

Diary of a journey from Iowa to Oregon, May 10–September 14, 1859, not following the usual route but taking unusual trails and cut-offs; the Mormon Trail from Council Bluffs to Fort Laramie; North Platte road to Platte Bridge, near the present town of Casper, Wyo., on the north bank of the river instead of the usual trail along the southern bank; the Oregon Trail to Gilbert's Station at the eastern approach to South Pass; Lander Cut-off to City of Rocks on the old California Trail; California Trail to the Great Bend of the Humboldt, and the Honey Lake–Applegate Trail to Oregon.

On the flyleaf, in a different hand, is the following note, dated April 26, 1859: "This chronicle records the first trip in 6 years (since 1853) over the Applegate cut-off, or 'Death route.'"

[Coe No. 48.]

119 CUMMINS, HENRY, 1840–

Diaries, journal, and notebook of Henry Cummins, January 1, 1857 to May 10, 1863.

6 vols. [i.e., 499 pp.] 19–40½ cm.

Henry Cummins was the son of William M. Cummins, who came to Oregon in 1853 and settled in Lane County, near Eugene. He assisted his father on the farm, attended school in Eugene, and worked from time to time in the city bookstore and the printing office of the *People's Press*. He accompanied Dr. A. W. Patterson on his geographical surveying expedition to the northern part of the state east of the Cascades, July 15–September 27, 1861, and returned to Eugene and to the printing office of the *State Republican*, edited by H. Shaw and later by Cummins' friend J. M. Gale. Cummins moved to Salem September 5, 1862, was appointed assistant clerk of the House of Representatives, and studied law in Lafayette and Salem.

The journal ends on the eve of starting on a tour through the states.

The diaries and journal give a daily record of Cummins' studies, his work and social life, and discuss local events and his keen interest in science and in spiritualism, especially in the works of Andrew Jackson Davis. The notebook contains his "Individual constitution, Dec. 10, 1861"; phrenological analysis of his character by Dr. Charles H. DeWolfe; synopses of lectures with dates of delivery; notes on his reading and various topics; the Constitution and Minutes of the Pantheon of Science [Eugene], June 24–October 22, 1861; meteorological records, November 4, 1861–December 1862; and other papers.

[Coe No. 49.]

120 CURRY, GEORGE LAW, 1820–1878

Letter to the editor of the *Oregonian* [William Lair Hill]. Portland, March 1, 1877.

Copy in an unidentified hand. 3 pp. 32 cm.

Curry, who was Governor of Oregon Territory, 1854–1859, knew Marcus Whitman personally and wrote this letter in denial of the legend that Whitman saved Oregon. The letter was published in the *Oregonian*, March 2, 1877.

[Miller Collection.]

121 CURTIS, EDWIN STYLES, *d.* 1901

"Military Reservation of Fort Kodiak" [Alaska, 1869]. Map, signed: "*Official* Edwin S. Curtis 2' Lieut. 2 Arty. Post Adjt." Accompanied by a manuscript index and a letter to the Hon. James Wickersham from Frederick Sargent, Deputy Collector of Customs at Kodiak, September 17, 1903.

Map, traced on linen, scale 30" to the mile. 76 x 75½ cm., folded and mounted in cloth covers, with typewritten copy of index pasted inside front cover. 32 cm.

SARGENT, FREDERICK. "Index to map of Kodiak Village drawn in 1868 from map made by Fritz Blotner," signed by Fredk. Sargent, Kodiak, September 17, 1903 [with official seal]. 4 pp. 25½ cm.

—— Letter to the Hon. James Wickersham, Valdese [Valdez]. Custom-House, Port of Kodiak, Alaska, Deputy Collector's Office, September 17, 1903. 1 p. 25½ cm.

Sargent, in signing the index, says that Kodiak was never accepted as a military reservation as orders were not to establish a post within one mile of a village. The accompanying letter to James Wickersham, who was appointed U.S. judge for the Third District of Alaska in 1900, transmitted the map and index and requested that the map be returned.

[Coe No. III, 56.]

122–125 CURTIS, SAMUEL RYAN, 1807–1866

Letters and papers of Major General Samuel Ryan Curtis and his two sons, Major Henry Z. Curtis and Colonel Samuel S. Curtis, 1846–1866.

416 letters and papers. 1,294 pp. 20½ x 9–32½ cm.

Samuel Ryan Curtis was born in New York State in 1807, and in 1809 moved with his family to Ohio. After graduation from West Point he was sent to Fort Gibson with the 7th Infantry. In 1832 he resigned, returned to Ohio, was employed as an engineer on the construction of the National Road, and took up the study of law. After service in the Mexican War he removed to Iowa as chief engineer for improvements in the Des Moines River; was city engineer of St. Louis, and became interested in railroading. He represented the First Congressional District of Iowa from 1856 to 1861, interesting himself especially in the promotion of the Pacific Railroad, but resigned his seat in Congress in August 1861 to report for duty to Major General Frémont at St. Louis. He commanded the Union Army at **Pea Ridge**, 1862; was in command of the Department of Missouri, but was later removed on account of friction between civil and military authorities. In 1864 he was assigned to command the Department of Kansas and in 1865 was sent to the Department of the Northwest. After the Civil War he was one of the commissioners to treat with the Indians along the Missouri, and also served on the commission to examine and report on the construction of the Union Pacific Railroad. While engaged on this survey he died at Council Bluffs, 1866.

Both of General Curtis' sons served in the Civil War. Major Henry Zarah Curtis was assistant adjutant general on his father's staff while he was in command of the Department of Missouri, and then was transferred to General Blunt's staff in Kansas. He was killed in 1863 by guerrillas under Quantrill. Samuel Stephen Curtis was aide-de-camp on his father's staff during the campaign in Arkansas and major of the 2d Colorado Regiment.

The collection contains General Curtis' intimate letters to his wife and children written at frequent intervals when he was away from them; letters from his wife and sons to him; his official correspondence, with copies of orders, telegrams, etc., while serving in the Mexican and Civil Wars and as a member of the Indian Commission to make treaties with the Sioux.

The papers are arranged in four groups:

122 —— Autobiographical material; family letters and papers covering his service in the Mexican War, on engineering projects in Iowa and Missouri, as representative in Congress from Iowa and his efforts in behalf of the Pacific Railroad; and a letter to Secretary of War Floyd regarding the Utah Expedition. 1846–1860.

CURTIS, SAMUEL RYAN. Two autobiographical statements, written about 1862 and 1864. 32 pp.

—— 18 letters to his wife. November 26, 1847–December 30, 1860. 66 pp. The letter of December 27, 1847 to Mrs. Curtis contains a rough map, "Rapids of the Mississippi," indicating property he has bought.

—— 11 letters to his children, Henry Z., Samuel Stephen and Cornelia. March 16, 1850–December 27, 1860. 56 pp.

—— Letter to L. M. Kennett, Mayor of St. Louis. July 19, 1850. 4 pp.

—— Letter to Secretary of War Floyd. January 29, 1858. Copy. 4 pp.

CURTIS, MRS. BELINDA. Letter to her husband. July 3, 1849. 3 pp.

CURTIS, HENRY Z. 24 letters to members of his family. March 21 [1851]–May 5, 1861. The letter to his father, March 29, 1858, contains a full-page drawing of the Missouri River for about five miles below Omaha. 103 pp.

CURTIS, SAMUEL STEPHEN. 14 letters to members of his family. January 23, 1854–April 25 [1865]. 42 pp.

—— 14 letters to his mother written from Europe. January 17, 1865 [i.e., 1866]– January 11, 1867. 135 pp.

TOMPKINS, DANIEL D. Two letters and invoices to Samuel R. Curtis. June 6–10, 1846. 6 pp.

WOOL, JOHN E. Letter to Adjutant General Curtis. June 7, 1846, with a copy of a letter to Major D. D. Tompkins, June 7, 1846, and a memorandum, June 8, 1846. 3 pp.

123 —— Letters about the discovery of gold in Colorado; Samuel Stephen Curtis' experiences going to Colorado by ox team, prospecting and trading at Cherry Creek, and during the early settlement of Auraria and Denver; and the attempt to establish Jefferson Territory, 1858–1860.

CURTIS, SAMUEL RYAN. Five letters to his sons. May 16, 1858–October 21, 1859. 29 pp.

CURTIS, HENRY ZARAH. Letter to his sister Sadie. September 7, 1858. 8 pp.

—— Three letters to his mother. September 24, 1858–November 6, 1859. 12 pp.

CURTIS, SAMUEL STEPHEN. Two letters to his brother Henry. November 22, 1858, March 28 [1860]; and a typewritten

copy of a letter to Henry, November 2, 1858 that was printed in the *Omaha Republican* and copied in the *Missouri Democrat*, December 4, 1858. 9 pp.

—— Letter to the editor. November 24, 1858, printed in the *Council Bluffs Nonpareil*, January 22, 1859. Typewritten copy. 2 pp.

—— Three letters to his mother and father. February 8–September 16, 1859. 12 pp.

124 —— The Civil War period, 1861–1865. Official correspondence of Major General S. R. Curtis, of the Departments of Missouri, Kansas, and the Northwest; field orders, telegrams, reports and other military papers of Major Samuel Stephen Curtis on the campaign of the Colorado Volunteers; military papers of Henry Z. Curtis; and family letters.

Map of the Battle of Pea Ridge. March 7 and 8, 1862. Printed. 56 x 43 cm.

CURTIS, SAMUEL RYAN. Letter to his daughter Sadie. April 22, 1861. 3 pp.

—— 40 letters to his wife. June 16, 1861–July 26, 1865. 150 pp.

—— Three letters and a telegram to

Samuel S. Curtis. November 4, 1863–April 10, 1865. 10 pp.

—— Two letters and a telegram to Lieutenant Colonel James K. Mills. April 3–7, 1862. Copies. 3 pp.

—— Six telegrams to General Halleck. April 5–September 25, 1862. 10 pp.

CURTIS, S. R. Two letters to Captain W. H. McLean. April 5, 1862. 2 pp.

—— Three letters to Captain J. C. Kelton. April 19–29, 1862. 4 pp.

—— Letter to Brigadier General George W. Cullum. April 20, 1862. 1 p.

—— Letter to Colonel Coates. October 21, 1864. "Copy." 1 p.

—— Letter to the editors of the *Cincinnati Commercial*. August 31, 1862. "A true copy." T. I. McKenny. 1 p.

—— Memoranda—Arkansas campaign. June 6–August 31, 1862; April 26–28, 1863. 13 pp.

CURTIS, MRS. BELINDA. Two letters to her husband. August 28, October 19, 1864. 8 pp.

CURTIS, HENRY Z. Telegram to his mother about Sadie's death. April 3, 1862. 1 p.

—— Orders to Major C. H. Perry and Lieutenant J. W. Noble. [April 6, 1862.] 1 p.

—— Telegram to Captain F. S. Winslow. April 19, 1862; letter, April 20, 1862. 3 pp.

—— Letter to Lieutenant Luke O'Reilly. April 20, 1862. 1 p.

BALDWIN, ELIAS B. Telegram to H. Z. Curtis. [April] 4 [1862].

BALLINGER, RICHARD H. Letter to Major H. Z. Curtis. December 1, 1862. Copy. 5 pp.

BOYD, SEMPRONIUS H. Telegram to General Curtis. April 7 [1862]. 1 p.

BUCKINGHAM, G. Letter to his sister, Mrs. S. R. Curtis, about Lincoln's death and its effect on the politicians. April 21, 1865. 4 pp.

CHIPMAN, NORTON PARKER. Telegram to General Curtis. October 10, 1863, announcing murder of Major Curtis.

FORMAN, JACOB G. Letter to Hon. Henry Wilson. [*ca.* November 29, 1862.] Copy. 4 pp.

—— Letter to Colonel N. P. Chipman. January 20, 1863. 2 pp.

HALLECK, HENRY WAGER. Eight telegrams to General Curtis. April 5, 1862–April 26, 1863. Five with drafts of answers on same sheet. 9 pp.

JOHNSON, P. R. Letter to Colonel Compton relating to attacks on Curtis. November 16, 1862. Copy. 5 pp.

MILLS, JAMES K. Seven letters to General Curtis. April 3–8, 1862. 7 pp.

—— Telegram to H. Z. Curtis. April 6, 1862, with answer on same sheet. 1 p.

PORTER, ASBURY B. Telegram to General Curtis. [April] 6, 1862. Telegram, General Curtis to Colonel Boyd. April 6, 1862, on verso. 2 pp.

STRONG, WILLIAM K. Two letters to General Curtis. "Private." November 17, December 23, 1862. 5 pp.

SULLY, ALFRED. Letter to General Curtis. July 25, 1865. 2 pp.

TAYLOR, HAWKINS. Letter to General Curtis. September 19, 1864. 4 pp.

TOWNSEND, EDWARD DAVIS. Telegram to General Curtis. January 2, 1863, with answer on verso.

WASHBURN, CADWALLADER C. Letter to General Curtis. "Private." September 13, 1862. 1 p. Certified, a true copy. T. I. McKenny.

WINSLOW, FREDERICK S. Letter to General Curtis. July 3, 1863. 3 pp.

CURTIS, SAMUEL STEPHEN. Commissions and discharge papers as Lieutenant Colonel of the 3d Regiment, Colorado Volunteers, Major, 2d Regiment of Cavalry, Colorado Volunteers, 1862–1865; proceedings of the Council of Administration, 3d Regiment of Colorado

Volunteers, 1863; special and general orders, 1863–1866; invoice of camp and garrison equipage, 1863; muster-in roll of Samuel S. Curtis, 1864; receipts for books; copy of a telegram to Colonel J. H. Ford, October 8, 1865 and letter to J. L. Davenport, acting commissioner of pensions, April 29, 1908. 52 pp. Some of the forms are of interest as examples of early printing in the West.

125 ——— The Dakota and Montana papers; Indian Commission, and survey of the Union Pacific Railroad. 1865–1866.

CURTIS, S. R. 68 letters to his wife. March 11, 1865–December 25, 1866. The letter of July 10, 1866 contains two small sketches. 240 pp.

——— Six letters to Samuel S. Curtis. August 21–December 24, 1865. 17 pp.

——— Telegram to General E. D. Townsend. August 4, 1865 and answer, August 5, 1865, signed: "T. M. Vincent, A.A.G." 2 pp.

——— Four letters to E. M. Stanton, Secretary of War. September 29–October 25, 1865. Copies. 15 pp.

——— Letter to Lieutenant J. O'Neill. October 10, 1865 and answer of the same date. Copies. 2 pp.

——— Six letters to Hon. James Harlan. October 10, 1865–May 25, 1866. Copies. 28 pp.

——— Two letters to Colonel Pattee. October 20, 1865, May 16, 1866; and Pattee to Curtis, October 22, 1865. Copy. 4 pp.

——— Telegram to General G. M. Dodge. October 16, 1865. 1 p.

——— Letter to Colonel E. B. Taylor. October 31, 1865. Copy. 4 pp.

——— Letter to Colonel Thornton. March 13, 1866. Copy. 2 pp.

——— Letter to General Sherman. March 14, 1866. Copy. 4 pp.

——— Letter to Colonel [John G. Clark] commanding at Fort Rice. March 14, 1866. Copy. 2 pp.

——— Letter to Captain Phinney. March 14, 1866. Copy. 1 p.

——— Letter to Colonel I. V. Reeve from Curtis and H. W. Reed. May 15, 1866. Copy. 4 pp.

——— Appointment of George C. Granger. May 21, 1866. 1 p.

——— Letter to Hon. O. Guernsey. May 22, 1866. 1 p.

——— Memorandum of a telegraphic conversation between Major General Curtis and Major General G. M. Dodge. September 18, 1865. 4 pp.

——— Memorandum—Agenda for the first day at Fort Sully. May 26, 1866. 2 pp.

——— Abstract of obligations contemplated by the treaties entered into by the Commission . . . 1866. 3 pp.

U.S. COMMISSION to negotiate with the Indians along the Upper Missouri River. Articles of a treaty made and concluded at Fort Sully between the commissioners on the part of the United States and the chiefs and head men of the Minneconjou Band of the Dakota or Sioux Indians. October 10, 1865. Attested a true copy by E. F. Ruth. 5 pp.

——— Articles of a treaty . . . [with] the chiefs and head men of the Two Kettles Band of Dakota or Sioux Indians. October 19, 1865. Attested a true copy by E. F. Ruth. 5 pp.

——— Signatories to all the treaties, United States, Blackfeet, Two Kettles, Lower Brulés (Sichangu), Yanktonais (Lower), Upper Yanktonais,

Sans Arcs, Minneconjous, Ogalallas, Onk-pah-pahs. A list. 11 pp.

U.S. SECRETARY OF THE INTERIOR. [Instructions to the commissioners to make treaties with the Indians of the South West] Washington, August 16, 1865. Printed. 4 pp.

CURTIS, MRS. BELINDA. Letter to her husband. July 25, 1865. 4 pp.

—— Letter to her son, Samuel S. December 26, 1866. 4 pp.

CURTIS, SAMUEL S. Letter to his father. October 27 [1865]. 2 pp.

BURTON, R. P., Master of steamer *Calypso*. Letter to Brigadier General H. H. Sibley, H. W. Reed and E. B. Taylor. October 31, 1868. Copy [?] 1 p.

CLARK, JOHN G. Two letters to General S. R. Curtis. November 29, 1865, May 17, 1866. 11 pp.

COOLEY, D. N. Letter to Hon. Newton Edmunds, Office of Indian Affairs, relating to the Blackfeet Indians. April 17, 1866. Copy. 3 pp.

—— Two letters to General Curtis. April 25, May 8, 1866. 4 pp.

DODGE, GRENVILLE M. Telegram to General Curtis. [August] 28, 1865. 1 p.

ECKERT, THOMAS T. Letter to Hon. James Harlan. August 19, 1865. Copy. 1 p.

EDMUNDS, NEWTON. Letter to General Curtis. September 8, 1865. 3 pp.

—— Letter to General Curtis and the Rev. H. W. Reed. May 19, 1866. Copy [?] 2 pp.

GOODRIDGE, MOSES H. Letter to Colonel E. B. Taylor. November 10, 1865. Two copies. 2 pp.

GUERNSEY, ORRIN. Telegram and letter to General Curtis. September 12, 1865, May 14, 1866. 3 pp.

HARLAN, JAMES, Secretary of the Interior. Letter to Major General S. R. Curtis. August 17, 1865, enclosing a copy of President Johnson's order, August 15, 1865, appointing commissioners to negotiate treaties with the Sioux and Cheyennes of the Upper Missouri. 3 pp.

—— Five letters to General Curtis. August 17, 1865–May 11, 1866. Copies of a letter and telegram from General Pope, and a telegram from General Sibley, August 16 and 18, enclosed with two of the letters. 11 pp.

—— Letter to Hon. E. M. Stanton. August 16, 1865. Copy. 1 p.

HAY, JOHN. Letter to Samuel S. Curtis. January 10, 1866 [i.e., 1867], about the death of his father. 1 p.

HITT, R. R. Letter to Colonel E. B. Taylor. October 28, 1865. Copy. 1 p.

MAJORS, ALEXANDER. Letter to General Curtis. July 10, 1866. 3 pp.

NORTON, MARTIN. Letter to Colonel Taylor. November 10, 1865. Copy. 1 p.

PLIMPTON, JOHN G. Letter to General Curtis. August 27, 1865. 1 p.

POPE, JOHN. Circular to officers of the Department of the Missouri to cooperate with the Indian Commission, signed by John T. Sprague, Colonel and Chief of Staff. August 29, 1865. Copy. 1 p.

REED, HENRY WALTER. Letter to Major W. S. Woods. November 10, 1865. Attest, "E. F. Ruth." Copy. 1 p.

—— Three letters to General Curtis. May 29–June 3, 1866, enclosing a list of property left at Crow Creek by J. W. Stone, Agt., May 30, 1866. 5 pp.

ROSE, ROBERT H. Letter to Indian Agent [J. W. Stone]. July 27, 1865. Copy. 1 p.

RUTH, E. F. Letter to Captain Burton, Steamer *Calypso*. October 21, 1865. Copy. 1 p.

SIMPSON, J. H. Telegram to General S. R. Curtis, asking him to serve on a commission to examine part of the Union Pacific Railroad. November 16, 1865. 1 p.

SULLY, ALFRED. Letter to Brigadier General H. H. Sibley. September 22, 1865. Copy. 2 pp.

—— Letter to General Curtis. October 12, 1865 [copy], enclosing a list of chiefs and principal men who made peace in 1863 and 1864. 3 pp.

—— Order to Captain M. H. Goodridge. April 4, 1866. Copy. 1 p.

TAYLOR, EDWARD B. Letter to Governor Newton Edmunds. October 28, 1865. Copy. 1 p.

—— Three letters to Captain Burton. October 29–30, 1865. Attested true copies, by E. F. Ruth. The letters of October 29, 30, 1865 signed by Sibley, Reed and Taylor. 5 pp.

—— Letter to M. H. Goodridge. November 10, 1865. Copy. 3 pp.

—— Letter to M. Norton, Esq. November 10, 1865. Copy. 1 p.

THORNTON, CHARLES C. G. Letter to General Sibley. October 9, 1865. Copy. 1 p.

VAN VALKENBURG, ROBERT B. Letter to E. F. Ruth. August 28, 1865. Copy. 2 pp.

—— Telegram to S. R. Curtis. September 9, 1865. 1 p.

A series of letters of General Curtis, including official correspondence and letters to his wife, has been edited and published in *Annals of Iowa*, 1942, 3d Ser. XXIV. The original letters are not in the Coe Collection but supplement those for the years 1861–1862. The official reports of the Indian Commission are printed in the *Report* of the Commissioner of Indian Affairs, 1865, pp. 537–542; and 1866, pp. 168–176.

[Coe No. III, 713.]

126 CUSTER, ELIZABETH BACON (MRS. GEORGE ARMSTRONG), 1842–1933

Journal of Elizabeth Clift Bacon, Monroe, Michigan, April 8, 1852 to December 31, 1860, and papers of General Custer.

137 pp. 19½ cm. Original binding.

The diary is inscribed on the flyleaf: "Presented to Elizabeth Clift Bacon by her Father on this 8th day of April, 1851, being her birthday, to be used by her in keeping a journal of events from this day forward, and to be kept and preserved by her as the wish of her Father Daniel S. Bacon."

Libbie Bacon commenced her journal on her tenth birthday, April 8, 1852, and continued it for several months, and then wrote only occasionally, usually making a New Year's resolution to continue it, but soon tiring.

The papers of General Custer include the following:

CUSTER, GEORGE ARMSTRONG. Parts of four letters to his wife. April 11, 1865– [September 1873]. 14 pp. 20½–24½ cm.

—— Parts of two letters to his father-in-law, Judge Daniel S. Bacon. [July]– December 18, 1865. 8 pp. 20–24½ cm.

—— Circular addressed to Captain F. W. Benteen, Captain L. M. Hamilton, 1st Lieutenant S. M. Robbins, 1st Lieutenant Owen Hale. Headquarters Fort Riley, March 23, 1867. 1 p. 31 cm.

[BARRETT, LAWRENCE]. Part of a letter to Custer. March 23 [1873]. 4 pp. 21 cm.

GREENE, [JACOB]. Letter to Custer. April 7, 1864. 4 pp. 20 cm.

SMITH, C. Ross. Order to Brigadier General Custer. Headquarters Cavalry Corps, Army of the Potomac. November 20, 186[3?]. 1 p. 25 cm.

Custer's letters to his wife tell of his life in the army and in New York; those to his father-in-law are largely about his horse Don Juan.

One brief extract from Mrs. Custer's journal is quoted by Mrs. Merington in *The Custer Story*, New York, 1950, p. 24; and parts of the letters of April 1865, July 1865, July 1871, July 1873, and September 1873 have been quoted or paraphrased. Mrs. Merington, when writing *The Custer Story*, was allowed by Mrs. Charles Elmer (Custer's niece, May Custer) to copy General and Mrs. Custer's letters on condition that the originals should then be destroyed, and to keep a few sheets, selected at random, as specimens of Custer's handwriting.

Gift of Mrs. Marguerite Merington.

127 CUSTER, ELIZABETH BACON (MRS. GEORGE ARMSTRONG), 1842–1933

Letter to Mr. Thomas A. Warburton of New York. Bronxville, N.Y., March 16 [1905].

3 pp. 17½ cm. With envelope.

Mounted in a loose-leaf scrapbook of clippings and illustrations from newspapers and magazines, manuscript copies of poems, letters, and quotations relating to General Custer and especially to his last battle, and including a typewritten letter from Cyrus Townsend Brady to T. A. Warburton, Brooklyn, N.Y., January 9, 1905 [1 p.]. 122 pp. 6 plates. 28 cm.

Manuscript captions, notes, and copies are in the hand of the collector of the material, Thomas A. Warburton.

Mrs. Custer's letter deals with her large correspondence regarding her husband and her failure to recall much about his horses.

The letter from Mr. Brady is with regard to Mrs. Custer's rejoinder to General Robert P. Hughes, "The Campaign against the Sioux in 1876," Military Service Institution *Journal*, 1896, XVIII, 1–44. This rejoinder, June 21, 1897, was printed but not published. It is copied in the scrapbook with a copy of Mrs. Custer's letter to the Librarian of the [Lenox] Library in New York transmitting a copy of the pamphlet, December 6, 1897.

[Coe No. IV, 1276.]

128 CUSTER, GEORGE ARMSTRONG, 1839–1876

Black Hills Expedition, order and dispatch book, July 1 to August 25, 1874.

pp. 27–46. 31½ cm.

Twenty pages of the original records of the 7th U.S. Cavalry, General Custer commanding, on the Black Hills Expedition, 1874. The orders (the first to 2d Lieutenant H. M. Harrington, Fort Lincoln, July 1, 1874) are signed by 1st Lieutenant James Calhoun, A.A.A. General. The reports of the progress of the expedition to the Assistant Adjutant General, Department of Dakota [July 15], August 2, and August 15, 1874, are signed by General Custer.

The expedition, under the authority of General Terry, was to reconnoiter a route to the Black Hills and explore their interior. It left Fort Lincoln July 2 and returned August 30. In his report of August 2 Custer records the discovery of gold in the Black Hills. The military command was accompanied by Captain William Ludlow as chief engineer, Professor N. H. Winchell as geologist, Professor A. B. Donaldson, assistant, Mr. George Bird Grinnell as naturalist, and others including Charles Reynolds, guide, and two miners. Lieutenant Calhoun, Custer's adjutant, was his brother-in-law.

The reports to the Assistant Adjutant General at St. Paul [Oliver Duff Greene] are printed in full with slight variations in C. C. O'Harra's "Custer's Black Hills Expedition of 1874," *The Black Hills Engineer*, 1929, XVII, 263–286; the reports of August 2 and 15 are printed in *Letter from the Secretary of War Transmitting . . . a Report of the Expedition to the Black Hills* (43d Congress, 2d Session, Senate Ex. Doc. No. 32, 1875).

[Coe No. III, 714.]

129 CUSTER, GEORGE ARMSTRONG, 1839–1876

Medal. *Obverse:* "Custer's 3 Cav. Div. 3 [profile bust of Custer, facing left, in wreath, laurel and oak]." *Reverse:* "The history of this war / when truthfully / written, will contain no / [star] brighter [star] / page / than that upon which is / recorded the chivalrous / deeds, the glorious / triumphs / of the / soldiers of the / Third Division. / Cedar Creek 19. Oct. 1864. G. A. Custer."

3½ cm. in diam.

Medal of white metal with ring.

[Coe No. I, 435.]

130 CUTLER, RUFUS PUTNAM, 1818–1877

Two letters to Joseph G. E. Larned. Portland [Maine], August 23, and 25, 1864, about his life during the twenty-five years since graduating from Yale College.

17 pp. 20½ cm.

After graduation Cutler entered the Divinity School in Cambridge, Mass. From 1854 to 1859 he was in charge of the First Unitarian Church in San Francisco, and describes vividly conditions there at a critical period. He returned to the East, living in Portland, Me., Charleston, S.C., and Brooklyn, N.Y.

[Yale Memorabilia, Class of 1839.]

131 DALLAM, RICHARD

Diary of Richard Dallam, cattle drover, over the trail from Texas to California, and in California and Oregon from December 5, 1852 to May 26, 1864.

484 pp. 19 cm. Bound in undressed sheepskin by the owner with tie to carry in his saddle bag.

Accompanied by the original articles of agreement with George Wentworth to perform certain duties on the journey to California, March 26, 1853, and signed by Dallam and 31 others. 2 pp. 25 cm.

The diary, which is preceded by 11 pages of accounts, covers the journey from St. Louis, December 5, 1852, by boat, for New Orleans and from there to Texas; the stay near San Antonio gathering the herd; the departure for California, March 30, 1853, by way of Devil's River, Pecos Crossing, Ojo Escondido, San Elizario, Franklin [El Paso], San Diego, Ojo de Vaca, Guadaloupe Pass, Tucson, Pima, Gila River, Colorado River ferry, Warner's Ranch, and Los Angeles November 7. They camped near "Chimecola" [Temecula?] for the winter, and in the spring worked north into the neighborhood of San José. December 4, 1856, Dallam sailed on the S.S. *Columbia* with Mr. Wentworth for Portland and remained in the Willamette Valley collecting a new herd which they drove back to California in the spring of 1858, returning to the

camp near San José. Dallam spent some time in San Francisco on his return, suffering from chills and fever, herded cattle in the Sacramento and Feather River valleys in 1859 and 1860, returning to the San Isobel camp in July 1860, where he remained most of the time until the diary breaks off on May 26, 1864.

He records the weather, the miles covered, details of the trail and camps, the places visited, the people met, and the Vigilante excitement in San Francisco.

The journal is described in the Anderson Galleries, sale No. 1711, *Americana, Mainly the Collection of a New Jersey Historian and California Pioneer*. February 1923.

[Coe No. 51.]

132 DANA, JAMES DWIGHT, 1813–1895

Seventeen letters written by James Dwight Dana while serving as geologist and mineralogist on the U.S. Exploring Expedition under Captain Wilkes, July 21, 1838 to October 24, 1846.

51 pp. 18–27 cm.

James Dwight Dana left Yale College shortly before graduation to serve as instructor in the Navy. Shortly after his return he was appointed geologist and mineralogist of the U.S. Exploring Expedition. He later became professor of geology and mineralogy at Yale College.

—— 12 letters to Edward C. Herrick of New Haven. July 21, 1838–June 11, 1842. 34 pp.

James Dwight Dana wrote frequently

to his friend Edward C. Herrick, librarian of Yale College. These letters form part of that correspondence.

—— Five letters to William C. Redfield of New York. August 14, 1838–October 24, 1846. 17 pp.

The letters to Mr. Redfield are chiefly about the scientific observations made on the expedition.

Gift of J. H. Redfield.

[Rare Book Room.]

133 DANA, JAMES DWIGHT, 1813–1895

Notebooks kept while serving as geologist on the U.S. Exploring Expedition, 1838–1842.

3 vols. [i.e., 375 pp.] 15½ cm. Original bindings.

—— Miscellaneous notes and a few sketches, dealing largely with the Islands of the Pacific and the Mediterranean, and scientific articles for the *American Journal of Science*.

59 pp. 11–32½ cm.

—— Portfolio of drawings and sketches of scenes in the Pacific Islands, New South Wales and the Pacific Northwest.

50 drawings. 2 maps. 11 x 6–44 x 19½ cm.

The notebooks cover the expedition from New Zealand, Tonga, Fijis and Sandwich Islands, March 9–October 28, 1840; Sandwich Islands, Samoa, Kingsmills, November 13, 1840–November 17, 1841; Oregon and the Northwest Coast, December 20, 1841–October 24, 1842. They include descriptions of places, geological formations, and the wreck of the *Peacock;* sketches, maps and diagrams; a vocabulary of the Shasta Indians, and native music.

Among the miscellaneous notes are a table of "Latitudes and Longitudes of the U.S. Ship *Peacock,*" August 19, 1838–April 24, 1842; morning report of prisoners, Captain Wm. L. Hudson, Com., March 3, 1840; and "List of Coral Islands visited by the expedition" with notes. 16 pp.

The drawings are largely in pencil, but some are in ink and a few in wash or color. Some are signed J.D.D., some marked "Copied," and some "Rejected." One map (printed) is "Chart of Oceanic Migration" by H. Hale; the other is a tracing of Clatsop Prairie from a map by J. Drayton.

Much of the material in the notebooks and sketches was published in Dana's reports of the Expedition, *Crustacea,* 1852, vol. XIII; *Geology* [1849], vol. X, of the U.S. Exploring Expedition, and in Dana, *Corals and Coral Islands,* New York, 1872.

Gift of Miss Maria T. Dana.

[Rare Book Room.]

134 DARLEY, FELIX OCTAVIUS CARR, 1822–1888

"The Life of an Indian" followed by 5 lines from Bryant's "The Prairies," and signed: "F. O. C. Darley fecit /42."

Title page, 14 original drawings in pen and ink and one in pencil. 34½ x 24 cm.

—— *Scenes in Indian Life: A Series of Original Designs Etched on Stone.* By Felix O. C. Darley. Philadelphia, J. R. Colon [1843].

The original pen and ink drawings and those etched on the stone and printed by T. S. Sinclair of Philadelphia differ widely in detail, but the subject matter is the same except in No. 7.

[Coe No. 52.]

135 DAVIDSON, A. F.

A series of twenty-two maps of the emigrant route along the Platte River and east to St. Joseph, drawn in the summer of 1846, with descriptive notes followed by eight pages of notes and four attestations to the accuracy of the maps.

30 pp. 20 x 11 cm.

Davidson went to Oregon in 1845, and in 1846 returned to the East over the same route. He made detailed maps showing the location of the road and changes in the route, the type of country, location of water and fuel, and the camps, with some 1845 camps as well. The journey took 104 days. These maps cover the last five weeks, from June 26 or 27 to August 1. The first two maps are undated, the third shows the camp on June 28.

Among the notes at the end are a record

of his marriage, November 6, 1851, to Mary Elizabeth Mumfert [?]; a brief record of events, November 6–20, 1851; pencil sketches of Chimney Rock and Castle Rock; and attestations to the accuracy of the maps written and signed by four of Davidson's companions, S. Eikenburg [no date], J. B. Holliday, August 2, 1846; J. A. Hunt, August 3, 1846; Henry Williamson, August 3, 1846.

[Coe Collection.]

136 DELANO, ALONZO, 1806–1874

Journal of an overland journey from St. Joseph to California and life in the mines, April 5, 1849 to February 1851.

192 pp. 32½ cm.

Alonzo Delano was the son of Frederick Delano of Aurora, N.Y., and was living in Ottawa, Illinois, in 1849 when he decided to try his luck in California. He tried mining and store keeping and banking, settling finally in Grass Valley, where he died in 1874.

Delano devotes the first few pages to his preparations for the journey to California and his passage by steamboat from Peru, Ill., to St. Louis and St. Joseph, where he was to join a company under Captain Jesse Green from Dayton, Ill. From May 3 he keeps a daily record of the route followed by the Platte and Sweetwater Rivers, Sublette's Cut-off, to Fort Hall, the Humboldt River and Lassen Route to the Sacramento Valley, September 17, 1849, when he writes: "And here my journal should properly end. I may continue to make remarks as I pass along, but the journey is made & California par excellence is reached." He continues to record his experiences in the mines, at Sacramento and San Francisco, with entries under occasional dates to February 22, 1851.

The journal appears to have been written at some later date for publication, as it is divided into chapters and has some alterations and corrections, and some comments before an event. The last three pages are headed "Anecdotes of California."

Laid in the volume and mounted on blank leaves are 16 clippings from newspapers, the *New Orleans True Delta*, *Ottawa Free Trader* and *Constitutionalist*, and the San Francisco *Pacific News*, containing correspondence from Delano about California.

In 1854 Delano published his *Life on the Plains and among the Diggings; Being Scenes and Adventures of an Overland Journey to California; with Particular Incidents of the Route, Mistakes and Sufferings of the Emigrants, the Indian Tribes . . .*, Auburn and Buffalo, 1854. Many passages from the manuscript are printed verbatim or with slight alterations, others are omitted entirely, and still others extensively expanded. The manuscript was evidently used as the basis of the published work.

[Coe No. 53.]

137 DELLENBAUGH, FREDERICK SAMUEL, 1853–1935

"A canyon voyage" [New York and London, 1908]. Galley proofs with the author's corrections.

95 pp. *ca.* 18 x 69 cm.

Dellenbaugh at 17 was chosen a member of Major John Powell's second Colorado River Expedition, 1871–1873. He was its artist and assistant topographer.

Later he became the historian of the Expedition and published *Romance of the* *Colorado River*, 1902, and *A Canyon Voyage*, 1908.

[Coe No. III, 306.]

138 DENVER, PEOPLE'S GOVERNMENT

Minutes of the meetings of the People's Government of the City of Denver, October 8, 1860 to November 19, 1861.

112 pp., and 3 loose leaves laid in. 31½ cm. Original binding. With typewritten transcript.

In 1859, when the Provisional Government of Jefferson Territory was unable to enforce its laws, local governments sprang up in the towns, similar to the governments in the mining districts. The People's Government Council elected judges, sheriffs, the recorder, held elections, assessed property, established a fire department, and maintained law and order until the establishment of Colorado Territory in 1861.

The minutes are signed by the Secretary, A. H. Mayer, and President, A. C. Hunt, to November 6, 1860, and by the Secretary alone to February 16, 1861. A. C. Hunt's resignation was accepted Decem-ber 11, 1860 and William M. Slaughter was elected president; after April 1861, R. Sopris was president, John C. Spencer secretary. The minutes of the three meetings, September 4, 10, and November 19, 1861, on loose leaves, were recorded by Spencer.

The pages are badly water stained and show traces of mud and silt, probably from the Cherry Creek flood of May 1864, when the City Hall was completely destroyed. Only a few passages are illegible but many of the blank pages in the front and back of the volume are stained and still stuck together.

[Coe No. 36.]

139 "DESCRIPCION geographico historica de la California, y Tierras situadas al Nord-Ouest de la America hasta el Estrecho de Anian, segun las ultimas observaciones: y de las Islas de Anadir, Eleuteras, y de Bering." [*ca.* 1790.]

241 pp. Folded map. 31 cm. Original binding.

"Carta reducida de los payses del norte, en que se demuestra el verdadero Estrecho de Anian, ó Paso del Norte, . . . y las costas è islas del Mar del Sud, particularmente donde hacen el comercio los Rusos por el Kams-chat-ka." 51½ x 35½ cm.

In preparing the map, which is a very finished production in ink and watercolor, the author has used the best information available at the time and has indicated the courses of the English, Russian, and Spanish explorations.

The manuscript is written in a very neat hand throughout, and is divided into 15 chapters. It is signed on the last page with a rubric but no name.

The anonymous author in his "Advertencia" says that his work is in two parts: the first describes the Spanish voyages and discoveries from Hernando Cortés to the present, the settlements, the land and the rivers from Cape St. Lucas to the mouth of the Trinidad; the second part describes the voyages and discoveries of the Russians.

The author seems to have had access to all the published accounts of voyages of the sixteenth, seventeenth, and eighteenth centuries, and to the reports of the Spanish expeditions in the Spanish Archives, and has cited his sources in footnotes. He summarizes the extent of the discoveries from California north to the Strait of Anian; describes the geography of California and the coast from Cape St. Lucas to the Arctic Circle, the earliest accounts and voyages of discovery of California, the settlement of Lower California and establishment of the missions; the mis-sions and harbors of northern California, the new discoveries of Captain Cook, the Russian discoveries and settlements and their trade in America, and the character, government, religion, manners, and customs of the people of California.

In 1937 the "Descripción" was in the possession of Maggs Bros. of London.

[Coe Collection.]

140 DOUGLAS, SIR JAMES, 1803–1877

Letter to Mr. Kittson. Fort Vancouver, April 4, 1839. Signature only.

2 pp. 32 cm.

James Douglas at 17 entered the service of the North West Company and at its coalition with the Hudson's Bay Company remained with the Company under Dr. McLaughlin. He later succeeded him as chief factor at Fort Vancouver, removed to Victoria in 1849, and served as governor of the Company on Vancouver Island until his retirement in 1859, when he was appointed governor of British Columbia.

The letter informs Mr. Kittson that the Rev. Mr. Leslie is on his way to Fort Nisqually to establish a missionary settlement; outlines the Hudson's Bay Company's tract of land, and directs Mr. Kittson to make over part of the tract north of Fort Nisqually for the mission.

141 —— Letter to William F. Tolmie. Fort Vancouver, December 9, 1847. Signature only.

4 pp. 32 cm.

The letter announces to Mr. Tolmie the destruction of the Whitman mission and describes the massacre as reported to him.

[Miller Collection.]

142 DOWELL, BENJAMIN FRANKLIN, 1826–1897

Journal of a trip by ox team from St. Joseph, Missouri, to California, May 10 to September 9, 1850.

31 pp. 18 cm. With typewritten transcript.

In a letter [unsigned] to his friend Greensville, Sacramento City, Calif., September 27, 1850, Dowell includes a copy of the journal of his overland trip from St. Joseph, Mo., to California, by the Little Blue, the Big Blue, and the Platte Rivers, Fort Laramie, Sublette's Cut-off, Fort Hall, the Humboldt and Truckee Rivers, 1,933 miles in 109 days. In his rather terse account he gives the route and daily mileage, records the deaths in his company, and comments on conditions as to grazing, game, water supply, etc.

In 1850 Dowell moved on to Portland, Ore., and in 1852 to Jacksonville. He took part in the Rogue River Indian War in 1853 and the Yakima War in 1855, and operated a pack train between the Willamette Valley and the gold mines. He bought and edited the *Oregon Sentinel*, and in 1885 returned to Portland.

[Coe No. 54.]

143 DOWELL, BENJAMIN FRANKLIN, 1826–1897

The Heirs of George W. Harris and Mary A. Harris, Indian Depredation Claimants vs. the Rogue River Indians . . . Petition and Argument. [Washington, 1888.]

64 pp. 21½ cm.

The author's personal copy with his manuscript notes.

[Coe No. III, 1456.]

—— A second copy with the Appendix. 96 pp.

Presentation copy to Elwood Evans with annotations and corrections by the author. Attested at the end by D. S. Holton and Charles K. Chansler, clerk of Josephine County.

[Miller Collection.]

144 DOYLE, SIMON

Journals and letters of Simon Doyle describing his overland journeys from Rushville, Illinois, to California in 1849 and 1854, his life in the mines, and his return journey in 1856 by the Isthmus of Panama.

3 vols. [i.e., 289 pp.] 18½–22 cm. With typewritten transcripts.

Simon Doyle, son of Edward Doyle of Rushville, served in the Mexican War as 2d lieutenant in Dunlap's Company of Illinois Cavalry. He with his brother James and a company of Rushville friends joined the emigration to California in 1849. James returned home in the fall of 1851 and Manville joined his brother in California. A. J. Doyle accompanied him on his second journey across the Plains.

—— Journal of an overland journey from Rushville to the Feather River Valley, April 2–October 4, 1849, and his stay in the mines until January 1, 1852, followed by a "Waibill of distances, encampments and all important points and streams from the Missouri River at old Fort Kearney across the Plains to California or the new El Dorado of the Far West." 172 pp. Original binding.

With a letter to his father, Edward Doyle, Fort Bridger, July 19, 1849. 3 pp.

The journal describes in detail the journey from Rushville across Iowa to the Missouri opposite Fort Kearney, along the Platte River trail, Fort Laramie, Sweetwater, South Pass, Fort Bridger,

Salt Lake City, Bear River Ferry, Goose Creek, Humboldt River to Lassen's Cutoff, the Oregon Route to Goose Lake, September 19, and the Feather River Valley, October 4; his experiences at Long's Bar, Oregon Bar, and Union Bar to January 1, 1852.

The journal was written in part at least at a later date. The last entry, January 1, 1852, is a summary of events since January 1, 1850. It contains also a rough list in pencil of the members of the party.

—— Diary of a journey from Rushville to Petaluma, Calif., March 27–August 24, 1854; record of the weather, December 31, 1854–February 10, 1856; and return journey from San Francisco by the Isthmus of Panama, May 21–June 13, 1856. 64 pp. Original binding.

The entries in the diary are very brief, noting weather, distance covered, route, other trains on the road. This time Doyle followed Sublette's Cut-off and the Soda Springs, Raft River, Humboldt and Truckee River route to the Sacramento Valley.

The diary, which is written hurriedly in

pencil, is followed by 12 pages of memoranda—number of cattle, value, letters written, rough plans of a house, etc. The record of weather, December 31, 1854–February 10, 1856, is not included in the transcript.

DOYLE, SIMON. Four letters to his parents. November 11[–25], 1849–May 14, 1853. 20 pp.

—— Letter to his brother [Manville]. January 20, 1850. 4 pp.

—— Two letters to his brother [James].

November 12[–16], 1851, December 9, 1852. 7 pp.

—— Letter to Sam. May 21, 1850. 4 pp. (First sheet only, rest missing.)

—— Two letters to his father. July 18, 1850, April 22, 1853. 8 pp.

These journals and letters were formerly in the collection of the late Frederick A. C. Baker and were sold at auction at the Ritter-Hopson Galleries, March 24, 1932.

[Coe No. 55.]

145 DRAKE, JOHN M. and McCALL, JOHN M.

Two letters to Lieutenant Apperson describing the Crooked River Indian battle and the murder of Lieutenant Watson. Camp Maury, May 18 and 20, 1864.

17 pp. 20½ cm. With typewritten transcript.

These two letters describe in detail the attack on a camp of Indians at Crooked River and the death of Lieutenant Watson.

[Coe No. 56.]

146 DRAKE, SAMUEL ADAMS, 1833–1905

"Recollections of the Old Army in Kansas."

26 pp. 27 cm.

Samuel Adams Drake was born in Boston. Soon after his marriage in 1858 he moved to Kansas where he worked on a newspaper. He served in the Civil War, attaining the rank of colonel in the Kansas Volunteers.

The manuscript is in two handwritings and is a condensed copy of another manuscript, as some pages have two or three numbers. The 26 pages cover pages 1–34.

The recollections describe Fort Leavenworth in 1858 and during the Mormon War, incidents in the Free State War and the Civil War in Kansas, and many of the men taking part in these events.

147 DRUMMOND, WILLIAM W.

Letter to the Hon. C. Cushing. Great Salt Lake City, Utah Territory, October 1, 1855.

2 pp. 25 cm.

In 1854 W. W. Drummond and George P. Stiles were appointed associate judges and John F. Kinney chief justice of the Supreme Court in Utah Territory. Drummond antagonized the Mormons from the start by his behavior, and they believed that he did more than any other person to bring about the Mormon War. He resigned in March, 1857.

This letter to the Hon. Caleb Cushing,

Attorney General in Washington, describes the situation of gentile federal officials under a Mormon governor and their inability to enforce the laws of the United States.

[Coe Collection.]

148 DuBOIS, JOHN VAN DEUSEN, 1833–1879

Journals of John Van D. DuBois recording his experiences in the army in the West from 1857 to April 1862; thirty letters to members of his family, 1849–1869, and five of his commissions in the Army, signed by the Presidents and Secretaries of War.

3 vols. 25½–31½ cm. With typewritten transcript.

John Van Deusen DuBois was the son of Henry A. and Eveline (Van Deusen) DuBois, born in 1833. He graduated from West Point in 1855 and served in the army until his retirement in 1876, when he returned to his home in Hudson, N.Y., where he died in 1879.

—— Journals, April 19, 1857–April 12, 1862. 2 vols. [i.e., 322 pp.] 25½–31½ cm. Original binding.

The journals cover the Gila Expedition from Fort Bliss, April 19–September 8, 1857, with manuscript map, June 20; the march to Fort Union, December 16, 1857–January 9, 1858; the march to join Captain Marcy on his return journey with supplies for the army in Utah; the expedition against the Navajos and the Comanches, September 30, 1858–December 1860; orders to report at Washington, April 12, 1861; the Missouri campaign against Price, with Frémont and Halleck, to April 1862.

Tipped in the first journal is the resolution on the death of Colonel DuBois, Military Order, Loyal Legion, United States, Circular No. 8, New York, January 10, 1880.

The second journal ends with a note in DuBois' hand, signed: "My journal of the war was burned under advice of General Rosencrans to whom I was chief of staff at the battle of Corinth for fear of its falling into the hands of the enemy. This was Oct. 2nd '62. I kept no personal journal afterwards."

—— Letters and original commissions. 30 letters, 116 pp., five parchment commissions.

DuBois, John Van Deusen. Nine letters to his sister Mary ["Mollie" or "Mate"]. January 7, 1850–December 25, 1861. 31 pp.

—— Six letters to his father. October 5, 1856–October 4, 1866. 30 pp.

—— 12 letters to his mother. November 8, 1856–February 8, 1869. 47 pp.

—— Letter to his uncle [Samuel T. DuBois]. September 2, 1862. 3 pp.

—— Regimental record from July 1, 1859 to March 3, 1866. 4 pp.

DuBois, Henry. Letter to his sister. [1861.] 3 pp.

DuBois, Henry A. Letter to his daughter Mary. July 21, 1849. 2 pp.

Engraved commissions, on parchment, filled in by hand and signed by the President and Secretary of War: As 2d lieutenant in the Regiment of Mounted Rifles, October 1, 1855, signed by Franklin Pierce and Jefferson Davis, recorded by Colonel S. Cooper, Adjutant General, July 11, 1856; as brevet captain, August 10, 1861; as brevet major, October 4, 1862; as brevet lieutenant colonel, March 13, 1865, signed by Andrew Johnson and Edwin M. Stanton, recorded by E. D. Townsend, Assistant Adjutant General, August 20, 1861; as major in the 3d Regiment of Cavalry, May 6, 1869, signed by U.S. Grant and William W. Belknap and recorded by E. D. Townsend, January 8, 1870. 38 x 44–40 x 49½ cm.

The journals and letters give detailed descriptions of his life in the army, the country through which he passes, the military campaigns, and frank opinions and criticisms of his fellow officers.

General Breck, in his obituary, says that shortly before his death Major DuBois consigned his diary and papers to his brother with injunctions to him to destroy them (*Annual Reunion*, Association of Graduates, U. S. Military Academy, 1880, XI, 42–51).

The journal from April 19, 1857 to March 30, 1861, and nine of the letters to his family are published in *Campaigns in the West, 1856–1861. The Journal and Letters of Colonel John Van Deusen DuBois, with Pencil Sketches by Joseph Heger.* Edited by George P. Hammond. Arizona Pioneers Historical Society, Tucson, 1949. (See No. 254.)

[Coe No. 57.]

149 DUTTON, CHESTER, 1814–1909

Sixteen letters to his Yale classmates, William W. Rodman and Theodore S. Gold, written from Riverside, Cloud County, Kansas, June 20, 1878 to February 1, 1906.

61 pp. 13½–32 cm.

After graduating from Yale Dutton taught for a few years, but later became a farmer in Wolcott, N.Y. In 1868 he and his family moved to Kansas, settling on the Republican River near Concordia.

The early letters describe the country, the life of the early settlers in Kansas, the depredations of the Indians; the later letters deal largely with farming conditions, crops, etc., and also with family affairs.

[Yale Memorabilia, Class of 1838.]

150 DUTTON, CLARENCE EDWARD, 1841–1912

Letter to James Dwight Dana. U.S. Geological Survey, Division of Colorado, Washington, December 29, 1881.

8 pp. 20 cm.

Clarence E. Dutton graduated from Yale College in 1860. After serving in the Ordnance Corps of the regular army during the Civil War and at Frankford and Washington Arsenals, he was detailed to the Survey of the Rocky Mountain Region under Major John W. Powell in 1875 and remained in the West until 1886.

The letter to Dana discusses the volcanic phenomena of the West.

[James Dwight Dana Scientific Correspondence, Rare Book Room.]

151 EELLS, CUSHING, 1810–1893

Letter to his son, Myron Eells. Tacoma, W.T., July 16, 1888.

2 pp. 20 cm.

The Rev. Cushing Eells crossed the Plains in 1838 with Elkanah Walker and their wives to join Whitman and Spalding in the Oregon mission. After the massacre he settled in Forest Grove, and in 1860 moved to Walla Walla where he founded Whitman Seminary.

The letter is personal, about his plan to go to Skokomish in a few days.

[Miller Collection.]

152 [EELLS, EDWIN] 1841–1917

"Eliza and the Nez Percé Indians." [1913].

14 pp. 32½ cm.

Typewritten manuscript with autograph alterations and comments. Attached to the manuscript is a note, "I believe Edwin Eells was the author of this sketch. He was one of the two sons of Cushing Eells . . . C. B. Bagley. Probably written about the year 1913."

A narrative of the life and work of Eliza Spalding Warren, the second white child born in Oregon Territory, with other facts relating to the coming of the early mission-aries from 1834 to 1838, the first printing press, the Indian tribes of the region, the Whitman Massacre, the conspiracy to kill Governor Stevens, and other events connected with the pioneer history of the Northwest.

Published, with some variations, with title: "Eliza and the Nez Percé Indians" by Edwin Eells, *Washington Historical Quarterly*, 1914, V, 288–299.

[Coe No. 58.]

153 EELLS, MYRON, 1843–1907

Two letters to the Hon. A. McKinlay. Skokomish, Mason County, Wash. Ter. [January], February 5, 1885.

9 pp. 25 cm.

The Rev. Myron Eells, youngest son of the Rev. Cushing Eells, was missionary to the Indians at Skokomish.

The earlier letter is undated but is en-dorsed: "Answered 19th January 1885." Both letters are about Whitman and the purpose of his journey east.

[Miller Collection.]

154 EELLS, MYRON, 1843–1907

Two letters to the Hon. A. Hinman. Union City, Mason County, Washington, April 14, 25, 1891.

5 pp. 26–26½ cm.

The letter of April 14 is folded and tipped into his *The Relations of the Congregational Colleges to the Congregational Churches . . . Read before the Congregational Council of the Pacific Coast, at Portland, Oregon, June 27, 1888.* New York, 1889.

The letter of April 25, written in pencil, concerns the crisis in the affairs of Tualatin Academy, later Pacific University, at the time of the controversy over denomina-tional or undenominational control and the resignation of President Jacob F. Ellis, and Mr. Hinman's personal attitude toward President Ellis.

The letter was formerly laid in a copy of Myron Eells, *Ten Years of Missionary Work among the Indians at Skokomish, Washington Territory*, Boston [1886], which was purchased from Fred Lockley of Portland, Ore.

[Coe No. III, 1470.]

155 EELLS, MYRON, 1843–1907

Notes on tools, utensils, clothing and other objects used by the Indians of the Pacific Northwest, signed by M. Eells.

31 pp. 22 cm.

The notes, in pencil on various kinds of scrap paper and backs of letters, were written after December 26, 1884. They describe briefly the Indians' loom, spinning wheel, snowshoes, combs, fishing implements, dyes, and their use of plants, birds, and animals.

[Miller Collection.]

156 EGAN, HOWARD, 1815–1878

Journals of Howard Egan, April 8, 1847 to January 5, 1856.

4 vols. [i.e., 403 pp.] 11½–15 cm.

Howard Egan was born in Ireland in 1815, and after his mother's death was brought to Canada by his father, who died in 1828. Howard went to sea for several years, later settling in Salem, Mass., where he made rope. In 1838 he married Tamson Parshley, a girl 14 years old. In 1842 he and his wife were converted to Mormonism and baptized, and moved to Nauvoo the same year. He became a major in the Nauvoo Legion; was captain of the Ninth Ten in the exodus from Winter Quarters to Great Salt Lake in 1847; repeating the journey with his family in 1848. In 1855 he was engaged in the cattle trade, driving cattle to California to sell. In 1862 he was superintendent of the Overland Mail Line from Salt Lake City to Carson, and was an experienced guide and mountaineer. After 1871 he tried mining with little success and later became a special guard for Brigham Young; at the time of his last illness he was a guard at Brigham Young's grave.

—— "A journal kept by Howard Egan, on the pioneer expedition to the westward, commencing Thursday, April the 8th, 1847." 180 pp. Original binding. With typewritten transcript.

The diary, covering the period from April 8 to July 27, 1847, gives in detail Major Egan's part in the Mormon exodus from Winter Quarters at Florence, Neb.,

to Salt Lake City. The party of 144 followed the Mormon Trail to Utah by the Platte River, Ash Hollow, Scott's Bluff, Fort Laramie, Sweetwater, Fort Bridger, where they met Jim Bridger himself, and on through the Great Divide to the valley of Great Salt Lake—1,055¾ miles. In the diary Major Egan describes the journey in detail, lists the names of the members of the party, quotes Brigham Young's sermons, gives an inventory of the provisions, and includes a table of distances.

—— Journal, July 28–September 6, 1847, kept during his stay in Salt Lake City until August 26 and the return journey to Winter Quarters as far as Pacific Springs. 38 pp. Original binding.

Major Egan describes the planning of Salt Lake City and its first buildings, the plans for the winter, and the organization of the pioneers.

—— "Jour. kept by H. Egan on a trip from fort Utah to California." November 18, 1849–February 23, 1850, followed by a table of distances. 57 pp.

The journal records events of an expedition from Fort Utah (Provo) to California, by the Sevier, Santa Clara and Virgin Rivers to Los Angeles and north to the San Joaquin and Merced Rivers, where the journal breaks off. The table of distances notes all springs and streams on the route, miles traveled from camp to camp, and the location of fuel and feed. The last leaf contains a "Bill of provisions laid in by Howard Egan January 1850."

—— Diary for 1855, kept by Howard Egan while in California trading in cattle, January 1–July 1; during the journey from California to Salt Lake, by the Humboldt River, July 1–20, and the return trip from Salt Lake to Sacramento, September 19–29, with brief entries from September 30 through [January] 5 [1856]. 125 pp. Original binding.

The diary is written in pencil recording very briefly the weather and Egan's transactions in the cattle business. There are no entries from July 21 until September 19, when he records his journey to Salt Lake and return, and adds a rough map at the end with no place names indicated.

With the journals is the leather knapsack carried by Howard Egan on the Plains. 31½ x 31 x 8 cm.

The journals and diaries have been published with many alterations in *Pioneering the West, 1846 to 1878. Major Howard Egan's Diary: Also Thrilling Experiences of the Pre-frontier Life among Indians; Their Traits, Civil and Savage, and Part of Autobiography, Interrelated to His Father's*, by Howard R. Egan. Edited . . . by William M. Egan. Richmond, Utah, 1917.

[Coe Nos. 59–62, 65.]

157 EGAN, WILLIAM MONROE, 1851–

"Journal" or, Reminiscences of his childhood in Salt Lake City [1851–1863].

24 pp. 14½ cm. Original paper covers.

—— "Trip from Salt Lake to Carson City, Nevada" in 1863, with a list of stations and distances on the Overland Mail route and reminiscences of the Pony Express, the Deep Creek Ranch, and his life from 1863 to 1886.

60 pp. 15 cm.

William Monroe Egan was the fifth son of Major Howard Egan and his first wife, Tamson Parshley. He was born in Salt Lake City in 1851. At 12 he went as a night herder of two teams of six mules each to Carson City with his brothers Erastus and Howard, helped with the cattle at the Deep Creek Ranch, returned to Salt Lake City to continue his education, was baptized in 1869, became interested in beekeeping, tried editing two journals, first, *Our Deseret Home*, second, *The Utah Industrialist*, and in 1886 married and moved to Provo.

The journal is in pencil in narrative form, describing briefly events from his birth, schools, his father's cattle trading, General Johnston's army, life at Lehi, loss of the barn at Salt Lake City by fire, the Pony Express, a trip to Fort Douglas, skating and swimming, etc.

The account of the trip was written from memory at a later date, and occupies pages 37–96. The remaining pages contain notes on prophecies, origin and organization of the Mormon Church, hymns, baptism, ordination, blessings, etc.

The list of stations and distances is printed in Howard R. Egan, *Pioneering the West*, 1917, pp. 197–198.

[Coe Nos. 63–64.]

158 EGAN, WILLIAM MONROE, 1851–

Family letters and papers, a daguerreotype, photographs, and material relating to the publication of the diary of Howard Egan, April 19, 1852 to March 11, 1918.

170 pp. Various sizes.

In addition to the letters of Howard Ransom Egan, William Monroe Egan, and other members of the family on personal affairs and the proposed publication of their father's diaries, the following letters and papers are included:

CHURCH OF JESUS CHRIST OF LATTER-DAY SAINTS. Deed transferring property at Fort Ephraim to Brigham Young, Trustee in Trust for the Church of Jesus Christ of Latter-day Saints, by Peder Nielssen, March 1, 1858. Witnesses, Parlan McFarlane, H. F. Petersen [?], J. Jensen. John Eagar, county recorder. Broadside, endorsed March 13. 1 p.

COOK, FREDERICK. Appointment of Major Egan as superintendent of the Overland Mail Line from Salt Lake City to Carson, July 1, 1862. 1 p.

CUMMING, ALFRED. Letter to the Commanding Officer at Fort Laramie [Captain F. N. Clarke]. May 12, 1858, signed: "A. Cumming, Governor of Utah Territory." 1 p.

ELLERBECK, THOMAS W. Receipt for powder, Ordnance Department, Nauvoo Legion, Great Salt Lake City, February 3, 1858. 1 p.

EMIGRATION OFFICE, Florence, N. T. Two orders to pay in rations, dated June 13, 1863, and signed: "F. Little by L. S. Hills, to Caroline Larsen and Cornelius Tipple." Printed forms filled in. 2 pp.

FORNEY, JACOB. Letter to Howard Egan, general mail agent. June 15, 1879. 1 p.

FOX, ISAAC. Promissory note to George Q. Cannon, signed: "Florence, July 19, 1860, Isaac Fox." 1 p.

HOLT, ROBERT. Subscription list for transporting Elder Holt from England. Great Salt Lake City, October 7, 1854, signed by Samuel W. Richards, P. G. Sessions, Jonathan Midgley, Thomas Hall, Hugh Hilton, John Mellen, Leon W. Hardy and followed by the names of subscribers. 2 pp.

LYNCH, PATRICK. Appointment of Howard Egan as deputy clerk of the U.S. Court of the Third Judicial District, Great Salt Lake City, April 21, 1862. 1 p.

McKEAN, THEODORE. Notice of appointment of Howard Egan as deputy sheriff of Salt Lake County, January 9, 1876. 1 p.

PERPETUAL EMIGRATING FUND COMPANY. Record of attendance of members, September 15, 1850–September 11, 1851; accounts with George Q. Cannon, "All transferred to H. Cart & other Immigrants Pass Bk. 1860"; balance sheet, etc. 8 pp.

U. S. MAIL LINE. Receipt for freight on steamer *Lady Franklin* to Mr. C. Layton, April 19, 1852, signed by Ben R. Kerby. Printed form. 1 p.

YOUNG, JOSEPH W. Letter to William C. Staines. May 11, 1864. 4 pp.

A few of these letters and papers, the daguerreotype and photographs are reproduced in *Pioneering the West, 1846 to 1878*, by Howard R. Egan, edited by William M. Egan, Richmond, Utah, 1917.

[Coe No. 65.]

159 EGAN, WILLIAM MONROE, 1851–

"Brigham Young. An historical Sketch by W. M. Egan." Salt Lake, *ca.* 1880.

64 pp. 20 cm.

The manuscript, in pencil, is a brief summary of the life of Brigham Young from his birth to his death, 1801–1877.

[Coe No. 66.]

160 EGAN, WILLIAM MONROE, 1851–

Papers of William M. Egan. I, "Native Utes of Utah"; II, "Pony Express; My recollections of it"; III, "Pioneering and biography of Major Howard Egan and sons. Supplement and sequel to *Pioneering the West.*"

23, 27, 12 pp. 28 cm. With typewritten transcripts of I and II.

The first and second manuscripts are in pencil. The third is typewritten, and, except for the first two pages, a carbon copy.

Some of the material on the Pony Express is included in Howard Egan, *Pioneering the West* (see p. 281). "Pioneering and biography" contains details not included in the printed volume and family history to 1921. Some of this material is contained also in W. M. Egan's "Trip from Salt Lake to Carson City and Reminiscences."

[Coe No. 66A.]

161 ELD, HENRY, 1814–1850

Journal of Henry Eld, Jr., U.S. Navy. September 6 to October 29 [1841].

126 pp., including 43 original maps. 2 folded maps, printed. 33 cm. Original binding.

—— Journal of an expedition to survey Gray's Harbor and Shoalwater Bay, August 11 to September 7, 1841. Incomplete.

30 pp. 31½ cm. Bound in the back of the journal of the Oregon and California overland expedition.

Accompanied by 3 paper-covered sketchbooks containing 48 original drawings on 43 loose leaves, each with guard sheet. 29 x 22½ cm.

Henry Eld was born in New Haven, June 2, 1814, and died at sea on the U.S.S. *Ohio*, March 12, 1850. As Passed Midshipman he accompanied Wilkes on the U.S. Exploring Expedition, 1838–1842, assigned first to the *Peacock*, and joined the *Vincennes* at Fiji. He was ordered by Charles Wilkes, commander of the expedition, to join the special overland expedition under Lieutenant George F. Emmons, from Vancouver, Wash., to San Francisco.

As second in command, when the expedition separated at Sutter's, he led the overland party to San Francisco.

The journal of the overland expedition covers the details of the expedition and its route from the Willamette Mission, south of Vancouver, September 7, to San Francisco, October 28, 1841; it is illustrated with 43 manuscript maps (three of them double page).

The two folded maps are:

"Map of the Oregon Territory by U.S. Ex. Ex. and the Columbia River, reduced from a survey made by the U.S.

Ex. Ex. 1841. J. H. Young & Sherman V. Smith, New York." 91½ x 63 cm. (*See* Wilkes' *Atlas*, Map [4].)

"Map of Upper California by U.S. Ex. Ex. and best authorities, 1841." 31 x 27 cm. (*See* Wilkes, V, 151.)

The manuscript of the Grays Harbor expedition is preceded by an extract from the Appendix of Wilkes' *Narrative*, IV, 533–536, including the letter from Wilkes ordering Eld to undertake this survey, with Colvocoresses as his second in command, and to proceed to join the ships in Baker's Bay after carrying out the orders.

The three sketchbooks are labeled "Henry Eld, Jr. U.S. Exploring Exped. 1838–1842. No. 1" [No. 2 and No. 3], and contain 11 sketches of scenes in Oregon and Washington, 5 of the Fiji Islands, 3 of other South Pacific Islands, 1 of California, and 28 untitled. On the inside of the cover of No. 3 there is a pencil plan of San Francisco. The sketches are not reproduced in the Wilkes *Narrative* of the Expedition.

—— Diary of Passed Midshipman Henry Eld, September 7 1841–October 29, 1841. Typewritten manuscript (carbon). 86 pp. 28 cm.

Transcript by Alfred N. Meiss of a diary kept by Henry Eld of the Wilkes Expedition overland journey from Vancouver to San Francisco that is now in the possession of the New Haven Colony Historical Society, which owns five manuscript journals of Henry Eld containing accounts of his experiences on the *John Adams* and the *Delaware*, on the Wilkes Expedition, on the Antarctic cruise, and on the overland expedition from Vancouver to California. The last journal is apparently a copy of the one in the Coe collection. It has some variations and insertions but includes additions which are in the Coe manuscript and omits passages crossed out.

The official report of the Expedition and Wilkes' *Narrative* contain accounts of the overland expedition to California and the survey of Grays Harbor, but Henry Eld's journal, with its series of maps of the route from Vancouver to San Francisco, and his sketches have not been published except for extracts, one page in facsimile, and three sketches reproduced in E. Eberstadt, *The Northwest Coast*, New York [1941].

[Coe No. 67.]

162 ELD, HENRY, 1814–1850

One hundred letters, orders, and other papers of Lieutenant Henry Eld during his service in the United States Navy, 1832–1851; and eleven letters written by or to Edward Eld while he was in California or Nebraska Territory, 1845–1858.

112 pieces. 188 pp. 25–33 cm.

The collection contains the following papers:

—— Letter to his brother, Edward, February 3, 1836. 3 pp.

—— Three letters to his father. April 15, 1839–February 21, 1850. 11 pp.

—— Report to Captain Hudson on observations taken on the ice in Antarctica, January 23, 1840; expenditure of provisions, etc., June 15, 1842; provisions on board U.S.S. *Vincennes*, June 17, 1842; list of articles remaining on hand, June [21], 1842; list of chronometers delivered to the Navy Yard, June 21, 1842. 9 pp.

—— Letter to Captain Wilkes. August 31, 1840, with Wilkes' answer of the same date. 2 pp.

—— Draft of his report of the expedition from Nisqually to Gray's Harbor [after August 11, 1841]. 4 pp.

—— Request for supplies, September 1, 1841. Approved by Charles Wilkes. 1 p.

—— Copy of the Resolution of the Senate and House, conferring medals on the members of the Exploring Expedition. 1 p.

—— Letter to Captain Gregory. June 26, 1842. 2 pp.

—— Report to John A. Davis on the bowsprit and jib boom of the U.S. Schooner *Flirt*, Porto Rico Harbor, May 8, 1843. Signed also by Chas. E. Fleming, acting lieutenant, H. F. Porter, acting master, Thomas King, carpenter. 1 p.

—— Letter to the Gentlemen of the Court [of Enquiry] with regard to the log of the *Somers*, January 14, 1843, a preliminary draft, and the summons to the Naval Court of Enquiry, unsigned and undated, 3 pp.

—— Draft or copy of an unsigned letter, Honolulu, November 10, 1840. 1 p.

ALMY, JOHN JAY. Two letters to Henry Eld, Sr. May 4, 29, 1850. 7 pp.

—— Letter to Miss Eld. May 28, 1850. 3 pp.

BANCROFT, GEORGE. Two letters to Henry Eld, Jr. August 21, 1845 [printed form, signed], May 12, 1846. 2 pp.

CLARK, PETER G. Letter to Henry Eld, Sr. May 4, 1850. 2 pp.

CRANE, WILLIAM MONTGOMERY. List of nautical instruments allowed to ships of each class. Printed circular, signed by W. M. Crane to Captain F. H. Gregory, with added note by M. C. Perry. 2 pp.

DAYTON, A. O. Two letters to Henry Eld. March 22, 30, 1843. 2 pp.

DICKERSON, MAHLON. Seven orders, etc., to Henry Eld. March 7, 1836–June 28, 1838. 7 pp.

ELD, ANN MANSFIELD (MRS. HENRY, SR.). Letter to her son Edward. February 17, 1850. 3 pp.

ELD, EDWARD. Letter to his mother. September 20, 1845. 2 pp.

—— Letter to his brother, Henry Eld. July 12, 1850. 2 pp.

—— Six letters to his father, Henry Eld, Sr. October 30, 1854–June 20, 1858. 10 pp.

ELD, HENRY, SR. Unsigned draft of a letter to John Boyle, Acting Secretary of the Navy, with a copy of a certificate from Dr. J. Knight. May 8, 1833. 2 pp.

—— Seven letters to his son, Henry Eld. November 4, 1846–November 20, 1849. 18 pp.

—— Two letters to his son, Edward Eld. June 23, 1849, February 15, 1855. 6 pp.

—— Three drafts of an epitaph for his son Henry, and family records. 8 pp.

ELLIOTT, JESSE DUNCAN. Orders to Henry Eld, Jr. May 20, 1836, 1 p.

EMMONS, GEORGE FOSTER. Instructions to Henry Eld. October 26 [1841]. 1 p.

—— Summons to appear at Naval Court of Enquiry. February 21, 1842. 1 p.

FORBES, ROBERT BENNET. Letter to Henry Eld, Sr. January 13, 1851. 1 p.

HENSHAW, DAVID. Orders to Henry Eld, Jr. July 27, August 1, 1843. 2 pp.

HOFFMAN, O., Judge Advocate. Document certifying that Henry Eld performed the duties of provost marshal to the Court of Enquiry, U.S.S. *North Carolina*, January 20, 1843. 1 p.

HUNT, TIMOTHY A. Letter to Henry Eld, Sr. May 27, 1850. 3 pp.

INGERSOLL, RALPH ISAACS. Two letters to Henry Eld, Sr. January 8, 1832, enclosing appointment of Henry Eld, Jr., as acting midshipman, January 7, 1832 [printed form signed by Levi Woodbury] ; and January 20, 1832, enclosing a letter to him from Levi Woodbury, January 19, 1832. 5 pp.

MANSFIELD, LOUISA. Letter to Henry Eld, Jr. July 24, 1833. 2 pp.

MASON, JOHN YOUNG. Orders to Henry Eld, Jr. November 13, 1846. 1 p.

NELSON, SAMUEL. Habeas Corpus ordering Captain Gregory, Captain Moorehead or the officer commanding the *North Carolina* to produce the body of Alexander Fullerton at the office of Frederick A. Talmadge, recorder of the City of New York on the 24th day of August. July 1, 1842. 2 pp.

PATTERSON, DANIEL TODD. Orders to Henry Eld, Jr. October 23, 1835. 1 p.

PAULDING, JAMES KIRKE. Letter to Henry Eld, Jr. July 6, 1838 [printed form] ; orders, July 12, 1838. 2 pp.

REYNOLDS, WILLIAM. Letter to Henry Eld, Jr. January 22, 1843. 4 pp.

RIDGELY, CHARLES GOODWIN. Four orders to Henry Eld, Jr. July 1, 1837–June 5, 1839. 4 pp.

STRIBLING, CORNELIUS K. Letter to Henry Eld, Sr. March 28, 1850. 2 pp.

UPSHUR, ABEL PARKER. Seven orders to Henry Eld, Jr. June 17, 1842–April 10, 1843. 7 pp.

WARRINGTON, LEWIS. Letter to Henry Eld, Jr. February 23, 1847. 1 p.

WILKES, CHARLES. Seven orders to Henry Eld, Jr. June 18, 1838–May 23, 1842. 10 pp.

—— Lists of equipment and provisions for the Grays Harbor expedition. Ap-

proved by Wilkes, July 18, 1841. 3 pp.

—— Two letters to Henry Eld, Jr. August 15, 1841, June 11, 1846. 5 pp.

WINDER, CHARLES H., Judge Advocate. Summons to Henry Eld to testify at the General Court Martial of Charles Wilkes, U.S. Ship *North Carolina*, July 30, 1842. Printed form. 1 p.

WOODBURY, LEVI. Letter to the Hon. R. I. Ingersoll. October 16, 1832. 1 p.

—— Letter to Henry Eld, Jr. April 2, 1833. 1 p.

WYMAN, THOMAS W. Certificate of Eld's correct deportment, October 31, 1835. 1 p.

The Eld papers fall into five groups: Henry Eld's early years in the Navy, 1832–1837; the U.S. Exploring Expedition, Captain Wilkes commanding, 1838–1847; the mutiny on the *Somers*, 1842/43; correspondence of Henry Eld, Sr., with his son during the Mexican War, 1846–1849; letters to Henry Eld, Sr., after the death of his son, 1850–1851, family records and genealogy, and correspondence of Edward Eld with his family while in California and the Middle West, 1849–1858.

Henry Eld, Jr., kept copies of all letters connected with his service in the Navy, and, with few exceptions, it is these copies that have been preserved by the family. With the manuscripts there is a red morocco portfolio, handmade, with Arabic decorations. It is possible that Eld got this portfolio in Morocco when he served in the Mediterranean. 23½ x 36 cm.

Captain Wilkes' order of July 17, 1841, for Eld to command the expedition to survey Grays Harbor, is printed in Wilkes' *Narrative*, Philadelphia, 1845, IV, 534.

[Coe Collection.]

163 ELLIS, WILLIAM, 1821–1905

Five letters to his Yale classmate Nathan Witter Williams from Washington Territory, March 3, 1884 to March 8, 1891.

12 pp. 21–25 cm.

Ellis studied medicine and practiced in Wisconsin until 1868. He then tried farming in Kansas, but later moved on to the Pacific Coast, finally settling near Willapa, W.T.

The letters, especially the first two, describe the country near Grays Harbor and the opportunities in farming and the lumber industry.

[Yale Memorabilia, Class of 1842.]

164 ELLSWORTH, HENRY LEAVITT, 1791–1858

Journal from October 8 to November 17, 1832, written in the form of a letter to his wife, Nancy Allen Goodrich. Fort Gibson, November 17, 1832.

114 pp. Sketch. 41½ cm.

Henry L. Ellsworth, Yale 1810, lawyer, and prominent citizen of Hartford, was appointed by President Jackson, in 1832, as a commissioner to superintend the settlement of the Indian tribes being moved to the south and west. On his way to Fort Gibson he met Washington Irving, Charles J. Latrobe and Count Pourtalès, who accompanied him. He was later appointed commissioner of patents by President Jackson.

The letter consists of copies of extracts from Ellsworth's journal kept while on tour of the Southwest, from Fort Gibson up the Arkansas and Cimarron Rivers to "Cross Timbers" and the Canadian River, and back across the prairie to Fort Gibson. His party was escorted by Captain Jesse Bean and his company of Mounted Rangers. The sketch is a diagram of an encounter with wild horses.

The journal has been edited by Stanley T. Williams and Barbara D. Simison and published with title: *Washington Irving on the Prairie; or, A Narrative of the Southwest in the Year 1832*, New York, 1937.

—— "Journal of Hon. H. L. Ellsworth, Commissioner to the Indians, in a series of letters written in the years 1832–3. Describing the manners & customs of various Indian tribes, and likewise incidents connected with the formation of treaties with them." 91 pp. 20½ cm. Original binding.

"This (so far as it goes) is a duplicate of the Ellsworth manuscript copied out (but never completed) by Mrs. H. L. Ellsworth, née C. C. Smith, his third wife. The 'dear N.' to whom the manuscript letters are addressed was Mr. Ellsworth's first wife, Nancy Goodrich. This copy was commenced with the intention of publishing it as of historical interest and perhaps value, but Mrs. Ellsworth died in 1869 and it was never completed."—Note in an unidentified hand pasted on the flyleaf. The copy breaks off in the middle of page 37 of the original manuscript.

Gift of Mrs. C. G. Rockwood.
[In the Ellsworth papers, Historical Manuscripts Collection.]

165 ELLSWORTH, HENRY LEAVITT, 1791–1858

Letter to Professor Benjamin Silliman. Fort Gibson on the Arkansaw River, December 5, 1832.

4 pp. 41½ cm. With a positive photostat, and typewritten transcript.

The letter to Professor Silliman describes briefly the journey to Fort Gibson, the meeting with Irving, Latrobe, and

Pourtalès, and the expedition with the Mounted Rangers up the Arkansas and Cimarron Rivers, south to the Canadian

River and back, the hunting of buffalo and wild horses, and the condition of the Indians in that region. Ellsworth left Canandaigua late in August, reaching Fort Gibson October 8, leaving again on October 10 for the West and returning November 9.

The letter to Professor Silliman is printed in full, with title: "A Journey through Oklahoma in 1832: A letter from Henry L. Ellsworth to Professor Benjamin Silliman. Edited by Stanley T. Williams and Barbara D. Simison," *Mississippi Valley Historical Review*, 1942, XXIX, 387–393.

[Coe No. 69.]

166–169 EMMONS, GEORGE FOSTER, 1811–1884

Manuscript journals kept while attached to the South Sea Surveying and Exploring Expedition under the command of Charles Wilkes, 1838–1842, on the U.S. Sloop of War *Peacock* and, after the wreck of the *Peacock*, on the *Vincennes;* two portfolios of original drawings; and letters and documents.

7 vols. Various sizes.

George Foster Emmons was appointed a midshipman in 1828. He served on the frigate *Brandywine* in the Mediterranean, 1830–1833, and in 1838 joined the Wilkes Exploring Expedition as acting lieutenant of the *Peacock*. He later served on the *Boston* of the Brazil Squadron and the *Ohio* of the Pacific Squadron. In 1868 he was commissioned commodore and spent the rest of his active duty on shore, chiefly as head of the Hydrographic Office in Washington and as commandant of the Philadelphia Navy Yard.

166 —— Three journals kept while on board the U.S. Sloop of War *Peacock*, W. L. Hudson, Commander, August 12, 1838 to June 10, 1842.

3 vols. [i.e., 931 pp.] 27–39 cm. Original bindings.

The journals contain an account of the expedition with detailed descriptions of the special surveys made by the *Peacock*, original drawings of the harbors, and a number of small drawings and diagrams, and are further illustrated by the insertion of portraits, engravings, maps, and extracts from Wilkes' *Narrative*.

No. 3 contains a detailed account of the overland expedition, Emmons commanding, from Vancouver to San Francisco, August–October, 1841, which is supplemented by the journal kept by Henry Eld (*see* No. 161).

The following letters and documents are inserted chronologically in the journals:

EMMONS, GEORGE FOSTER. Letter to S. P. Lee. February 23, 1839. True copy, signed S. P. Lee. 1 p.

—— Five letters to Lieutenant Wilkes. February [25], 1839–April 20, 1842. Copies. 6 pp.

—— Letter to Captain Hudson. April 6, 1840. Copy. 2 pp.

—— Letter to J. P. Couthouy. November 14, 1840. Copy. 1 p.

—— Court Martial, U.S.S. *Peacock*. Trial of Sweeney, Ward, and Riley, October 2–28, 1840. Charges and specifications preferred by Lieutenant George F. Emmons. Finding and sentences of the Court. Copy. 22 pp.

—— Plan of wedding party and guests, January 10, 1843. 2 pp.

—— Family of Frances Thornton (Mrs. Emmons). 1 p.

ALDEN, JAMES. Letter to Emmons. August 23, 1845. 2 pp.

BACON, FREDERICK A. Note to Emmons. [February 20? 1839.] 1 p. With note added by Emmons.

BALDWIN, AUGUSTUS S. Letter to Emmons. [December 19, 1839.] 1 p.

CARPENDER, E. W. Letter to Emmons. June 14, 1842. 1 p.

CARR, OVERTON. Letter to Emmons. December 29, 1842. 3 pp.

CASE, AUGUST LUDLOW. Letter to Wilkes. April 20, 1842, signed by A. L. Case, G. F. Emmons, and W. M. Walker. Copy. 1 p.

CHANDLER, WILLIAM. Letter to Emmons. January 9, 1843. 1 p.

COUTHOUY, JOSEPH PITTY. Letter to Emmons. November 10, 1840. 1 p.

DANA, JAMES DWIGHT. Letter to Emmons. August 15, 1841. 1 p.

DAYTON, A. O. Notification from Treasury Department, August 23, 1842, to Emmons. Printed form. 1 p.

DEHAVEN, EDWIN JESSE. Letter to Emmons. December 28, 1842. 1 p.

DRAYTON, HARRY J. Letter to Emmons. January 10, 1843. 1 p.

DYES, JOHN W. W. Receipt for elk and antelope horns. October 29, 1841. 1 p.

—— Letter to Emmons. June 10, 1842. 1 p.

FISHER, PETER, Lieutenant, Royal Navy. Note to Emmons. [December 7, 1839.] 1 p.

GILCHRIST, EDWARD. Note to Emmons. [December] 9 [1838]. 1 p.

GUILLOU, CHARLES F. B. Letter to Emmons. November 23, 1841. 1 p.

HARWOOD, ANDREW A. Letter to Emmons. June 21, 1842. 1 p.

HUDSON, WILLIAM L. Seven letters to Emmons. October 21, 1839–August 2, 1841. 12 pp.

—— Orders to Officers of *Peacock*, June 21, 1841. 1 p.

—— Orders to Emmons. [August 4, 1841.] 1 p.

JOHNSON, ROBERT E. Letter to Emmons. October 20 [1841]. 3 pp.

LEE, SAMUEL PHILLIPS. Letter to Emmons. February 23, 1839. 1 p.

LINN, LEWIS FIELDS. Letter to Emmons. January 6, 1843. 2 pp.

MCKAY, THOMAS. Letter to Emmons. [September 6, 1841.] 2 pp.

MCLOUGHLIN, JOHN. Letter to Samuel Taylor. August 5, 1841. 1 p.

—— Letter to Emmons. August 15, 1841. 1 p.

MAGRUDER, GEORGE A. Letter to the Secretary of the Navy [J. K. Paulding] from the petty officers of the *Macedonian*. April 16, 1838. Copy. Endorsed by Lieutenant G. A. Magruder. 2 pp.

MAURY, WILLIAM L. Letter to Emmons. September 3, 1842. 2 pp.

PAULDING, JAMES KIRKE. Two form letters filled in by hand, enclosing commissions to Lieutenant G. F. Emmons. July 11, 1838, March 2, 1841. 2 pp.

PICKERING, CHARLES. Letter to Emmons. January 11, 1843. 1 p.

REYNOLDS, WILLIAM. Letter to Emmons. August 3[?], 1846. 1 p.

RINGGOLD, CADWALADER. Letter to Emmons, notifying him of appointment as judge advocate. [February 20, 1842.] 1 p.

ROGERS, CORNELIUS. Letter to Emmons. August 30, 1841, with note at end by Emmons. 3 pp.

SAWYER, H. B. Letter to Emmons. July 13, 1840. 2 pp.

SAWYER, R. W. (MRS. H. B.). Letter to Emmons. [July 13, 1840.] 1 p.

SICKLES, J. FREDERICK. Letter to Emmons. November 14, 1839. 1 p.

TOTTEN, G. M. Letter to Emmons. July 30, 1841. 2 pp.

UNDERWOOD, JOSEPH A. Two letters to Emmons. December 13, 1838, May 3, 1839. 2 pp.

UPSHUR, ABEL PARKER. Letter to Emmons, detaching him from the *Vincennes.* June 17, 1842. 1 p.

UPSHUR, GEORGE P. Letter to Emmons. January 15, 1843. 2 pp.

WALDRON, RICHARD R. Summons to witnesses to a General Court Martial, October 13, 1840. On verso of Emmons to Wilkes, October 8, 1840. Copy.

—— Letter to Emmons. October 20, 1841, with Emmons' comment. 2 pp.

—— Letter to Secretary of the Navy. January 10, 1842. Copy. 1 p.

WALKER, WILLIAM M. Two letters to Wilkes. November 5, 1840, April 20, 1842. Copies. 2 pp.

WILKES, CHARLES. Seven orders to Emmons. July 14, 1838–October 20 [1841]. 19 pp.

—— Letter to Emmons. October 6, 1840, with copy of answer. Accompanied by *Defence of Lieutenant R. F. Pinkney before the Court Martial* . . . 3 pp.

—— Letter to Lieutenants Walker and Emmons. November 6, 1840. Signature only. 1 p.

—— Letter to Emmons and others. May 30, 1842, and copy of answer, with map. 2 pp.

—— Two letters to Emmons. [October 27, 1841], February 20, 1842, appointing him judge advocate at Court of Inquiry, February 21, 1842. 2 pp.

—— Letter to Ringgold. [February 20, 1842] enclosing "Inquiries for the Court and Proceedings of the naval court," signed by Ringgold and Emmons. Copy [?] 30 pp.

—— Letter to Walker, Case, and Emmons. April 19, 1842. Copy, with copy of the answer, April 20, 1842, enclosing copy of a letter to the Secretary of the Navy from 41 petty officers of the frigate *Macedonian*, endorsed and signed by Lieutenant G. A. Magruder, April 6, 1838. 4 pp.

—— Court Martial, Minutes, trials of Sweeney, Ward, and Riley, October 2–28, 1840. 22 pp.

167 —— Two sketchbooks of original drawings made while attached to the South Seas Surveying and Exploring Expedition on board the U.S. Sloop of War *Peacock*, 1838–1842.

2 vols [i.e., 31 leaves] 29½ x 22½ cm.

The 34 sketches include drawings of icebergs in the Antarctic, harbors entered, incidents of the voyage, pictures of the natives, etc.

168 —— Scrapbook of official letters received from 1828 to 1850, and memorabilia.

97 pieces. 28 cm.

The collection includes invitations, calling cards, and the following orders, letters, and documents, arranged chronologically in three groups: 1828–1837; correspondence relative to the Exploring Expedition, 1836–1838; and 1842–1848.

EMMONS, GEORGE FOSTER. Resolutions passed at a meeting of midshipmen, addressed to the Naval Lyceum, New York. December 28, 1838, signed by Emmons and 18 others. Copy. 1 p.

—— Letter to Ridgely. December 30, 1833, signed by Emmons and 12 others. Copy. 1 p.

—— Request to Navy Department for lessons in swordsmanship at N.Y. Navy Yard. February 10, 1834, signed by Emmons and 26 others. Copy. 1 p.

—— Certificate of admission to bar in Indiana, May 1836, signed by Samuel Bigger and Williams W. Wick. 1 p.

—— Letter to Glynn. January 28, 1838, signed by Emmons, Hartstene and Reid. Copy. 1 p.

—— Letter to Tattnall. February 15, 1838. Copy. 1 p.

APPLETON, JOHN. Letter to Emmons. May 6, 1847. 1 p.

BALLARD, HENRY E. Letter to Emmons. September 20, 1830. 1 p.

BALTIMORE CLUB. Invitation. February 18, 1845, signed by Columbus O'Donnelly. Printed form. 1 p.

BARRON, JAMES. Letter to Emmons. July 12, 1830. Signature only. 1 p.

BIDDLE, JAMES. Letter to Emmons. August 8, 1845. Signature only. 1 p.

BOYLE, JOHN. Letter to Emmons. September 8, 1834. Printed form. 1 p.

—— Letter to Emmons. August 6, 1836. Signature only. 1 p.

BRANCH, JOHN. Three orders to Emmons. May 16, 1829–August 23, 1830. Signatures only. 3 pp.

—— Letter to Emmons. August 26, 1830. Printed form. 1 p.

CHAUNCEY, ISAAC. Four orders to Emmons. August 11, 1828–August 25, 1830. Signatures only. 4 pp.

CINCINNATI COLLEGE. Letter certifying that Emmons has fulfilled the requirements for the B.L. degree, April 20, 1836. 1 p.

CLAIBORNE, M. G. L. Letter to Emmons. July 5, 1838. 2 pp.

CLARK, JAMES H. Note on orders from Isaac Chauncey to Emmons. January 25, 1830.

DALE, JOHN B. Letter to Emmons. April 17, 1838. 2 pp.

DAYTON, A. O. Letter to Emmons. November 14, 1842. Signature only. 1 p.

DICKERSON, MAHLON. Orders to Emmons. November 16, 1836. Signature only. 1 p.

DOWNES, JOHN. Orders to Emmons. October 14, 1836. Signature only. 1 p.

GARRETT SOCIETY. Appointment of Emmons as Treasurer, September 13, 1676 [sic], with note on verso: "Considered a good joke. G.F.E." Broadside. 39 x 33½ cm.

GILLIS, JAMES MELVILLE. Two letters to Emmons. July 29, 1833, September 22, 1842. Signatures only. 2 pp.

GLYNN, JAMES. Letter to Emmons. October 21, 1837. 3 pp.

—— Certificate with regard to Emmons, May 12, 1838. Copy. 1 p. With copy of Emmons to Pickett, June 4, 1838, on verso.

HALSEY, JAMES M. Letter to Emmons. June 1, 1835. Printed form. 1 p.

HARTSTENE, H. J. Orders to Emmons. June 2, 1837. 1 p.

—— Letter to Emmons. June 14, 1838. 1 p.

Henshaw, David. Letter to Emmons. September 28, 1843. Signature only. 1 p.

Jones, Thomas Ap Catesby. Letter to Emmons. August 12, 1837, granting leave, endorsed by M. Dickerson, August 14, 1837, with note added by Emmons.

—— Orders to Emmons. October 22, 1837. Signature only. 1 p.

Kendall, Amos. Two letters to Emmons. June 28, August 6, 1834. Signatures only. 2 pp.

Kennedy, Edmund Pendleton. Letter to Emmons. August 22, 1833. 1 p.

—— Orders to Emmons. October 22, 1842; revoked, October 24, 1842. Signatures only. 2 pp.

Le Compte, Samuel W. Letter to Emmons. September 19, 1843. 1 p.

Markoe [?], Francis, Jr. Letter to Emmons. September 29, 1843, acknowledging gifts to the Naval Institute, Washington. Signature only. 1 p.

Mason, John Young. Orders to Emmons. October 13, 1846. Printed form. 1 p.

—— Letter to Emmons. May 5, 1847, granting leave. 1 p.

Mix, Marvine P. Letter to Board of Examiners. April 18, 1834, recommending Emmons. Signature only. 1 p.

Ohio Medical College. Certificate of Emmons' matriculation, October 24, 1835, signed by J. Cobb. Printed form.

Pendergrast, G. J. Two letters to Emmons. October 20, 1843, July 4, 1845. Signature only on latter. 2 pp.

Perry, Matthew Calbraith. Two orders to Emmons. October 12, 1833, March 10, 1834. Signatures only. 2 pp.

—— Letter to Emmons. March 26, 1834. Signature only. 1 p.

Pickett, James Chamberlayne. Seven letters to Emmons. January 12, 1837–June 8, 1838. Signatures only. With copies of Emmons' answers to two of them. 7 pp.

Renshaw [?], James. Letter to Board of Examiners. July 8, 1833, recommending Emmons. 1 p.

Ridgely, Charles Goodwin. Letter to midshipmen attached to the New York station. December 30, 1833. Copy [?] With copy of answer, signed by Emmons and 12 others. 1 p.

—— Orders to W. I. McCluney. December 30, 1833. Copy. 1 p.

—— Two letters to Emmons. March 24, June 11, 1834. 2 pp.

—— Three orders to Emmons. June 6, 1834–May 23, 1843. 3 pp.

Sawyer, George. Letter to Emmons. May 23, 1838. 2 pp.

Sawyer, H. B. Three letters to Emmons. December 11, 1837–July 6, 1843. 5 pp.

Semmes, Raphael. Letter to Emmons. February 21, 1838. 3 pp.

Smith, A. Thomas. Orders to Emmons. September 16, 1843, signed also by Ridgely. Printed form. 1 p.

Smith, Joseph. Letter to Commander H. B. Sawyer. September 16, 1843. 1 p.

Smith, William. Receipt, to Emmons. October 21, 1842. Signature only. 1 p.

Southard, Samuel Lewis. Printed form to Emmons. April 1, 1828, appointing him acting midshipman. 1 p.

—— Orders to Emmons. July 18, 1828, to attend Naval School in New York. 1 p.

Tatnall, Josiah. Letter to Auditor, Treasury Department. August 21, 1837. 1 p.

—— Letter to Emmons. March 13, 1838. 3 pp.

TURNER, DANIEL. Two orders to Emmons. June 6, November 11, 1845. Signatures only. 2 pp.

UNDERWOOD, JOSEPH A. Three letters to Emmons. April 20–November 21, 1837. 5 pp.

U.S. CONGRESS, 30th. H.R. 536, June 14, 1848. *A Bill . . . for the Relief of the Heirs and Legal Representatives of Captain Presley Thornton, deceased.* [Washington, 1848.] 2 pp.

U.S. NAVY. Midshipman's oath, manuscript copy, signed by Emmons, April 17, 1828. 1 p.

—— *General Order*, on uniform dress, May 10, 1820. Printed. 4 pp.

—— *General Order*, May 1, 1830. Printed. 4 pp.

—— *Petition* to Van Buren from the Navy Yard, January 8, 1838. Printed. 1 p.

UPSHUR, ABEL PARKER. Orders to Emmons. September 1, 1842, endorsed by H. B. Sawyer. Printed form. 1 p.

WOODBURY, LEVI. Four form letters to Emmons. July 11, 1833–June 28, 1834. 4 pp.

—— Permission to Emmons to attend Naval School, October 10, 1833. Signature only. 1 p.

169 —— Scrapbook of mounted clippings from the *New York Express*, reporting the proceedings of the Naval General Court Martial on board the U.S. Ship *North Carolina*, at New York, July 27 to September 15, 1842.

34 pp. 31 cm.

In addition to the Wilkes trial, the report covers the trials of Midshipman William May, Lieutenant Robert E. Johnson, Surgeon C. F. B. Guillou, and Lieutenant Robert F. Pinkney, all members of the Exploring Expedition, which preceded the Wilkes trial (August 17), and a few trials following that of Wilkes. There are also a few clippings on miscellaneous topics in the volume.

"Extracts from the Emmons Journal," describing Fort Vancouver and the courtesy of Mr. Douglas and Dr. McLoughlin, edited by George Thornton Emmons, is published in *Oregon Historical Quarterly*, 1925, XXVI, 263–273, covering journal entries of July 25 to August 2, 1841.

[Coe No. 68.]

170 ENGLE, PAUL MAX, *d.* 1862

"Sketches and surveys made during the exploratory tour of 1857 to Nebraska and Dakota under Lt. G. K. Warren, by P. M. Engle, Topographer to the expedition. 1857."

127 colored charts. 17½ cm. Original binding.

P. M. Engle, spelled Engel in the printed report, and J. H. Snowden were the topographers on the expedition.

The original maps (scale, 1 inch to the mile) represent the first official survey of the part of Nebraska and Dakota covered. The route taken by the party is indicated, with the camping places and dates, July 6–November 3, 1857. The maps fall into four groups: the route from Sioux City to Loup

Fork near its entrance into the Platte; from Fort Laramie west to Laramie Peak and back; from Fort Laramie to the Black Hills, the Cheyenne River and Niobrara River; and down the Niobrara to the Missouri. A few of the drawings are profiles or views of the mountain ranges.

The "Key Map" has the added notation: "Engraving carefully revised, G. K. Warren, Lt."

The position of the 127 sketches is indicated in red ink on this "Key Map":

". . . Military map of Nebraska and Dakota, by Lieut. G. K. Warren, Topl. Engrs. From the explorations made by him in 1855–6 while attached to the staff of Brig. Gen. W. S. Harney . . . and in 1857 under the direction of the Office, Explorations and Surveys," Washing-

ton, N. Peters, Photo. Lithograph. (35th Congress, 1st Session.) 84 x 116 cm.

Accompanied by Gouverneur Kemble Warren's "Preliminary Report of Explorations in Nebraska and Dakota, in the Years 1855–'56–'57 . . ." *Annual Report of Captain A. A. Humphreys, Topographical Engineers, in Charge of Office of Explorations and Surveys, War Department,* Washington, 1859, pp. [43]–173, uncut and unbound. 25½ cm.

While the sketches have not been published, the report of the explorations was printed [see above] with the documents accompanying the *Annual Report* of the Secretary of War, 1858. It was later reprinted with the map, without the key to the sketches, by order of the Secretary of War.

[Coe No. 70.]

171 ENGLISH, WILLIAM L., *ca.* 1842–1877

"Field diary of 1st Lt. Wm. L. English, 7th. Infantry 1876 campaign . . ." March 17 to September 5 [1876].

106 pp., oblong, hinged at top. 9 x 15 cm. Original binding. With typewritten transcript.

Lieutenant English was born in Jacksonville, Ill., *ca.* 1842. He served as 1st lieutenant of Co.I, 7th U.S. Infantry, during the Indian campaigns. He died at Deer Lodge, Mont., August 9, 1877, from wounds received at the battle of the Big Hole in the Nez Percé War.

The diary is a daily record of the march under command of Colonel Gibbon of the 7th Infantry from Fort Shaw, March 17, 1876, to join General Terry in his campaign against the hostile Sioux in the Yellowstone country, briefly noting camping places, distances, conditions of the roads, the receipt of news of Custer's defeat, the march to the scene and burial of the dead, the rescue of Major Reno, until September 5, when orders were received to return to Fort Shaw. From March 27 to June 27, except for a few special details to which

Lieutenant English was assigned, the diary parallels the journal of Lieutenant James H. Bradley, which is much more detailed and was published, with additions, in the *Contributions* to the Historical Society of Montana, 1896, vol. II, and Captain Freeman's journal (see No. 204).

The transcript contains a folded map, 24 x 19½ cm.: "The Gold Regions of the Black Hills, showing the scene of the massacre of General Custer's troops, and the Indian reservations and military forts in the western portion of the United States," Russell & Struthers, New York; a portrait of Major George A. Custer; and a folded clipping, "The Montana Slaughter," from *Harper's Weekly,* July 22, 1876, XX, 598.

[Coe No. V, 12.]

172 EVANS, ELWOOD, 1828–1898

Journal and notes kept by Elwood Evans while a member of the Northern Pacific Railroad Exploration and Survey under the command of Governor Isaac I. Stevens. May 9 to December 6, 1853.

162 pp. 14½ cm. Original binding.

Elwood Evans, born in Philadelphia in 1828, went to Oregon Territory in 1851 as deputy collector of customs at Nisqually. He returned to Philadelphia the next year, but went west again in 1853, as secretary to Governor Stevens. He took an active part in the development of the Territory and served as territorial secretary. He contributed many historical articles to the local papers, and planned to write an extensive history of Oregon and Washington (see Nos. 181–184).

In the Winlock W. Miller, Jr., Collection there are scrapbooks of clippings on various topics of western history compiled by Evans and annotated by him.

The journal commences with a record of Elwood Evans' movements from May 10 to 16, continued briefly from May 28 to June 16, 1853, when he had been left in Washington to finish up business connected with the survey and to follow Governor Stevens. He then records Governor Stevens' movements from May 9, when he left Washington, to May 16, and June 17 to July 26, about 100 miles east of Fort Union; and finally his own experiences from October 2 to December 6, 1853, from Fort Owen with Lieutenant Donelson's party, by the Jocko River, Clark's Fork and Palouse River to Walla Walla; the Columbia River to The Dalles, Vancouver, Portland and Olympia, December 4, 1853.

The journal is written in pencil and ink, sometimes beginning toward the front of the volume, sometimes toward the back, and interspersed with inventories of equipment and supplies, accounts, and other memoranda.

[Miller Collection.]

173 EVANS, ELWOOD, 1828–1898

Correspondence and papers of Elwood Evans, 1843–1894.

212 letters and papers. 782 pp. 19–35 cm.

Some of the letters are on legal matters or official business of the Secretary of the Territory, but the majority are concerned with the history of the Northwest, the early settlement of Oregon Territory, the Oregon missions and the controversy over Whitman's journey to Washington, D.C., relations with the Catholic missions and with the Hudson's Bay Company, and political affairs in Washington Territory.

The following letters and documents are included:

—— Copies of two letters to his father, Charles Evans. February 2, July 2, 1862. Without signatures. 8 pp.

—— Copy or draft of a letter to the Rev. J. H.[i.e., S.] Griffin. February 26, 1862. 4 pp.

—— Drafts of two letters to Charles H. Phelps, editor of the *Californian*. [Earlier undated,] November 19, 1880. 6 pp.

ABERNETHY, ALEXANDER S. 30 letters to Evans. March 3, 1857–February 18, 1855. 71 pp.

BLANCHET, AUGUSTIN M. A., Bishop of Nisqually. Letter to Evans, March 13, 1862, unsigned and in an unidentified hand. 2 pp.

BRONDEL, JOHN BAPTIST, Bishop of Helena. Letter to Evans. February 17, 1880. 1 p.

BROUILLET, JOHN BAPTIST ABRAHAM. Letter to Evans. February 11, 1861. 1 p.

BUSH, ASAHEL. Four letters to Evans with regard to collecting bills for subscriptions to the *Oregon Statesman*, March 9–October 13, 1856; draft of a letter to Bush from Evans, March 15, 1856; receipt signed by J. & C. E. Williams, August 6, 1856; and a letter to Evans from A. Benton Moses, September 21, 1855. 15 pp.

CALDWELL, WILLIAM S. "The Oregon American and Evangelical Unionist." Copy of the Introduction from the first number of the journal, with notes signed: "W. S. C[aldwell]." 5 pp.

CLARKE, SAMUEL ASAHEL. Letter to Evans. May 10, 1885. With draft of Evans' answer, May 11, 1885. 4 pp.

CORBETT, HENRY WINSLOW. "Private" letter to Evans. April 7, 1869. 1 p.

CRAIGHEAD, JAMES GEDDES. Two letters to Evans. April 10, July 1, 1879. With a pencil draft of Evans' answer [May ? 1879]. 16 pp.

CRAWFORD, MEDOREM. Two letters to Evans. January 11, 30, 1885. 4 pp.

DEADY, MATTHEW PAUL. Letter to Evans. February 28, 1878. 2 pp.

EELLS, CUSHING. Letter to Evans. January 16, 1862. With a draft of Evans' letter of January 6, 1862. 7 pp.

EELLS, MYRON. Seven letters to Evans. February 25, 1881–March 7, 1883, the last enclosing a photograph of his father, Cushing Eells. With drafts of three answers, March 14, 1881–May 10, 1882. 36 pp.

FARRAR, WILLIAM H. Two letters to Evans. August 8, 15, 1861. 5 pp.

FLETT, JOHN. Letter to Evans. May 19, 1890, and a manuscript on the religion of the Indians. 7 pp.

FOLEY, WILLIAM. Letter to Evans. October 5, 1894, enclosing biographical notes of Brouillet, Blanchet and Demers. 4 pp.

FROST, JOHN. Eight letters to Evans, the first undated but prior to December 16, December 16–25, 1857. 17 pp.

GARFIELDE, SELUCIUS. Letter to Evans. January 4, 1864. 4 pp.

GOODWIN, JOHN N. Letter to Evans. July 7, 1872. 4 pp.

GRAY, WILLIAM HENRY. Four letters to Evans. June 8, 1880–September 30, 1882. 11 pp.

HILL, GEORGE D. Letter to Evans. January 9, 1881. 1 p.

HINES, HARVEY KIMBALL, Editor of *Pacific Christian Advocate*. Three letters, April 9, 1884–September 29, 1885. With a typewritten transcript (carbon) of Evans' letter to Hines, April 12, 1884, unsigned. 11 pp.

HOLMES, LEANDER. Two letters to Evans. March 15, April 15, 1863. 6 pp.

HUGGINS, EDWARD. Letter to Evans. June 29, 1880, enclosing a copy of extracts from the journal of the Puget Sound Agricultural Company, describing the Snoqualmie attack on the Fort in May, 1849. 6 pp.

JESTER, JAMES E. D. Two letters to Evans. September 10, 1863, March 28, 1864. 2 pp.

KAPUS, WILLIAM. Seven letters to Evans. October 20, 1862–April 30, 1864, with a list of officers of the 1st Regiment, Washington Volunteer Infantry, clipped from a paper. 14 pp.

LANCASTER, COLUMBIA. Letter to Evans. July 12, 1854. 3 pp.

LANDER, EDWARD. Letter to Evans. June 30, 1858. 4 pp.

LANE, JOSEPH. Letter to Evans. December 17, 1857. 1 p.

McKINLAY, ARCHIBALD. Letter to Evans. May 1, 1881, enclosing Peter H. Burnett, letter to Archibald McKinlay, October 12, 1843; Archibald McKinlay, cattle contract with Jesse Applegate and Company, to John McLoughlin, October 27, 1843, endorsed (in James Douglas' hand) canceling the agreement, signed by John McLoughlin, Fort Vancouver, November 11, 1843; Jesse Applegate, letter to Archibald McKinlay, December 19, 1843; John McLoughlin, two letters to Archibald McKinlay, December 29, 1843, November 30, 1847. 16 pp.

—— 18 letters to Evans, not in McKinlay's hand. August 2, 1880–March 28, 1889. Accompanied by a small photograph of "Pioneer printing office of the Pacific Northwest—Lapwai Creek" [7 x 6 cm.]; draft of a letter from Evans to McKinlay, February 5, 1882; copy of a letter from McKinlay to Dr. Tolmie, December 9, 1854; typewritten copy of a letter to McKinlay from Myron Eells [n.d.], with a copy of McKinlay's answer, January 19, 1885; and copy of a letter to McKinlay from the North Pacific History Company, March 8, 1889. 162 pp. Archibald McKinlay at this time was growing blind and only a few of the letters are signed by him personally.

MARSHALL, WILLIAM ISAAC. Three letters to Evans. September 12, 1884–July 24, 1887, and a draft of a letter from Evans to Marshall, August 11, 1882. The first two are written on printed and illustrated circulars of his lectures. 26 pp.

NESMITH, JAMES WILLIS. Three letters to Evans. October 20, 1862–July 27, 1864, and draft of a letter from Evans to Nesmith, December 18, 1862. 6 pp.

NEWELL, ROBERT. Letter to Evans. May 7, 1867, enclosing a clipping from the *Oregon Herald*, March 8, 1867, of a letter from Newell to the editor. 2 pp.

PARKER, SAMUEL J. Five letters and a note to Evans. July 31–December 22, 1882, and a draft of Evans' answer to the first, August 19, 1882. 91 pp.

PARKER, WILDER W. Letter to Evans. March 2, 1867. 1 p.

RAMSEY, ALEXANDER. Two letters to Evans. June 9, August 3, 1882, and a draft of Evans' letter to Ramsey, May 10, 1882. 8 pp.

RAYNOR, JAMES O. Letter to Evans. June 10, 1863. 1 p. With a copy of the broadside notice of the Union convention at Vancouver [21½ x 30½ cm.] and a note by Evans on "The Canvass for Delegates." 1 p.

ROBERTS, GEORGE B. Two letters to Evans. November 22, 1860, August 25, 1880, 6 pp., and mounted clippings listing vessels trading on the coast, 1788–1809.

SMITH, SOLOMON HOWARD. Letter to Evans. November 11, 1865. 4 pp.

SPALDING, HENRY HARMON. 15 letters to Evans. April 1866–September 15, 1870, and a copy of an unsigned letter in Spalding's hand, to the Hon. Mr. Lasater, October 29, 1869. 104 pp.

STEEL, W. G. Letter to Evans. April 4, 1890. 1 p.

STEINBERGER, C. M. Letter to Evans. March 13, 1863. 1 p.

STEINBERGER, JUSTUS. Two letters to Evans. November 29, 1860, December 22, 1862. 7 pp.

SWAN, JAMES GILCHRIST. Four letters to Evans and a note appended to an account of "General Wool & the Indian War." October 11, 1864–June 17, 1885. 14 pp.

SWAN, JOHN M. Letter to Evans. May 26, 1885. 2 pp.

TARBELL, FRANK. Invitation from the American residents of Victoria to Governor Evans to attend a dinner to be given for the Hon. Schuyler Colfax. Victoria, July 21, 1865. Frank Tarbell, Secretary. 1 p.

TILDEN, DANIEL R. Letter to Evans. August 31, 1882. 1 p.

TOLMIE, WILLIAM FRASER. Two letters to Evans. December 26, 1878, February 16, 1879. 8 pp.

TUCKER, EGBERT H. Two letters to Evans. July 12, 14, 1863. 3 pp.

VICTOR, FRANCES FULLER. Eight letters to Evans. November 15, 1865–September 23, 1886, and enclosed with the letter of December 1, 1880, extracts copied from a letter from P. L. Edwards to Dr. J. M. Bacon, September 1842. 40 pp.

WARNER, FITZ HENRY. Letter to Evans. September 4 [1852]. Signature only. 1 p.

WESTERN WASHINGTON INDUSTRIAL ASSOCIATION, Olympia, W.T. Printed certificate, No. 84, for one share of capital stock, made out to Elwood Evans, October 4, 1872 and signed by C. C. Hewitt, President, Albert A. Manning, Secretary. Printed by R. H. Hewitt, printer, Olympia [1872].

WEYMAN, FREDERICK. Letter to Evans. August 9, 1865. 4 pp.

WHITE, ELIJAH. Letter to Evans. March 11, 1863. 2 pp.

The cattle contract and letters of Peter H. Burnett, October 12, 1843, Jesse Applegate, December 29, 1843, and John McLoughlin, December 29, 1843, to Archibald McKinlay, are quoted in full or in part in Evans, *History of the Pacific Northwest* [Portland, 1889], I, 258–260; the letter of Solomon H. Smith, November 11, 1865, *idem*, I, 117–118; Archibald McKinlay's letter of March 14, 1882 is printed with the title: "The Gun Powder Story" and editorial notes by T. C. Elliott in the *Quarterly* of the Oregon Historical Society, 1911, XII, 369–374, and a passage from his letter of March 7, 1882, is quoted in Elliott, "Peter Skene Ogden, Fur Trader," *idem*, 1910, XII, 268.

[Miller Collection.]

174 EVANS, ELWOOD, 1828–1898

Correspondence, notes, and memoranda about the proposed History of Oregon, 1867.

22 letters and papers. 94 pp. 20½–32 cm.

In 1867 Evans had Chapter XVII of his *History*, on "The Americanization of Oregon," printed and sent proofs for criticism to the survivors of the band of settlers who established the Provisional Government of Oregon. Some of this correspondence survives:

APPLEGATE, JESSE. Two letters to Evans. July 26, October 13, 1867. With the printed copy of Chapter XVII (pp. 201–211), Applegate's notes on the chapter,

transmitted through Judge Deady; and two drafts of a letter from Evans to Applegate, August 8, 1867, with his answers to the notes. 16 pp.

DEADY, MATTHEW PAUL. Two letters to Evans. September 7, October 5, 1867, and a draft of Evans' answer, September 24, 1867. 21 pp.

NEWELL, ROBERT. Letter to Evans. August 8, 1867, and drafts of two letters to him from Evans, July 20, August 24, 1867. 16 pp.

SHORTESS, ROBERT. Letter to Evans. September 1, 1867. 4 pp.

The letter of Robert Shortess, September 1, 1867, is quoted in part in Evans, *History of the Pacific Northwest* [Portland, 1889], I, 243.

[Miller Collection.]

175 EVANS, ELWOOD, 1828–1898

Address delivered at Olympia, Washington, July 4, 1859.

17 pp. 20 x 32 cm.

The manuscript is accompanied by a letter requesting a copy of the address for publication, Olympia, July 6, 1859, signed by Butler P. Anderson, Jos. Cushman and 12 others, and a copy of Evans' answer, Olympia, July 8, 1859. 2 pp.

[Miller Collection.]

176 EVANS, ELWOOD, 1828–1898

"Campaign of Maj. Gen. John E. Wool, U.S. Army, against the people and authorities of Oregon and Washington, 1855–6. *And not contained in the official correspondence.*"

24 pp. 26 cm. Bound with an extract (pp. 193–256) from *Indian Affairs on the Pacific* (34th Congress, 3d Session, House Ex. Doc. No. 76, 1857).

Scrapbook of manuscript notes by Elwood Evans and mounted clippings dealing with the Indian Wars in Oregon.

[Miller Collection.]

177 EVANS, ELWOOD, 1828–1898

Columbia River Centennial. Address by Elwood Evans, Astoria, May 11, 1892.

Typewritten manuscript. 10 pp. 33 cm.

Elwood Evans had been asked by the committee in charge of the celebration to represent the State of Washington as its orator.

With the manuscript is the printed invitation of the Columbia River Centennial Celebration Society to the exercises at Astoria, May 10, 11, and 12, 1892, signed in facsimile by Curtis C. Strong, President, John Adair, Recording Secretary, Geo. H. Himes, Secretary.

[Miller Collection.]

178 EVANS, ELWOOD, 1828–1898

"The Fraser River excitement, 1858." Scrapbook of manuscript notes and mounted clippings, compiled by Elwood Evans.

48 pp. 26 cm.

Evans' manuscript notes occupy about 21 pages. Bound in the volume are copies of the following letter and printed document:

WALKER, RUDOLPH M., Secretary of Washington Territory. Letter to Lewis Cass, Secretary of State. [Olympia] June 18, 1858, reporting the discovery of gold on the Fraser. 6 pp. 33 cm.

Message of the President of the United

States, Communicating . . . the Report of the Special Agent of the United States [John Nugent] *Recently Sent to Vancouver's Island and British Columbia* (35th Congress, 2d Session, Senate Ex. Doc. No. 29 [Washington, 1859]).

[Miller Collection.]

179 EVANS, ELWOOD, 1828–1898

Historical reminiscences and memoranda.

262 pp. 26 cm.

Scrapbook of clippings from western newspapers, documents and papers on the early history of the Pacific Northwest, including the following manuscripts:

THURSTON COUNTY, W. T. CITIZENS. Minutes of a public meeting held at Olympia February 7, 1852, of the Citizens of Thurston County, and the passengers and crew of the late sloop *Georgiana*, recently rescued and returned from Queen Charlotte's Island.

Copy, in pencil, in an unidentified hand. 9 pp. 23 cm.

SARGEANT, ASHER. Detailed bill for services and advice to Daniel Show while on the sloop *Georgiana* and in the hands of the Haida Indians on Queen Charlotte's Island. November 1851, signed: "Asher Sargeant." 3 pp. pasted together. 55 cm.

[Miller Collection.]

180 EVANS, ELWOOD, 1828–1898

Scrapbook of articles by Elwood Evans clipped from newspapers, and manuscript notes in his hand, with an outline of a proposed "History of Oregon and Washington in four parts." 1880.

200 pp. 25 cm.

These notes represent Elwood Evans' research in the history of the Northwest, and, arranged chronologically, formed the basis of the first and second parts of his proposed history, which was published in 1889 with the title: *History of the Pacific Northwest: Oregon and Washington.*

Compiled and published by the North Pacific History Company of Portland, Ore. [1889].

An introductory note by W. W. Miller, Jr., is tipped in the scrapbook.

[Miller Collection.]

181 EVANS, ELWOOD, 1828–1898

History of the Pacific Northwest: Oregon and Washington compiled and published by the North Pacific History Company of Portland, Oregon, 1889; with extensive manuscript alterations and insertions in the first volume.

2 vols. 30½ cm.

"This is the copy used by Elwood Evans, the author of the major portion of this work, for the revision which resulted in his unpublished History." Note by W. W. M[iller] Jr.

In addition to the notes and alterations in the text over 100 pages of revisions are laid in Vol. I.

[Miller Collection.]

182 EVANS, ELWOOD, 1828–1898

History of Washington and Oregon, by Elwood Evans. Unpublished manuscript, 1894.

2 vols. [i.e., 875 pp.] Various sizes, mounted and bound. 44 cm.

Holograph and typewritten manuscript of a proposed revision of Parts I–V of the *History* published in 1889, with a Foreword by Winlock W. Miller, Jr. The manuscript is almost entirely rewritten from the 1889 edition, which, contrary to Evans' wishes, had been published as a commercial venture.

183 —— History of Oregon and Washington. Unpublished typescript, 1894.

2 vols. [i.e., 667 pp.] Various sizes, mounted and bound. 40 cm.

Revised typewritten manuscript, with manuscript pages and clippings from newspapers inserted, and corrections and alterations by the author in Volume I; Volume II has few changes in the typescript.

184 —— History of Washington and Oregon. Unpublished final revision of Volume I, 1894.

382 pp. Various sizes, mounted and bound. 44 cm.

Elwood Evans had gathered together a great deal of information and many letters and documents in preparing his history but died before completing it. After his death in 1898 a portion of his papers were in the hands of H. H. Bancroft, other parts came into the hands of C. B. Bagley, and the remainder, including the History, had apparently disappeared. In 1932, however, an old trunk was found in Tacoma full of letters, pamphlets, scrapbooks, and historical documents, which proved to be Evans' working collection. At the bottom of the trunk was a "jumble of manuscript and typewritten pages in apparently hopeless disorder." Mr. Miller secured these manuscripts and after careful study was able to sort them into the three revisions.

[Miller Collection.]

185 EVANS, ELWOOD, 1828–1898

"Hudson's Bay & Puget Sound Agricultural Companies. Data & excerpts—showing their acts and motives, their policy as to settlements, and especially bearing on Oregon & Washington." Compiled from various sources by Elwood Evans. 1859–1860.

47 pp. 25 cm.

Scrapbook of newspaper clippings, containing also a copy in Evans' hand of a letter from W. F. Tolmie, Chief Factor of the Hudson's Bay Company, to A. G. Dallas, Esq., Victoria, V.I., April 12, 1861 [13 pp.], in which he discusses the recently published reports of James Tilton, Surveyor General of Washington Territory, and the Secretary of the Interior on the land claims of the Puget Sound Agricultural Company.

[Miller Collection.]

186 EVANS, ELWOOD, 1828–1898

"The Indian War. 1855–56. 'Newspaper details in weekly instalments.' "

127 pp. 26 cm.

Scrapbook of mounted clippings, largely from the Olympia *Pioneer and Democrat* and the Portland *Oregonian*, and pages from the official reports of the Secretary of War, with extensive annotations by Elwood Evans.

[Miller Collection.]

187 EVANS, ELWOOD, 1828–1898

"Martial law in Washington Territory, April 1856. A true narrative, and the documents. Collected by Elwood Evans."

390 pp. 25 cm.

Manuscript notes and documents, newspaper clippings, printed documents and reports, including the following manuscripts:

PROCLAMATION, May 24, 1856, signed by Isaac I. Stevens, Governor, Territory of Washington, abrogating Martial Law in Pierce and Thurston Counties. In the handwriting of Andrew Jackson Cain. 1 p. 24 cm.

STEVENS, ISAAC INGALLS. Petition for a change of venue to the First Judicial District for trial of the United States vs. Isaac I. Stevens. Attachment for contempt, signed by Isaac I. Stevens, with affidavit, Territory of Washington, County of Thurston, in the Second Judicial District July 4, 1856, W. W. Miller, Clerk. In the handwriting of Judge William Strong. 1 p. 32 cm.

—— Motion signed by Isaac I. Stevens [defendant] filing a respite, signed by Isaac I. Stevens, Governor of the Territory, before the Hon. Edward Lander, July 10, 1856. 1 p. 25 cm.

—— [The respite] signed by Isaac I. Stevens, Governor, Territory of Washington, and Isaac W. Smith, Acting Secretary, Washington Territory. July 10, 1856, with the Territorial seal affixed. 2 pp. 32½ cm.

The Proclamation is printed in the *Message from the President of the United States, Communicating . . . Information respecting the Proclamation of Martial Law in the Territory of Washington* (34th Congress, 3d Session, Senate Ex. Doc. No. 41, 1857, pp. 38–39). Stevens' pardon or respite is printed with an introductory note by E. S. Meany under "Documents. Governor Stevens' Famous Pardon of Himself." *Washington Historical Quarterly*, 1934, XXV, 229, and in Samuel F. Cohn, "Martial Law in Washington Territory," *Pacific Northwest Quarterly*, 1936, XXVII, 214.

[Miller Collection.]

188 EVANS, ELWOOD, 1828–1898

"Oregon Missions." History & Spirit. Whitman's Massacre & Winter Journey.

2 vols. 24 cm.

Two scrapbooks, compiled by Elwood Evans with his manuscript annotations, containing mounted newspaper clippings, pamphlets, and documents relating to the Oregon missions, letters copied by Evans, and the following original manuscripts:

EELLS, CUSHING. Letter to Evans. August 29, 1867. 4 pp.

LOVEJOY, ASA LAWRENCE. Letter to Evans. September 28, 1867. 3 pp.

MCKINLAY, ARCHIBALD. Two letters to Evans, signed by Archibald McKinlay. June 21, July 19, 1880. 4 pp.

WHITMAN, MARCUS. Copy in Evans' hand of a letter to Archibald McKinlay. September 30, 1841. 5 pp. The original letter was in 1937 owned by Mr. G. H. Plummer of Seattle.

[Miller Collection.]

189 EVANS, ELWOOD, 1828–1898

Three notebooks, compiled from various sources by Elwood Evans, on Alaska, early settlers on the Columbia River, and southern Oregon.

3 vols. [i.e. *ca.* 242 pp.] 11 x 21 cm.

The notes, written in pencil, are largely taken from published works by Bancroft and other writers. They are written on the blank pages of the *Calendar . . . of the District Court of the Second Judicial District, Wash. Ter. Holding Terms at Ta-coma*, for the February and June terms, 1889. Some of the entries in the *Calendar* are annotated by Evans with brief notes such as "Under advisement," "settled," "jury trial," etc.

[Miller Collection.]

190 EVANS, ELWOOD, 1828–1898

" 'The trial of Leschi,' and the matter of George Williams, J. M. Bachelder, Frank Clark, F. R. Kautz, and D. B. McKibbin—for contempt and obstruction of process. An epoch in the history of Washington Territory" [1857–1858].

48 pp. 24½ cm.

An account of the trial of Leschi, Nisqually chief, compiled by Elwood Evans by mounting reports of the trial and related material clipped from the Steilacoom *Washington Republican* and the Olympia *Pioneer and Democrat*, 1857–1858, with manuscript copies of extracts from the court records and his own notes and com-ments; and the following letter and papers:

WALLACE, W. H. Letter to Colonel Wright, U.S.A. July 8, 1857. 2 pp.

Truth Teller. Devoted to the Dissemination of Truth, and Suppression of Humbug. Edited by Ann Onymous. Vol. No.

ooo. Steilacoom, W.T., February 3, 1858, and February 25, 1858. Two leaflets of four pages each issued for free distribution by Frank Clark, George Williams and their associates.

[Coe No. I, 944.]

191 EVANS, ELWOOD, 1828–1898

"The Trial of Yelm Jim for the murder of William White."

72 pp. 18½ cm. Original binding.

The account of the testimony at the trial of Yelm Jim for the murder of William White on March 2, 1856, as reported in the Olympia *Pioneer and Democrat*, April 29, 1859, is mounted on the first nine pages. The manuscript, which follows, is headed "Incidents of the trial and errors alleged," and details the reasons on which a motion for a new trial and arrest in judgment is based. It includes copies of affidavits accompanying the motion, the opinion of Associate Judge William Strong of the Supreme Court of Washington Territory that there were no grounds for a reversal of the verdict of the District Court, and the letter from Elwood Evans, counsel for the defendant, to the Governor, in the matter of the petition of Yelm Jim for a pardon.

The letter is accompanied by copies from the *Pioneer and Democrat* [1855–1860] of the following proclamations and notices to prove that a state of war existed between the Yakima Indians and the United States in March, 1856:

MASON, CHARLES H., Acting Governor. Proclamation, October 14, 1855, calling for volunteers.

—— Proclamation, October 22, 1855, calling for more volunteers.

SIMMONS, MICHAEL T., Special Indian Agent. Notice directing all friendly Indians in the Puget Sound District to rendezvous at special points to await orders, November 12, 1855.

STEVENS, ISAAC I., Governor. Proclamation, January 23, 1856, calling for volunteers.

TILTON, JAMES, Adjutant General, W.T.V. Orders to the commanding officer, Fort Steilacoom, to send men in search of the enemy in the vicinity of Nathan Eaton's, and reporting the attack on William White, March 2, 1856.

GHOLSON, RICHARD D., Governor. Proclamation, May 3, 1860, granting a reprieve to Yelm Jim.

The manuscript ends with a clipping about the reprieve from the *Pioneer and Democrat*, May 4, 1860, and a note stating that Yelm Jim was pardoned by Acting Governor H. M. McGill, August 9, 1860.

The handwriting on the cover, in the first few pages and the final note is that of Elwood Evans. The rest of the manuscript, the copies of affidavits, etc., are in a fine, copperplate hand.

Formerly the property of James Wickersham and contains his bookplate.

[Coe No. IV, 432.]

192 EVANS, JOHN, 1814–1897

Letter, signed by John Evans, Governor of Colorado Territory, to the Hon. Solomon Foot, U.S.S. Denver, August 14, 1865.

1 p. 25 cm.

The letter is laid in *Reply of Governor Evans, of the Territory of Colorado, to That Part Referring to Him, of the Report of "The Committee on the Conduct* of the War," Denver, August 6, 1865.

John Evans was born in Ohio, studied medicine and settled in Indiana, but in 1848 moved to Chicago to accept the chair of obstetrics in Rush Medical College. He became prominent in educational, political, religious and business affairs. On being appointed governor of Colorado Territory he moved to Denver.

In the letter Governor Evans calls Sena-

tor Foot's attention to misrepresentations in the report of the Committee on the Conduct of the War, states that he will shortly appeal to the public for a suspension of judgment until he can present his case to the Committee or some equally high authority, and hopes for the Senator's aid in securing justice.

[Coe No. II, 1230.]

193 EVERTS, F. D.

"A journal on & of the route to California," March 15 to June 30, 1849, when the entries break off suddenly.

31 pp. 31 cm. With typewritten transcript.

Everts, with ten companions, left Kingsbury, La Porte County, Ind., March 15, 1849, for the gold mines in California. They arrived in St. Joseph May 1, and started overland May 5 by way of Fort Kearney, Platte River, Fort Laramie, the North Platte and Willow Springs.

The journal records in detail the events of the journey, his meeting with Colonel Vaughan, agent for the Iowas, Sacs and Foxes, on the Nemeha River, the country through which they traveled and the sickness and hardships they encountered.

[Coe Collection.]

194 FALCONER, THOMAS, 1805–1882

Letter to Mr. Hawes [Mr. Doubleface added in parentheses in another hand]. Wootton, September 13, 1850.

4 pp. 19 cm.

Laid in the author's personal annotated copy of his On the Discovery of the Mississippi, and on the Southwestern, Oregon and Northwestern Boundary of the United States . . . , London, 1844.

Falconer, who had taken part in the Texas–Santa Fé expedition of 1841–1842, was in 1850 appointed arbitrator on behalf of Canada to determine boundaries

between Canada and New Brunswick. At the time of writing this letter he was judge of the county courts of Glamorganshire and Brecknockshire and of the district of Rhayader in Radnorshire, Wales.

The letter deals with his relations with Lord Grey.

[Coe No. III, 1480.]

195 FAULK, ANDREW JACKSON, 1814–1898

Official papers and correspondence of Andrew J. Faulk during his term as governor of Dakota Territory, 1866–1869; and business and family papers and letters, 1817–1896.

9 vols. [i.e., 532 pp.] 980 letters and papers. ca. 1,700 pp. 11–38 cm. 2 sketches, plan.

As a young man in Armstrong Co., Pa., Faulk learned the printing trade, studied

law, and took an active part in local politics. In 1861 Lincoln appointed him post-trader to the Yankton Indian Agency in Dakota Territory. In 1864 he returned to Pennsylvania and engaged in the oil business until 1866 when President Johnson appointed him governor of Dakota. He served in that office until 1869, when President Grant appointed John A. Burbank to succeed him. Faulk continued to live in Yankton until his death, and was active in local politics and in the opening and development of the Black Hills. He was associated, as an adviser, with the peace commission under General Sherman which concluded the treaty of Fort Laramie in 1868. He was appointed clerk of the U.S. District Court, Second Judicial District, in November 1873, and served until 1881.

The manuscripts deal mainly with Faulk's official duties in Dakota Territory as governor and superintendent of Indian affairs, and as clerk of the U.S. District Court. The letters to Faulk and Faulk's letters to his wife and family are in general the original letters; Faulk's letters to others are copies, usually signed, made for his official files.

In addition to the letters and documents listed below, the manuscripts include Faulk's commissions as justice of the peace in Armstrong Co., Pa., and as lieutenant colonel in the Pennsylvania Militia; deeds, indentures, leases, for property in Pennsylvania and in Dakota; accounts current of the Superintendent of Indian Affairs with the Commissioners N. G. Taylor, Charles E. Mix, L. V. Bogy, and Ely S. Parker, including vouchers, abstracts, receipts, property returns, reports on employees, 1866–1869, and correspondence with the Commissioner and auditors in the Treasury Department, 1866–1875; accounts current of the executive department of the Territory; emolument returns, 1875–1881, receipts, 1873–1881, correspondence with the Solicitor of the Treasury and U.S. Comptroller, decisions and reports of cases, and accounts of the clerk of the U.S. District Court; personal memoranda, notes, bills and receipts; and 25 photographs of friends and Indians.

FAULK, ANDREW JACKSON. Eight letters to his wife. April 21, 1865–April 3, 1882. 17 pp.

—— Letter to his son, T. B. Faulk. July 2, 1877. With T. B. Faulk's answer on the same sheet, July 6, 1877. 2 pp.

—— Letter to [Dr. Avery]. June 27, 1884. Signed copy. 1 p.

—— Letter to L. H. Bailey. July 18, 1887. Signed draft. 1 p.

—— Two letters to John S. Boutwell. March 11, May 17, 1869. Signed copies. 3 pp.

—— Four letters to Britton, Gray & Drummond. June 28, 1875–March 3, 1876. Signed copies. 7 pp.

—— Two letters to O. H. Browning. October 31, 1867, February 20, 1869. Signed copies. 2 pp.

—— Two drafts of a letter to L. F. Cavalier. April 18, 1892. Signed. 9 pp.

—— Letter to Duane B. Cooley. March 15, 1871. With "Extract from evidence taken touching the . . . contest of election for delegate —Burleigh vs. Armstrong." Signed by Phil K. Faulk, April 8, 1871. Copies. 6 pp.

—— Letter to Wills De Hass. March 21, 1849. Signed copy. 4 pp.

—— Letter to H. B. Denman. January 22, 1867. Signed copy. 2 pp.

—— Letter to E. W. Foster. April 26, 1892. Signed copy. 4 pp.

—— Draft of a letter to President Grant, recommending George W. Bible. March, 1869. Unsigned. 1 p.

—— Draft of a letter to President Hayes, urging the reappointment of Governor Pennington. Signed also by N. Edmunds "and some 20 others. Sent January 15, 1878." 1 p.

—— Letter to Alexander Hughes. September 25, 1877. With undated answer on the same page. 1 p.

—— Letter to H. A. Humphrey. May 26, 1884. Copy. 2 pp.

—— Letter to William Jayne. September 12, 1862. Signed copy. 3 pp.

—— Letter to President Johnson. [May 14, 1868.] Signed copy. 1 p.

—— Letter to Captain J. L. Kelly. March 3, 1867. 3 pp.

—— Draft of a letter to D. M. Mills and others. May 16, 1868. Signed. 5 pp.

—— Letter to G. L. Ordway. March 1884. Signed copy. 2 pp.

—— Letter to William H. Seward. September 24, 1866. Signed copy. 1 p.

—— Letter to Charles H. Sheldon. February 23, 1893. Signed copy. 4 pp.

—— Account books, with memoranda of arrivals and departures of friends, important events, and business records. January 5, 1863–March 1869. 3 vols. [i.e., 93 pp.] 12–17 cm. Original bindings.

—— To the sheriff of Yankton County, ordering the arrest of James D. Berger and his delivery to Charles W. W. Clark of Michigan. March 11, 1869. Signed by Faulk with the State seal affixed. Endorsed by George W. Black, sheriff, that he arrested Berger March 12, 1869 and delivered him to Clark. With a letter to Faulk from T. C. Carpenter, prosecuting attorney, St. Joseph Co., Mich., March 8, 1869, enclosing a requisition for the delivery of James D. Berger, signed by Henry P. Baldwin, Governor, P. L. Spalding, Secretary of State, February 24, 1869 [broadside. 26 x 42 cm.] ; and a letter from G. C. Moody to Faulk, March 11, 1869. 4 pp.

—— "A bill to amend Chapter 14 of the Session laws of 1865–6" and "An Act to create the tenth Representative dis-

trict and for other purposes." Endorsed by Horace J. Austin, President, George I. Foster, Secretary, Enos Stutsman, Speaker, P. H. Halnan, Chief Clerk. With note attached: "Jan. 10, 1868. Two bills received this day and not returned for want of time to consider them properly on account of objectionable features." 4 pp.

—— Veto message to G. C. Moody, Speaker of the House of Representatives, House Bill No. 48, January 14, 1869. Endorsed: "A copy taken and sent this retained." 4 pp.

—— Message to Enos Stutsman, Speaker of the House, vetoing a bill to simplify the proceedings of the courts of the Territory. January 6, 1868. With a note at the end that the bill had been amended and the veto withdrawn, January 7, 1868. Signed copy. 6 pp.

—— Report to D. N. Cooley, Commissioner of Indian Affairs, on the condition of the Dakota superintendency. October 10, 1866. "Office copy." 9 pp.

—— Report of N. G. Taylor, Commissioner of Indian Affairs. September 9, 1867. Draft. 22 pp.

—— Remarks to One-that-Kills-the-Eagle. Endorsed: "July 8, 1868. Orig. sent with other vouchers to Washington, D.C." Copy. 4 pp. With notes of Eagle's remarks. 2 pp.

—— "Schedule of claims of Yankton Indians" with accounts and memoranda. November 1861–June 1864. 14 pp. Original binding.

—— Receipt for payments to half breeds of the Yankton Sioux tribe under the treaty of April 19, 1858. Certified as correct by A. J. Faulk. December 31, 1868. Seventy names are listed with the amounts due and signatures or marks of the recipients and witnesses. Signature only. 1 p. 55½ x 82½ cm.

FAULK, A. J. Docket of the clerk of the U.S. District Court, Second Judicial District, September 24, 1875–August 13, 1881. The books, numbered A No. 2–A No. 5, include notations of a few personal or family events not in the legal calendar. 4 vols. [i.e., 385 pp.] 17 cm. Original bindings.

—— Oath as clerk of the U.S. District Court, Second Judicial District, November 29, 1873. Renewed January 12, 1874. Witnessed by P. C. Shannon. 2 pp.

—— Oath as clerk of the District Court of Yankton County. November 23, 1873. Renewed January 12, 1874. Witnessed by P. C. Shannon. 1 p.

ALBRIGHT, RICHARD. Letter to Mark Parmer. September 25, 1879. 4 pp.

ALLEN, D. K. Letter to Faulk. February 17, 1868. 2 pp.

ARCANGE, WALTER. Patent, certificate No. 478E, for land in Vermillion. May 21, 1867. Signed for Andrew Johnson by Frank Cowan, Secretary, and J. N. Granger, recorder. Certified a true copy, February 11, 1895, by S. W. Lamoreux, Commissioner of the General Land Office, and recorded February 18, 1895, by J. P. Serr. Printed form. 1 p. 46 x 32½ cm.

ARMSTRONG, MOSES KIMBALL. Four letters to Faulk. January 10, 1873–February 23, 1875. 7 pp.

BAILEY, L. H. Two letters to Faulk. July 12, October 5, 1887. 2 pp.

BALDWIN, MRS. MARY MCCOOK. Letter to Faulk. February 15, 1882. 3 pp.

BAYLESS, LOTT S. Letter to Mr. and Mrs. Faulk. March 3, 1882. 2 pp.

BEADLE, WILLIAM HENRY HARRISON. Letter to Faulk. November 27, 1871. Signature only. 3 pp.

BIBLE, GEORGE W. Letter to Faulk. February 15, 1869. 2 pp.

BLACK, T. D. Letter to Faulk. November 21, 1877. 1 p.

BLAKELEY, WILLIAM. Four letters to Faulk. October 13, 1866–April 25, 1890. 8 pp.

BLAKELEY & MILLER. Letter to Faulk. May 6, 1868. 1 p.

BOYLE, JOHN W. Letter to Faulk. November 17, 1868. 3 pp.

BRADFORD, DANIEL P. Letter to Faulk. March 24, 1869. 4 pp.

BRISTOL, WILLIAM M. Letter to Faulk, transmitting a resolution of the Board of Education of Yankton. May 16, 1877. With a duplicate of the report of the case, County of Yankton vs. A. J. Faulk, signed by F. Schnauber, May 26, 1877. 6 pp.

BRITTON, GRAY & DRUMMOND. Six letters to Faulk. June 14, 1875–March 9, 1876. 10 pp.

BRODHEAD, J. J. Letter to Faulk. April 13, 1875. 2 pp.

BRODHEAD, J. M. Letter to Faulk. June 2, 1875. With a four-page memorandum. Signed: "per J.D.T." 5 pp.

BRODHEAD, JOHN F. Two letters to Faulk. October 26, November 28, 1866. 4 pp.

BRODHEAD, JOHN H. Nine letters to Faulk. October 17, 1866–June 19, 1878. 21 pp.

BROOKINGS, WILMOT WOOD. Letter to W. A. Burleigh. February 26, 1869. 2 pp.

BROWN, JASON BREVOORT. Three letters to Faulk. September 6–9, 1875. 3 pp.

BROWNING, ORVILLE HICKMAN. Three letters to Faulk. October 3, 1866–April 4, 1867. Signatures only. 4 pp.

—— Letter to Charles E. Mix. November 16, 1865. Copy. 3 pp.

—— Instructions to N. G. Taylor. August 8, 1867, under the Act of July 29, 1867, to establish peace with the hostile Indians. Copy by Faulk, who accompanied the commission by invitation. 11 pp.

BRUGUIER, CHARLES, EUGENE, and JOSEPH. Three powers of attorney to W. A. Burleigh to collect money due under the Yankton treaty of April 19, 1858. Each signed with the other two as witnesses, December 23, 1868. With affidavits by John W. Boyle and endorsed: "Received the above . . . 12 March 1869. Chas B. Wing." 12 pp.

BURBANK, JOHN A. Letter to Mr. Walters. December 12, 1871. 1 p.

BURLEIGH, ANDREW F. Seven letters to his grandfather, A. J. Faulk. December 16, 1876–October 7, 1883. 18 pp.

—— Letter to his grandmother, Mrs. Faulk. September 27 [1879]. 2 pp.

BURLEIGH, CAROLINE FAULK (MRS. WALTER A.). Letter to Faulk. [n.p., n.d.] Endorsed: "Answered October 31, 1867." 1 p.

—— Notice served on Simon Eisenman and Charles Eisenman. October 2, 1878. Endorsed: "Original Notice served by copy October 2, 1878 . . . To Chas. Eisenman in his store room. A. J. Faulk." 1 p.

BURLEIGH, WALTER A. 63 letters to Faulk. December 30, 1863–December 14, 1884. 128 pp.

—— Letter to Lewis V. Bogy. January 3, 1866. Copy. 6 pp.

BURLEIGH, WALTER A., JR. Letter to his grandfather, A. J. Faulk. December 20, 1882. 2 pp.

BUTLER, DAVID. Letter to Governor Faulk. October 10, 1867, transmitting a copy of the resolution ratifying the amendment to the Constitution of the United States, June 15, 1867. Certified a true copy by Thomas P. Kennard, Secretary of the State of Nebraska. Printed. 3 pp.

BUTT, WILLIAM. Certificate that A. J. Faulk is a member of the Methodist Church at Kittanning, Armstrong Co., Pa. November 8, 1835. 1 p.

BYLES, C. N. Letter to the clerk of the District Court. Montesana, W.T., February 21, 1874. 2 pp.

CALLAN, JOHN F. Letter to W. A. Burleigh. February 5, 1869. 1 p.

CAMERON, JAMES DONALD. Letter to Faulk. December 10, 1881. 2 pp.

CAMPBELL, C. T. Three letters to Faulk. March 18, 1878–March 24, 1885. 3 pp.

CARY, J. E. Two letters to Faulk. August 5, 30, 1867. 4 pp.

—— Letter to F. B. Van Vleck. May 26, 1871. 3 pp.

CHANDLER, WILLIAM EATON. Five letters to Faulk. May 8, 1889–January 21, 1896. Two of the letters are typewritten. 5 pp.

CHURCH, LOUIS KOSSUTH. Letter to Faulk. May 7, 1887. Typewritten. 1 p.

CLEVENGER, SHOBAL VAIL. Letter to Faulk. May 14, 1874. 1 p.

CONANT, CHARLES P. Letter to Faulk. August 11, 1874. With a copy on verso of Faulk's letter to 3d Asst. Postmaster General, August 17, 1874. 2 pp.

CONGER, PATRICK H. Two letters to Faulk. January 31, 1867, November 26, 1868. 2 pp.

CONINGSBY, ROBERT. Letter to Faulk, enclosing a circular explaining his purpose in coming to America, "An English Enquiry into American Manufactures and the Condition of the Working Classes." [Broadside. 25½ cm.] Cooper Institute [New York], July 22, 1868. 1 p.

Cook, Charles. Letter to Faulk. April 1, 1867. 1 p.

Cook, John. Letter to Faulk. March 18, 1863. 1 p.

Cooley, Duane B. Letter to Faulk. March 15, 1871. With supporting statements signed by L. Congleton, March 15, 1871, and C. G. Irish, March 27, 1871. 4 pp.

Copley, Josiah. Letter to Faulk. April 27, 1868. 5 pp.

Cowles, N. M. H. Letter to Faulk. December 22, 1871. 1 p.

Cowles, Warren. Letter to W. A. Burleigh. June 24, 1869. 2 pp.

—— Two letters to Faulk. December 20, 23, 1870. 2 pp.

Crawford, G. T [?]. Letter to Faulk. June 13, 1878. 1 p.

Curriden, Samuel W. Power of attorney for William E. Chandler to Faulk, with abstract of mortgages of Joseph G. Chandler and William E. Chandler signed by J. G. Chandler. October 11, 1886. Typewritten. 7 pp.

Dakota Territory. Legislative Assembly. *Council File No. 1. Joint Resolution*, recommending the appointment of Faulk as governor. [Broadside. 21½ x 35½ cm.] Certified a true copy by George W. Kingsbury, and on the verso copy of the concurring statement by the judges of the Supreme Court. Signed by the three justices and five other territorial officials. December 7, 1866.

Davis, W. Wallace. Letter to Faulk. November 15, 1866. 2 pp.

DeGray, Charles. Power of attorney to Walter A. Burleigh, to collect money under the Yankton treaty of April 19, 1858. Signed by his mark before J. L. Kelly and Ara Bartlett, with affidavit by Ara Bartlett, September 7, 1868. 3 pp.

DeKay, Drake. Three military passes signed by DeKay, issued to W. A. Burleigh and A. J. Faulk, General Lane and General Pomeroy, and Charles Mason. July 6, 1861. 3 pp.

Del Mar, Alexander. Letter to Faulk. December 5, 1867. Signature only. 2 pp.

Denman, H. B. Letter to Faulk. January 17, 1867. 2 pp.

Dewey, William P. Appointment of Faulk as justice of the peace of Yankton County during absence of George W. Roberts. October 11, 1883. Attested by E. T. White, city clerk, per Blatt. 1 p.

Dorion, Paul. Document assigning to W. A. Burleigh, money due under the Yankton treaty of April 19, 1858. Signed by his mark before P. H. Conger and A. C. Guyon, May 19, 1865. Printed form. 1 p.

Dougherty, Maria L. Two letters to Faulk. September 10, 1882, April 22, 1883. 8 pp.

Drew, Joe [?]. Letter to Mark Parmer. September 20, 1879. 4 pp.

Dunlap, W. W. Letter to Faulk. September 23, 1869. 4 pp.

Durley, P. B. Two letters to Faulk. June 27, July 21, 1884. 3 pp.

Ellsworth, Orlando F. Patent, certificate No. 667, for land in Vermillion. September 10, 1870. Signed by President Grant, E. A. Fiske, Assistant Secretary, and J. N. Granger, recorder. Filed for record, May 28, 1872, J. G. Mead, register. Printed form. 40½ x 25 cm.

Emmons, James A. Letter to Faulk. March 29 [n.y.]. 1 p.

Faulk, Jasper H. Power of attorney to A. J. Faulk. September 22, 1842. Witnessed by J. G. Parsons, Leonard Edelen, and Rutherford H. Rountree, clerk of County Court, by Th. J. Purdy, deputy clerk. Filed November 8, 1842. 1 p.

FAULK, JOHN. Two letters to his son, A. J. Faulk. March 21, 1840, June 2, 1853. 4 pp.

—— Commission as justice of the peace, Armstrong Co., Pa., March 4, 1817. Printed form signed by N. B. Boileau, secretary. Filed August 5, 1817, Eben Smith Kelley, recorder. 40 x 34 cm.

FAULK, MAY. Letter to her grandmother, Mrs. A. J. Faulk. October 7, 1886. 8 pp.

FAULK, SAMUEL J. Letter to his brother, A. J. Faulk. February 11, 1839. 3 pp.

FAULK, SARAH (MRS. THOMAS B.). Letter to her son, Andrew J. Faulk, 2d. November 12, 1871. 3 pp.

FAULK, THOMAS B. 49 letters to his father, Andrew J. Faulk, or his parents. November 26, 1868–June 20, 1887. 118 pp.

—— Five letters to his mother. January 16, 1870–January 11, 1874. 12 pp.

—— Note on John Gilpin. August 24 [n.y.]. 1 p.

—— Petition to President Garfield. Resolution of the Republican County Executive Committee of Armstrong Co., Pa., commending Peter C. Shannon for reappointment as chief justice of Dakota Territory. May 14, 1881. Copy, signed by T. B. Faulk, chairman, A. P. Neale, secretary. 2 pp.

FENTON, REUBEN EATON. Letter to Governor Faulk recommending the appointment of Colonel William S. Rowland as special commissioner to represent the interests of the Northwest at the Paris Exhibition in 1867. September 4, 1866. Signed by the governors of eight states, and attested a true copy by Governor Fenton. September 8, 1866. Parchment. 1 p.

FLETCHER, MINNIE E. Four letters to Faulk. February 12, 1878–June 17, 1879. 15 pp.

FOSTER, E. W. Letter to Faulk. April 22, 1892. 1 p.

FULLER, ALPHEUS G. Letter to Faulk. February 6, 1867. 1 p.

FULLER, PERRY. Letter to W. A. Burleigh. September 10, 1868. 1 p.

FULTON, J. ALEXANDER. Letter to Faulk. February 8, 1885. 3 pp.

GIFFORD, OSCAR SHERMAN. Letter to clerk of the District Court. May 13, 1879. 1 p.

GRAFTON, ABBIE (MRS. BEN). Letter to Faulk. July 27 [1866?]. 4 pp.

GREAT EUROPEAN-AMERICAN EMIGRATION LAND COMPANY. Letter to Governor Faulk. February 2, 1869. Signed by J. D. Reymert, secretary. 1 p.

GREGORY, J. SHAW. Four letters to Faulk. March 1, 1868–April 4, 1869. 10 pp.

GUYON, ALEXANDER C. Letter to Faulk. November 15, 1868. 1 p.

—— Power of attorney to W. W. Brookings, witnessed by C. F. Picotte, John Treadway. December 26, 1868. Printed form. 1 p.

HAMPTON, HUGH. Two letters to Faulk. December 20, 1879, [n.d.]. 2 pp.

HAND, GEORGE H. Two letters to Faulk. [n.p., n.d.] 2 pp.

—— Letter to Faulk. January 20, 1869. Enclosing pardon and warrant for release of Lewis E. Monger, with 29 signatures. Cheyenne, November 27, 1868. 4 pp.

HANSON, JOSEPH R. Letter to Faulk. November 14, 1866. 2 pp.

HATHAWAY, T[?]. Letter to Faulk. September 28, 1879. 4 pp.

HAWLEY, LUCY (MRS. A. F.). Letter to Faulk. April 16, 1871. 4 pp.

HAYDEN, FERDINAND VANDIVEER. Letter to Faulk. February 22, 1867. 1 p.

HEDGES, CHARLES E. Letter to Faulk. October 23, 1867. 1 p.

—— Contract with Faulk. February 5, 1868. 2 pp.

HEDGES, CHARLES E., and D. T. Letter to Faulk. September 30, 1868. Signed: "J.D.S." 1 p.

HEINER, ROBERT GRAHAM. Three letters to Faulk. March 4, 1867–September 10, 1874. 9 pp.

HELM, DU PLESSIS M. Letter to Faulk. August 5, 1867. 1 p.

HERRING, C. F. Two letters to Faulk. September 23, 1871, September 9, 1875. Signed: "per A.F.W." 1 p.

HOFFMAN, CHARLES W. Letter to Faulk. April 14, 1869. 1 p.

HOLLEY, FRANCES C. Letter and post card to Faulk. July 20, August 4, 1891. 1 p.

HOOKER, C. D. Letter to J. M. Stone. February 24, 1871. Signed: "A." 2 pp.

HUBBARD, DANA L. Letter to Faulk. February 12, 1869. With postscript by W. A. Burleigh. 1 p.

HUGHES, ALEXANDER. Two letters to Faulk. April 7, 1877, December 28, 1888. 2 pp.

HUMPHREY, H. A. Nine letters to Faulk. March 21, 1883–March 18, 1895. 18 pp.

HUMPHREY, S. E. B. (MRS. H. A.). Two letters to Faulk. May 11, 1884, June 4, 1886. 4 pp.

HUNTER, W. Letter to Faulk. June 17, 1886. 1 p.

JAYNE, WILLIAM. Letter to Faulk. December 16, 1866. 1 p.

JOHNSON, HENRY. Four letters to Faulk. September 5, 1853–March 29, 1869. 6 pp.

JOLLEY, JOHN L. Letter to Faulk. October 18, 1867. 1 p.

KELLOGG, N. G. Two letters to Faulk. May 10, 1866, February 7, 1868. 2 pp.

KELLY, JAMES LOUDEN. Three letters to his father-in-law, A. J. Faulk. December 18, 1876–February 24, 1877. 10 pp.

—— Letter to Mark Parmer. September 14, 1879. 3 pp.

—— Affidavit regarding accounts of Dakota Territory, July 23, 1875. Certified by Joel A. Potter, July 26, 1875. 6 pp.

KELLY, LANE FAULK (MRS. JAMES L.). Letter to her parents. July 4, 1884. 4 pp.

KELLY, R. M. Letter to Faulk. September 30, 1877. 2 pp.

KIDDER, JEFFERSON PARISH. Three letters to Faulk. May 7, 1868–December 30, 1882. 3 pp.

KIPP, LOUISA. Power of attorney to W. W. Brookings, December 26, 1868. Signed by her mark, witnesses C. F. Picotte and A. C. Guyon. 1 p.

KLOTZ, E. Letter to Faulk. November 15, 1866. 2 pp.

KOUNTZ, WILLIAM J. Letter to Faulk. December 16, 1882. 1 p.

LABAREE, JOHN. Three letters to Faulk. April 26–September 11, 1880. 6 pp.

LAMONT, S. COLIN. Power of attorney to W. W. Brookings. December 15, 1868. Witnessed by B. E. Wood, C. F. Picotte. Printed form. 1 p.

LANPHERE, WEBSTER BENTON. Three letters to Faulk. October 4, 1872–August 30, 1873. 6 pp.

LEWIS, SARAH DAVIS FAULK (MRS. J. A.). Two letters to her father, A. J. Faulk. March 18, 1867, July 17, 1868. 8 pp.

—— Letter to her mother. April 20, 1868. 4 pp.

LITTLE, THOMAS. Letter to Brevet Brigadier General O. D. Greene. March 5,

1869, enclosing a letter to Governor Faulk, March 3, 1869, and sworn statements of Peter Frank, February 7 and March 4, 1869, Henry J. Blunt, February 7, 1869, Frederic Brandt, March 4, 1869, Wakon-ja-kea, March 5, 1869, and Charles Boegehold, March 5, 1869, sustaining the accusations against John B. Gerard. 18 pp.

The letter to General Greene was endorsed by Colonel De Trobriand, forwarded to General Terry, and forwarded by him to Governor Faulk, April 9, 1869.

McCook, Edwin Stanton. Letter to W. A. Burleigh. February 22, 1872. With note on verso from Burleigh to Faulk. 1 p.

McCormick, Richard C. Letter to Faulk. August 15, 1868. 1 p.

McCoy, A. A. Letter to Faulk. June 28, 1887. Signed also by John Bulman. 1 p.

Mann, William L. Letter to Faulk. January 30, 1863. 2 pp.

Maxwell, H. A. Letter to Faulk. November 16, 1869. 2 pp.

Mechling, Frank. Two letters to Faulk. February 26, November 3, 1869. 7 pp.

Meckling, J. S. Letter to J. M. Stone. July 31, 1875. 2 pp.

Merrill, George D. Letter to Faulk. November 20, 1868. 3 pp.

Millard, Ezra. Letter to Faulk. December 11, 1867. 1 p.

Mills, David M. Letter to Faulk. April 11, 1869. 1 p.

Moody, Gideon Curtis. Two letters to Faulk. February 20, 1871, June 20, 1878. 2 pp.

—— Letter to P. C. Shannon. March 27, 1878. 1 p.

—— Letter to the editors of the Press and Dakotan, endorsing Judge Shannon.

January 18, 1876. Signed by Moody and 13 others. 2 pp.

Morrison, A. H. Letter to J. M. Stone. January 23, 1878. 1 p.

Morse, A. W. Letter to Faulk. December 16, 1886. 1 p.

Morton, Oliver Perry. Letter to Faulk. November 1, 1866, recommending Luther R. Martin. Signed also by Charles A. Ray and Thomas A. Hendricks. 1 p.

Nagler, Robert. Letter to Faulk. March 4, 1868. Enclosing a recommendation signed by Governor Butler of Nebraska, February 26, 1862. 5 pp.

Ordway, George L. Five letters to Faulk. December 26, 1883–January 9, 1885. 7 pp.

Ordway, Nehemiah G. Two letters to Faulk. November 8, 21, 1882. Signed also by J. C. McVay and George R. Scougal. Copies. 3 pp.

Packard, Samuel W. Letter to Faulk. February 22, 1879. 1 p.

Padelford, Seth. Letter to Governor Faulk, transmitting a copy of the resolution of the General Assembly of Rhode Island ratifying the Fifteenth Amendment to the Constitution. Certified by John R. Bartlett, Secretary of State. January 20, 1870. Printed. 2 pp.

Painter, John V. Letter to Faulk. May 26, 1870. 1 p.

Parker, O. H. Letter to Faulk. April 30, 1891. Written on the verso of a broadside, "Historical Society of South Dakota. Circular No. 1." 1891. 22 x 28 cm.

Parmer, Charlotte Faulk (Mrs. Mark M.) "Pet." Two letters to her father, A. J. Faulk. January 25, 1883, April 9, 1885. 5 pp.

—— Two letters to her mother. November 3, 1885, March 21, 1886. 8 pp.

PARMER, MARK M. Three letters to Faulk. January 30, 1868–September 14, 1879. 9 pp.

—— Letter to Mrs. Faulk. August 20, 1881. 2 pp.

PHILIPS, W. C. Letter to Governor Faulk. December 8, 1868. Printed form. 1 p.

PICKLER, JOHN ALFRED. Letter to Faulk. July 1, 1884. 1 p.

PICOTTE, CHARLES F. Letter to Faulk. April 25, 1892. 2 pp.

PICOTTE, MARGARET. Power of attorney to W. W. Brookings. December 26, 1868. Witnessed by C. F. Picotte and A. G. Guyon. Printed form. 1 p.

PIERCE, H. A. Letter to Faulk. March 9, 1870. 4 pp.

PREBLE, GEORGE HENRY. Letter to Faulk. January 26, 1867. Signature only. 2 pp.

RAYMOND, JOHN BALDWIN. Two letters to Faulk. August 31, 1877, October 29, 1879. 3 pp.

RAYNER, KENNETH. Two letters to Faulk. December 17, 1877, June 4, 1879. 2 pp.

REED, WILLIAM M. Letter to Faulk. October 10, 1879. 2 pp.

REILLY, EDWARD. Letter to Faulk. August 6, 1866. 2 pp.

RENCONTRE, ZEPHYR. Letters patent. A grant of land to Rencontre under treaty of April 19, 1858, signed by Abraham Lincoln, President, Edward D. Neill, Secretary, G. W. Granger, recorder. Recorded May 4, 1870. Certified a true copy by W. W. Warford, recorder of deeds, March 5, 1878. 3 pp.

REYNOLDS, M. H. (MRS. ABSALOM). Letter to Faulk. September 28, 1879. 4 pp.

ROBINSON, J. F. Two letters to Faulk. December 6, 1866, September 21, 1869. 2 pp.

ROSSTEUSCHER, CHARLES F. Letter to Governor Faulk. January 4, 1868. 1 p.

ROWLAND, WILLIAM S. Letter to Faulk. October 20, 1866. 2 pp.

SEWARD, FREDERICK WILLIAM. Three letters to Faulk. October 2, 1866–February 17, 1869. Signatures only. 4 pp.

SHANNON, PETER C. Four letters to Faulk. May 27 [1873]–May 22, 1894. 4 pp.

—— Appointment of Faulk as clerk of the District Court of the United States, Second Judicial District of Dakota Territory, and register in Chancery. November 29, 1873, renewed January 12, 1874. 1 p.

—— Appointment of Faulk as clerk of the District Court for Yankton County. November 29, 1873, renewed January 12, 1874. 1 p.

—— Appointment of Faulk as U.S. commissioner for the Second Judicial District. March 2, 1874. 1 p.

SHELDON, CHARLES H. Two letters to Faulk. February 9, 20, 1895. Typewritten. 2 pp.

—— Letter to Captain H. A. Humphrey. February 20, 1893. Copy. 3 pp.

SMITH, EDWARD W. Letter to Faulk. August 5, 1867. Signature only. 1 p.

SMITH, R. W. Two letters to Faulk. October 6, 1876, August 26, 1878. 4 pp.

SPINK, SOLOMON LEWIS. Two letters to Faulk. June 16, 1867, March 22, 1869. 3 pp.

STEVENS, THADDEUS. Letter to H[?] K[?] Fowler. February 21, 1867. 1 p.

STEIN, WILLIAM I. Letter to Faulk. August 28, 1874. 1 p.

STRIKE-THE-REE (Palaneapape). Letter to Faulk. April 21, 1879. 1 p.

STUTSMAN, ENOS. Six letters to Faulk. October 1, 1866–June 6, 1870. 16 pp.

—— Two letters to W. A. Burleigh. May 10, 1866, May 31, 1869. With reprints of Burleigh's speeches in the House of Representatives on the Indian question, July 21, 1868, and on the bill to provide a territorial government for Wyoming, July 23, 1868. 11 pp.

SULLY, ALFRED. Note of the delivery of one ambulance to Governor Faulk, August 1, 1867. Endorsed: "Turned over to John A. Burbank Gov. etc. May 1, 1869. A. J. Faulk, Governor." 1 p.

SWETT, LEONARD B. Letter to Faulk. November 18, 1875. 1 p.

TERRY, ALFRED HOWE. Letter to General E. D. Townsend. May 29, 1867. "Official" copy by Edward Smith. 1 p.

[THOMAS], CAMILLA. Two letters to Faulk. July 30, 1871, March 5, 1875. 9 pp.

THOMAS, ROBERT I. Letter to Faulk. January 3, 1867. 2 pp.

THOMPSON, CLARK W. Letter to Faulk. January 20, 1864. 1 p.

TODD, JOHN BLAIR SMITH. Letter to Faulk. September 9, 1866. 1 p.

TRIPP, BARTLETT. Letter to Faulk. January 19, 1877. 1 p.

TURNER[?], S. S. Letter to Faulk. September 1, 1873. 1 p.

TYNDALE, SHARON. Letter to Faulk. December 8, 1868. Signed: "per Lotus Viles." 1 p.

U. S. PRESIDENT (ANDREW JOHNSON). Appointment of Faulk as governor of Dakota Territory. August 4, 1866. Signed by Andrew Johnson and William H. Seward. Engraved on vellum. 50 x 35 cm. With letter of transmittal, August 9, 1866. Form letter signed by W. H. Seward. [Before confirmation by the Senate.] 1 p.

—— Appointment of Faulk as governor "by and with the advice and consent of the Senate." March 2, 1867. Signed by Andrew Johnson and William H. Seward. Engraved on vellum. 49½ x 35 cm.

VAN VALZALS, S. B. Letter to Faulk. March 24, 1872. 3 pp.

VAN VLECK, FREDERICK B. Five letters to Faulk. May 30, 1866–May 27, 1871. 16 pp.

WADDELL, WILLIAM COVENTRY H. Letter to Faulk. August 3, 1871. 1 p.

WARD, MORRIS E. Letter to Faulk. December 22, 1867. 1 p.

WARNER, OLIVER. Letter to Faulk. March 29, 1867, transmitting a copy of the resolution of the Massachusetts Legislature ratifying the amendment to the Constitution of the United States passed March 20, 1867. Printed. 3 pp.

WASHABAUGH, FRANK J. Letter to Faulk. November 23, 1879. 3 pp.

WEITZEL, MRS. ELIZA B. Letter to Faulk. February 23, 1881. 3 pp.

WHITE, ASHTON J. H. Two letters to Faulk. September 7, November 19, 1868. Signature only. 3 pp.

WHITNEY, OSCAR. Letter to Faulk. December 3, 1879. 2 pp.

—— Letter to Columbus Delano. December 11, 1873. Copy by Faulk, signed by Whitney. 8 pp.

WICKER, J. H. Eight letters to J. M. Stone. June 27, 1872–November 14, 1878. 14 pp.

WICKER, MECKLING & Co. Letter to J. M. Stone. January 2, 1875. 1 p.

WILKINS, TURNEY M. Letter to Faulk. January 21, 1872. 4 pp.

WILKINSON, MAHLON. Two letters to Faulk. April 27, 1868, April 14, 1869. Signature only. 2 pp.

WILLAMOV. Letter to the District Court of Dakota. Imperial Russian Legation, May 2, 1878. With copy of letter in answer addressed to J. P. Kidder, signed by Faulk, May 17, 1878. 4 pp.

WILLIAMS, JOHN. Letter to Faulk. January 23, 1867. 1 p.

WILLIAMS, THOMAS. Letter to Faulk. December 20, 1866. 2 pp.

WILSON, JAMES S. Four letters to Faulk. General Land Office. January 28, 1867– August 10, 1868. 8 pp.

WOODWARD, JOSEPH T. Letter to Governor Faulk, transmitting a copy of "Acts and Resolves of Maine for 1868." December 23, 1868. Printed. 1 p.

"Plan of grounds of Major J. M. Stone,

Yankton. Cleveland & French, March 1874, Landscape Architects, Chicago." 43½ x 63 cm.

Pencil sketch in color, inscribed: "This view of an Indian camp was made by a son of Congressman Burleigh." [n.d.] 32½ x 16½ cm.

Pencil sketch of Governor Faulk's mother, Mrs. Margaret Faulk, drawn on the back of an unsigned draft of a letter to W. M. Watson. July 9, 1832. 19 x 18 cm.

The report of the Superintendent of Indian Affairs, September 9, 1867, is printed in the *Report on Indian Affairs by the Acting Commissioner, for the Year 1867*, Washington, 1868, pp. 225–228.

[Coe Collection.]

196 FITCH, C. WELLINGTON

Journal of C. Wellington Fitch, Acting Assistant Surgeon, U.S. Army, during the campaign against the Bannock Indians, June 10 to October 22 [1878].

38 pp. 14 cm. Original binding.

The journal opens with Dr. Fitch's departure from San Francisco June 10, under Special Order No. 82, for Carlin, Nev., to join Captain Viven at the Shoshone Reservation, and records the daily marches and stopping places. On August 10 he was ordered to join Captain Sumner at Camas Prairie and then Major Green's command, reporting to him August 21. He continued with the battalion, scouting and pursuing the Indians until October 7, when he was ordered to Walla Walla, arriving October 18, where he was relieved of duty by General Howard and ordered to report at Division Headquarters in San Francisco.

The journal is preceded and followed by 23 pages of accounts and memoranda.

[Coe No. IV, 434.]

197 FLETCHER, CHARLES FOSDICK

Letter to Hon. I. I. Stevens. Kalorama, Washington, D.C., March 17, 1859.

1 p. 25 cm.

Written on the third page of a leaflet containing on the first page a printed circular: "Atlantic and Pacific Railroad— Northern Route. Importance of the Northern Route for a Railroad to the Pacific Ocean" by St. Paul and Fort Benton and appealing to all merchants and capitalists to build the road.

The letter asks for an appointment to discuss the project.

[Coe No. IV, 556.]

198 FLETT, JOHN, 1815–

Notes on the religions of the Indians of the Northwest. Signed: "John Flett. July 11, 1890."

Typewritten manuscript. 4 pp. 33 cm.

John Flett emigrated from the Selkirk settlement on the Red River in 1841 under the auspices of the Puget Sound Agricultural Company. In 1854 he was appointed Indian interpreter under General Joel Palmer, and later subagent, attending all of the Indian councils with Superintendent Palmer. In 1859 he returned to farming in Washington Territory and finally settled at Lakeview, near Tacoma.

The manuscript has many corrections and alterations in Elwood Evans' hand and is dated by him: "Lake View, Pierce County, July 11, 1890." It is similar in content to a manuscript sent to Evans with a letter of May 19, 1890, but differently phrased. (See Evans' Correspondence, No. 173.)

[Miller Collection.]

199 FOOTE, HENRY STUART, 1804–1880

Letter to Colonel William Hickey, undated [1850] and headed "(Confidential)."

2 pp. 25 cm. With typewritten transcript.

Endorsed: "From Hon: H. S. Foot Senator U.S. requesting W. Hickey to draw a bill providing for the governments of California, New Mexico, Utah &c."

H. S. Foote was elected U.S. senator from Mississippi in 1847, and later governor. He supported the compromise measures of 1850; spent some years in California, being defeated in an election for U.S. senator in 1856; and returned to Mississippi. "Col." Hickey had been a captain in the militia, but was often called colonel or general. He was assistant secretary of the Senate.

[Coe No. 71.]

200 FORT LARAMIE

Watercolor painting of Fort Laramie between 1863 and 1868 [?] by an unknown artist.

32½ x 14 cm.

[Coe Collection.]

201 FORT RECORDS OF THE NORTHWEST

Original manuscript records of Forts Dalles, Hoskins, Klamath, Simcoe, Vancouver, and Yamhill in Oregon and Washington Territories, 1850–1879, including Proceedings of the Councils of Administration, post orders, morning report books, reports of guard mounted, letter books of the commanding officers, and other records.

19 vols. 33–40½ cm.

FORT DALLES. Proceedings of the Council of Administration, August 9, 1850–December 31, 1859; post orders, March 26, 1856–December 30, 1863; morning report book, December 19, 1862–May 24, 1866; report of the guard mounted, kept by the officer of the day, August 28, 1858–December 6, 1865. 8 vols. [i.e., 1,525 pp.] 32½–45 cm. Original bindings.

FORT KLAMATH. "Record Book of Interment in Post Cemetery at Fort Klamath, Oregon," 1863–1890; "Letter Book 'B' Quartermasters Dept. Fort Klamath," January 5, 1871–September 25, 1872. 2 vols. [i.e., 185 pp.] 31½–39½ cm. Original bindings.

FORT YAMHILL. Morning report book, February 12, 1858–August 7, 1860; report of the guard mounted, March 1–September 9, 1860; "Fort Yamhill Commander's letter book" [Lieutenant W. J. Shipley], September 9, 1865–June 30, 1866. 3 vols. [i.e., 440 pp.] 33½–37½ cm. Original bindings.

FORT HOSKINS. Morning report book, March 18–April 10, 1865; report of the guard mounted, June 1, 1862–February 9, 1863. 2 vols. [i.e., 270 pp.] 32½ cm. Original bindings.

FORT SIMCOE. Morning report book, 9th Inf., November 22, 1856–June 27, 1857; November 19, 1857–May 8, 1859; report of guard mounted, 9th Inf., May 24–November 17, 1857. 3 vols. [i.e., 419 pp.] 33–40½ cm. Original bindings.

FORT VANCOUVER. "Cash blotter, Office of disbursing quartermaster. Bannock expedition, Fort Vancouver, W. January 1st, 1879." 98 pp. 38½ cm. Original binding.

These manuscripts are the official records kept by the commanding officers, the adjutants and the officers of the day, of the activities at the forts in the Northwest, which were occupied at various times by companies of the Regiment of Mounted Riflemen, the 1st Cavalry Oregon Volunteers, 1st Washington Volunteer Infantry, 1st Oregon Infantry, 1st Oregon Cavalry, 2d, 3d, and 4th California Infantry, and the 4th, 9th, 14th, 21st, and 23d U.S. Infantry.

[Coe No. 74.]

202 FORT SMITH, ARKANSAS, and FORT GIBSON, INDIAN TERRITORY

"Account Book of the Post Trader at Forts Gibson and Smith, 1823, 1824, and 1825."

370 pp. 41½ cm. Original binding.

Fort Smith was established in 1817 to protect the Indian lands from encroachments of white settlers and to restrain the Indians, and was occupied until April 1824, when it was determined to move the troops nearer to the warlike Osage Indians and Fort Gibson was established. Fort Smith was again occupied by troops in 1833. From 1861 to 1863 it was occupied by Confederate troops, and was finally abandoned in 1871.

The Post Trader's account book contains records of sales to the officers and soldiers stationed at Fort Smith from September 27, 1823 to May 10, 1824, and at Fort Gibson, May 29, 1824–May 7, 1825, and to settlers and traders. The forts were manned by several companies of the 7th U.S. Infantry under Colonel Mathew Arbuckle.

Colonel John Nicks was sutler at Fort Gibson and, with John Rogers, maintained trading establishments at Fort Gibson and Fort Smith.

[Coe No. 72.]

203 FRANCIS, SAMUEL DEXTER, 1814–1891

Journal of Samuel Dexter Francis, describing life in Vermont, 1841–1845; travels in the midwest and his stay in Illinois, 1845–1852; and the daily record of his trip across the Plains and life in Oregon, 1852–1862.

209 pp. 32 cm. With typewritten transcript.

From November 19, 1841 to September 9, 1845, the diary of this farmer of Barnard, Vt., is a leisurely account of country life. September 9, 1845, he set out for Geneva, Ill., where he hired out as a farmhand. The following year he returned to Vermont for his family, and they lived in Illinois until 1852. The entries for this period are brief and largely concerned with details of weather and crops with occasional political observations.

In April 1852 Mr. Francis, his wife, and five children, in company with the Wilson and Sheppard families, began their wagon trip to Oregon, across Illinois to the Mississippi, to Des Moines, Kanesville, along the Platte to Fort Laramie, the Salt Lake Road, Fort Boise, to Oregon City, arriving October 15, 1852. The entries that follow and end abruptly on March 23, 1862, are laconic, with comments on weather and farm duties, and some concern, as always, for the state of the nation, notably, at this period, the impending outbreak of the Civil War.

Notarized attestation of the author's daughter, Dora Francis Frazer, April 1936, is bound with the manuscript.

[Coe No. 75.]

204 FREEMAN, HENRY BLANCHARD

Journal kept by Captain Henry B. Freeman, 7th U.S. Infantry, in the campaign against the Sioux in 1876, covering the period from March 21 to October 6.

79 pp. Map. 19 cm. Original binding.

Captain Freeman began his journal March 21, 1876, at camp between Fort Shaw and Fort Ellis, two days after he succeeded Captain Rawn in command of the six companies of the 7th Infantry. The expedition, under the command of Colonel John Gibbon, was to march down the Yellowstone and get in communication with General Terry and General Custer. The journal describes the daily march, Colonel Gibbon's council with the Crows, his meeting with Terry, arrival at Big Horn, the news of Custer's fate, June 26, meeting with Major Reno, June 27, arrival at the battlefield, care of wounded and burial of those killed, June 28 and 29. On July 1 the command started the march back to the mouth of the Rosebud, joined Crook's command August 10, and, after a month of pursuing the Indians, arrived again at Fort Shaw, October 6, when the journal breaks off.

The journal contains a manuscript map of the battlefield, June 29, 1876. 12 x 5 cm.

This journal corroborates that of Lieutenant William L. English (see No. 171), which covers the campaign from March 17 to September 5, and the journal of Lieutenant James H. Bradley, March 17–June 27, printed in the *Contributions* to the Historical Society of Montana, 1896, II, 140–225.

[Coe No. 76.]

205 FRÉMONT, JOHN CHARLES, 1813–1890

"Articulos de capitulacion hecha el dia trece de Enero de mil ochocientos, cuarenta y siete por D. José Antonio Carrillo Comandante de Escuadron y D. Agustin Olvera Diputado comicionados nombrados por D. Andres Pico Comandante en Gefe de las fuersas de California pertenecientes al Gobierno Mejicano, y P. B. Picading [Reading] Mayor del Batallon de California y Luis Mailane [McLane] J. Capitan de Artilleria, y W. H. Rusel Capitan de ordenes, comicionados nombrados por el Teniente Coronel del Ejercito de los Estados Unidos de norte America, J. C. Frémont militar Comandante del territorio de California." Cuidad de los Angeles dia diez y seis de Enero, 1847.

2 pp. 31 cm.

This copy, entirely in the handwriting of Narciso Botello, is signed: "Es copia de sus original, que sertifico como Srio. del Gobierno y Comandante Gral. Angeles Marzo 8 de 1847."

At the time of the signing of the articles Narciso Botello was secretary to Governor Flores. He had served as secretary of the Ayuntamientos in 1836 and had taken an active part in public affairs and against the American invasion.

The manuscript contains the seven articles signed at Campo de Cahuengua, January 13, 1849 and the additional article signed January 16.

These articles signed by the commissioners appointed by Pico to represent the Californians and by Frémont to represent the United States, marked the final capitulation of California.

The original of the Articles of Capitulation now in the Bancroft Library is reproduced in facsimile followed by an English translation in the *Annual Publications* of the Historical Society of Southern California, 1932, XV, 305–310; and the English text alone appears in the *Report of the Secretary of the Navy Communicating Copies of Commodore Stockton's Despatches relating to the Military and Naval Operations in California* (30th Congress, 2d Session, Senate Ex. No. 31, pp. 22–23 [Washington, 1849]).

[Coe Collection.]

206 FRUSH, WILLIAM H.

Diary of William H. Frush on his journey across the Plains to Oregon, with observations on the country passed through, details of the route, and information and advice to emigrants on the overland trail, May 15 to September 25, 1850.

108 pp., illus., map. 12 cm. With typewritten transcript of the diary.

William H. Frush left his home in Newark, Mo., alone for California, hoping to overtake his brother, John H. Frush. He followed the Oregon Trail by St. Joseph, Blue River, North Platte to Fort Laramie, where he met his brother. While at Fort Laramie he met Kit Carson, who advised them to go to California by way of Oregon. They continued by South Pass, Bear River, Soda Springs, Fort Hall, Fort Boise, and The Dalles, arriving in Portland September 25, 1850. He recorded full names and dates on all graves passed on the trail, and the names and homes of travelers they met. Frush was one of the organizers of the Pacific Telegraph Company in 1855, and is buried in Lone Fir Cemetery, Portland, Oregon.

The diary [87 pp.] is preceded by tables of distances, two drawings, and a page with the note "Property of Wm. H. Frush of Newark Knox Co. Missouri." It is fol-lowed by two pages describing the snow of December 1852, an account of trouble with J. Knott over ferrying, January–March, 1851, and contains drawings of Chimney Rock, Court House Rock, profile of Snake River, and a map of Burnt River.

[Coe No. 77.]

207 FURGERSON, SAMUEL

"Journal of a voyage from Boston to the North-West Coast of America, in the Brig *Otter*, Samuel Hill Commander. Kept by Samuel Furgerson Ship's Carpenter." March 31, 1809 to March 24, 1811.

129 pp., 1 folded chart. 33 cm. Original binding.

"A chart shewing the track to & cruising grounds on the northwest coast of America during a voyage of the Brig Otter, Samuel Hill Commander, 1809–1811." Original chart in color. 47½ x 66½ cm.

A daily journal of the voyage, kept in tabular form from April 1 to May 4, 1809, and then in narrative form, becoming much more detailed on arrival in the Sandwich Islands in September, and on the Northwest Coast, November 1, 1809, and describing the places visited, the natives, and the traffic with the Indians while trading principally on the coast of Alaska and the Queen Charlotte Islands. The journal ends with the entry for March 24, 1811, in Thanikyloo Bay.

[Coe No. IV, 433.]

208 GAINES, ARCHIBALD KINKEAD, 1823–

Journal of the voyage of Governor John P. Gaines and his family from New York to San Francisco on the U.S. Store Ship *Supply*, and from San Francisco to Astoria, Oregon Territory, on the Sloop of War *Falmouth*, January 3 to August 15, 1850, kept by his son, Archibald K. Gaines; together with a summary of their life in Oregon, his father's career as governor, and death. The last entry is dated February 17, 1858.

100 pp. 25½ cm. Original binding.

The first entry is January 3, when the party sailed from New York, followed by daily entries for January 21–27, 1850 and May 28–October 27, 1854.

On June 27, 1850, the author reversed the volume, beginning the account of the voyage again, and continued the entries at intervals until February 17, 1858. It is followed by a record of the dates of birth, etc., of members of the family, the last entry being the death of his brother Richard, January 28, 1866.

[Coe No. 79.]

209 GAINES, JOHN POLLARD, 1795–1857

Document authorizing and empowering the Hon. Alvin T. Smith of Washington County to serve as Judge of the Probate Court of the County, July 3,

1851, signed by Jno. P. Gaines, Governor, and E. Hamilton, Secretary of Oregon Territory.

1 p. 33 cm.

The document is in the handwriting of Edward Hamilton, Secretary, and bears the official seal of the Territory.

[Coe No. 78.]

210 GARDNER, WILLIAM P.

Letter to Henry [Cummins]. Sand Creek Salmon Mines [Idaho], April 19, 1862.

2 pp. 31½ cm.

William P. Gardner settled in Lane County, Ore., in 1853. In the fall of 1861 he was at Oro Fino, Idaho, and moved on to the Salmon River mines in January 1862.

The letter describes conditions in the Salmon River gold mines during the winter and spring following their discovery.

The letter was accompanied by a copy of the *Salmon River Guide*, San Francisco, April 1862.

[Coe IV, 900.]

211 GARNETT, ROBERT SELDEN, 1819–1861

Letter to Major Gilmore Hays, W.T.V. Post at Muckleshuts Prairie, W.T., April 13, 1856.

2 pp. 25 cm.

Major Garnett served in the Mexican War, in Texas, and as commandant of cadets at West Point. In 1855 he was commissioned Major and sent to the Northwest where he was in command of the Puget Sound and Yakima Expeditions. He later resigned and joined the Confederate Army.

The letter, which is probably a copy, is endorsed in the same hand: "Post at Muckleshuts Prairie, W.T., April 13, 1856. R. S. Garnett, Maj. 9 Infy, commandg. Under instructions from Lt. Col. Casey, proposes the occupation of the Block House at Porter's Prairie by troops from Muckleshuts Prairie."

[Miller Collection.]

212 GEARY, JOHN WHITE, 1819–1873

The "executive minutes" and official correspondence of John W. Geary, Governor of Kansas Territory, 1856–1857; and a few personal letters and papers, 1855–1871.

3 vols. [i.e., 653 pp.] 667 letters and papers. 1,387 pp. 16½–33 cm. With typewritten transcript of the more important papers.

Governor Geary served during the Mexican War in the 2d Pennsylvania Infantry. In 1849 President Polk appointed him postmaster at San Francisco, but he had hardly begun his duties when his Whig successor, appointed by President Taylor, arrived. Geary was elected first alcalde of San Francisco and appointed judge, and later became the first mayor. In 1852 he returned to his home in Pennsylvania and in 1856 when Kansas was in a state of civil war he accepted the appointment as governor of the Territory. He made great advances at first, but aroused the enmity of the pro-slavery politicians and, when he did not receive the necessary military and official support from the government, he resigned and in 1857 returned to Pennsylvania. He later served as colonel of the 28th Pennsylvania Regiment during the Civil War and was twice elected governor of the state, 1867–1873.

The manuscripts give a vivid picture of conditions in Kansas during the Free State War. They include petitions from citizens of other states in behalf of the Free State prisoners, congratulatory letters on his accomplishment in restoring peace in Kansas, documents and receipts relating to the building of the capitol, and a few personal and family papers.

The letters from Governor Geary are copies, usually in his secretary's hand. The correspondence, with the exception of five letters written in 1862–1871, is dated from April 22, 1856 to December 4, 1857.

GEARY, JOHN WHITE. Executive minutes kept by Governor Geary's private secretary, John H. Gihon, September 9, 1856–March 20, 1857. 2 vols. [i.e., 533 pp.] Original bindings. 31–33 cm.

The minutes, which are almost entirely in Gihon's handwriting, contain copies of official letters to and from the governor, his messages to the legislature and other official acts, with records of events in diary form inserted chronologically.

—— Governor Geary's personal letters and reports to Secretary of State William L. Marcy, Secretary of the Treasury James Guthrie, President Pierce, and President Buchanan. September 6, 1856–February 12, 1857. Copied by his secretary. 130 pp. Original binding. 20½ cm.

—— Letter to James Buchanan. April 27, 1857. Copy. 3 pp.

—— Two letters to Lewis Cass. April 20, December 4, 1857. Copies. 4 pp.

—— Letter to George W. Clarke. December 22, 1856. Copy. 2 pp.

—— Letter to William Flinn. January 7, 1857. Copy. 2 pp.

—— Letter to John B. Floyd. April 17, 1857. Copy. 2 pp.

—— Letter to John A. Halderman, F. Renick, William A. Shannon, Committee. September 9, 1856. Copy. 1 p.

—— Letter to L. S. Hall. October 11, 1856. Copy. 1 p.

—— Power of attorney to Andrew J. Jones. August 28, 1856. Witnessed by Richard McAllister and Theodore Adams, and signed by Jones before the same witnesses. 3 pp.

—— Letter to the Hon. W. Medill. July 8, 1857. Copy. 1 p.

—— Three letters to Franklin Pierce, President of the United States. August 9–December 10, 1856. Copies. 6 pp.

—— Letter to William P. Richardson. August 21, 1856. Copy. 1 p.

—— Letter to Governor Charles Robinson. July 13, 1857. Copy. 2 pp.

—— Two letters to Persifor F. Smith. October 6, November 11, 1856. Copies. 4 pp.

—— Letter to H. T. Titus. November 8, 1856. Copy. 1 p.

—— Letter to Elisha Whittlesey. February 4, 1857. With statement of account to June 30, 1857. Copy. 2 pp.

—— Abstract of account in disbursement for the capitol. April 16, 1857. 2 copies. 2 pp.

—— Abstract statement of expenditures [ca. July 7, 1856]. 2 copies. 4 pp.

—— Abstract of expenditures in the purchase of library for Kansas Territory

[December 1, 1856]. With the receipted bill for the books signed by James L. Gihon, December 2, 1856. 12 pp.

GEARY, J. W. Affidavit for the arrest of William T. Sherrard before S. G. Cato, February 9, 1857. Copy. 2 pp.

—— Bill for expenses, September 9, 1856–March 5, 1857. Copy. With unsigned copy of accompanying affidavit, April 16, 1857. 4 pp.

—— Estimate by counties of the probable population of the Territory. November 27, 1856. Copy. 1 p.

—— Memorandum of payments made to Kansas Militia. December 3, 1856. Copy. 1 p.

—— Memorandum of testimony, Territory vs. J. A. W. Jones. February 28, 1857. 1 p.

—— "Opinions & notes." [August 9, 1856.] Not Geary's hand. 1 p.

—— Statement of conditions in Kansas Territory. Endorsed: "Notes prepared by JON." [n.d.] 18 pp.

ABRĒO, MRS. CORNELIA M. Letter to Geary. December 9, 1856. 2 pp.

ADAMS, THEODORE. 13 letters to Geary. August 22, 1856–July 8, 1857. 28 pp.

ANDERSON, ROBERT. Letter to Geary. September 19, 1856. 1 p.

ARNY, WILLIAM F. M. Two letters to Geary. December 8, 1856, February 2, 1857. 12 pp.

"Atcherson County." Letter to Geary about Charles M. Hays. February 6, 1857. Signed: "Atcherson County." 2 pp.

BABCOCK, CARMI W. Letter to Colonel McAllister. February 16, 1857. 2 pp.

BACHMAN, B. C. Letter to Geary. March 10, 1857. With note added from Josephine Stuart. 2 pp.

BAILEY, JAMES G. Letter to Geary. October 9, 1856. 2 pp.

BAINTER, EPHRAIM. Territory of Kansas vs. Ephraim Bainter. November 3, 1856. Certified copy of judgment, February 17, 1857, James R. Whitehead, clerk, by W. L. Kuykendall, deputy. 2 pp.

BAKER, ARTHUR J. Two letters to Geary. January 12, February 10, 1857. 4 pp.

BANKS, E. A. Letter to Geary. January 26, 1857. 1 p.

BARDWELL, GEORGE H. Letter to Geary. January 19, 1857. 2 pp.

BARNETT, WARD B. Letter to Geary. September 26, 1856. 1 p.

BARNUM, HERON. Letter to Geary. October 11, 1856. 1 p.

BARTON, JOHN T. Letter to Geary. House of Representatives, January 1, 1857. 1 p.

BASHFORD, COLES. Letter to Geary. November 29, 1856. 1 p.

BEACH, ASHAEL. Letter to Geary. October 4, 1856. 2 pp.

BEESON, RICHARD. Letter to Geary. October 23, 1856. 2 pp.

BETTS, ROYSTON. Letter to Geary. December 31, 1856. 2 pp.

BIG SPRINGS. CITIZENS. Report of a meeting upholding Geary. February 17, 1857. Signed by Charles D. Jones, chairman, Charles A. Allen, secretary, and 22 others. 2 pp.

BIGHAM, JOHN. Letter to Geary. September 15, 1857. Signed also by Joseph Cook, John B. Davison, George Gallagher. 1 p.

BIGLER, WILLIAM. Two letters and a telegram to Geary. July 23–November 14, 1856. 5 pp.

BINGHAM, E. F. Letter to Geary. January 15, 1857. 3 pp.

BINGHAM, GEORGE. Letter to Geary. January 24, 1857. 1 p.

BLADEN, WASHINGTON. Letter to Geary. August 26, 1856. 2 pp.

BOONE, ALBERT G. Letter to Geary. March 5, 1857. 1 p.

BOWMAN, GEORGE W. Three letters to Geary. January 21–March 11, 1857. 6 pp.

BOYLE, J. A. Letter to Geary. March 7, 1857. 2 pp.

BRADSHAW, WILLIAM. Letter to Geary. August 4, 1856. 1 p.

BREECE, S. D. Letter to Geary. September 1, 1856. 1 p.

BRETZ, C. Letter to Geary. November 15, 1856. 1 p.

BRIGHT, J. D. Letter to Geary. November 5, 1856. Signature only. 1 p.

BRIGHT, M. G. Letter to Geary. November 7, 1856. 3 pp.

BRINDLE, WILLIAM. Four letters to Geary. May 15, 1856–January 17, 1857. 7 pp.

BROOKBANK, JOHN B. Letter to Geary. September 12, 1856. 1 p.

BROWN, GEORGE W. Seven letters to Geary. September 1, 1856–January 15, 1857. 13 pp.

BROWN, JAMES W. Letter to Geary. February 8, 1857. 1 p.

BROWNE, O. H. Letter to Geary. September 13, 1856. 2 pp.

BRUNSWICK, ME. CITIZENS. To the President of the United States. Petition in behalf of prisoners. Endorsed: "Referred to Gov. Geary for any suggestions he may think the case warrants. F.P." [November 1856?] With 30 signatures. 2 pp.

BUCHANAN, JAMES. Letter to Geary. November 3, 1856. Signature only. 1 p.

BULLOCK, CHARLES P. Letter to Geary. January 13, 1857. 2 pp.

BURGESS, R. Letter to Geary. January 14, 1857. 6 pp.

BUTLER, DAVID. Letter to Geary. April 28, 1871. 1 p.

CALDWELL, A. Letter to Geary. August 30, 1856. 3 pp.

CALHOUN, JOHN. "Proceedings of a meeting said to have been held at Council House, Wyandot." John Calhoun chairman and McLean secretary. Notes in an unidentified hand [July? 1856]. 1 p.

CALOHAN, WILLIAM S. Letter to Geary. August 2, 1856. 1 p.

CARPENTER, SAMUEL L. Letter to Geary. January 29, 1857. 2 pp.

CASS, LEWIS. Four letters to Geary. October 23, 1856–November 28, 1857. 9 pp.

—— Letter to Hon. Howell Cobb. May 22, 1857. Copy. 1 p.

CASTLEMAN, BENJAMIN D. Letter to Geary. September 16, 1856. 1 p.

CATO, STERLING G. Letter to Geary. November 10, 1856. 2 pp.

CHRISTIAN, JAMES. Letter to Geary. June 21, 1857. 2 pp.

CLEGG, B. Letter to Geary. February 10, 1857. 2 pp.

COFFEY, A. M. Letter to Geary. March 7, 1857. Signed also by M. McCaslin. 2 pp.

COLEMAN, WILLIAM. Letter to Geary. June 27, 1857. 1 p.

COLLINS, THOMAS. Letter to Geary. January 28, 1857. 1 p.

COOK, WILLIAM A. Letter to Geary. July 27, 1857. 1 p.

COOKE, PHILIP ST. GEORGE. Five letters to Geary. [September 12, 1856]–March 14, 1857. 8 pp.

CORLEY, JOHN. Letter to Geary. February 3 [1857]. 1 p.

COYLE, JOHN. Three letters to Geary. September 20, 1856–January 26 [i.e., 29], 1857. The letter of September 20 is signed also by William Bryant, Charles King, and J. B. Todd. 6 pp.

CRAIG, HENRY KNOX. Letter to Geary. November 13, 1856. 1 p.

CRANE, JOHN M. Letter to Geary. November 3, 1856. 2 pp.

CUNARD, L. M. Letter to Geary. November 6, 1856. 1 p.

CUNNINGHAM, THOMAS. Letter to Geary. February 15, 1857. 2 pp.

CURRY, WILLIAM B. Three letters to Geary. August 13–September 3, 1856. 3 pp.

CUSHMAN, C. A. Letter to Geary. September 12, 1856. 2 pp.

CUTLER, ANDREW S. Two letters to Geary. October 22, 29, 1856. 4 pp.

DANFORTH, C. H. Letter to Geary. January 12, 1857. 3 pp.

DANIELS, EDWARD. Letter to Geary. December 11, 1856. 2 pp.

DAVIDSON, H. O. Letter to Geary. August 17, 1856. 2 pp.

DAVIS, B. F. Letter to Geary. February 9, 1857. 4 pp.

DAVIS, ISAAC. Letter to Geary. November 13, 1856. 2 pp.

DAVIS, JOHN W. Letter to Geary. July 29, 1856. 4 pp.

DELAHAY, MARK W. Letter to Geary. February 4, 1857. 2 pp.

DESELDING, CHARLES. Letter to Geary. January 17, 1857. 1 p.

DEWEY, S. P. Letter to Geary. August 2, 1856. 2 pp.

DEWOLFE, EZEKIEL. Letter to Geary. September 7, 1856. 3 pp.

DICK, JOHN T. Letter to Geary. February 16, 1857. 2 pp.

DONOUGHE, CORNELIUS. Two letters to Geary. August 9, October 22, 1856. 9 pp.

DOUGHERTY, B. A. Letter to Geary. July 29, 1856. 1 p.

DOWNER, JAMES P. Three letters to Geary. October 4, 1856–January 30, 1856 [i.e., 1857]. 7 pp.

DRUM, RICHARD C. Letter to Geary. November 3, 1856. 1 p.

DULL, J. J. Two letters to Geary. January 22, February 23, 1857. 3 pp.

DUNCAN, WILLIAM M. Letter to Geary. January 30, 1857. 2 pp.

DUNDAS, WILLIAM H. Letter to Geary. November 26, 1856. 1 p.

DUNN, RICHARD C. Letter to Geary. February 17, 1857. 2 pp.

DUTTON, BENJAMIN F. Letter to Geary. July 29, 1856. 1 p.

DYER, WILLIAM F. Letter to Geary. January 26, 1857. 1 p.

EASTIN, LUCIEN J. Letter to Geary. February 26, 1857. 2 pp.

EBERHART, A. G. Two letters to Geary. October 30, 1856, February 11, 1857. 3 pp.

EDGAR, WILLIAM. Letter to Geary. November 3, 1856. 2 pp.

ELDRIDGE, SHALER W. Two letters to Geary. December 18, 1856, February 9, 1857. 2 pp.

ELLIOTT, ARCHIBALD. Letter to Geary. September 19, 1856. 2 pp.

ELLIOTT, JOHN A. Letter to Geary. January 19, 1857. 2 pp.

EMERSON, W. A. G. Letter to Geary. February 12, 1857. 3 pp.

EMORY, W. H. Letter to Geary. September 12, 1856. 2 pp.

EMRICK, SIMON. Letter to Geary. February 7, 1857. 1 p.

FISH, HAMILTON. Form letter to Geary. April 15, 1871. With a printed copy of the Act of Congress providing for the commemoration of the centennial. 1 p.

FLENNIKEN, ROBERT P. Letter to Geary. January 15, 1857. 1 p.

FLINT, F. F. Letter to Geary. January 27, 1857. 2 pp.

FORMAN, JOHN W. Petition to Governor Geary. [September, 1856?] Signed also by William P. Richardson, F. J. Marshall, D. A. N. Grover, B. O. Driscoll, and Thomas W. Waterson. 1 p.

FORSTER, JOHN T. Letter to Geary. January 5, 1857. 3 pp.

FOX, GEORGE K. Letter to Geary. June 6, 1857. 1 p.

FRAIN, WILLIAM P. Letter to Geary. March 9, 1857. 2 pp.

Friend to the oppressed, A. Letter to Geary. November 21, 1856. 4 pp.

FULLER, PERRY. Letter to Geary. March 4, 1857. 2 pp.

FURCEY, WILLIAM. Letter to Geary. February 6, 1857. 1 p.

GARRETT, R. Letter to Governor Geary on the division of Riley County. February 16, 1857. Signed also by Thomas Reynolds and Stephen B. Williams. 1 p.

GARVEY, EDWARD C. K. Letter to Geary. November 24, 1856. 1 p.

GATES, MRS. LOUISE W. Letter to Geary. February 9, 1857. 2 pp.

GEARY, EDWARD R. Five letters to his brother, John W. Geary. September 17, 1856–February 19, 1857. 18 pp.

GEARY, EDWARD R., 2d. Eight letters to his father, J. W. Geary. June 13, 1856–September 2, 1857. 21 pp.

GEARY, JOHN. Letter to his uncle, J. W. Geary. November 1 [1855]. Signed by his mark and written by his father, E. R. Geary, with note added on the same sheet. 2 pp.

GEORGE, GEORGE W. Letter to Geary. November 3, 1856. 2 pp.

GIHON, JOHN H. 14 letters to Geary. October 28 [i.e., 18], 1856–July 29, 1857. 47 pp.

GIHON, JOHN L. Letter to Geary. July 15, 1857. 1 p.

GILMAN, CHARLES. Letter to Geary. October 23, 1856. 4 pp.

GOETSCH, OSCAR. Letter in German to Geary. January 29, 1857. Signed also by Maria Goetsch. 4 pp.

GOODIN, JOEL KISHLER. Two letters to Geary. February 12, 18, 1857. 4 pp.

GORLEY, J. Letter to Geary. November 14, 1856. 2 pp.

GRAHAM, A. D. Letter to Geary. February 28, 1857. 1 p.

GRANT, EDWIN H. Letter to Geary. July 30, 1857. 4 pp.

GREATHOUSE, J. S. Letter to Geary. January 30, 1857. 2 pp.

GUTHRIE, JOHN B. Letter to Geary. August 4, 1856. 4 pp.

HALDEMAN, CYRUS S. Six letters to Geary. November 13, 1856–May 22 [1857]. 14 pp.

HALDEMAN, HORACE. Letter to Geary. February 9, 1857. 3 pp.

HALDERMAN, JOHN A. Two letters to Geary. September 9, 1856, January 20, 1857. The earlier letter is signed also by O. F. Renick and W. A. Shannon. 3 pp.

HALL, L. S. Two letters to Geary. October 10, November 24 [1856]. 4 pp.

HAMPTON, LEVI J. Two letters to Geary. March 16, 23, 1857. 4 pp.

HARVEY, JOHN A. Two letters to Geary. November 22, 1856, March 4, 1857. 5 pp.

HASTINGS, JOHN. Letter to Geary. September 20, 1856. 1 p.

HATCH, J. M. Letter to Geary. April 10, 1857. 3 pp.

HAWKE, GEORGE. Letter to Geary. February 9, 1857. 2 pp.

HAYS, JOHN. Letter to Geary. January 3, 1857. 1 p.

HEBERTON, EDWARD P. Letter to Geary. [September 1856.] Enclosing a letter of introduction to Governor Geary from David R. Porter, September 6, 1856. 3 pp.

HEISKELL, WILLIAM A. Letter to Geary. March 5, 1857. Signed also by L. D. Williams. 2 pp.

HEISTER, A. O. Letter to Geary. September 18, 1856. 1 p.

HENSHAW, JOHN C. Letter to Geary. July 29, 1856. 1 p.

HEWITT, GIRART. Letter to Geary. November 6, 1856. 3 pp.

HICKORY POINT, JEFFERSON CO., K. T. "Names of Convicts who were convicted for acts committed at Hickory Point, Jefferson County, K.T." [October? 1856.] In an unidentified hand. 1 p.

HICKS, SARAH (MRS. JOSEPH). Letter to Geary. November 9, 1856, with added note, November 24. 3 pp.

HIGGINS, SILAS PARSONS. Letter to Geary. November 29, 1856. 3 pp.

HODGE, WILLIAM L. Letter to Geary. August 12, 1856. 2 pp.

HOLMES, WILLIAM W. Letter to Geary. January 29, 1857. 1 p.

HOOGLAND, EDWARD. 11 letters to Geary. August 18 [1856]–April 19, 1857. 43 pp.

HORRELL, IRWIN. Letter to Geary. February 16, 1857. Signature only. 2 pp.

HORNSBY, BRINKLY. Letter to Geary. October 27, 1856. 1 p.

HOSCROFT, JOHN I. Letter to Geary. February 16, 1857. 1 p.

HUGHES, H. COURTENAY. Letter to Geary. January 7, 1857. 1 p.

HULBURD, A. N. Letter to Geary. February 14, 1857. 3 pp.

HULSE, GEORGE T. Letter to Geary. March 3, 1857. 1 p.

HUMPHREY, JOHN. Letter to Geary. February 2, 1857. 2 pp.

HUNTER, ALEXANDER. Letter to Geary. October 23, 1856. 3 pp.

HURD, H. B. Two letters to Geary. October 8, November 22, 1856. 3 pp.

HYATT, THADDEUS. Two letters to Geary. December 5, 8, 1856. Signatures only. 5 pp.

IOWA COUNTY, WIS. CITIZENS. Petition in behalf of William H. Gill. November 8, 1856. With 37 signatures. 3 pp.

IRVINE, JAMES. Two letters to Geary. August 10, 1856, January 19, 1857. 6 pp.

IVES, TIMOTHY. Two letters to Geary. October 24, November 5, 1856. 2 pp.

IVORY, WILLIAM W. Letter to Geary. August 7, 1856. 3 pp.

JACKSON, ISAIAH H. Letter to Geary. November 6, 1856. 2 pp.

JAMES, BURTON A. Two letters to Geary. January 7, February 23, 1857. 2 pp.

JAMES, HENRY. Letter to Geary. January 11, 1857. 2 pp.

JEFFERSON COUNTY, K. T. CITIZENS. Petition in behalf of Ephraim Bainter. [October? 1856.] With 87 signatures. 5 pp.

JEFFERSON, IND. COMMITTEE. Petition for clemency for Otis Mason Marsh. November 5, 1856. Signed by Levi Sparks and nine citizens, with a letter from Joseph A. Wright, Governor of Indiana, November 7, 1856. 2 pp.

JOHNS, HENRY F. Letter to Geary. March 30, 1857. 6 pp.

JOHNSON, JAMES NEELY. Letter to Geary. March 18, 1857. Signature only. 1 p.

JOHNSON, L. M. Letter to Geary. February 3, 1857. 2 pp.

JOHNSTON, B. K. Letter to Geary. September 14, 1856. 2 pp.

JOHNSTONE, EDWARD. Three letters to Geary. September 14–October 22, 1856. 6 pp.

JONES, A. W. Letter to Geary. December 1, 1856. 1 p.

JONES, ANDREW J. 21 letters to Geary. July 21, 1856–July 8, 1857. 47 pp.

JONES, JOHN A. W. Three letters to Geary. October 6, 1856–July 6, 1857. The letter of July 6 encloses a copy of Medill's letter to Jones, July 3, 1857. 8 pp.

JONES, SARAH L. Letter to Geary. January 24, 1857. 2 pp.

KANSAS TERRITORY. CITIZENS. Petition in behalf of William Partridge. December 22, 1856. With 70 signatures. 3 pp.

—— Petition for the release of Free State prisoners, with the names of the prisoners [January 13, 1857]. Signed by G. W. Brown, Richard J. Hinton, James F. Walker, L. S. Hall, A. W. Gleason. 5 pp.

KANSAS TERRITORY. LEGISLATURE. COM-MITTEE. Notes of remarks about Geary [by John Calhoun?] during the 3d Session of the House. [After January 12, 1857.] Endorsed by Geary [?]: "This paper was blown by the wind from Surveyor Genl. Calhoun's office to mine." 1 p.

KEAN, JOHN. Two letters to Geary. January 25, February 20, 1857. 2 pp.

KERR, LEANDER. Letter to Geary. October 23, 1856. 3 pp.

KEY, THOMAS K. Two letters to Geary. January 26, February 20, 1857. 4 pp.

KILLEN, DANIEL. Letter to Geary. March 8, 1857. Signed, with postscript by Killen. 1 p.

KING, HORATIO. Letter to Geary. October 29, 1856. 2 pp.

KING, JOHN A. Letter to Geary. January 9, 1857. 3 pp.

KIRKPATRICK, JOHN M. Four letters to Geary. August 23, 1856–April 2, 1857. 10 pp.

KLOTZ, ROBERT. Letter to Geary. March 25, 1857. 1 p.

LADD, ERASTUS D. Letter to Geary. January 30, 1857. 3 pp.

LADIES SEWING CIRCLE, LAWRENCE. Invitation to Geary. November 14, 1856. Signed by L. S. Hall, corresponding secretary. 1 p.

LAIRD, J. M. Letter to Geary. January 10, 1857. 3 pp.

LANZ, ALFRED. Letter to Geary. February 1857. 1 p.

—— Petition for pardon for men convicted for their part in the attack on Hickory Point. [n.d., October? 1856.] Signed also by J. M. Bernard, W. W. Spratt, D. K. Stout, M. P. Randall, Matthew R. Walker, G. N. Reis. 1 p.

LATHAM, R. W. Letter to Geary. January 22, 1857. 2 pp.

LAWRENCE, AMOS A. Two letters to Geary. November 8, 1856, February 5, 1857. 3 pp.

LEAVITT, STEPHEN. Letter to Geary. January 8, 1857. 1 p.

LeCOMPTE, SAMUEL DEXTER. Letter to Geary. September 17, 1856. 3 pp.

LLOYD, WILLIAM M. Letter to Geary. October 9, 1856. 1 p.

LOGAN, SAMUEL. Letter to his brother-in-law, J. W. Geary. June 23, 1856. 1 p.

LOGAN, WILLIAM W. Three letters to Geary. July 9–August 5, 1856. 4 pp.

LOWRY, M. B. Letter to Geary. July 30, 1856. Signature only. 2 pp.

McALEER, JOSEPH L. Letter to Geary. January 9, 1857. 1 p.

McALLISTER, JOHN H. Letter to Geary. December 6, 1856. 4 pp.

McALLISTER, RICHARD. Nine letters to Geary. July 14, 1856–May 13, 1857. 28 pp.

McCANDLESS, WILSON. Letter to Geary. September 19, 1856. 1 p.

McCANN, THOMAS K. Three letters to Geary. July 31, 1856–March 27, 1857. 8 pp.

McCASLIN, MAXWELL. Seven letters to Geary. August 9, 1856–February 25, 1857. 17 pp.

McCLINTOCK, JONAS R. Letter to Geary. [n.d.] Endorsed: "August 1, 1856." 1 p.

McFADIN, ANDREW H. Three letters to Geary about Henry Sherman. March 3–9, 1857. The last letter is signed also by L. D. Williams, Henry Tuley, Thomas Totten, George Wilson and S. P. Boon before Henry W. Peck. 4 pp.

McFARREN, SAMUEL. Letter to Geary. February 4, 1857. 2 pp.

McGEE, E. M. Letter to Geary. January 10, 1857. 3 pp.

McKOWEN, SAMUEL. Two letters to Geary. October 8, 1856, February 16, 1857. 3 pp.

McLURE, C. C. Letter to Geary. September 9, 1856. 1 p.

McNAMARA, THOMAS. Two letters to Geary. October 16, 1856, February 23, 1857. 5 pp.

McQUAIDE, JAMES G. Letter to Geary. September 15, 1856. 2 pp.

MAGUIRE, THOMAS A. Two letters to Geary. August 6, September 14, 1856. 2 pp.

MARCY, WILLIAM LEARNED. Two letters to Geary. August 26, September 2, 1856. Signatures only. 5 pp.

MARKOE, FRANCIS. Three letters to Geary. August 8–October 24, 1856. 4 pp.

MARSH, SAMUEL. Two letters to Geary. October 13, 1856. Enclosing a letter of the same date to his brother, Otis Mason Marsh. 4 pp.

—— Letter to President Pierce. October 13, 1856. Endorsed: "Referred to Gov. Geary. F.P." 1 p.

MARSHALL, FRANK J. Letter to Geary. September 16, 1856. 2 pp.

—— Agreement with Governor Shannon to transport from St. Louis material for the capitol at Lecompton, April 22, 1856. Signed by Marshall and Wilson Shannon, witnessed by R. C. Bishop, C. A. Perry, Elias H. Perry, and H. Basye. Copy. 3 pp.

—— Receipt for transporting material for the capitol. January 13, 1857. Certified by Wilson Shannon. 1 p.

MARYE, SIMON B. Letter to Geary. August 15, 1856. 3 pp.

MATHIAS, WILLIAM G. Letter to Geary. February 18, 1857. 1 p.

MATTESON, JOEL ALDRICH. Letter to Geary. December 25, 1856. Signature only. 1 p.

MAYNADIER, HENRY. Letter to Geary. March 19, 1857. Signature only. 1 p.

MEDARY, SAMUEL. Letter to Geary. January 22, 1857. 1 p.

MEDILL, WILLIAM. Three letters to Geary. May 27–July 17, 1857. Signatures only. 6 pp.

MERRILL, ABEL. Letter to Geary. January 13, 1857. 3 pp.

MILLAR, I. Letter to Geary. November 16, 1856. 1 p.

MILLER, GEORGE W. Letter to Geary. February 11, 1857. 2 pp.

MITCHELL, A. M. Letter to Geary. January 7, 1857. 1 p.

MITCHELL, D., JR. Letter to Geary. February 4, 1856 [i.e., 1857]. 3 pp.

MITCHELL, EDWARD P. Letter to Geary. October 25, 1862. 1 p.

MITCHELL, JAMES. Two letters to Geary. November 7, December 12, 1856. 3 pp.

MONTAGUE, ISAAC W., and HANNAH S. Letter to Geary. October 17, 1856. 1 p.

MOORE, J. D. Letter to Geary. February 24, 1857. 1 p.

MOORE, W. W. Letter to Geary. February 11, 1857. 1 p.

MORRISON, J. Letter to Governor Wright. November 12, 1856. With postscript by N. Hayden. 2 pp.

MURPHY, WILLIAM E. Letter to Geary. January 21, 1857. 1 p.

NICHOLS, JULIA A. Letter to Geary. November 21, 1856. 3 pp.

NICHOLS, R. D. Letter to Geary. February 26, 1857. 1 p.

NONES, J. H. Letter to C. S. Haldeman. April 8, 1857. 2 pp.

[NUTE, EPHRAIM.] Statement of treatment received from the "Border Ruffians" on August 28, 1856, when he was traveling with his sister-in-law, whose husband, William C. Hoppe, had been murdered a few days before. September 15, 1857. Unsigned. 5 pp.

O'HERN, M. P. Two telegrams and a letter to Geary. July 23–August 27, 1856. 3 pp.

ORR, JOHN M. Letter to Geary. August 19, 1856. 1 p.

OTTAWA CREEK, K. T. Proceedings of a meeting at Otaway [sic] Creek, February 14, 1857, S. Mewhinney, chairman, John W. Griffith, secretary. Copy. 1 p.

PAINE, ALFRED J. et al. vs. Territory of Kansas. Copy of the judgment rendered, certified February 17, 1857, James R. Whitehead, clerk, by W. L. Kuykendall, deputy clerk, 2 pp.

PAINTER, C. R. Letter to Geary. January 15, 1857. 1 p.

PAINTER, ISRAEL. Invitation to a dinner in Pittsburgh. March 19, 1857. Signed by Israel Painter, P. C. Shannon and 18 other citizens. 3 pp.

PARDEE, A. W. Two letters to Geary. January 28, February 3, 1857. 5 pp.

PARROTT, MARCUS J. Two letters to Geary. September 13, October 5, 1856. 2 pp.

PARSONS, THEOPHILUS. Letter to Geary, introducing John Coffey Douglass, Yale 1853. October 29, 1856. 1 p.

PARTRIDGE, WILLIAM. Letter to Geary. January 24, 1857. 3 pp.

PATRICK, ALBERT G. Letter to Geary. December 2, 1856. 2 pp.

PATTERSON, ALMIS B. Letter to Geary. October 30, 1856. 3 pp.

PATTERSON, FINDLEY. Letter to Geary. November 3, 1856. 2 pp.

PAYNTER, REECE. Letter to Geary. February 20, 1857. 1 p.

PECK, JOHN. Two letters to Geary. October 24, 1856, January 30, 1857. 4 pp.

PELLIT, SARAH. Two letters to Geary. January 15, 1856 [i.e., 1857], February 3, 1857. 5 pp.

PETERSON, T. B. Letter to John H. Gihon. January 5, 1857. 2 pp.

Petition to Governor Geary to pardon Elias Roark. November 24, 1856. With 101 signatures. 4 pp.

PHILLIPS, E. A. Letter to Geary. November 8, 1856. 2 pp.

PIERCE, FRANKLIN. Telegram and letter to Geary. August 26, 1856, March 25 [1857]. 2 pp.

PLEASANT GROVE, IND. CITIZENS. Petition to Governor Joseph A. Wright in behalf of William Updegraff. October 27, 1857. With 42 signatures. 2 pp.

PLUMLEY, GEORGE R. Two letters to Geary. January 14, March 2, 1857. 2 pp.

POMEROY, PHINEHAS. Letter to Geary. February 2, 1857. 1 p.

POMEROY, SAMUEL CLARKE. Letter to Geary. February 10, 1857. 1 p.

PORTER, DAVID R. Letter to Geary. August 1, 1856. 1 p.

PRICE, THOMAS B. Two letters to Geary. August 28, 1856, July 1857. 5 pp.

PRICE, WILLIAM. Letter to Geary. November 5, 1856. 3 pp.

Prisoners at Lecompton, November 12, 1856. A list. 4 pp.

PURSE, WILLIAM A. Two letters to Geary. May 19, 1856, February 20, 1857. 3 pp.

RAINEY, WILLIAM. Letter to Geary. November 17, 1856. 2 pp.

RAY, ALEXANDER. Letter to Geary. February 16, 1857. 1 p.

REEDER, ANDREW H. Letter to Geary. May 19, 1857. 2 pp.

REPUBLICAN CENTRAL COMMITTEE OF THE CITY AND COUNTY OF NEW YORK. Resolution adopted March 25, 1857. Signed by John A. Kennedy, president, William Peel, J. L. Woodford, secretaries. Copy. 1 p.

REYNOLDS, L. C. Letter to Geary. October 26, 1856. 1 p.

RICE, JOHN T. Affidavit. Leavenworth Co., K.T., January 8, 1857, about the sacking of the post office at Alexandria, September 1856, Jos. L. McAleer, postmaster. Sworn before Richard R. Rees, with a note signed by Lewis N. Reis, postmaster, Leavenworth City. 1 p.

RICHARDSON, WILLIAM P. Letter to Nathaniel Pascall. February 10, 1857. Copy. 3 pp.

RICHMOND, L. Three letters to Geary. October 18–November 28, 1856. 8 pp.

RITCHEY, A. J. Letter to Geary. September 27, 1856. 1 p.

ROARK, ELIAS vs. Territory of Kansas. Copy of judgment, certified February 16, 1857 by James R. Whitehead, clerk, W. L. Kuykendall, deputy. 2 pp.

ROBERTS, WILLIAM G. Letter to Geary. November 5, 1856. 2 pp.

ROBERTS, WILLIAM YOUNG. Two letters to Geary of same date. February 1, 1857. 3 pp.

ROBINSON, CHARLES. Four letters to Geary. September 14–December 20, 1856. 7 pp.

—— Letter to Geary about the postmaster at Lawrence. December 26, 1856. With added notes, December 27, by G. W. Brown, S. B. Prentiss and C. W. Babcock. 4 pp.

RODGERS, GEORGE J[?]. Letter to Geary. September 27, 1856. 2 pp.

RODRIGUE, ARISTIDES. Letter to Geary. February 4, 1857. 1 p.

—— Agreement, March 9, 1857, canceling contract of December 27, 1855 for building the capitol. Witnessed by John H. Gihon. 1 p.

—— Statement of settlement. March 9, 1857. 1 p.

—— Abstract of settlement of capitol building contract with Rodrigue. [April 16, 1857.] Copy. 1 p.

ROGERS, A. A. Letter to Geary. September 30, 1856. 1 p.

ROSS, RANDAL. Letter to Geary. January 20, 1857. 2 pp.

ROWE, GEORGE J. Letter to Geary. January 14, 1857. Signed also by Jacob Rowe. 2 pp.

RUFF, B. F. Letter to Geary. November 21, 1856. 1 p.

RUMBOLD, WILLIAM. Two letters to Geary. September 15, 1856, March 14, 1857. 2 pp.

RUSSELL, WILLIAM HEPBURN. Seven letters and a telegram to Geary. December 1, 1856–February 16, 1857. 13 pp.

SANSOM, J. B. Two letters to Geary. January 12, March 16, 1857. 5 pp.

SCAMMAN, T. Letter to Geary. January 10, 1857. 1 p.

SCHLEY, JAMES M. Letter to Geary. August 18, 1856. 1 p.

SEEGAR, JOHN R. L. Letter to Geary. November 3, 1856. 2 pp.

SETTLE, WILLIAM H. Letter to Geary. December 1, 1856. 1 p.

SEXTON, CHARLES A. Letter to Geary. November 13, 1856. 1 p.

SHEARER, CRAWFORD W. Letter to Geary. August 7, 1856. 1 p.

SHERRARD, WILLIAM T. Letter to Geary. December 22, 1856. 2 pp.

—— Territory of Kansas vs. William T. Sherrard. Writ of arrest, signed by S. G. Cato, assistant justice of the Supreme Court, K.T., February 9, 1857. 2 pp.

SHORE, S. T. Letter to Geary. November 5, 1856. 4 pp.

SIBLEY, HENRY HASTINGS. Two letters to Geary. December 5, 1856, January 12, 1857. 7 pp.

SMITH, HAMILTON. Letter to Geary. December 30, 1856. 2 pp.

SMITH, PERSIFOR FRAZER. Nine letters to Geary. September 16, 1856–February 16, 1857. 28 pp.

SMITH, SAMUEL O. Letter to Geary. September 16, 1856. 1 p.

SONS OF TEMPERANCE. Friendship Division No. 19. Resolution of thanks to Governor Geary, April 5, 1870. Signed by Oliver Martin and A. G. Little. Broadside. 36 x 47½ cm.

SPEER, W. R. Letter to Geary. September 16, 1857. 2 pp.

SPENCER, JOHN C. Letter to Geary. January 1, 1857. 1 p.

SPENCER, WILLIAM. Letter to Geary. January 17, 1857. 2 pp.

SPERING, JOSHUA. Letter to Geary. January 5, 1857. 2 pp.

SPICER, JOHN. Letter to Geary. Unsigned and undated. Endorsed: "Private. John Spicer, Decr. 21st, 1856." 2 pp.

Squatter Sovereign, Atchison, K.T. Bill for printing proclamations and advertisement for proposals for building the capitol, February 9, 1857. Receipted by Stringfellow, Kelly & Lasey, and certified February 21, 1857, by Wilson Shannon. Duplicate. 1 p.

STERETT, SAMUEL H. Letter to Geary. September 12, 1856. 4 pp.

STERETT, WILLIAM A. Letter to Geary. September 29, 1856. 3 pp.

STEVENS, WILLIAM. Letter to Geary. March 21, 1857. 2 pp.

STEWART, CHARLES. Letter to Geary. August 7, 1856. Written and signed by B. K. Johnston. 1 p.

STEWART, OWEN C. Letter to Geary. February 18, 1857. 1 p.

STEWART, SAMUEL. Letter to Geary. November 15, 1856. 2 pp.

STEWART, T. G. Letter to Geary. January 27, 1857. 2 pp.

STILLMAN, E. A. Letter to Geary. December 25, 1856. 2 pp.

STORRS, N. S. Letter to Geary. February 20, 1857. 2 pp.

STRICKLER, HIRAM JACKSON. Two letters to Geary. May 11, August 11, 1857. 3 pp.

STRONG, D. Letter to Geary. July 30, 1856. 3 pp.

STROUD, R. P. Letter to Geary. July 31, 1856. 2 pp.

STUMP, JOHN M. Two letters to Geary. August 20, November 12, 1856. 2 pp.

STURGEON, ISAAC H. Three letters to Geary. September 9, 1856–January 29, 1857. 3 pp.

—— Letter to Wilson Shannon. January 27, 1857. Signed by J. W. Wills, 1 p.

SWIFT, A. C. Letter to Geary. January 18, 1857. 1 p.

SWISS COLONIZATION SOCIETY, Cincinnati. Two letters to Geary. January 19, 1857, signed by J. C. Christian and Felix Schelling; March 7, 1857, signed by Felix Schelling. 6 pp.

TANNER, WILLIAM. Letter to Geary. February 22, 1857. 1 p.

TASSEY, MRS. EMILY E. Letter to Geary. January 12, 1857. 2 pp.

TEBBS, A. SIDNEY. Three letters to Geary. August 4, 1856–March 19, 1857. 7 pp.

TEN EYCK, ANTHONY. Two letters to Geary. November 7, December 12, 1856. 7 pp.

THOMAS, CHARLES H. Letter to Geary. January 12, 1857. 1 p.

THOMAS, FRANCIS JOHN. Letter to Geary. January 20, 1857. 3 pp.

THOMAS, LEWIS A. Letter to Geary. January 30, 1857. 4 pp.

TITUS, HENRY T. Letter to Geary. November 8, 1856. 1 p.

—— Statement regarding the attack on him sworn to before R. B. Nelson, J.P. August 25, 1856. 1 p.

TODD, J. M. Letter to Geary. August 3, 1856. 2 pp.

TOPEKA, LADIES OF. Petition for the pardon and release of Free State prisoners. [October ? 1856.] With 19 signatures. 1 p.

TOTTEN, THOMAS. Complaint to Governor Geary against Partridge and Holmes. February 25, 1857. Signed also by Henry Tuley, A. H. McFadin, H. W. Peck and Baptis Peora. 2 pp.

UPTON, JOHN. Letter to Geary [?]. August 7, 1856. With postscript by S. F. Tappan. 2 pp.

VAN NOSTRAND, A. M. Letter to Geary. January 14, 1857. 3 pp.

WATTLES, AUGUSTUS. Letter to Geary. January 25, 1857. 1 p.

WEA EMIGRANTS. Address to Governor Geary. Wea Plains, Ind., [1857]. Signed by Daniel H. Roberts, John O. Wattles, Milton Hollingsworth. 4 pp.

—— Constitution and list of members. [n.d.] 5 pp.

WHITFIELD, JOHN W. Letter to Geary. January 18, 1857. 3 pp.

WHITTLESEY, ELISHA. 15 letters to Geary. October 23, 1856–April 25, 1857. Signatures only. 30 pp. Enclosed with the letter of January 28, 1857 are a statement of differences in the account of Governor Shannon; copy of a letter from Whittlesey to Shannon, January 27, 1857; and two copies of Owen C. Stewart's bill for services on the capitol building, certified, January 23, 1857, by Wilson Shannon. 8 pp.

WILLIAMS, LORANGE D. Letter to Geary. January 30, 1857. 1 p.

—— Affidavit before A. H. McFadin about the death of Henry Sherman. March 3, 1857. 1 p.

WILLIAMS, WILLIAM. Letter to Geary. August 27, 1856. 2 pp.

WILSON, GEORGE. Letter to Colonel Boone. March 3, 1857. Signed also by Thomas Totten, and forwarded by Boone to Geary. 2 pp.

WILSON, JOHN A. Letter to Geary. November 4, 1856. 1 p.

WINSTON, J. Letter to Geary. February 10 [1857]. 1 p.

WINSTON, THOMAS B. Letter to Geary. January 21, 1857. 1 p.

WISE, HENRY ALEXANDER. Requisition to Governor Geary for delivery of Joseph L. McCubbin. January 3, 1857. Signed by Henry A. Wise, Governor, and George W. Munford, Secretary, with the seal of the state of Virginia. Accompanied by Governor Wise's appointment of Charles P. Arnold as agent to demand and receive Joseph L. McCubbin, signed by Governor Wise and Secretary Munford, January 3, 1857; and statement of Charles P. Arnold before Thomas S. Wood, December 29, 1856. 4 pp.

WOMACK, GEORGE W. Letter to Geary. March 9, 1857. 4 pp.

—— Letter to "Tommy." January 15, 1857. 4 pp.

WOODBRIDGE, F. H. Letter to Geary. January 3, 1857. 1 p.

WOODRUFF, W. D. Letter to Geary. February 16, 1857. 2 pp.

WOODS, SAMUEL. Letter to Geary. February 15, 1857. 2 pp.

WRIGHT, JOSEPH ALBERT. Letter to Geary. November 11, 1856. Signature only. 1 p.

WRIGHT, W. W. Letter to Geary. February 19, 1857. 1 p.

ZIGLER, I. Telegram and letter to Geary. August 8, September 8, 1856. 2 pp.

Some of these letters have been copied into the "executive minutes" but the majority have not.

Governor Geary transmitted copies of his executive minutes to William L. Marcy, Secretary of State, from time to time for the information of the President and Congress. The minutes for September 9–30, 1856 were printed in the *Message from the President . . . to the Two Houses of Congress* (34th Congress, 3d Session, House Ex. Doc. No. 1, 1856, pp. 86–173); those for October 1–16, 1856 and November 21, 1856–March 12, 1857 in the *Message of the President* (35th Congress, 1st Session, Senate Ex. Doc. No. 17, 1858, pp. 27–208); and those for October 1–16, 1856 in *Kansas Territory, Message from the President* (34th Congress, 3d Session, House Ex. Doc. No. 10, 1856). The minutes have been reprinted in full in the *Transactions* of the Kansas State Historical Society, 1890, IV, 520–742. Correspondence dealing with Governor Geary's administration, including the letter from Halderman, Renick and W. A. Shannon and Geary's answer, is printed in the *Transactions*, 1896, V, 264–289. Dr. John H. Gihon quoted extensively from the minutes and correspondence in his *Geary and Kansas*, Philadelphia, 1857.

[Coe Collection.]

213 GEE, PERRY

"Aug. 7th 1853. Perry Gee's Journal of travels across the Plaines to California. Directed to Sarah Ann Gee, Geneva, Ashtabula Co., Ohio," and his stay in the mines. April 6, 1852 to February 3, 1853.

128 pp. 15½ cm. Original binding. With typewritten transcript.

The diary opens April 6, 1852, with the departure from Madison for Independence. The party started overland for California May 4 by the Platte River, Sweetwater, South Pass, Sublette's Cut-off to Soda Springs, Humboldt and Carson Rivers to the Sierra Nevadas, September 19, when with Akaman and Lovelan[d] Gee went up through Hope Valley and Weaver to Hangtown, September 24. After September 25 he prospected and mined in the diggings in the neighborhood of Ringgold. The diary breaks off February 3, 1853.

The diary describes in detail the route, camping places, and happenings on the way, and notes many of the graves passed. It is preceded by six pages of accounts and memoranda, including "My individual expenses aside from our company concerns," and is followed by seven pages of accounts, including a record of gold dust sold.

[Coe No. V, 14.]

214 GEIGER, VINCENT EPLY, 1823?–1869, and BRYARLY, WAKEMAN, 1820-1869

"Journal of the route of the Charlestown Va. Ming. Co. from St. Josephs, Mo. to California—Frank Smith as guide." May 10, 1849 to August 30, 1849.

277 pp. 19 cm. Original binding. With typewritten transcript.

Geiger was a Virginian and Bryarly from Maryland; both served in the Mexican War and sought adventure in this journey.

The journal of the Charlestown Company was kept by Vincent E. Geiger from the departure from St. Joseph to the point where the trail left the North Platte, June 22; and continued from June 23 by Dr. Wakeman Bryarly, surgeon of the company. They followed the route by the Little Blue, Platte, and Sweetwater Rivers to South Pass, Sublette's Cut-off to Fort Hall, the California Trail along the Raft River, Goose Creek to the Humboldt River, and the Truckee River to the mines and Johnson's ranch.

It is preceded by Geiger's diary of his trip from Staunton, Va., February 8, to Lexington, Mo., April 11, 1849.

The journal has been edited with introduction and notes by Professor David M. Potter and was published in the series Yale Historical Publications. Manuscripts and Edited Texts, New Haven, 1945, Vol. XX.

[Coe No. 80.]

215 ——, GEORGE

Letter, signed "George," to his cousin [a woman]. Cuming City, N.T., May 20, 1859.

3 pp. 25 cm.

"Map of the Gold Region, with the routes thereto" and "Table of distances from Omaha to Cherry Creek," printed on the fourth page of the sheet.

The letter tells of the miners passing to and from the mines, family affairs, and his life in Nebraska Territory.

The map, 19 x 10 cm., drawn by G. R. DeForest, engraved by N. Orr Co., is the same as the frontispiece in William N. Byers and John H. Kellom, *A Handbook to the Gold Fields of Nebraska and Kansas* . . . Chicago, New York, 1859.

[Coe No. I, 1016.]

216 GHENT, WILLIAM JAMES, 1866–

Two letters to F. S. Dellenbaugh. Washington, D.C., August 15 and August 27, 1933.

9 pp. 21½ cm.

The letters, written to F. S. Dellenbaugh, Custer's biographer, relate to E. A. Brininstool's pamphlet *The Custer Fight. Captain Benteen's Story of the Battle of* *the Big Horn*, Hollywood, 1933, and the Custer-Benteen-Brininstool-Reno Controversy.

[Coe No. I, 426.]

217 GIBBS, GEORGE, 1815–1873

Twenty-two letters to George Gibbs and a draft of one letter from Gibbs, 1853–1856.

42 pp. 17–25½ cm.

George Gibbs crossed the Plains from St. Louis to Oregon with the Mounted Rifles and was active in Whig politics. He later settled near Fort Steilacoom and devoted himself to the study of the languages and customs of the Indians.

The letters are about the Indian War, the settlement of Lieutenant Slaughter's estate, specimens of the flora and fauna of the Territory, the native languages and the Nez Percé laws, and local business affairs. They include the following:

—— Draft of a letter to Captain William L. Dall. February 10, 1856. Unsigned. 1 p.

BACHELDER, JAMES M. Letter to Gibbs. February 4, 1856. 2 pp.

BALLENDEN, JOHN. Letter to Gibbs. February 12, 1853. 1 p.

COOPER, JAMES GRAHAM. Letter to Gibbs. November 4, 1855. 4 pp.

GARDNER, CHARLES KITCHEL. Letter to Gibbs. December 6, 1855. Signature and postscript in his hand. 1 p.

GOLDSBOROUGH, HUGH A. Four letters to Gibbs. December 23, 1855–February 2, 1856. 4 pp.

GRIFFIN, JOHN SMITH. Letter to Gibbs. January 7, 1854. 2 pp.

HODGES, HENRY C. Letter to Gibbs. January 3, 1856. 1 p.

HOLMAN, JAMES DUVAL. Letter to Gibbs. November 24, 1855. 1 p.

LANE, D. E. Letter to Gibbs. December 2, 1855. 1 p.

McCLELLAN, J. H. B. Letter to Gibbs. August 28, 1855. 3 pp.

McDONALD, ANGUS. Letter to Gibbs. September 27, 1855. 3 pp.

MANHEIM & STERN. Letter to Gibbs. July 20, 1855. 1 p.

NUGEN, JOHN. Two letters to Gibbs. December 21, 1855, January 14, 1856. 8 pp.

SUCKLEY, GEORGE. Two letters to Gibbs. November 1855, signature only [February 4, 1856]. 5 pp.

WHITTLESEY, ELISHA. Letter to Gibbs. August 27, 1855. 2 pp.

WILSON, JOSEPH S. Letter to Gibbs. September 2, 1855. 1 p.

WOOD, WILLIAM HENRY. Letter to Gibbs. February 4, 1856. 1 p.

[Miller Collection.]

218 GILMAN, DANIEL S.

Six letters to members of his family written while on the voyage from Massachusetts to California and after his arrival, February 14, 1849 to August 26, 1850; and a letter from his brother, Moses D. Gilman, to his parents, March 21, 1850.

7 letters. 21 pp. 25–26½ cm.

Daniel S. Gilman of Lowell, Mass., sailed from Boston on the bark *Oxford* January 10, 1849 for California. He spent some time in the mines and in August 1850 was back in San Francisco working for Dr. J. Whitmore, formerly of Lowell.

The letters from Daniel describe the events of the voyage, Rio de Janeiro, Talcahuano and Concepcion, life in San Francisco, and conditions in California. The last letter to his mother and father tells of the death of his brother Moses and of his own financial situation.

Moses had sailed from New York, March 13, 1850, to join his brother in California. His letter, dated Havana, March 21 and continued after his arrival at Panama April 1, 1850, describes the passage, the town of Havana, the arrival at Chagres and Panama, and his proposed sailing for California on the bark *Augusta* April 1, 1850.

[Coe Collection.]

219 GINN, JOHN I.

"Mormon and Indian wars: The Mountain Meadows Massacre, and other tragedies and transactions incident to the Mormon rebellion of 1857. Together with the personal recollection of a civilian who witnessed many of the thrilling scenes described."

Typewritten manuscript. 161 pp. 27½ cm.

John I. Ginn, a printer by trade, of Acworth, Ga., set out from Independence, Mo., in June 1857, as a member of Magraw's Pacific Wagon Road Expedition but left it at Fort Laramie, when it went into camp for the winter, and was employed in the Commissary Department of the 10th U.S. Infantry until the command was planning to leave for Fort Hall. As Ginn wished to reach California he resigned and made his way to Fort Bridger, where the Mormon militia was in command.

The reminiscences describe the journey

from Independence to Fort Laramie; his stay with the Mormons in Salt Lake City, where he was befriended by Porter Rockwell; his departure for California in the fall of 1857, passing through the site of the Mountain Meadows Massacre; troubles with the Indians; the Utah Expedition; the Navajo Expedition, and the Indian Wars in Washington Territory.

The reminiscences were acquired from the heirs of Captain Ginn. They were evidently written for publication, with some footnotes and directions for the printer. Captain Ginn kept a diary of his adventures, which in 1934 was in the possession of Richard B. Shepard of Salt Lake City. That diary was used extensively by Charles Kelly and Hoffman Birney in writing *Holy Murder. The Story of Porter Rockwell*, New York, 1934. Passages quoted by Kelly and Birney are the same as passages in the typewritten reminiscences.

[Coe No. 81.]

220 GISH, JOHN

Correspondence of John Gish while in California in 1850–1851; letters to him after his return to the East from his associates at the mines, 1852–1856; and the original "article of agreement" of a partnership for the purpose of migrating to California in search of gold, February 14, 1850.

28 letters and 1 document. 78 pp. 21½–31½ cm.

John Gish, of Logan County, Ohio, formed a partnership with four friends to go to California. They planned to leave by Port Jefferson, Ohio, March 20, 1850, and traveled by St. Joseph and the Sweetwater. About 150 miles west of Salt Lake the company broke up and Gish, Hill, and Hodge joined with S. Perry and traveled down the Humboldt to California, to Weber Creek and later to Mud Springs, where Hill and Hodge died. Gish moved on to the north and in the fall of 1851 returned by sea to his home in the East.

Gish's earlier letters give some account of the journey west. His later letters and those from his associates after he returned to Ohio describe life in the mines, their failures and successes, and conditions in California.

"Article of agreement," February 14, 1850. Signed by John S. Hodge, Jacob Singer, Joseph Hill, Abraham Mayes, John Gish. 1 p.

The document, apparently in Hodge's hand, binds each of the partners to pay $200 into the company and, in case of death of any member of the company, to pay his share of the proceeds to the heirs.

—— Five letters to his wife, Mary Gish. December 29, 1850–July 27, 1851. 12 pp.

HILL, G. K. Letter to friends and brothers, addressed to John Gish. August 13, 1850. 3 pp.

MEKEMSON, JOSEPH S. Eight letters to John Gish. January 6, 1852–June 15, 1853. 31 pp.

POMROY, H. B. Three letters to John Gish. January 17, 1852–May 24, 1853. 5 pp.

The letter of January 17 is written on the verso of Van Derveer's letter of January 16, 1852.

POWERS, J. T. Letter to John Gish. December 30, 1855. 2 pp.

VAN DERVEER, W. Four letters to John Gish. January 16, 1852–December 20, 1853. 7 pp.

WISE, JOHN H. Six letters to John Gish. April 25, 1852–April 30, 1856. 17 pp.

[Coe Collection.]

221 GLASS, ANTHONY

"Copy of a journal of a voyage from Nackitosh into the interior of Louisiana on the waters of Red River, Trinity, Brassos, Colorado & the Sabine performed between the first of July 1808 & May 1809. By Capt. Anthony Glass of the Territory of Mississippi."

28 pp. 25½ cm.

Captain Glass, having obtained a passport and license from John Sibley, Indian Agent for Orleans Territory, set out from Natchitoches, July 5, 1808, with ten companions, to trade with the Pawnee and Hietan Indians. They followed the Red River northwest to the Pawnee villages, where they remained some time and heard of a mysterious piece of metal found by the Pawnees in the Hietan country. Wishing to see this metal they left the Pawnee villages October 3, traveling southwest to a Hietan camp near the Brazos River, and saw the metal. Being unable to trade for horses the party broke up, leaving Glass with two companions, Peter Young and Joseph Lucas, interpreter, to make his way back to the settlements from the Hietan country. The journal breaks off at the end of March 1809 when they left the Pawnee villages for Natchitoches.

Glass describes the country, the customs of the Indians, his experiences as a trader, the efforts of the Spaniards from San Antonio to influence the Indians against the United States, and the meteoric iron found in Texas.

The iron was transported to Natchitoches and New Orleans in 1810 and sold to Colonel Gibbs, who deposited it in the Museum of the Lyceum of New York. After his death Mrs. Gibbs presented the mass to the Cabinet of Mineralogy of Yale College.

With this manuscript there is a second journal by John Maley (see No. 324) and the following correspondence:

DARBY, WILLIAM. Letter to Benjamin Silliman, Sr. February 28, 1822. 3 pp.

JOHNSON, WILLIAM. Letter to Benjamin Silliman, Sr. August 18, 1821. 5 pp.

SIBLEY, JOHN. Letter to Benjamin Silliman, Sr. June 2, 1822. 4 pp.

SILLIMAN, BENJAMIN, SR. Notes on the accounts of the native iron [1822?]. 1 p.

SILLIMAN, BENJAMIN, JR. Letter to Edward S. Dana. November 16, 1877. 1 p.

Professor Silliman of Yale College had written to Judge Johnson, Mr. Darby and Dr. Sibley for information about the malleable iron found in Texas for publication in the *American Journal of Science*. From Dr. Sibley he obtained the copy of Anthony Glass' Journal and an account of the removal of the mass, and through Judge Johnson the Maley Journal, then owned by Mr. Isaac Riley of Philadelphia. Glass' original journal was, in 1822, in the possession of Dr. John Sibley, and was copied by "a very young lady" in his family for Professor Silliman.

Extracts from the journals and letters are quoted in "Notice of the Malleable Iron of Louisiana," *American Journal of Science*, 1824, VIII, 218–225.

[Silliman Family Collection, Historical Manuscripts Collection.]

222 GORRILL, WILLIAM H., 1836–1874

Diary of a journey on horseback from Walla Walla, Washington Territory, to San Francisco. October 17 to December 16, 1869.

180 pp., maps, sketches. 18½ cm. Original binding. With typewritten transcript.

William H. Gorrill was on his way to prominence at the bar in Toledo but developed tuberculosis and in 1869 sought health in California, where he established the Pacific Bridge Company. He died in Oakland in 1874.

He left Helena, Mont., on horseback, September 17, 1869. The diary records in detail the journey from Walla Walla down the Columbia Valley to The Dalles, and by boat to Portland. From Portland the party rode up the Willamette Valley, crossed the Umpqua and Rogue Rivers, to Yreka, Calif.; continued south to Shasta, Red Bluffs, and Sacramento, where they took the steamboat *Yosemite* for San Francisco. December 5 they left San Francisco for Stockton, Mariposa and the big trees, and Yosemite, returning to San Francisco by the San Joaquin Valley and Stockton December 16, when the diary ends.

It contains 16 maps of parts of the route and 27 small sketches of scenery and types of faces of Indians, and describes the country, its industries, labor conditions, etc.

[Coe No. 82.]

223 GOUDY, JAMES H.

Letter to Colonel M. T. Simmons. Muckleshoot Reserve, W.T., January 9, 1859. "Copy."

4 pp. 33 cm.

Endorsed in the same hand: "Report of Jas. H. Goudy to M. T. Simmons, Indn. Agt. relative to the arrest of Kitsap."

Goudy was an employee of the Indian agent at Fort Kitsap in 1857 and was put in charge of the D'Wamish Indians. In 1859 he was in charge of the Muckleshoot Reservation.

The report describes the arrest of Kitsap, the escape of Nelson, and the attitude of the Indians on the Reserve toward the arrest.

[Miller Collection.]

224 GOUDY, JAMES H.

"Account of the capture and killing of Qui-e-muth."

4 pp. 25½ cm.

The manuscript is probably a copy, and is endorsed: "Killing of Quiemuth," with the date "Nov. 18, 1856" added in a different hand. It is unsigned but attributed to Sub-Indian Agent Goudy.

Quiemuth voluntarily surrendered to Governor Stevens and was killed while waiting in his home in Olympia to be taken to Fort Steilacoom.

[Miller Collection.]

225 GOULDING, WILLIAM R.

Journal of the expedition of the Knickerbocker Exploring Company of the City of New York from Fort Smith overland to California. March 10 to September 18, 1849.

328 pp. 20½–32 cm.

Accompanied by a printed broadside of the Knickerbocker Exploring Company's Constitution and list of members [12½ x 31 cm.] and two clippings from the *Fort Smith Herald*, March 10 and 16, 1849.

William R. Goulding was 42, married,

and engaged in the manufacture of surgical instruments in New York when he joined the Knickerbocker Company. He met with financial reverses and later secured an appointment from the Surgeon General at McClennon Hospital near Philadelphia. On October 3, 1864, he enlisted in the U.S. Army, and on January 27, 1865, was appointed to the U.S. Medical Museum in Washington.

The manuscript was evidently written at a later date. It is divided into 21 chapters, with a summary of the contents at the beginning of each one, and has some corrections and alterations. The writer refers often to sketches that he made in his notebook on the journey and he was probably planning to publish the account of his travels to California. The first 17 chapters are on loose sheets; chapters 18–21 are in a notebook that also contains copies or drafts of letters; record of letters written and received, October 11, 1864–April 30, 1865; family expenses and hospital accounts. Laid in the notebook are four pencil sketches of scenes along the way.

Goulding describes his trip from New York, February 18, 1849, by rail, wagon, and the steamer *Hudson*, to Fort Smith, March 10. The journal records the organization of the company, the preparations for the journey, the route from Fort Smith, March 26, on the road followed a few weeks later by Captain Marcy, along the Arkansas River, Gregg's road to Little River, along the Canadian River and the Santa Fé Trail, to Albuquerque, the Rio Grande, the Rio Membres, the Chihuahua road to Tucson and the Gila River, crossing the Colorado and the desert to Warner's ranch and San Diego, Santa Barbara, Monterey, and San Francisco, September 18, when the journal breaks off.

Goulding describes in detail the country, flora and fauna, settlements of the Indians and the events of the journey, mirages in the desert, the Mexican fandangos; and has included a few small sketches. In Chapter 19 he copied Mr. Hoyt's notes of his travels after he left the party at Santa Fé to take the Northern, or Spanish Trail, his return to Socorro and then west to the Gila River.

[Coe No. V, 15.]

226 GOVE, JESSE AUGUSTUS, 1824–1862

Journal of the march of the Utah Expedition from Fort Bridger to Fort Leavenworth. August 9 to October 6, 1861.

23 pp. including 2 original pencil drawings. 32 cm. With typewritten transcript.

Original yellow wrappers lettered in manuscript: "Order book for the battalions of the 10. Infantry and 4th Artillery en route to Fort Leavenworth commanded by Capt. Jesse A. Gove 10th regt."

Record of the return journey of the Utah Expedition sent out by President Buchanan in 1857 to conquer the Mormons. The expedition left Fort Bridger August 9, 1861, and proceeded by Green River, Big and Little Sandy, Pacific Pony Express Station, South Pass, Devil's Gate, Platte Bridge to Fort Laramie, where it remained several days; then along the old river trail to Dripp's Trading Post, Scott's Bluffs, Fort Kearney and Leavenworth.

This journal was unknown in 1928 when Otis G. Hammond published "The Utah Expedition 1857–58; Letters of Capt. Jesse A. Gove . . . to Mrs. Gove," New Hampshire Historical Society *Collections*, Vol. XII, but it constitutes an important supplement as it continues the narrative from the point where the printed record ended to the disbanding of the company at Fort Leavenworth.

[Coe No. 83.]

227 GRAHAM, WILLIAM ALEXANDER, 1875–

"The story of Trumpeter John Martin. He carried Custer's last message to Benteen in the Battle of the Little Big Horn, and was the last man to see General Custer alive, June 25, 1876. By Lieut.-Col. W. A. Graham, J.A., U.S.A. With introductory comments and closing remarks by Colonel Graham," June 12, 1922.

Typewritten manuscript. 24 pp. 28½ cm.

A note by E. A. Brininstool reads: "The following story or interview given by Sergeant Martin to Colonel Graham, took place June 12th, 1922. Sergeant Martin died at his home in Brooklyn in December of that same year." A note on page 15 states that the story was signed by Martin in Graham's presence after it was read to and corrected by Martin, June 12, 1922.

The manuscript, which formed part of the library of Bishop Thomas of Wyo-ming, was sold at the Thomas sale at the Anderson Galleries, January 30, 1929. With some additions and alterations, it is published in *The Cavalry Journal*, 1923, XXXII, 303–317, with the title: " 'Come on! Be Quick! Bring Packs!' Custer's Battle Plan. The Story of His Last Message as Told by the Man Who Carried It. With commentary by Brigadier General Edward S. Godfrey."

[Coe No. I, 441.]

228 GRANVILLE COMPANY

"Granville Company Diary," from Zanesville, Ohio, to the Feather River Valley, April 3 to September 18, 1849, with a table of distances from Independence to San Francisco.

158 pp. 12½ cm. Original binding. With typewritten transcript.

The name of the writer of the diary does not appear. There were 32 in the party.

The diary was evidently written on the road but not every day. It records briefly the journey from Zanesville, Ohio, to Independence, April 3–18, and in more detail the preparations for the journey at Inde-pendence, the start on May 1, the country traversed and the camping places along the Platte and Sweetwater Rivers, Sublette's and Hudspeth's Cut-offs, and the Applegate Trail and Lassen Road to the Feather River Valley, where the diary breaks off on September 18.

[Coe No. 81 A.]

229 GRAY, WILLIAM HENRY, 1810–1889

Letter to the editor of the *Pacific Tribune*. Astoria, September 15, 1865, enclosing "A leaf from the History of Oregon in August 1836."

11 pp. 32 cm.

William H. Gray crossed the Plains to Oregon with Whitman in 1836. He published *A History of Oregon, 1792–1849* in 1870.

In answer to a statement in the *Pacific Tribune* of September 9, by H. S. D. Day, counsel for the Hudson's Bay Company, about its claims in Washington Territory and those of the Puget Sound Agricultural Company, Mr. Gray sends the editor his notes on the relations between the Hudson's Bay Company and the missionaries and early settlers, and expresses the hope that they may be placed before the commission which was to determine the amount that should be paid the company for its claims.

Formerly among the Elwood Evans manuscripts.

[Miller Collection.]

230 GREENE, FRANCIS VINTON, 1850–1921

Voyage from the Sweet Grass Hills, Montana Territory, to Bismarck, Dakota Territory, along the Missouri River. September 2 to September 30, 1874.

63 pp. 19 cm. Original binding. With typewritten transcript.

Lieutenant Greene was detailed in 1872 to serve under the Department of State on a joint commission for the survey and demarcation of the boundary line along the 49th parallel. Archibald Campbell was appointed commissioner, Captain W. J. Twining, Corps of Engineers, chief astronomer, Captain J. F. Gregory, assistant astronomer, and Lieutenant F. V. Greene, assistant.

The manuscript is written in the form of a letter to Lieutenant Greene's parents, George Sears and Martha Barrett (Dana) Greene, "On the Missouri River," September 13, 1874, and continues in journal form to September 30 at Bismarck.

The first three pages contain a list of the dates and camps from Fort Benton to Bismarck.

The letter begins with a description of Sweet Grass Hills, where he arrived September 2, and tells of his overland journey to Fort Shaw and Fort Benton, where he joined the rest of his party, and on the 12th left in a fleet of six mackinaw boats for Bismarck, N.D. The manuscript describes the various forts, courtesies of the officers, especially General Gibbon, the animal life, and the country through which the party traveled. The transcript contains a manuscript map of the route [not by Greene].

[Coe No. 84.]

231 GREENE, FRANCIS VINTON, 1850–1921

Two letters to his parents. Virginia City, Montana, August 25, 1875; Washington, September 4, 1875.

21 pp. 26 cm.

The first letter breaks off with a note "(to be continued FVG)," the second is signed "Frank." They describe his trip with Lieutenant Doane through Yellowstone National Park in July and August, 1875, and the return journey to Washington with brief stops in Virginia City, Mont., Denver, and St. Louis.

[Coe Collection.]

232 GRIFFIN, JOHN SMITH, 1807–1899

"History of Tualatin Plains, by J. S. Griffin, Pastor of First Con. Church." August 2, 1842 to January 1, 1843; and at the back, accounts of J. S. Griffin, January 1, 1845 to April 28, 1851.

48 pp. 32 cm. Original boards.

Griffin was sent as a missionary to Oregon in 1839 by the North Litchfield Association of Connecticut. He married in St. Louis on the way west, and after a winter at Lapwai, a summer in the Snake country, and a winter in Vancouver, they took up farming on Tualatin Plains. In 1848 he secured the Lapwai press from H. H. Spalding and issued eight numbers of a magazine, *The Oregon American and Evangelical Unionist.*

In 1842 Griffin planned to write a history of Tualatin Plains but completed only three pages. He used the same volume for his farm accounts from January 1, 1845 to April 28, 1851.

The manuscript formerly belonged to Dr. Skiff, who secured it from a friend, another collector, L. B. Cole. The "History of Tualatin Plains" is printed in full in F. W. Skiff, *Adventures in Americana,* Portland, 1935, pp. 232–233.

[Coe Collection.]

233 GRINDELL, JOHN

"The overland narrative of John Grindell. Platteville, Wis., to California." March 25 to August 1, 1850.

Typewritten copy (carbon). 18 pp. 28 cm.

John Grindell left Platteville, Grant County, Wis., March 25, 1850 for St. Joseph and California, following the route to Fort Kearney, the Platte and Sweetwater Rivers, Sublette's Cut-off, Hudspeth's Cut-off, and the Humboldt and Carson Rivers to Hangtown, July 31, 1850.

Grindell, who is a man of very little education, begins his account with a sum-

mary of the journey to Fort Laramie and a description of Independence Rock, June 11. He then goes back to March 25 and gives a daily account of the journey, camping places, the country, distances traveled, etc., until he closes his journal August 1. It is followed by a record of the mileage and of the expense of the journey.

Gift of Michael J. Walsh.

234 GRISWOLD, CORNELIUS

Thirteen letters to his mother and father, April 26, 1860 to May 13, 1862.

32 pp. 20–25 cm. Mounted with ten of the original envelopes. With typewritten transcripts.

Cornelius Griswold was the son of Willard Griswold, owner of a clothing and carding machine shop and a starch factory in Jeffersonville, Lamoille County, Vt. He left home in 1860 for the Colorado gold fields.

——— Letter to his mother, Mrs. Willard Griswold. April 26, 1860. 2 pp.

——— 12 letters to his father. May 27, 1861–May 13, 1862. 30 pp.

The letters describe briefly his experiences in a severe storm on the Plains, in

Denver, in Cañon City, and in the mines in Arkansas and Independent Districts. The last, in May, 1862, says he is going to go to the recently discovered gold mines in Washington Territory.

The covers of the first three letters to his father bear the postmark of the Central Overland California & Pike's Peak Express Company, which in 1860 absorbed the Leavenworth & Pike's Peak Express and secured the U.S. mail contract.

[Coe No. 85.]

235 GROW, S. L.

Journal of the overland march from Clinton, Wisconsin, to Fort Laramie, April 8 to June 7, 1850, kept by Dr. S. L. Grow of Clinton and sent back in three instalments to A. Richardson.

37 pp. 25–27 cm.

One page of the journal, May 8–10, is written on the back of a broadside, printed by the *Frontier Guardian* and dated Kanesville, May 7, 1852, containing the resolutions adopted by the Beloit Company and the names of the members of the company. 21 x 27 cm.

The first instalment dated Lyons, Iowa, April 14, 1850, covers the journey from Clinton, April 7, through Beloit, DeWitt, Iowa, to "The Bluffs" April 30; the second, May 1–11, sent back from Kanesville, describes the formation of the Beloit Company, the preparation for the journey west and the addition of new members, among them Mr. Newcomb (see No. 359); the third instalment covers the journey from Kanesville to Fort Laramie, May 14–June 7, 1850.

[Coe No. 86.]

236 HAIGHT, HORTON DAVID, 1832–1900

"Captain Horton D. Haight's Company that served in the Salmon River Expedition, 1858," and "Persons who furnished outfits for the Salmon River Expedition, 1858."

2 pp. 61½ and 31½ cm.

The list of Captain Haight's company is endorsed: "Horton D. Haight's Return, Salmon R—Expedition March 9th till April 8th, 1858."

Captain Haight and 1st Lieutenant Hirum Judd were officers in the Nauvoo Legion, and many of those furnishing outfits were prominent members of the Church of Jesus Christ of Latter-day Saints.

In May 1855 a party of men left Ogden, Utah, to establish a settlement among the Flathead or Shoshone Indians in Washington Territory. They settled on the Lemhi River in the Salmon River Valley and named their stockade Fort Limhi. In 1857 the crops were abundant and the settlement was prosperous, but the Shoshone Indians began stealing the cattle and in February 1858 murdered two white herders. The Mormon settlers decided to abandon the settlement and sent two messengers to President Young to ask permission to return to Utah. An escort of soldiers under Captain Haight was sent to the Salmon River and by April 11, 1858 the settlers were safely back in Ogden.

[Coe Collection.]

237 HALKETT, KATHERINE (MRS. JOHN), *d.* 1848

Note to Viscountess Melville. 5 Seymour Place, Curzon St. [London, 1817].

3 pp. 18½ cm.

Laid in *Statement Respecting the Earl of Selkirk's Settlement upon the Red River, in North America*, London, 1817 [by John Halkett].

Lord Selkirk's sister, Katherine Dunbar, married John Halkett who wrote the *Statement*.

The note was evidently sent by hand with the book, which bears the Melville bookplate, asking Lady Melville as a friend to read the statement of Selkirk's defense.

[Coe No. III, 584.]

238 HALLER, GRANVILLE OWEN, 1819–1897

A brief account of the anti-Chinese riot in Seattle, February 7, 1886, written by Colonel G. O. Haller on the back of a photograph of Governor Squire and his military staff appointed for the emergency.

Photograph. 20 x 15 cm.

Colonel Haller was commissioned a 2d Lieutenant in 1839, served in the Mexican War and in 1852 was ordered to the Pacific Coast. After the Civil War he returned to Washington and at the time of the anti-Chinese riots served as adjutant general on Governor Squire's staff.

[Miller Collection.]

239 HAMELIN, JOSEPH P., JR., 1823–

"Journal. Jos. P. Hamelin jr. of Lexington, Missouri," describing his overland journey from Lexington to Los Angeles, April 12, 1849 to February 17, 1850 and up the coast to Sacramento, March 15 to April 12, 1850, with guide and table of distances; his journey from Leavenworth City to Fort Laramie, May 19 to June 22, 1856, his year at Laramie as agent for Majors, Russell Co., and his return to Leavenworth, June 5 to July 5, 1857.

126 pp. 32½ cm. Original boards. With typewritten transcript.

Joseph P. Hamelin, Jr., had been in the Southwest as early as 1842 and in Santa Fé as an employee of James Aull.

The journal, or "Notes," is dedicated to his friend Mrs. Deborah Fleetwood Boulware with a request that it be sent to her in case of his death. Signed: "J. P. H. Centre of Grand Island, May 25, 1849."

The journal records the details of the journey and route from Lexington, Mo., on the *Highland Mary* to old Fort Kearney, overland to Salt Lake City by the south bank of the Platte, Sweetwater River, and Fort Bridger; from Salt Lake City to Los Angeles over the southern trail to the Virgin River and Cajon Pass, February 17, 1850; and up the coast to Sacramento, March 15–April 12, 1850. It is continued in 1856, when Hamelin, partly on account of his health, went to Fort Laramie as agent for Majors, Russell Co., freighters, leaving Leavenworth May 19, 1856, at Fort Laramie June 22, 1856–June 5, 1857, and his return journey reaching Leavenworth July 5, 1857.

During Hamelin's stays in Salt Lake City, where he had intermittent fever, in Los Angeles, and in Fort Laramie, he made only occasional entries in his journal.

[Coe No. IV, 435.]

240 HANCOCK, SAMUEL, 1824?–

"The narrative of Samuel Hancock: Being a description of his overland journey to Oregon in 1845: his adventures and sufferings: his escape from the Indians: his gold seeking expedition to California and encounters with robbers there: the wreck of the *Cayuga* and his near starvation: and his life as a trader among the Indians. Together with an account of his captivity among the savages: a description of the war dances, marriage ceremonies, methods of house-building, medicinal practices, whaling, fishing, and other manners and customs. And also a recital of the massacre of Whitman and the other missionaries, and of the facts connected with the proposed murder, by the Indians, of himself and Lieutenant Lawson's party."

127 pp. 34½ cm.

Typewritten manuscript with note signed by C. B. Bagley, ". . . This is one [of] two copies—all that have been made, as I believe." Originally written by Hancock in longhand at Whidby's Island and dated February 17, 1860.

Samuel Hancock settled at Tumwater in 1847 and later at Whidby Island. According to his wife's brother, Samuel D. Crock-ett, Henry Y. Sewell, a schoolmaster, prepared in Hancock's name a manuscript descriptive of the latter's adventures.

The narrative is published in full, with an Introduction by Arthur D. Howden Smith, with the title: *The Narrative of Samuel Hancock, 1845–1860*, New York, 1927.

[Coe No. 87.]

241 HARBIDGE, GEORGE

"Journal of a voyage from Gravesend to Hudson's-Bay North America and Inland journey to the Red-River Colony in the year 1820, with a few particulars during 5 years residence in the Colony, and homeward-bound voyage in the year 1825." Followed by extract from a letter from the Rev. D. T. Jones, missionary at the Red River Settlement, to Mr. Harbidge, July 10, 1826.

296 pp. 2 illus. 17½ cm.

George Harbidge sailed with the Rev. John West, chaplain of the Hudson's Bay Company, on the company's ship *Eddystone*, Captain Bell, to become the schoolteacher at the Red River Settlement.

The journal is a daily account of the voyage from England, May 27, 1820, through Hudson's Straits to York Fort, August 15, the stay at York Fort, and the journey to Red River, arriving October 16, 1820; followed by an account of his life in the settlement, marriage, troubles with Mr. Jones who succeeded Mr. West as missionary, and his return to England with his family, arriving September 22, 1825.

The illustrations mounted in the journal are the same as two of those in West, *Substance of a Journal during a Residence at the Red River Colony*, London, 1824, although the captions differ slightly and the execution of the woodcuts is cruder.

[Coe No. 88.]

242 HARDY, FRANCIS A., 1819–1915

"Journal of Francis A. Hardy, Piqua Mar 25, 1850" to Saturday, August 31, 1850 at Auburn, California.

2 vols. [i.e., 240 pp.] 15½ cm. Original bindings. With typewritten transcript.

Hardy was the son of a poor New Hampshire farmer. He learned the trade of a cooper at 14 and in 1843 went to Piqua, Ohio, as a journeyman cooper. He served as a volunteer in the Mexican War, and after financial losses decided to look for gold in California. He reached California almost destitute and worked in a grocery store in Auburn for some months. After his return to Piqua he taught school for a time, worked at his trade as a cooper, and held many public offices in the town. He died in Piqua in 1915.

The journal, written very neatly in ink, does not appear to have been written on the road. Hardy may have written it up from time to time, or after his return.

He records his departure from Piqua March 25, 1850 for Weston, Mo., by boat, the departure from Weston, April 23, on foot, the formation of the Piqua Independent California Company and its by-laws; and describes in detail the characteristics of the country, location of water and fuel along the trail from Weston to the Little Blue, the Platte, and Sweetwater Rivers, Sublette's and Hudspeth's Cut-offs, and the Humboldt River to Hang-town, August 23, followed by brief entries for August 27 and 31 when he reached Auburn.

[Coe No. 89.]

243 HARE, WILLIAM HOBART, 1839–1909

Correspondence of the Right Reverend William H. Hare, Missionary Bishop of South Dakota, and other papers relating to the Crow Creek Indian Reservation, 1883–1885.

16 pieces. 37 pp. 20–23 cm.

Bishop Hare, known as the "Apostle to the Sioux," was appointed Bishop of Nio-brara in 1872. Later the district was extended and the name changed to the Missionary District of South Dakota. Bishop Hare continued his work in Dakota until his death in 1909.

The correspondence deals with the rights of the Indians to the land in the reservation under the treaty of 1868 and the agreement of 1882; the influx of speculators and settlers under President Arthur's executive order of February 27, 1885; the rights of the settlers who entered the reservation in good faith under Arthur's order but were dispossessed by President Cleveland's proclamation of April 17, 1885.

BURT, REV. HACHALIAH, Presbyter at Crow Creek Agency. Letter to Bishop Hare. March 9, 1885. 5 pp.

DAWES, HENRY LAURENS, Senator from Massachusetts. Letter to Bishop Hare. March 2, 1885. Signature only. 1 p.

GASMANN, REV. JOHN G., U.S. Indian Agent at Crow Creek. Letter to Bishop Hare. March 11, 1885. 5 pp.

HARE, WILLIAM HOBART. Draft of a letter in Hare's hand, to the Secretary of the Interior [H. M. Teller]. 4/5/83 [i.e., March 5, 1883]. 2 pp.

—— Draft of a note in Hare's hand, 5/1 [1885?] possibly to the Secretary of the Interior [Lamar] in behalf of the white settlers who entered the reservation in good faith after the executive order of President Arthur. 1 p.

—— "Copy of a letter to H. Welsh, Esq., dated about May 28 [1885] W. H. H." 3 pp.

—— Quotation in Bishop Hare's hand from the *Report* of the Commissioner of Indian Affairs for the year 1883, October 10, 1883 [p. xlvii of printed report].

[INDIAN RIGHTS ASSOCIATION.] *The Sioux Bill* [1884]. Printed leaflet with manuscript annotations. 4 pp.

INDIAN RIGHTS ASSOCIATION. *Provisions of the Sioux Bill*. Philadelphia, December 16, 1885. Printed leaflet, 4 pp.

PANCOAST, HENRY SPACKMAN, recording secretary of the Indian Rights Association. Letter to Bishop Hare, quoting a communication from Professor Painter. March 3, 1885. 2 pp.

Plat in pencil of the Crow Creek Reservation. 1 p. 20 x 33 cm.

PRICE, HIRAM, Commissioner of Indian Affairs. Letter to Bishop Hare in answer to his letter of the 5th ultimo. April 13, 1883. Signature only. 3 pp.

QUINTON, MRS. AMELIA STONE. *The Mohonk Indian Conference* [1885] (leaflets of the Women's National Indian Association). 12 pp.

U.S. PRESIDENT (Chester Alan Arthur). The Executive proclamation regarding the Crow Creek Reservation, February 27, 1885. Typewritten copy (carbon). 1 p.

WELSH, HERBERT, corresponding secretary, Indian Rights Association. Letter to Bishop Hare. July 6, 1885, enclosing typewritten copies (carbon) of a letter from Mr. Welsh to John H. King, July 2, 1885, and two letters from H. L. Dawes to Mr. Welsh, June 16, 23, 1885. "PRIVATE" 13 pp.

The papers formerly belonged to the Rt. Rev. Nathaniel Seymour Thomas, Bishop of Wyoming. Bishop Hare's letter of March 5, 1883 is printed in full in Indian Rights Association, *Crow Creek Reservation*, 1885, pp. 11–12.

[Coe No. 47.]

244 HARMON, DANIEL WILLIAM, 1778–1845

"A Journal of travels in the Interior of North America, between 47° and 58° North Latitude, extending from Montreal, nearly to the Pacific Ocean."

Photostat. 6 pp. 19½ cm.

Harmon spent the years 1800–1819 in the Northwest as a clerk in the North West Fur Company. The year after his return to Vermont his journal was edited and published by the Rev. Daniel Haskel of Burlington.

The photostat copy of the first few pages of the original journal covering the beginning of his journey west, April 29–May 14, 1800, was procured from the Public Archives of Canada.

Gift of Edward Eberstadt.

245 HARRIOTT, JOHN EDWARD, 1797–1877

Memoirs of life and adventure in the Hudson's Bay Company's territories, 1819–1825.

111 pp. 18 x 27 cm. Original binding, hinge at top.

Written about 1860, the manuscript includes the narrative of his journey on foot from Fort Carlton to Edmonton in 1819; his expedition from Fort Chesterfield toward the Pacific in 1822; his journey from the South Saskatchewan to Fort Carlton in 1823; and his overland trip from York Factory to New Caledonia and the Columbia River in 1828.

[Coe No. 90.]

246 HARRIS, EDWARD, 1799–1863

Letter to "My dear Dr." New Orleans, December 1, 1843, with additions to December 21.

Typewritten copy. 20 pp. 28 cm.

Edward Harris was born in Moorestown, N.J., in 1799, a quiet, unassuming gentleman farmer of means, deeply interested in birds. He met Audubon in 1824 in Philadelphia and bought all the drawings on hand at the time. He accompanied Audubon on his expedition to the Upper Missouri as manager and treasurer, and was his friend and patron.

The letter, to his brother-in-law, John J. Spencer, who was looking after Mr. Harris' affairs during his absence, describes his first experiences in hunting buffalo while near Fort Union, in July 1843, with John James Audubon on his expedition to the Upper Missouri and Yellowstone. The last few pages deal with his personal affairs and his stay in New Orleans.

The greater part of the letter, from a typescript in the W. U. Harris Collection of the Department of Archives and History at Montgomery, Ala., is printed in *Up the Missouri with Audubon, The Journal of Edward Harris*, edited and annotated by John Francis McDermott, Norman, University of Oklahoma Press, 1951, pp. 28–38.   [Coe No. II, 767.]

247 HARTMAN, SARAH McALLISTER (MRS. DAVIS)

Reminiscences of early days on Puget Sound, the friendliness of the local Indians, and experiences during the Indian War of 1855.

Typewritten copy. 28 pp. 33 cm.

The first page of Mrs. Hartman's manuscript was so mutilated that it could not be copied, but it has been supplied by a photostat of the original.

James McAllister and his family accompanied M. T. Simmons to Puget Sound in October 1845, settled at Tumwater but soon moved to the Nisqually valley.

The manuscript, written many years later, describes the home life of the family, their friendly relations with the Indians, the outbreak of Indian hostilities, the departure of their father to join the rangers, the imprisonment of the family in their home, the final escape to Fort Nisqually, and the death of their father.

[Miller Collection.]

248 HASTINGS, LOREN B., 1814–1881

Journal of L. B. Hastings while traveling from LaHarpe, Hancock County, Illinois, to Portland, Oregon Territory, in the summer of 1847.

Typewritten copy (carbon). 39 pp. 28 cm.

Loren B. Hastings settled first at Portland but in 1851 moved to Puget Sound and took a claim near Port Townsend. He was one of the first commissioners appointed for Jefferson County.

The journal, written for his brothers and sisters in Vermont, describes the journey from LaHarpe, Ill., to Portland, Ore., April 23–December 3, 1847. He joined his company near Carthage, traveled overland to St. Joseph, the Independence road to the Platte, Fort Laramie and the Sweetwater, Fort Bridger route to Soda Springs and Fort Hall, and the Oregon

Trail to The Dalles, October 20; made a boat for the rest of the journey, reaching Vancouver November 27; received news of the Whitman massacre; arrived at Portland, December 3, 1847.

[Miller Collection.]

249 HAUSER, SAMUEL THOMAS, 1833–1914

Diary, August 17 to September 4, 1870, by Samuel T. Hauser, a member of the Washburn-Langford Expedition to the Yellowstone.

55 pp., 6 maps and 2 sketches. 13 cm. Original binding. With three printed accounts of the expedition.

Hauser was born in Kentucky in 1833; in 1854 he moved to Missouri and engaged in engineering. He was a member of the Yellowstone Expedition of 1863, and in 1870 of the Washburn-Langford-Doane Expedition to the Upper Yellowstone. He settled in Montana, played an important part in its development, and in 1885 was appointed governor. He died in 1914.

The diary, written hurriedly in pencil, occupies 23 pages. It is followed by 32 pages of miscellaneous notes, addresses, mathematical calculations and accounts (some in ink and some of a later date); and 6 maps and 2 sketches in pencil. The diary covers the expedition from its departure from Helena to the arrival at Yellowstone Lake.

DOANE, GUSTAVUS CHEENY. *Letter from the Secretary of War Communicating the Report of Lieutenant Gustavus C. Doane upon the So-called Yellowstone Expedition of 1870* (41st Congress, 3d Session, Senate Ex. Doc. No. 51 [Washington, 1871]).

LANGFORD, NATHANIEL PITT. *Diary of the Washburn Expedition to the Yellowstone and Firehole Rivers in the Year 1870* [n.p., ca. 1905].

EVERTS, TRUMAN C. *Thirty-seven Days of Peril. A Narrative of the Early Days of the Yellowstone*, San Francisco, Edwin & Robert Grabhorn and James McDonald, 1923, No. 42.

[Coe Collection.]

250 HAUSER, SAMUEL THOMAS, 1833–1914

Three letters to his sister [Susan Emeline Hauser] written on a voyage up the Missouri from St. Joseph to Fort Benton, and overland to the Bitter Root Mountains, May 20 to September 9, 1862.

38 pp. 25 cm. With a typewritten transcript and biographical sketch.

In the spring of 1862 Hauser and a party planned an expedition to the Salmon River mines, taking the new steamboat *Emilie*, recently purchased by LaBarge Harkness & Co. for trading on the upper Missouri. The *Emilie* left St. Louis May 14. Hauser and James Harkness went by train to St. Joseph and joined the *Emilie* there. The letters relate the events of the voyage, especially the race with the *Spread Eagle* on June 6; the arrival at Fort Ben-

ton and preparations for the overland trip to the Salmon River mines; the journey to Deer Lodge, Fort Owen, and the Bitter Root Mountains, where they gave up the attempt to reach Salmon River and returned to Deer Lodge.

A diary of the voyage from St. Joseph to Fort Benton kept by James Harkness is published in Historical Society of Montana, *Contributions*, 1896, II, 343–361.

[Coe Collection.]

251 HAYDEN, CHARLES W.

Journal of the trip across the Plains from Wisconsin to Oregon. March 23, 1852 to January 8, 1853.

82 pp. 14 cm. Original binding. With typewritten transcript.

The entries are brief but give details of the route from Jefferson, Wis., March 23 [1852], by Council Bluffs, Platte River, Scotts Bluffs, Fort Laramie, The Sweetwater, South Pass, Soda Springs, Fort Hall, Boise, Cascades, arriving at Vancouver August 26, where he found his brother, Gay Hayden. The diary continues through January 8, 1853, records letters written and received, and includes some accounts at the end, and at the beginning the names and addresses of members of his family.

[Coe No. 91.]

252 HAYS, GILMORE, *d.* 1880

Letter to J. W. Wiley. Salem County, Missouri, October 30, 1856.

4 pp. 25 cm.

Gilmore Hays in 1852 led a train of immigrants to Oregon, losing his wife and two children from cholera on the way. He was of great service to the Territory during the Indian War.

The letter takes exception to statements made by Mr. Wiley in an editorial in his paper [*Pioneer and Democrat*, Olympia] on a letter from Hays printed in the *Union* [Washington, D.C.] of July 10 on the causes of the Indian War. That letter was not written to the editor of the *Union* but to Joseph Lane, delegate in Congress, in answer to a request for the information.

[Miller Collection.]

253 HECLA CONSOLIDATED MINING COMPANY

Account books of the Hecla Consolidated Mining Company, Montana, July 1876 to June 1877, August 1879 to June 1880, January 1891 to June 1906.

3 vols. [i.e., 696 pp.] 31–45 cm.

The volumes include accounts at Trapper City, Lion City, and Lion Hall, 1876–1877; Lion Mountain, 1879–1880; and Glendale and Melrose, 1891–1906, all in Beaverhead County, Mont. The chief mines mentioned are Atlantis, Cleve, Cleopatra, Trapper, Franklin, True Fissure. The first mention of the Hecla Consolidated Mining Company occurs on April 7, 1877. The mines were closed down on June 30, 1904, and the company was unable to meet its payroll or expenses. The properties were purchased by Henry Knippenberg at a stockholders' sale, May 1, 1906. At the time the officers of the company were Henry Knippenberg, president, John C. Wright, vice-president and treasurer, J. C. McCutcheon, secretary.

Gift of Mrs. Joanna C. Moore.

254 HEGER, JOSEPH, 1835–

Portfolio of original pencil sketches of scenes in Utah and on the return march to Fort Union with Lieutenant DuBois' detachment of Mounted

Rifles after escorting Captain Marcy and his supply train from New Mexico to the Army of Utah at Camp Scott [Fort Bridger].

24 drawings. Various sizes. Mounted to 38 x 30 cm.

Heger served also with DuBois in the Arizona–New Mexico campaign of 1859–1860 as a private in Co. K. of the 1st Regiment of Mounted Riflemen. Born in Hesse, he came to America as a child, enlisted in the army in 1855 from Jefferson, Wis.

The expedition camped on Yellow Creek, June 19, 1858, on the march from Camp Scott to Salt Lake City with General Johnston, and on June 21 learned that President Buchanan had pardoned the Mormons. The return journey from Camp Floyd to Fort Union started July 19, through Goshen, Ephraim, the Wasatch Mountains, Green River, etc., to San Luis Valley, River del Norte, Taos, and Fort Union, September 13, 1858. (See Lieutenant DuBois' Journal, No. 148.)

Heger signs and dates nearly every drawing. They include the following:

Camp of the Army of Utah on Yellow
  Creek
Goshen, Utah
Nephi, Utah
Ephraim, Utah
Manti, Utah
Manti, Utah

Near the summit of Wahsatch [*sic*] Mts.
Camp Floyd, Cedar Valley, Utah
Near Wahsatch Mts.
Leaving Wahsatch Mts.
Near the Tanks
Green R[iver]
Near Green R.
Camp an[*sic*] Grand R.
Near Grand R.
Crossing Blue R.
Spring an[*sic*] Cedar Creek
The Twin Rivers
Near Camp
Grand R.
Eagle Tail Valley
In Sawatch Pass
In Sawatch Pass
San Luis Valley

Four of these drawings are reproduced in DuBois, *Campaigns in the West, 1856–1861. The Journal and Letters of Colonel John Van Deusen DuBois with Pencil Sketches by Joseph Heger.* Ed. by George P. Hammond, Tucson, Ariz., Pioneers Historical Society, 1949.

[Coe No. IV, 436.]

255 HILL, JOHN BIRNEY, *d.* 1919

Diary of an overland journey from St. Joseph to California, May 10 to August 11, 1850. Typewritten copy made by Marian Adaire, granddaughter of the writer, March 4, 1940.

14 pp. 28 cm.

John Birney Hill was born in Indiana. In 1850 he joined a party for California from Prairieton, Ind., with Dr. W. Ogle, Elijah Montgomery, Sidney Young, John Kirby, and James Hale. He later settled in Coles County, Ill., and engaged in the meat-packing business.

Entries are brief but comment on the soil and vegetation, the accessibility of water, fuel, and forage, and the weather.

The writer started from Terre Haute, Ind., and left St. Joseph on March 10, 1850, traveling by the Platte and Sweetwater Rivers, South Pass, Sublette's Cutoff to Fort Hall, and the California Trail to the Humboldt River, where the diary ends.

A narrative account of the journey from Scott's Bluff, June 14, to the Lewis Fork beyond Fort Hall about July 21 is printed in *Annals of Wyoming*, 1935, IX, No. 4, 35–42, with title: "Gold. A Story of the Plains in 1850." It was evidently written from memory as he calls the California Trail from Fort Hall "Sublette's Cut-off." The story was contributed by Mr. Hill's son-in-law, J. B. Lutz of Cheyenne.

[Coe No. II, 700.]

256 HINMAN, ALANSON, 1822–1908

Account book kept by Alanson Hinman at the Bannock Boise mines, Idaho City, 1863–1864; and a record of disbursements of customs money and on account of Revenue Cutters, June to December [1867?].

117 pp. 33½ cm. Original binding.

Alanson Hinman went to Oregon in 1844, spent his first winter as teacher at the Whitman Mission, and later settled in the Willamette Valley, at Forest Grove, where he engaged in a mercantile business. In 1860 he went to San Francisco to buy stock for his business; on the return voyage the ship was wrecked, the cargo lost, but he was saved. He went to the mines in Idaho and there repaired his fortunes. From 1867 to 1873 he was collector of customs at Astoria and then returned to Forest Grove for the rest of his life.

Four pages (in the middle of the volume) belong to the Astoria period, 1867–1873. The accounts are with many of the leading firms of Portland.

[Coe No. 92.]

257 HITCHCOCK, SOPHRONIA SUMNER (MRS. ASA), 1800–1828

Manuscript map of the Dwight Mission to the Cherokee Indians, in what is now Pope County, Arkansas. [1823?]

41 x 32 cm.

Sophronia Sumner, a missionary at Dwight (named after President Dwight the elder of Yale College), sent this map home to her friends. It was probably drawn in 1823 prior to her marriage to Asa Hitchcock, a fellow missionary at Dwight, in that year. In her "Refferences" on the map she mentions the winter of 1822 and speaks of "bro." Asa whom she married in October 1823.

Gift of Frederick J. Shepard.

258 HOFFMANN, WILHELM

"Reise Skitzen von Wilhelm Hoffmann." Account of an overland journey from St. Louis and experiences in California, March 30, 1849 to October 8, 1850, when he sailed for the Sandwich Islands, his brief stay on the island of Maui, and arrival at Honolulu, November 7, 1850.

32 pp. 24½ cm. With typewritten translation of the account of the journey to and stay in California.

The manuscript is written in German script in a fine, neat hand, two columns to a page. The journey and California experiences occupy 27½ pages. Wilhelm Hoffmann, with Bernhard Schneider, John Gelshaüsser, and Dietrich and Paul Hoffmann, left St. Louis with their wagon and oxen, March 30, 1849, and traveled by St. Joseph, the Platte and Sweetwater Rivers, Sublette's Cut-off and the California Trail to the Humboldt River, and Lassen's Route to the Sacramento Valley and Lassen's on Deer Creek, September 27. Hoffmann sailed to the Sandwich Islands, October 8, 1850, on the steamer *Edward.* At the island of Maui, where they first anchored, he found most of the desirable land had already been bought up by American and English sugar planters. He then went to Honolulu where he again sought land on which to settle. The account breaks off before he has succeeded.

[Coe No. III, 662.]

259 HOLLADAY, BEN, 1819–1877

Two letters to Nat Stein. New York, December 15, 1862, and February 16, 1863.

2 pp. 27 cm.

Ben Holladay, friend of the Mormons, after the Mexican War traded in Salt Lake City; bought the Central Overland Express Co.; organized the pony express to carry the overland mails; and became a leader in transportation development in the West and Northwest.

The earlier letter, signed by Holladay but written in another hand, praises Stein for his work for Holladay in Colorado, and asks him to take charge of the Central City Office until a qualified person is appointed. The second, all in his hand, addressed to Stein at G.S.L. City [Great Salt Lake], advising him how to deal with his friends, the Mormons, enclosed a letter of introduction to Governor Young [not in the collection].

[Coe No. 93.]

260 HOLMES, SILAS, *d.* 1849

"Journal kept by Assistant Surgeon Silas Holmes during a cruise in the U.S. Ship *Peacock* and Brigs *Porpoise* and *Oregon.* 1838–1839–1840–1841–1842 Exploring Expedition."

3 vols. [i.e., 730 pp.] 26–27½ cm. Original bindings.

Each volume has a title page, printed in part with an imprint: Sold by C. Hall, Norfolk. The name of the author and other details are filled in by hand.

Silas Holmes was assistant surgeon on the U.S. Exploring Expedition, serving on the Sloop of War *Peacock*, William L. Hudson, commanding, from August 10, 1838 to December 9, 1839, at Sydney, where he joined the Brig *Porpoise;* on October 25 he joined the Brig *Oregon* at San Francisco.

During the expedition Holmes assisted the scientists with astronomical calculations and observations and in his journal described in detail the events of the voyage, the countries visited, customs of the natives, etc.

The journal is a daily record of the expedition. Vol. I covers the period August 20, 1838–May 20, 1840, Hampton Roads, via Cape Horn, the Antarctic, Sydney, to the Fiji Islands; Vol. II, May 21, 1840–August 29, 1841, Fiji Islands to Northwest Coast, Fort Nisqually, Fort Vancouver; Vol. III, September 15, 1841–June 4, 1842, from Vancouver to San Francisco, Singapore, St. Helena, Rio de Janeiro to the Equator. The journal closes with a copy of the orders of June 12 that all journals, specimens, etc., be surrendered. It is followed by a three-page note on the Polynesian Indians.

This journal covers the entire expedition in such detail (except for the overland expeditions) that it is an important supplement to the journals of Blair, Colvocoresses, Eld, Emmons, and Underwood (see Nos. 35, 101, 161, 166–169, 480).

[Coe No. IV, 437.]

261 HOSKINS, JOHN BOX, 1768–

"The narrative of a voyage to the North West Coast of America and China on trade and discoveries by John Hoskins, performed in the ship Columbia Rediviva, 1790, 1791, 1792 & 1793."

Typewritten transcript. 206 pp. 27½ cm.

John Hoskins, protégé of Joseph Barrell, chief organizer of the expeditions, was sent as ship's clerk or supercargo on the second voyage of the *Columbia Rediviva*, Captain Robert Gray commanding. The "Narrative" opens with a summary of the events of the first voyage, 1787–1790, of the *Columbia Rediviva*, Captain John Kendrick in command, and the *Lady Washington*, Captain Robert Gray in command; and continues with an account of the second voyage from Boston, September 28, 1790, until it breaks off suddenly on March 29, 1792, in the midst of a description of the country and Indians of Clayoquot Sound.

The original manuscript narrative is now in the library of the Massachusetts Historical Society. This copy was made from a transcript in the University of Washington Library, October 2, 1922. Published in *Voyages of the "Columbia" to the Northwest Coast 1787–1790 and 1790–1793*, edited by Frederic W. Howay [Boston], 1941 (Massachusetts Historical Society. *Collections*, Vol. 79).

[Coe No. 94.]

262 HOSMER, HEZEKIAH LORD, 1814–1893

Notebook containing "Distances on the Missouri" from St. Louis to Fort Benton and an address to the citizens of Montana; ten letters to Judge Hosmer and a document; and part of the manuscript account of his journey to the States in 1865, written by his son J. A. Hosmer.

1 vol. [i.e., 45 pp.] 14½ cm. Original binding. 44 pp. 18–33 cm.

Hezekiah L. Hosmer was appointed as the first chief justice of Montana Territory by President Lincoln in 1864, and served for four years. In 1869 he was appointed postmaster at Virginia City and held that office until 1872 when he moved to California. In September 1865 he left for the East with his son, John Allen Hosmer, traveling down the Yellowstone and Missouri Rivers, and returned the following spring.

The address to his fellow citizens of Montana [12 pp.] was delivered soon after his return and in it he strongly advocated the building of a northern railroad to the Pacific Coast.

The letters and document deal with the establishment of the courts in the Territory, local political questions, and mining claims. They are as follows:

BAGG, CHARLES S. Letter to Judge Hosmer. December 3, 1865. 2 pp.

CARROLL & STEELE. Letter to Judge Hosmer. July 12, 1865. 1 p.

EVERTS, TRUMAN C. Two letters to Judge Hosmer. January 6, 12, 1865. 6 pp.

GIDDINGS, AMMI. Letter to Judge Hosmer. May 5, 1865. 3 pp.

JOHNSON, STANTON C. Document binding Stanton C. Johnson and his heirs to pay H. L. Hosmer and T. C. Everts $6,000, dated May 23, 1865, and listing claims on quartz lodes in Montana placed in the hands of Hosmer and Everts. 2 pp.

McBAIN, D. Letter to Judge Hosmer. March 6, 1865. 1 p.

MILLER, WILLIAM H. Letter to Judge Hosmer. July 14, 1865. 2 pp.

NEALLEY, EDWARD B. Letter to Judge Hosmer. May 7, 1865. 4 pp.

SNELL, CHARLES H. Letter to Judge Hosmer. February 17, 1865. 4 pp.

TORBET, A. M. Letter to Judge Hosmer. July 15, 1865. 1 p.

The manuscript of "A trip to the States" is typewritten with manuscript corrections, the pages numbered 21–42. The entire manuscript was printed with the title: *A Trip to the States, by the Way of the Yellowstone and Missouri, by J. Allen Hosmer, with a Table of Distances*, Virginia City, M.T., 1867.

The table of distances printed on 12 pages at the end of the volume agrees almost exactly with Hezekiah Hosmer's table except that it is reversed and reads from Fort Benton to St. Louis.

[Coe Collection.]

263 HUDSON'S BAY COMPANY

Seventy-five official and confidential letters written by Sir James Douglas, Roderick Finlayson, Dr. John McLoughlin, and others, to Dr. William Fraser Tolmie, in charge at Nisqually, and a few to his predecessors at Nisqually, A. C. Anderson and Angus McDonald, 1841–1859.

165 pp. 18–32½ cm. With typewritten transcript.

The letters relate to the company's attitude toward the settlement of Oregon and its newly established Provisional Government, the quarrel between McLoughlin and Simpson, the establishment of the Puget Sound Agricultural Company at Nisqually, the Boundary Treaty, the attitude toward the U.S. Government and the American people, the seizure of the *Beaver*, the company's land claims, and the San Juan Island and Haro Strait difficulty.

The letters are:

DOUGLAS, SIR JAMES. Two letters to Angus McDonald. December 28, 1841, February 8, 1842. 2 pp.

—— 41 letters to Dr. Tolmie. March 11, 1850–December 18, 1857. 105 pp.

—— Letter to John Work. December 27, 1851. 6 pp.

—— Letter to Henry N. Peers. September 19, 1854. 1 p.

—— Letter to Mr. Huggins. October 3, 1854. 1 p.

FINLAYSON, RODERICK. Ten letters to Dr. Tolmie. May 26, 1845–November 13, 1854. 16 pp.

—— Letter to Mr. Huggins. October 4, 1854. 1 p.

—— Affidavit, George Harvey, January 26, 1852, certified by James Douglas. 1 p.

HAWKINS, J. S. Three letters to Dr. William F. Tolmie. February 24–March 8, 1859. 6 pp.

McKENZIE, KENNETH. Letter to Dr. W. F. Tolmie. July 28, 1856. 3 pp.

McLOUGHLIN, JOHN. Letter to A. C. Anderson. January 4, 1841. 2 pp.

—— Letter to Angus McDonald. November 12, 1841. 3 pp.

—— Two letters to Dr. Tolmie. October 10, November 25, 1843. 3 pp.

MACTAVISH, DUGALD. Letter to A. McDonald. September 10, 1842. 1 p.

OGDEN, PETER SKENE. Five letters to Dr. Tolmie. January 12, 1846–July 25, 1853. The first three letters are signed also by James Douglas. 11 pp.

PEMBERTON, J. DESPARD. Letter to William F. Tolmie. July 29, 1856. 1 p.

SIMPSON, SIR GEORGE. Letter to William F. Tolmie. March 17, 1859. 1 p.

WORK, JOHN. Letter to Dr. Tolmie. March 30, 1848. 1 p.

[Coe No. 144.]

264 HUGGINS, EDWARD, 1832–

"The origin of the Puget Sound Agricultural Company, from mem: left at Nisqually by A. C. Anderson, who was in charge of Fort Nisqually for two or three years (1840, 41.)"

5 pp. 34½ cm. With negative photostat.

The manuscript is endorsed: "The origin of the Puget Sound Agricultural Comp'y, Fort Nisqually, by Mr. A. C. Anderson, prepared by him for the use of the Commission appointed to examine and report upon the claims of the Hudson Bay and Puget Sound Ag. Comp'y under the Treaty of 1846. 1865."

A note accompanying the manuscript states: "This manuscript was compiled by Edward Huggins clerk of the Puget Sound Agricultural Co. from memoranda left at Nisqually by Mr. Anderson. It was later left or given to Mr. Bagley who presented it to me in 1928. Winlock Miller Jr."

Edward Huggins arrived in Nisqually in 1850 to serve as trader and clerk for the Hudson's Bay Company and the Puget Sound Agricultural Company under Dr. Tolmie. In 1859 he succeeded Dr. Tolmie as manager of the company's affairs in Pierce County.

With the manuscript are photostats of two maps:

"Plan of the Pugets Sound Agricultural

Company's land claim at Nisqually, Washington Territory. Fort Nisqually May 10th 1852, W. F. Tolmie, Agent Puget's Sound Agricl. Co. Filed May 7th 1855. James Tilton, Sur. Gen. W.T." 42 x 28½ cm.

An added note on the plan reads: "I hereby certify that the above map, and the papers attached thereto are true copies of the originals on file in this office. Surveyor General's Office, Olympia, W.T. August 18, 1865. E. Giddings, Acting Surveyor General."

"Sketch of the prairie land about Nisqually." 37½ x 30½ cm.

The photostat of this sketch was given to Mr. Miller by F. A. Wellman, August 8, 1929.

A brief extract from the manuscript is quoted by Mr. Bagley in his *In the Beginning. A Sketch of Some Early Events in Western Washington*, Seattle, 1905, pp. 17–18.

[Miller Collection.]

265 HUGGINS, EDWARD, 1832–

"The story of the seizure of the Hudson Bay Company's steamer 'Beaver' and the brigantine 'Mary Dare,' by the Custom House authorities at Olympia, Wash. Ter. (then Oregon Territory) in November 1851," by Edward Huggins. July 11, 1901.

Typewritten manuscript (carbon). 7 pp. 28 cm.

The Hudson's Bay Company's steamer *Beaver* and brigantine *Mary Dare* were seized by the U.S. Collector of Customs for infringement of the revenue laws. The case was tried before Judge William Strong and the ships were later released.

Mr. Huggins added accounts of other incidents showing the attitude of the government officials of Washington Territory toward the Hudson's Bay Company.

[Miller Collection.]

266 HUMPHREYS, L.

"Over Land Guide from Kanesville Iowa to Oregon City &c." Signed: "L. Humphreys of Ohio. Willammette Forks, Oregon T. May 4, 1853."

25 pp. 23 cm.

Accompanied by three pen and ink maps of the route drawn by L. Humphreys:

Across Iowa to Kanesville to Prairie Creek, with notes of Indian tribes and game, with distances on the verso. 20 x 30½ cm.

From Loupe Fork and Prairie Creek to Soda Springs and Fort Hall. 39½ x 31 cm.

From Fort Hall to the coast, showing the various routes to Oregon and the Humboldt River route to California with rivers and towns identified. 39½ x 31 cm.

The guide gives details of distances, width and depth of streams, camping places, landmarks, etc. Humphreys adds the distances to Sacramento taken, after leaving the Oregon Trail, from "the most approved authors"; distances from Burlington, Iowa, to Kanesville; a "List of places where the face of the country & soil &c denotes the existence of gold," notes on the Indians; and notes "To Emigrants."

On the last leaf are statements certifying the value and accuracy of the guide signed by R. B. Willoughby, W. W. Neilson, Alfred Humphrey.

In 1927 this manuscript was sold by John R. Humphreys, the writer's son.

[Coe No. 95.]

267 HUNTINGTON, CHARLES ANDREW, 1812–

Memoir of the life of C. A. Huntington written for the benefit of his children with no expectation of its being seen outside the family. April 1899.

Typewritten manuscript. 224 pp. 33 cm.

The memoir covers the writer's early life and education in Vergennes, Vt., and Perry, N.Y.; his marriage, and years in Rockford, Ill.; his experience in Vicksburg during the Civil War. In 1864 he sailed for the Pacific Coast, by the Isthmus, to act as clerk for his brother-in-law, William H. Waterman, Superintendent of Indian Affairs in Washington; settled at Olympia, and in 1881 accepted a call to the pastorate of the Congregational Church in Eureka, Calif. The memoir gives details of life in Olympia and Eureka, conditions of the Indians in Washington Territory and the Agency at Neah Bay, the expulsion of Chinese from Eureka and Humboldt County, and his views on theology.

The Rev. C. A. Huntington evidently began writing his reminiscences before 1899 because he published in 1892 *The University of Vermont Fifty Years Ago.*

"A Chapter From the Unpublished Reminiscences of One of the Oldest of Surviving Graduates . . . Followed by Thirteen Select Sermons of the Author," Burlington, Vt., Eureka, Calif.

[Coe No. 96.]

268 HUSKISSON, WILLIAM, 1770–1830

Papers and documents relating to the affairs of America, printed and manuscript, used by William Huskisson during negotiations with the United States. 1824–1826.

417 pp. Map. 23½–34 cm.

William Huskisson, prominent statesman, was president of the Board of Trade from 1823 to 1827. He and Stratford Canning were appointed by the Foreign Secretary, George Canning, as the British Plenipotentiaries to carry on negotiations with Richard Rush, Minister Plenipotentiary in London for the United States. In this volume, bearing his bookplate, Huskisson has gathered documents needed during the negotiations.

Message of President Monroe to the Senate of the United States Transmitting the Report of the Secretary of State, with Accompanying Documents, of Negotiations between Richard Rush, Envoy Extraordinary and Minister Plenipotentiary of the United States in London, and William Huskisson and Stratford Canning, Plenipotentiaries of Great Britain. Printed with heading: 18th Congress, 2d Session [Confidential], *In Senate of the United States. January 20, 1825. Read and Printed in Confidence, for the Use of the Members.* 172 pp.

Richard Rush's autographed copy, accompanied by a letter from Rush to William Huskisson, saying that a few copies of the account of their negotiations were printed for the use of the Senate, and he is sending his own copy, November 2, 1825, "Private." 3 pp. Endorsed: "Washington 2 Nov 1825. Mr. Rush Rd 17 Dec. with a Pamphlet."

Northwest Coast of America. May 15, 1826. Report of Mr. Baylies of the Select Committee "to be Referred to the Committee of the Whole House, to Which Is Committed the Bill to Authorize the Establishment of a Military Post or Posts . . . on the Pacific Ocean" (19th Congress, 1st Session, House of Representatives [Rep. 213]). 22 pp.

Manuscript note at top of page 1: "Enclosure F in Mr. Baker's No. 35 of 1826." This report was probably sent to William Huskisson from the British Legation in Washington where Anthony St. John Baker was secretary, and contains information about the Northwest Coast derived from Samuel Adams Ruddock who in 1821 traveled overland from Council Bluffs to the mouth of the Columbia River, and an extract from the logbook of the *Columbia*.

"Sketch. Exhibiting the Claims of Boundary, on the Part of the British and American Governments under the 5th Article of the Treaty of Ghent." Printed by Harrison & Son, Lithog., Lancaster Court, Strand. 46½ x 50 cm.

Map showing claims of the two governments between the St. Lawrence and the ocean east of Quebec and the headwaters of the Connecticut River.

"The 5th Article of the Treaty of Ghent," and extracts from other documents. 46 pp.

Manuscript copy. Endorsed on last leaf: "Compendium of arguments &c," probably prepared for Mr. Huskisson's use during the negotiations.

*Private. Papers Relating to the Negotia-
tion, in London, between the British
Plenipotentiaries and the Plenipotentiary on the Part of the United States
of America. January to August, 1824.*
108 pp.

Manuscript note on title page: "Private
& Confidential. For Mr. Huskisson."

The papers included are the correspondence between the Secretary of State for
Foreign Affairs, the Rt. Hon. George Canning, and the British Plenipotentiaries,
and the report of the Plenipotentiaries to
the Secretary on the negotiations to August, 1824. Some passages are marked, and
there are a few marginal notes. With the
papers is a two-page manuscript: "American Memorandum of subjects for negotia-
tion, referred to in the first conference."

*Private. Additional Papers Respecting the
North-West Coast of America,* West-
minster [1826]. 14 pp. Endorsed:
"Private & Confidential."

These papers include a letter from J. H.
Pelly, Governor of the Hudson's Bay
Company, December 9, 1825, enclosing

documents relating to the sale of the Pacific Fur Company to the North West
Company.

Private. A letter from C. R. Vaughan, of
the British Legation at Washington,
June 6, 1826, to Mr. Secretary Canning,
enclosing the Baylies report on the
Northwest Coast of America [1826].
17 pp. Endorsed on last leaf: "Private
& confidential." Paged continuously
with the preceding, but issued later.

*Private. Message of the President of the
United States to the House of Representatives, Transmitting the Correspondence with the British Government
in Relation to the Boundary of the
United States on the Pacific Ocean,
January 31, 1826,* Westminster [1826].
33 pp. Paged continuously with the two
preceding.

Endorsed: "Private and Confidential.
Port Discovery a most admirable and safe
Harbour . . . A work on Cape Disappt.
would effectually prevent a Vessel entering the Columbia," presumably in Huskisson's hand.

[Coe No. IV, 438.]

269 HUTCHINSON, FRANCIS McCREDY, *d.* 1924

Journal of F. M. Hutchinson, while in Minnesota and Dakota employed on
the construction of the Northern Pacific Railroad. May 20, 1871 to February 21, 1872 and June 6, 1872 to January 1, 1873.

438 pp. [i.e., 436, pp. 1–2 missing] 64 photographs, 4 drawings, 2 maps, 49 clippings.
28½ cm. Original binding.

Francis McC. Hutchinson, a Philadel-
phian, attended the Agricultural College of Pennsylvania (later Pennsylvania
State College). He spent part of two years
in Minnesota and eastern Dakota, and
then returned home. After being employed by the Philadelphia *Record* for 17
years, in 1890 he entered the real estate
business.

The journal describes at length the details of Hutchinson's experiences from his
departure from Philadelphia, May 20,

1871 to his return home, February 21,
1872, after working seven months as a
chainman and rodsman under Colonel Gaw
on the construction of the Northern Pacific
Railroad from Brainerd to Moorhead,
Minn.; his return to Minnesota in June
1872, his employment as chainman by T.
G. Merrill on a government survey on the
Marsh and Sand Hill Rivers after failing
to secure a position with the railroad; and
his experiences as assistant inspector of
ties of the Dakota Division under P. B.

Winston, August 7–November 13, when he left to return to Philadelphia.

The journal gives a vivid picture of the places through which he passed and the life of the railroad camps. It is illustrated with a few drawings, many photographs of the scenery, the camps, Indians and their villages, and clippings from newspapers and magazines about the progress of the railroad and views of the cities and towns.

Hutchinson included after his western journal an account of a visit to Cape May, N.J., June 14–15, 1873 [pp. 439–449]; and "Adventures in Spain" [i.e., Berlin, N.J.], July 19–25, 1873 [pp. 451–460]; he included copies of poems composed in 1870–1871 and compositions written while a student at Pennsylvania Agricultural College, 1866–1869 [pp. 462–477].

Laid in the volume are four loose pages on the Indian problem; a pass on the Northern Pacific Railroad, June 13, 1872, signed by C. Hobart, superintendent; and the following letters relating to his employment by the railroad:

DAVIDSON, JOHN. Two letters to Frank Hutchinson. March 24, May 9, 1873. 2 pp.

DOUGLAS, H. H. Letter to Frank Hutchinson. March 24, 1872. 3 pp.

GAW, WILLIAM B. Letter to Frank M. Hutchinson. August 8, 1872. 1 p.

HUTCHINSON, F. M. Letter to conductors of the Pittsburgh, Fort Wayne & Chicago Railway Co., requesting their attention to F. M. Hutchinson, Jr. June 8, 1872. 1 p.

NEWPORT, R. M. Letter to F. M. Hutchinson. May 10, 1873. Not in his hand. 1 p.

ROBERTS, WILLIAM MILNOR. Four letters to F. M. Hutchinson. May 11, 1872– February 19, 1873. 4 pp.

The letter of May 11, 1872, is endorsed by C. B. Wright, Phil. June 1, 1872.

ROSSER, THOMAS L. Letter to F. M. Hutchinson. April 4, 1872. 1 p.

SPAULDING, IRA. Letter to F. M. Hutchinson. January 29, 1872. 1 p.

WINSTON, P. B. Two letters to F. M. Hutchinson. May 6, July 10, 1873. 6 pp.

[Coe Collection.]

270 INGALLS, RUFUS, 1820–1893

Letter to Major General Thomas S. Jesup, Quartermaster General U.S.A. Office of Assistant Quartermaster, Department of Oregon, Fort Vancouver, W.T., January 15, 1859.

Manuscript copy. 8 pp. 32 cm.

General Ingalls went to Oregon in 1849 as quartermaster with the rank of captain, under Major Hathaway, who established the post at Fort Vancouver.

The letter brings to the attention of General Jesup the facts regarding the site of Fort Vancouver, the claims of the Hudson's Bay Company, and the claims of the Catholic Mission recently set forth by Bishop Blanchet in a letter to the President of the United States.

[Miller Collection.]

271 INGRAHAM, JOSEPH, 1762–1800

Log of the brigantine *Hope* from Boston to the Northwest Coast of America, and journal of events. 1790–1792.

Photostat. 206 pp. and 31 full-page drawings, maps, and charts. With typewritten transcript.

Joseph Ingraham, formerly mate on the *Columbia*, was put in command of the brigantine *Hope* of Boston on a trading voyage to the Northwest Coast.

The journal covers the voyage from September 16, 1790, the day before the *Hope* sailed from Boston, to the Marquesas and Hawaiian Islands and to the Northwest Coast by the end of June 1791, where the summer was spent in trading with the Indians. The *Hope* sailed on September 2 for the Sandwich Islands and China, returned to the coast in July 1792, and sailed again for the Sandwich Islands October 12, 1792. The journal breaks off on November 5, on arrival at Owyhee.

Copies of the following letters are incorporated in the journal, and the original letter from Don J. F. de la Bodega y Quadra is inserted:

BODEGA Y QUADRA, JUAN FRANCISCO DE LA. Letter to S. Don Roberto Gray y Don Joh. Ingraham. Nutca, Agosto 2 de 1792, asking for information about the transactions between the English and Spaniards at Nootka in 1789. Signature only. 2 pp.

GRAY, ROBERT, and INGRAHAM, JOSEPH.

Letter to Don Juan Francisco de la Bodega y Quadra. Nootka Sound [August 3, 1792] in answer to the above. Copy. 5 pp.

INGRAHAM, JOSEPH. Letter to His Excellency the Governor of Port [Solodad, Falkland Islands, January 9, 1791] asking permission to run the *Hope* into the harbor. Copy, unsigned.

—— Letter to His Excellency, the Governor of Port Solodad. Brigantine *Hope*. January 9, 1791. Copy, unsigned.

The journal also contains a three-page vocabulary of the language of the Washington Isles.

The photostat reproduces 21 drawings and maps in the text as well as 31 full-page drawings, maps, and charts.

The original manuscript journal is in the Library of Congress. It has not been published in full. A brief account of the voyage, based on the journal, was published by F. W. Howay with the title: "The Voyage of the Hope: 1790–1792," *Washington Historical Quarterly*, 1920, XI, 3–28.

[Coe Nos. 97–98.]

272 JACKSON, WILLIAM HENRY, 1843–1942

Letter to his father and mother [George Hallock and Harriet Maria Allen Jackson]. Great Salt Lake City, October 30, 1866.

8 pp. [i.e., 10½ pp. as 3 are crossed]. 32 cm. With typewritten transcript.

Cut and mounted with the letter is an original wash drawing signed: "W. H. Jackson, 1866," with title: "Sawatch [i.e., Wasatch] Range, Utah. From West Side Utah Lake Dec 24—1866." 43½ x 21½ cm.

The letter describes Jackson's journey across the Plains as a "bullwhacker" from Nebraska City to Ham's Fork, June 26–September 7, when he left the wagon train, and his subsequent experiences with a second train to Great Salt Lake City.

[Coe No. I, 1055.]

273 JENNINGS, OLIVER

Journal of an overland trip from Oregon City to Vancouver and by the Columbia River and Blue Mountains to Fort Boise, Fort Hall, and Great Salt Lake City. March 5 to May 22, 1851.

88 pp. including a pencil sketch. 19½ cm. Original binding. With typewritten transcript.

The sketch depicts "Mount Hood from Vancouver."

After a stay of about a month at Fort Vancouver, where he fraternized with the soldiers and with the officials of the Hudson's Bay Company, Oliver Jennings, daguerreotypist, from Oregon City, abandoned his idea of taking pictures of the Cayuse Indians when his camera and pictures were stolen. Consequently he set out in company with Robert Wilson, Alexander McKay, McArthur, Pritchard, and Lieutenant Wood from the Fort and trading post for Fort Hall in three bateaux pushing up the Columbia past the Cascades, to The Dalles, Fort Hall, Fort Boise, Cantonment Loring, and with Major Owen to Salt Lake along the California Trail, Bear River, and Ogden River.

The most significant part of the journal begins on May 5, when he accompanied Major John Owen, the trader, to Salt Lake City, for the entries which end May 22 fill a gap in Owen's own journal (see *The Journals and Letters of Major John Owen* . . . ed. by S. Dunbar and P. C. Phillips . . . New York, 1937).

Jennings was an unusually acute observer and the resulting journal is a frank exposition of what he saw and heard with regard to such varied subjects as the Rifle Regiment, the Hudson's Bay Company, the Indians, the Mormons. Throughout the journal appear such names as Mr. Pritchard [i.e., Pritchette], former secretary of Oregon Territory, Peter Skene Ogden, chief factor of the Hudson's Bay Company, and Brigham Young.

A brief extract from the journal is printed in Harris K. Prior, "Art Note, Oliver Jennings, Daguerreotypist," *Oregon Historical Quarterly*, 1951, LII, 186–188.

[Coe No. 99.]

274 JOHNSON, JOHN LAWRENCE, 1830–1916

Diary of the overland journey of the Rev. Neill Johnson and his family from April 1 to August 31, 1851, from Mt. Pleasant, Iowa, to Oregon.

99 pp. 24 cm. Original binding.

J. L. Johnson was born November 15, 1830, in Pleasant Grove, Ill. His father, the Rev. Neill Johnson, was probate judge of Tazewell County, Ill., in 1838. When he was not re-elected for a third term, 1847, he accepted a call to the Cumberland Presbyterian Church in Mt. Pleasant, Iowa, later removing with his wife and ten children to Oregon, where he settled in Woodburn.

The Johnson party was followed the next year, 1852, over practically the same route from St. Joseph by Mr. Johnson's brother-in-law, John Tucker Scott, and his family.

The diary is headed: "J. L. Johnson, Woodburn Oregon," and is preceded by a brief outline of Johnson's childhood in Illinois, his father's removal to Iowa and finally to Oregon. The diary recounts the daily events of the journey from Mt. Pleasant, Iowa, to St. Joseph and over the Oregon Trail to the Cascades, where it breaks off on August 31 after the party had descended Laurel Hill with the help of William A. Jack and Thomas B. Allen, who had come to meet them.

The biographical material and the journal were written at a date after 1853, as Johnson mentions his cousin "Abigail Scott (now Mrs. Duniway)" who was married in 1853, and other later events.

[Coe No. 101.]

275 JOHNSON COUNTY, WYOMING. COUNTY CLERK

"Brand record A. Johnson County." May 11, 1881 to September 26, 1891, and re-recordings to December, 1896.

212 leaves. 41 cm. Original binding.

The volume records the brands of all cattle owners in Johnson County from its establishment in 1881 until 1891, when the volume was full. It also records sales and transfers of branded stock signed by the owners, and re-recording of brands up to December, 1896.

The names of all important stockmen and cattle companies of Johnson County appear in the volume.

The law required that all brands be recorded by the county clerk from 1867 to 1909, when the county records were abandoned and all brands were recorded in the books of the State Board of Livestock.

Laid in the volume are two letters: the first, To Whom it May Concern, April 14, 1894, certifies that the undersigned consent to the marriage of Myrtie May Hill to Dayton Hendrick, signed by David D. Collins, stepfather, Arlilian Collins, mother; the second, May 14 [n.y.] to Mr. O. J. Flagg, certifies that Jennie Pierce, the undersigned, consents to the marriage of her daughter Alida L. Brahm to Gardner L. Kimball. 2 pp. 20 cm.

The volume was formerly the property of Bert L. Pratt of Buffalo, Wyo.

[Coe No. 200.]

276 JOHNSTON, ALBERT SIDNEY, 1803–1862

Letter to the Assistant Adjutant General, Headquarters of the Army [Major Irvin McDowell]. Headquarters Army of Utah, Fort Leavenworth, September 11, 1857.

1 p. 24½ cm.

Colonel Johnston reports that he has assumed command of the Army of Utah and will leave Fort Leavenworth in a few days for Utah.

The letter is quoted in part in *The Month at Goodspeed's*, 1949, XXI, 11.

[Coe Collection.]

277 KAHLER, WILLIAM

"William Kahler's Diary, 1852"

93 pp. 14½ cm. Original binding.

William Kahler settled in Jacksonville, Ore. On August 4, 1853, the day of the murder of Richard Edwards by the Indians, his house was entered and rifled of its contents, and his name appears among the claimants on account of property destroyed.

The diary, written in pencil, records events of Kahler's journey overland from McConnellsville, Ohio, March 31, 1852,

to a point on the Oregon road beyond the turnoff for Shasta; it breaks off on September 14. The route was by boat from St. Louis to St. Joseph, where he bought 5 oxen, a cow, and a mare, and over the trail to the Platte River, Fort Laramie, the Sweetwater, Fort Hall and the Humboldt River to the Oregon road.

H. W. Scott, in his *History of the Oregon Country*, Cambridge, 1924, III, 235 *passim*, cites the diary a number of times and quotes a few words. He says the diary is unpublished and that Kahler's party left the Oregon Trail for California at Raft River, Idaho.

[Coe No. 102.]

278 KANE, PAUL, 1810–1871

A series of six paintings in oils of scenes in the Northwest, four of them attributed to Kane. [1846–1848.]

Six framed paintings.

[Fort Vancouver, Columbia River.] Artist unknown. 60 x 39½ cm.

[Mount Hood from the East.] Artist unknown. 52 x 39½ cm.

[Falls on the Palouse, Snake River.] 46½ x 30 cm.

[Kakkabakka Falls, near Fort William, Ontario.] 46½ x 30½ cm.

[Buffalo Hunt—half-breeds running buffalo.] 46 x 30½ cm.

[Buffalo resting—A group of buffalo.] Oval. 42 x 27½ cm.

Paul Kane, a young artist of Toronto, after four years in Europe, wished to devote his time to painting the Indians and scenes of the Northwest. He went first as far west as Sault Ste. Marie but returned to Toronto. He was encouraged to see Sir George Simpson, Governor of the Hudson's Bay Company's Territories in North America, who arranged for Kane to accompany the spring brigade in 1846 to the Northwest and is said to have commissioned him to paint a series of 12 pictures for him. Kane spent two years on his journey to Fort Vancouver, Fort Victoria, and Oregon Territory, returning with hundreds of sketches of Indians and Indian life, and of the country. Mr. George William Allan of Toronto commissioned Kane to paint 100 scenes in oil for him which are now in the Royal Ontario Museum in Toronto; and 12 were commissioned by the Legislative Council, of which 6 are now in the National Gallery at Ottawa, 5 in the Speaker's Chamber, House of Commons, Ottawa, and 1 is missing.

The paintings commissioned by Sir George Simpson were apparently shown in Buckingham Palace about 1858 and their favorable reception aided Kane in securing a publisher for his book, *Wanderings of an Artist*, London, 1859. These paintings have long been lost unless the four in this series were originally among them. They were acquired from the widow of a grandson of Sir George.

Mr. C. P. Wilson, in his article "Early Western Paintings," *The Beaver*, June, 1949, No. 280, pp. 12–13, ascribes the third, fourth, and fifth to Kane and suggests that the views of Vancouver and Mount Hood might be by or after Lieutenant Warre.

[Coe No. III, 1697.]

279 KANE, THOMAS LEIPER, 1822–1883

Papers and correspondence relating to the Mormons. [1846?]–1853, 1856–1860, 1884.

47 pieces. 142 pp. 13½–110 cm. With copies of *The Mormons* and *The Private Papers of Thomas Leiper Kane*.

Colonel Kane became interested in the Mormons in 1846 when he visited Nauvoo and the Mormon camp at Council Bluffs. In 1858 he visited Salt Lake City with special instructions from President Buchanan and was instrumental in preventing a clash between the army and the Mormons.

The papers consist of reports, drafts of speeches and letters by Colonel Kane ; and letters to him written chiefly by the leaders of the Mormon Church describing conditions in Utah and the relations between the federal officials and the army and the Mormons. They include the following letters and papers:

KANE, THOMAS LEIPER. Account of the inhuman treatment of the anti-Mormons in Illinois [in 1846]. 3 pp.

—— Report on the "Half breed track" of Indian land and the Mormons in Nauvoo [1846]. 3 pp.

—— Report to Hon. William Medill, Commissioner of Indian Affairs, April 21, 1847. A signed copy in Kane's hand. 3 pp.

—— Notes for an address on the Mormons introducing Elders Benson and Little as speakers at a meeting, probably in New York in the spring of 1848. 1 p.

—— Draft of a letter to President Buchanan. December 31, 1857. 1 p.

—— Cipher message to his father, Judge Kane. February 4, 1858, with added notes and postscript on verso [not in cipher]. 2 pp. and translation [not in Kane's hand]. 1 p.

—— Draft of a letter to Brigham Young. August 25, 1858. 2 pp.

—— Draft of a letter to Mrs. Cumming. August 25, 1858. Signed with initials. 2 pp.

—— Draft of a letter to Colonel William Cumming. August 28, 1858. Signed with initials. 2 pp.

—— Draft of a letter to Governor Cumming. March 22, 1859. Signed. 2 pp.

APPLEBY, WILLIAM I. Two letters to Colonel Kane. April 17, 1848, August 30, 1852. 4 pp.

—— Certificate that James Ferguson on the 18th day of November, 1851, was admitted by the Hon. Judge Snow to practice law in the Territory. W. I. Appleby, clerk. A true copy. 1 p.

—— Certificate that James Ferguson, on the fifth day of December, 1853, was admitted to practice in the Supreme Court of the United States. December 5, 1853, W. I. Appleby, clerk. 1 p.

BERNHISEL, JOHN MILTON. Two letters to Colonel Kane, listing proposed appointees for Utah. September 11, 1850, July 17, 1852. 2 pp.

BOLTON, CURTIS E. Deposition concerning R. Keith Johnson and Justice Eckels. June 21, 1860. 1 p.

BROWN, THOMAS D. Letter to Colonel Kane. February 14, 1859. 1 p.

CANNON, GEORGE QUAYLE. Letter to Mrs. Kane after the death of her husband. January 25, 1884. 3 pp.

ECKELS, DELANO R. Copy of a letter to Lieutenant Bennett. August 12, 1858. Attested a true copy by H. B. Clawson and James Ferguson. 1 p.

HAIGHT, ISAAC CHAUNCEY. Letter to Colonel Kane requesting seeds. December 31, 1858. 1 p.

HARVEY, THOMAS H., Superintendent of Indian Affairs. Letter to William Medill [December 3, 1846]. Extract in Kane's hand. 2 pp.

JOHNSON, LUKE S. Letter to Blair & Firkson. Signed by James Jordan, clerk, Luke Johnson, judge [n.p., n.d.], enclosing, on second leaf, an affidavit of John D. Peters, Shamship County, May 12, 1860, signed by Peters, Luke Johnson, judge, James Jordan, clerk. Letter and affidavit in James Jordan's hand. 2 pp.

PHELPS, WILLIAM WINES. Two letters to Colonel Kane. June 25, 1852, February 10, 1859, enclosing signed copies of a petition to the Hon. Aaron V. Brown, Postmaster General, for the removal of H. F. Morrell, and affidavits of Joseph Horne, Henry E. Phelps, and John G. Lynch, February 9, 1859 before Jeter Clinton, J.P. 17 pp.

PRATT, ORSON. Letter to Colonel Kane. May 12, 1853. 2 pp.

RICHARDS, FRANKLIN DEWEY. Letter to the Company of Latter-day Saints on board the *Enoch Train* for Boston, appointing James Ferguson to preside and E. Ellsworth and D. D. McArthur counselors on the journey. Liverpool, March 22, 1856. 2 pp.

RICHARDS, SAMUEL WHITNEY. Letter to Colonel Kane. September 16, 1857. 4 pp.

RICHARDS, WILLARD. Two letters to Colonel Kane. August 31, 1851, May 4, 1852. 3 pp.

ROCKWELL, ORRIN PORTER. Letter to Colonel Kane. November 20, 1858. 1 p.

SMITH, GEORGE ALBERT. Two letters to Colonel Kane. September 11, 1858, January 14, 1859. Signature only. 13 pp.

SMOOT, ABRAHAM OWEN. Petition to His Excellency, James Buchanan, to remove from office Chief Justice Eckels and other officials . . . Great Salt Lake City, June 25, 1858. Signed by A. O. Smoot, Mayor; J. C. Little, Marshal; Robert Campbell, City Recorder; and 57 other citizens. 3 pp.

TAYLOR, JOHN. Letter to his nephew, George [Q. Cannon]. January 12, 1859. Copy with a note added and signed J.T. 12 pp.

WELLS, DANIEL HANMER, and TAYLOR, JOHN. "Copy. Memorial for the admission of the State of Deseret. To the Honorable the Senate and House of Representatives in Congress Assembled." Signed by Daniel H. Wells, President of the Council, John Taylor, Speaker of the House of Representatives. January 14, 1859. 1 p.

WOODRUFF, WILFORD. Letter to Colonel Kane. March 8, 1859. Signature only. 4 pp.

YOUNG, BRIGHAM. Letter to Senator Stephen A. Douglas, introducing Dr. John M. Bernhisel. May 2, 1849. Signed also by Heber C. Kimball and Willard Richards. 1 p.

—— Five letters to Colonel Kane. January 7, 1857–November 22, 1858. Signatures only. 24 pp.

—— Extract copied in an unknown hand from a letter to Horace S. Eldredge. November 20, 1858. Unsigned. 2 pp.

—— Copies of two letters to George Q. Cannon. November 21, December 24, 1858. The second signed. 12 pp.

"Statistics—Comprising the necessary outfit to assist the emigrating Mormons now stationed at Mt. Pisgah—consisting of 200 Families including the widows and orphans . . ." [n.d.] 2 pp.

KANE, THOMAS LEIPER. *The Private Papers and Diary of Thomas Leiper Kane, A Friend of the Mormons.* Edited with an introduction by Oscar Osburn Winther, San Francisco, 1937.

—— *The Mormons. A Discourse Delivered before the Historical Society of Pennsylvania:* March 26, 1850, Philadelphia, 1850.

The papers and letters are arranged chronologically and accompanied by a copy of *The Collector*, December 1944–January 1945, containing a description of the Haiken Benjamin collection of Kane manuscripts offered for sale by Mary A. Benjamin. The remaining items are from the collection of the late Guido Bruno. Thomas H. Harvey's report to Medill is printed from another copy in the Stanford University Library in *The Private Papers*, pp. 25–29; Young's letter to Stephen A. Douglas introducing Dr. Bernhisel is quoted almost in full in D. L. Morgan, "The State of Deseret," *Utah Historical*

Quarterly, 1940, VIII, 113–114; and extensive extracts are printed in *The Collector*.

[Coe No. III, 1199.]

280 KELLER, JOSIAH P., 1812–1862

A collection of 104 letters and documents and two charts, relating to the establishment and early years of the Puget Mill Company at Teekalet [Port Gamble], W.T., written, with a few exceptions, by Captain Josiah P. Keller, Teekalet, 1853–1862, to his partner, Charles Foster of East Machias, Maine.

104 letters and documents, 2 charts. 340 pp. 24–32½ cm.

The charts (20 x 34 cm. and 21 x 33 cm.) are drawn in pencil on brown paper and show Hood's Canal, the harbor, and location of the mill buildings.

J. P. Keller of East Machias, Me., and Charles Foster, with W. C. Talbot and A. J. Pope of San Francisco, formed the Puget Mill Company. Captain Talbot fitted out the *Julius Pringle* in San Francisco and sailed to Puget Sound to select a site, settling on Port Gamble. On September 4, 1853, Captain Keller, with his family, arrived at Port Gamble in the schooner *L. P. Foster* and remained as superintendent.

The manuscripts include a copy of the indenture between Andrew J. Pope of San Francisco and William C. Talbot, Charles Foster, and Josiah P. Keller of East Machias, Me., December 20, 1852, entering into a partnership, to be the Puget Mill Company, to manufacture lumber in the Territory of Oregon at Puget Sound; with a supplementary agreement, June 4, 1857, to continue the partnership indefinitely; and the following letters:

KELLER, JOSIAH P. 101 letters to Charles Foster. February 24, 1853–April 23, 1862. 335 pp.

TALBOT, WILLIAM C. Two letters to Charles Foster. June 30, September 20, 1861. Copies by Charles Endicott, November 1, 1862. 2 pp.

Power of Attorney, Henry W. Alline for J. P. Keller. East Machias, Me., January 7, 1861. 1 p.

Some of Mr. Keller's letters to his partner are addressed to Foster and Keller, the others to Charles Foster. They give details of the plans of the Puget Mill Company, the building of the mill and wharf, the ships and cargoes, the development of the business, and accounts, with occasional references to personal and family affairs. The letter of September 7, 1853 describes Keller's voyage around Cape Horn in the schooner *L. P. Foster*. Some of the letters are marked "copy."

[Coe No. 103.]

281 KELLY, WILLIAM, *d.* 1871

Muster roll of Captain William Kelly's Company "A" of the Clarke District Regiment of Militia of Washington Territory, enrolled the first day of October, 1855, at Vancouver, W.T.

Printed form filled in by hand. 39½ x 31½ cm.

The muster roll is signed at the end: "I certify that this Roll exhibits a correct list of the Militia within my district as appears by the Census Roll for this year. William

Kelly, Captain Company 'A.' Clark Dist. R.M.W.T." The roll is endorsed, in

another hand: "Recd. Feby 8, 1856."

[Miller Collection.]

282 KENDRICK, JOHN, *ca.* 1740–1794

Power of Attorney to John Jolliffe, signed October 3, 1866 by sixteen heirs of John Kendrick, the signatures accompanied by affidavits, authorizing Jolliffe to petition Congress in their behalf for relief or compensation for Captain Kendrick's services and expenditures in the discovery of the Columbia River and its circumjacent territory, etc.

4 pp. 35 cm.

John Kendrick of Massachusetts commanded privateers during the Revolutionary War and was a pioneer in the maritime fur trade. He was in command of the first voyage of the *Columbia* and *Washington* to the Northwest Coast which sailed from Boston in September 1787 (see No. 261).

The document is accompanied by a specimen of the copper medal struck in 1787 by the owners in commemoration of the first American voyage to the Northwest Coast. The medals were carried on the voyage for distribution.

Obverse: The *Columbia* and *Washington* encircled by the words "Columbia and Washington. Commanded by J. Kendrick." *Reverse:* the names of the owners, "By/J. Barrell, /S. Brown, C. Bulfinch. /J. Darby, C. Hatch, /J. M. Pintard. 1787/" encircled by "Fitted at Boston, N. America for the Pacific Ocean."

The medal is reproduced in Bancroft, *The Northwest Coast*, San Francisco, 1884, I, 186.

[Coe No. 104.]

283 KERNER, ROBERT JOSEPH, 1887–

"Statement of Dr. Robert J. Kerner, Sather Professor of History, University of California, Berkeley. 414 Federal Court Bldg., Seattle, Washington. November 17, 1944. Given at hearing on November 17, in connection with petitions of Indians of Hydaburg, Kake, and Klawock, Alaska, conducted by the Department of the Interior.

Mimeographed. 43 pp. 28 cm.

The Alaskan Indians, supported by the Office of Indian Affairs of the Department of the Interior, claimed that they were deprived of their rights to fish in Alaskan waters by the canning industry and white residents, and hearings were held in Seattle before Judge Richard Hanna in November 1944.

The statement covers the source material on Russian-American relations to 1869 in American libraries; and discusses the attitude of the Russian Government toward the Indians, Russian claims to Alaska, the Russian American Company, Russian relations with America and with Great Britain and the treaties of 1824 and 1825, the terms of the purchase of Alaska in 1867, and the part the Washington Territorial Legislature played in the purchase.

A note on the title page reads: "This was given to me by Stephen V. Carey Esq., of Kerr, McCord & Carey of Seattle. W. W. M."

[Miller Collection.]

284 KEYES, ERASMUS DARWIN, 1810–1895

Letter to Captain B. L. Henness. Head Quarters, Puget Sound District, Fort Steilacoom, W.T., November 27, 1855, signed by E. D. Keyes, Captain 3rd Artillery, commanding; with a postscript in his own hand dated November 28.

2 pp. 25 cm.

The letter enclosed Orders No. 2 [not now with the letter] and instructed Captain Henness of "F" Company, Grand Mound Mounted Rangers, to examine the country for Indians in the direction of Mount Rainier and to keep headquarters informed of his movements. The postscript informs Henness of the attack on Lieutenant Slaughter's camp on the Puyallup and the need of vigilance.

[Miller Collection.]

285 KILGORE, MAGGIE

"Life of Jim Baker" [Savery, Wyo., 1917].

14 pp. 26 cm. With typewritten transcript.

A note at the end of the manuscript, in another hand, reads: "Written by Maggie Kilgore of Savery, Wyo., & read as her graduation essay from the 8th grade into the High School, June 1917. Data obtained from word of mouth in the vicinity of Jim Baker's home."

Two newspaper clippings are mounted with the transcript, one of Jim Baker's cabin "to be dedicated Monday" dated July 23, 1917; and the other dated April 5, 1920, about the gift of his canoe to the state.

The manuscript and transcript were formerly in the library of the Rt. Rev. Nathaniel Seymour Thomas, Bishop of Wyoming. The manuscript has been published, at least in part, in the *Wyoming Tribune* [Cheyenne], July 23, 1917; and in full in N. Mumey's *Life of Jim Baker*, Denver, 1931, pp. 191–203.

[Coe No. 105.]

286 KINGERY, SOLOMON

Three letters from Solomon Kingery to his parents and friends, giving an account of his travels to California, March 22 to April 12, 1852.

23 pp. 24½–31½ cm. With typewritten transcript.

Starting from Pine Creek, Ogle County, Ill., Kingery, with other local young men, traveled by team across Iowa to Kanesville, along the Platte and Sweetwater Rivers, Kinney's and Hudspeth's Cut-offs and the Shasta or Nobles Pass route, the first emigrant train to arrive in California by this route across the Sierra Nevadas, to Shasta City.

The first two letters are chiefly concerned with the daily incidents of the journey, camping places on the route, cost of ferriage and food, encounters with the Indians, records of sickness and deaths. He was impressed by his first sight of women in bloomers and by the welcoming dinner served by the citizens of Shasta City for the emigrants. The third letter recounts his experiences at storekeeping in Shasta City,

[Coe No. 106.]

287 KINGSBURY, JAMES WILKINSON, 1801–1853

Two letters to his parents General and Mrs. Jacob Kingsbury, of Franklin, Connecticut, June 18, July 6, 1825.

4 pp. 24½–25 cm. With typewritten transcripts.

James W. Kingsbury, son of General Jacob and Sarah Palmer (Ellis) Kingsbury, was graduated from the Military Academy at West Point in 1823 and served with distinction in the army during the Black Hawk War. In 1825 he accompanied General Atkinson on an expedition to the Upper Missouri to make treaties with the Indians. The expedition left St. Louis on the *Beaver* March 20, held councils with the Indian tribes, and reached the mouth of the Yellowstone August 17, 1825.

The letter of June 18, written on the "U.S. Transport *Beaver* near the Big Bend of the Mo.," and that of July 6, "60 miles above Big Bend of the Mo.," tell of the journey from Council Bluffs, the councils with the Poncas, Sioux, Ogalallas, and Cheyennes, and the scenery.

[Coe Collection.]

288 KRILL, ABRAM

Diary of an overland journey from Independence, Missouri, to Weaverville, California. May 14 to September 11, 1850.

2 vols. [i.e., 153 pp.] 15 cm. Original binding.

Accompanied by a daguerreotype of Krill & Bamber's grocery and provision store near Hangtown, with group on porch. 11½ x 8 cm.

The route followed was by the Platte and Sweetwater Rivers, Sublette's Cut-off, Hudspeth's Cut-off, Humboldt and Carson Rivers to Pleasant Valley and Weaverville.

The diary is written in pencil in a rather narrative form with observations by the way, from May 14 to August 24, 1850, in a calf-bound notebook with the inscription on the flyleaf: "Abram Krill's book. Residence Washington Township Wood Co., Ohio." The continuation from August 25 to September 11, 1850 occupies 32 pages in a memorandum book which contains also expenditures for April, 1850; accounts of Krill & Bamber, April 29–November 14, 1851; account of gold dug and washed, May 12–July 7, 1851; memoranda and a number of pressed flowers. The memorandum book contains also a note that Krill left Findley, April 19, arriving at Independence May 8, 1850.

[Coe No. 107.]

289 KUSSASS, Snoqualmie Chief

Papers relating to the trial of Kussass and five other Indians for the murder of Leander C. Wallace before the District Court of the United States, County of Lewis, Territory of Oregon, Steilacoom, October 1849.

6 pieces. 12 pp. 22½–31½ cm.

Mr. Wallace was shot by a party of Snoqualmie Indians who were trying to enter Fort Nisqually as he, with Charles Wren and another companion, approached the fort. The documents are the following:

UNITED STATES OF AMERICA VS. KUSSASS AND OTHER INDIANS. Bench warrant to the U.S. Marshal of the Territory of Oregon to produce in court the six Indian prisoners. Written and signed by

William Wallace, Clerk of the Court, October 2, 1849. Endorsed: "In obedience to the above order I have brot the six Indians before the court, Oct. 2, 1849. Joseph L. Meek, U.S. Marshal. O. Ty." 1 p.

—— Indictment for murder, by the Grand Jurors of the District Court of the United States. Signed by A. A. Skinner, District Attorney pro tem. Endorsed: "A true bill, John R. Jackson, Foreman of the Grand Jury." 4 pp.

—— Order book for the District Court of the United States. Report of the proceedings, October 1–3, signed by Wm.

P. Bryant. Endorsed: "Journal, Lewis County Octr. Term, A.D. 1849." 4 pp.

—— The finding of the jury, signed by all 12 jurors. 1 p.

—— The verdict of the jury, written and signed by Thomas M. Chambers, foreman. 1 p.

—— Statements of witnesses, in an unidentified hand. 1 p.

The court found Kussass and Quallawowt guilty and the other four not guilty. These documents formerly belonged to Elwood Evans.

[Miller Collection.]

290 LAIRD, MOSES F., 1835–

"Moses F. Laird's Book. A journal of a few items of my life: different situations: Travels, etc.," from Ohio to Oregon in 1852; life in Oregon to May 1855, and a Chinook jargon vocabulary.

131 pp. 13 cm. With typewritten transcript.

Following a brief sketch of his life in Ohio before leaving Zanesville, March 29, 1852 for Oregon, Laird gives a detailed account of his trip across the Plains as well as his subsequent experiences in the gold mines and in the saddling business. Going by the Muskingum, Mississippi and Missouri Rivers, at St. Joseph he joined a train of 16 wagons and followed the North Fork of the Platte, South Pass and Oregon Trail to Fort Hall, Fort Boise, and The Dalles on the Columbia River, arriving in September 1852. The following three years, until May 23, 1855 when he left to return to Ohio, were spent in various parts of Oregon Territory where his work ranged

from floating logs up the Willamette River to helping run a flourishing saddle business in Winchester.

The part of the diary describing the journey west gives the usual details of the route, mileage, weather, prices, etc. The latter part includes the more interesting incidents of his life in the West. He also lists commodity and stock prices in January 1854, as well as prices obtained for products in the saddle business. On May 3, 1855, he looks forward "in the next three years to enjoy my life more pleasantly" back home in Ohio.

[Coe No. 108.]

291 LAMB, HARVEY, 1829–1856

Letters written from California to members of his family, February 6, 1852 to July 18, 1856; and two letters to his mother, Mrs. D. H. Lamb, written after his death, from W. R. Harrison, Probate Judge, 1856 and 1857.

40 letters. 131 pp. 20½–27 cm.

Harvey Lamb had left his home in Cleveland and arrived in San Francisco,

by the Isthmus of Panama, February 5, 1852. He had evidently been leading a reckless life at home and incurred debts that he could not pay. He went to California hoping to pay these debts and to prove himself worthy to return to his home and family.

LAMB, HARVEY. 35 letters to his mother, Mrs. D. H. Lamb. February 6, 1852–February 19, 1854. 119 pp.

—— Two letters to his sister Mrs. Clara D. Lufkin. July 29, 1853, October 28, 1854. 6 pp.

—— Letter to his brother-in-law Amos Lufkin. January 6, 1856. 3 pp.

HARRISON, W. R., Probate Judge of Tehama County, Calif. Letter to Mrs.

D. H. Lamb [n.d.] announcing death of Harvey Lamb [July 1856]. 1 p.

—— Letter to D. H. and C. D. Lamb. August 2, 1857. 2 pp.

The letters to his mother describe his efforts to make money, conditions in San Francisco and life in the mines. He went to the Sandwich Islands and once to Astoria, Oregon, before going north to the mines. In spite of hard work he met with nothing but failure and longed to return home. He did prove himself worthy of his mother's faith. While in the mines "his character was irreproachable & of the highest moral firmness and courage" (*see* letter of W. R. Harrison).

[Coe No. IV, 439.]

292 LANSDALE, RICHARD HYATT, 1810–1897

Journal of Dr. Richard H. Lansdale, from October 4, 1854 to October 3, 1855; and his "official journal," August 30, 1855 to March 30, 1858.

2 vols. [i.e., 430 pp.] 12–15 cm. Original bindings.

Dr. Lansdale came to Oregon by way of California in 1849 and finally settled on Whidby Island, W.T., in 1852. He was justice of the peace for Lewis County and practiced medicine until appointed Indian agent by Governor Stevens, when his duties took him east of the Cascades. In 1855, with James Doty, he was sent to eastern Washington to arrange for a general council of the Indians, which was held at Walla Walla at the end of May. On the appointment of Nesmith as superintendent of Indian affairs for Oregon and Washington Territories, Lansdale was put

in charge of the Flathead district in eastern Washington.

The first volume contains Lansdale's personal journal to August 20, 1855, which is continued to October 3 in the back of the second volume. The second volume contains also the official journal and issues of goods to the Indians. A note at the beginning reads: "Official Diary, 1855. Hertofore my official acts have been recorded in my personal journal & otherwheres; I think it best to keep a separate official journal."

[Coe No. 109.]

293 LAPÉROUSE, JEAN FRANÇOIS DE GALAUP, 1741–1788

"Lapérouse, ses compagnons, ses rechercheurs. Autographes,—Portraits,—Poësies, &c."

28 pieces. Various sizes. Mounted in a quarto volume. 28 cm.

Lapérouse, a French navigator, sailed from Brest in August 1785 on the frigate *Boussole*, with the *Astrolabe* under M. de Langle, on a scientific exploring expedi-

tion around the world under the French Government. He visited the Hawaiian Islands, the California and Northwest Coast of America, the Northeast Coast of

Asia, the Pacific Islands and New Zealand. The whole expedition was shipwrecked and lost in 1788 off the island of Vanikoro. In 1791 a second expedition was sent out under Rear Admiral Entrecasteaux to search for traces of Lapérouse and his expedition.

This collection, formed about 1850 by A. Guichon de Grandpont, Commissaire de Marine, includes portraits (engravings) and autographs of members of the two expeditions, and papers about them or the ships. The manuscripts themselves have no direct connection with the expeditions, except the following:

Order for articles for the jardinier botaniste. Signed: "*La Boussole*, 25 juin 1785 Le chev. de Clonard." 16½ x 21 cm.

Order for supplies for the Marine Guards on the *Boussole*, 7 juillet 1785, signed by S. Céran and De Clonard. 18 x 9½ cm.

Order for supplies for the pilot of the *Astrolabe*, signed: "12 juillet, 1785, De Monti." Countersigned: "De L'Ainé, pilote." 18 x 13 cm.

Receipt for materials supplied to le chevalier de Lamanon and abbé Mongez, signed by them at Brest, 13 juillet 1785. 18 x 17½ cm.

DUPERRÉ, VICTOR GUY, Vice Admiral. Request to the Directeur d'Artillerie for information on the armaments of the *Boussole* and *Astrolabe* in 1785, signed and dated at Brest, 12 Avril 1827 [12½ x 20 cm.]. Accompanied by a statement: "Estimation des frigates la *Boussole* et l'*Astrolabe*," signed by de G [M. Godebert?]. 13½ x 21 cm.

Among the signatures and autographs are those of Lapérouse, Chevalier de Langle, Hesmivy d'Auribeau, Charles M. F. Boutin, Dumont d'Urville, Antoine de Bruni Entrecasteaux, Morel d'Escures, Charles H. Jacquinot, Jacques J. Labillardière, La Borde Marchainville, La Haie, Jean L'Ainé, Mel de St. Céran, Jérôme de Vaujuas, and Louis Ventenat.

[Coe No. 110.]

294 LASSUS DE LUZIÈRE, CHARLES DEHAULT DE, *d.* 1842

Letter in French to Don Manuel de Salcedo and Marquis de Casa Calvo, Commissioners of the King of Spain for the recession of Louisiana to France. A La Nelle. Bourbon des Illinois le 27 février 1804. Signed with rubric.

2 pp. 32½ cm.

De Lassus, Spanish Lieutenant Governor of Upper Louisiana at St. Louis, writes to the Commissioners at New Orleans that he will carry out their instructions of December 31, 1803, and those of Laussat, the French Commissioner, to turn Upper Louisiana over to the representative of the French Republic, Amos Stoddard, or his agent, who in turn will accept it for the United States (see Nos. 295, 323).

[Coe Collection.]

295 LAUSSAT, PIERRE CLÉMENT DE, 1756–

"Actes publics de la domination française. Nouvelle Orleans 1803–1804." Record of the official acts and proclamations of the French Commissioner during France's brief occupancy following the transfer from Spain. November 30 to December 6, 1803.

15 pp. 34½ cm.

Pierre Clément de Laussat, born at Pau in 1756, was receiver-general at Pau in 1789, and was arrested as a suspect in 1793. He was soon released, became paymaster general of the army of the Pyrénées Orientales, 1793, and member of the Conseil des Cinq-Cents, 1797. In 1802, at his own request, he was appointed préfet coloniale de la Louisiane. He left New Orleans on April 21, 1804, after the cession to the United States, for Martinique, was captured by the British in 1809, exchanged and returned to Paris, January 1810. From 1823 to his retirement in 1825 he was commandant and administrator of French Guiana.

Many, if not all, of these Actes were printed as broadsides and in the *Moniteur de la Louisiane*, which was called the "dépôt" of government acts.

[Coe No. 111.]

296 LAW, WILLIAM, 1809–1892

"Day Book, Nauvoo, Ill." April 27, 1841 to July 9, 1842.

290 pp. 20 x 13½ cm. Original binding.

William Law came to Nauvoo in 1839, served on the municipal council and as captain in the Legion. He was associated in business with his brother, Wilson Law, and owned several mills, a brickyard and a store. He was later one of the owners and publisher of the *Nauvoo Expositor* and was excommunicated from the church in 1844.

The handwriting in the daybook varies. Accounts with practically all the prominent citizens of Nauvoo are included, especially with Joseph Smith. On leaves 140–141 are agreements for labor in return for goods, etc., some unsigned, others signed by Jeremiah Levitt, Patrick Norris, Salmon Warner, Hervey Green.

[Coe No. 133.]

297 LEAVENWORTH, MELINES CONKLIN, 1796–1862

Letter to Mr. Hezekiah Howe. Camp near the mouth of the False Washita, June 5, 1834.

1 p. 25 cm.

Dr. Leavenworth graduated from the Yale Medical School in 1817. He served as assistant surgeon in the army from 1833 to 1840 and was with his uncle, General Henry Leavenworth, at the time of his death at Cross Timbers, near the Falls of the Washita, in July 1834, while on an expedition against the hostile Pawnees and Comanches.

Dr. Leavenworth was particularly interested in botany and while in New Haven was in charge of the botanical garden attached to the Medical College. The letter is to Hezekiah Howe, bookseller of New Haven, thanking him for sending him some botanical works, and telling him of the progress of the expedition in opening a road from Fort Towson, and troubles with the Pawnees.

[Coe Collection.]

298 LEE, JASON, 1803–1845

Letter to the Rev. Gustavus Hines. Walamette, November 18, 1841.

2 pp. 24½ cm.

The letter written by the superintendent of the Oregon Mission defines in detail the duties and responsibilities of Mr. Hines' position in charge of the Manual Labor School.

[Miller Collection.]

299 LEFFINGWELL FAMILY LETTERS

Letters of Mrs. Frances Noyes Leffingwell and Henry L. Leffingwell; and two letters to Christopher S. Leffingwell, 1853–1876.

5 letters. 23 pp. 20–25½ cm.

Mr. and Mrs. William Leffingwell and Henry L. Leffingwell were living in San Francisco in 1853. Henry's wife had died at Fort Laramie the year before, and his two young daughters, Emily and Lucy, had been sent east from San Francisco to his mother and father in Cleveland. Christopher Starr Leffingwell remained in the East, attended Trinity College, 1854, and the Berkeley Divinity School. In 1859 he was rector in Fairfield, Conn., and in 1876 at Gardiner, Me. "Gregory" was mate on a clipper and Mrs. Hatch a former parishioner who had moved to Santa Barbara, Calif.

LEFFINGWELL, FRANCES NOYES HOWLAND (MRS. WILLIAM). Letter to her brother-in-law, Christopher Starr Leffingwell. June 14, 1853. 4 pp.

LEFFINGWELL, HENRY LUCIUS. Two letters to his father, Lucius W. Leffingwell. November 14, 1853, October 11, 1854. 8 pp.

"GREGORY." Letter to "Leff" [the Rev. C. S. Leffingwell]. July 20, 1859. 4 pp.

HATCH, MRS. IDA. Letter to the Rev. C. S. Leffingwell. February 29, 1876. 7 pp.

Frances Leffingwell's and Henry L. Leffingwell's letters discuss family affairs and conditions in San Francisco; Gregory's letter describes San Francisco in 1859; and Mrs. Hatch's gives a detailed description of Santa Barbara, especially its churches.

Gift of the Misses Leffingwell and Mrs. Kenneth McKenzie.

300 LEIBEE, DANIEL

Letter to his wife, Sarah Enyart Leibee, of Middletown, Ohio. California, Sonora, November 24, 1850.

4 pp. 32 cm.

The letter describes his cabin at the mines, his three partners from Cincinnati, and his chances of success.

—— Letter to his son-in-law, Horace P. Clough. San Francisco, April 8, 1863. 1 p. 26½ cm.

The writer says he did not think his family would care to hear from a father or husband who was a traitor to his country, as they termed it. He has a "mission" and is writing a series of pamphlets that throw an entirely new light on the Bible (see No. 93).

Gift of Stuart W. Jackson.

301 LEWIS, JOHN F.

Journal of an overland journey written in the form of a letter to his sister Sarah, begun at St. Joseph, May 12, 1849, and ending at Deer Creek, California, December 31, 1849. Followed by a "Continuation of journal of John F. Lewis, January 1, 1852" to October 31, 1854.

91 pp. 33½ cm. With typewritten transcript of the journal for 1849.

The journal covers the journey from Huntsville, Randolph County, Mo., to St. Joseph, overland to the Platte and Sweetwater Rivers, Fort Bridger, Salt Lake City, Mormon Route to Goose Creek and the Humboldt, and the Truckee River Route to Donner Pass, Yuba River and Deer Creek; and his life in the mines until December 31, 1849.

The "Continuation" describes his life on his farm near Glasgow, Howard County, Mo., after his return from California, where he grew hemp and the usual farm products.

[Coe No. 112.]

—— Another copy (carbon) of the transcript.

Gift of Michael J. Walsh.

302 LEWIS, THOMAS COTTON, 1805–1891

"Memorandum or Notes of Thos. C. Lewis & Son," April 12, 1852 to March 24, 1853, on an overland journey from Portsmouth, Ohio, to California; Mr. Lewis' return by Panama in 1853; and seven letters from Mr. Lewis to his wife, Mrs. Nancy A. Lewis, written on the road and from California. April 27 to September 29, 1852.

94 pp. 24½–27 cm. With typewritten transcript.

Thomas C. Lewis was born in Wales in 1805, came to Portsmouth in 1832 and worked in the Gaylord mill. In 1852 he and his eldest son, Charles, crossed the Plains to the mines. He died in Portsmouth in his 87th year.

The transcript contains a foreword by the Argonaut's granddaughter, and as an appendix [ix pp.] a copy of "Summary of expenses and random jottings," and a list of the passengers on the schooner *Mary Howard* lost December 6, 1852, on the Quinto Sena Banks, copied from a pocket notebook retained by the Lewis family.

The journal and letters describe in detail the journey by boat from Portsmouth to Cincinnati, St. Louis, and St. Joseph; the start overland, April 29, by the Platte, Sublette's Cut-off, Soda Springs, Hudspeth's Cut-off, Humboldt River to Carson River, Scott's Cut-off to the mines; experiences at the mines and in California; his determination to return home leaving his son at the mines; his voyage from San Francisco to Nicaragua on the *New Orleans*, and from Graytown on the *Mary Howard*, the wreck, December 6, and his final arrival at New Orleans and Portsmouth, March 24, 1853.

[Coe No. 110 B.]

303 LEWIS AND CLARK EXPEDITION, 1804–1806

Fifty-four manuscript maps of the route of the Lewis and Clark Expedition to the Pacific Coast and back, 1804–1806; and a detailed map by Clark of the continent from the Mississippi Valley to the Pacific and from the junction of the Missouri and Mississippi Rivers and the Gila River to the Great Lakes and Vancouver Island.

55 maps. 15½ x 9½–129 x 73½ cm.

Some of the maps were carried on the expedition by Lewis and Clark, but the majority were drawn by William Clark en route. They are in four groups:

I. Three maps copied from contemporary Spanish and French maps [Thwaites, Nos. 2–4]:

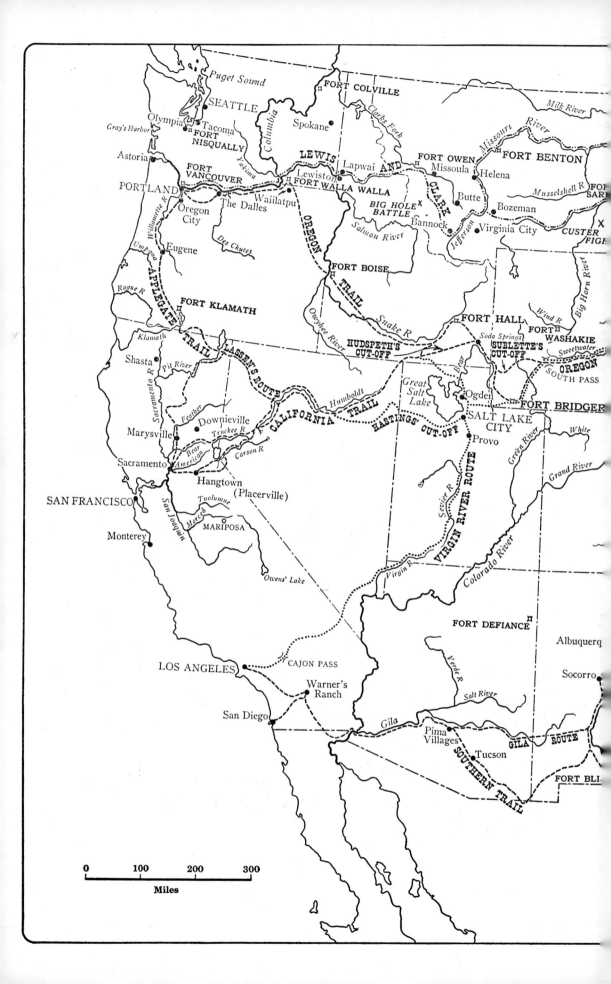

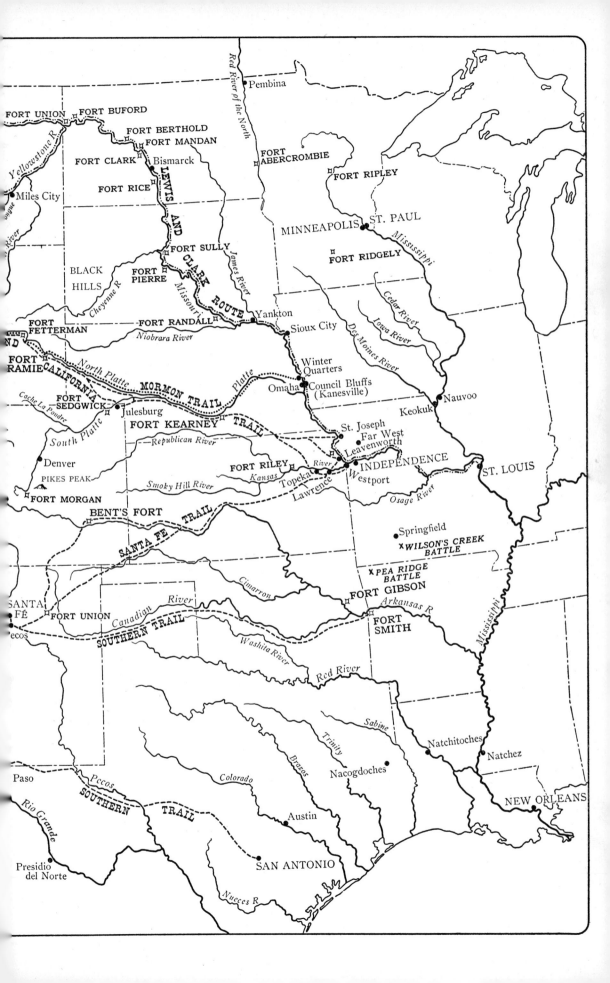

"A topogr[aphical] sketch of the Missouri and Upper Mississippi," showing the Indian nations, "copied from the original Spanish MS. map." 52½ x 42 cm.

The Upper Mississippi and the Missouri as far as the Mandans. 42 x 36 cm.

The neighborhood of Camp River Dubois. 21 x 14 cm.

On the verso of this map, in Clark's hand, there is "A Memorandum of Articles in readiness for the Voyage." 21 x 31 cm.

II. Seven maps of the Missouri River from Fort Charles to the Mandans, marked Nos. 1–6, No. 4 is in two parts [Thwaites, Nos. 5–11]. These cover the route taken by Lewis and Clark from August 13 to October 21, 1804, when they camped for the winter at Fort Mandan. 15½ x 9½–40½ x 25½ cm.

Mr. Aubrey Diller, author of "Maps of the Missouri River before Lewis and Clark" in *Studies and Essays . . . in Honor of George Sarton* (New York [1946?]), believes that this group is the map by John Evans sent to Lewis and Clark by President Jefferson, January 13, 1804, or a copy of it. In the Office of Indian Affairs in Washington another map was found among some William Clark papers that covers the route from St. Charles, Mo., to the Mandans, May 21–October 21, 1804. It has been attributed to John Evans, 1795 or 1796, by Miss Annie H. Abel (*Geographical Review*, 1916, I, 329–345). It may be the map sent to Lewis, and the six smaller maps copies of that portion beyond Fort Charles for use on the way.

III. Two maps based on information secured from the Indians during the winter at Fort Mandan: The trail from the Mandans to the Yellowstone; and from the Mandans to the Rockies [Thwaites Nos. 12–13]. 30 x 21–38½ x 24 cm.

IV. 42 maps of the route followed by the expedition from Fort Mandan through the Rockies, down the Columbia to the Pacific, and on the return journey. They were all, probably with one exception, drawn by William Clark, the recognized draftsman of the party. The exception is Lewis' sketch map of Vancouver Island and Nootka Sound [Thwaites No. 37]. 47½ x 38 cm.

William Clark indicated each day's march and camping place on the maps from April 7, when they left Fort Mandan, to November 26, 1805 and the camps on the return journey from April to August 1806 [Thwaites Nos. 14–53]. 18½ x 23–46 x 36 cm.

The majority of the maps are drawn on sheets of paper, 30 x 20½ cm., or double sheets, 30 x 41 cm., which are pasted together to follow the route of the journey. The smaller maps are sometimes on both sides of the sheets, and many are accompanied by notes about the country and the Indians.

CLARK, WILLIAM. "A map of part of the Continent of North America . . . Compiled from the information of the best informed travellers through that quarter of the Globe in which the Missouri Jefferson's Lewis's & the upper part of Clark's river and the lower part of the Columbia river is partially Corrected by celestial observations from the Junction of the Missouri and Mississippi to the entrance of the Columbia into the Pacific Ocean in Longitude 47° 57′ West of Washington City and 124° 57′ W. of Greenwich and in Latitude 46° 19′ 11″ North Shewing Lewis & Clark's rout over the Rocky Mountains in 1805 on their rout to the Pacific from the United States. By William Clark Laid down by a Scale of 50 Miles to the inch." [1806–1811.] 129 x 73½ cm.

Clark drew this map, based on his field maps and notes, after the return of the expedition in 1806, with additions after 1811, as he indicates the route taken by Wilson P. Hunt, commander of the Astoria overland expedition that started from Missouri in April 1811, reaching Astoria in January 1812.

In 1903, when Reuben Gold Thwaites was preparing his edition of the Lewis and Clark journals, he approached General William Clark's heirs, his granddaughter, Mrs. Julia Clark Voorhis, and her daughter, Miss Eleanor Glasgow Voorhis, of New York. In their collection of General Clark's papers were the maps of the expedition. Mr. Thwaites published all of these maps, except Clark's large map of the entire journey, in Vol. VIII of his edition of *Original Journals of the Lewis and Clark Expedition*, 1804–1806, New York, 1904. Clark's "Memorandum of Articles" is printed in Vol. I, 15–16. A collotype reproduction of William Clark's large manuscript map was published in four sections by the Yale University Library in 1950.

[Coe Collection.]

304 LEWIS AND CLARK EXPEDITION

Draft of a receipt for compensation, headed: "We the subscribers do acknowledge to have received of [space] the several sums set opposit to our names, the same being due us from the War department pursuant to an Act of Congress bearing date March the 3rd. 1807, entitled 'an Act makeing compensation to Messrs. Lewis & Clark and their companions.'—Signed Duplicates."

1 p. 50 x 40 cm.

The receipt lists the names of 31 members of the expedition, their rank, dates and length of service, rate of pay, amount of pay received, and has blank columns for the signatures and for a witness.

This manuscript was formerly in the possession of Mrs. Julia Clark Voorhis and Miss Eleanor Glasgow Voorhis. It is printed as Appendix LXX in Thwaites' edition of the Lewis and Clark *Journals*, VII, 360–361.

[Coe Collection.]

305 LIVINGSTON, HENRY FARRAND, 1843–1913

Diaries kept by Dr. Henry F. Livingston from 1866 to 1879 [except 1870 and 1872].

12 vols. 12½–19 cm.

Dr. Livingston went to Dakota in 1865 from Davenport, Iowa, and located in Yankton. In 1867 he was appointed surgeon at the Crow Creek Agency, then in charge of Major Joseph R. Hanson, and continued until 1870, when he was appointed Indian agent at Crow Creek. This was regarded as one of the largest and most important agencies on the Missouri River and Dr. Livingston had been highly commended for his administration when in March 1878 the agency was seized, without warning, by a squad of U.S. soldiers under Lieutenant Dougherty. All of his official, private, and personal papers were seized as well as the papers and property of the trader, E. E. Hudson, and were put in the custody of General J. H. Hammond, Superintendent of Indian Affairs for Dakota. Charges were brought against Dr. Livingston, but in each case the verdict was not guilty or the case was dismissed.

These journals record briefly the life in Dakota Territory from 1866 to 1879; the duties of an Indian agent, the business transactions and relations with the trader on the reservation [E. E. Hudson], the arrival and departures of steamers on the Missouri, the movements of officers and troops at the forts and in the Black Hills; receipt of news of Custer's defeat and other events; visits of Bishop Hare and Mr. Burt; family and personal affairs; the seizure of the Crow Creek Reservation by Lieutenant Dougherty, the conspiracy of General Hammond, and the subsequent trial; accounts and prescriptions; and the building of his home in Yankton, 1879.

[Coe No. 113.]

306 LIVINGSTON, ROBERT R., 1746–1813

Letter to Jy. [i.e., William] MacClure, I. C. Barnet, and J. Mercer. Paris, December 23, 1803.

1 p. 25 cm.

With a portrait of Livingston engraved by H. B. Hall, printed by W. Pate. 14 x 20½ cm.

Robert R. Livingston was minister plenipotentiary in Paris during the negotiations for the purchase of Louisiana.

The letter informs the three gentlemen of the ratification of the Treaty of Paris and the President's approbation of their nomination to act as commissioners under the convention providing for the payment of debts due by France to the citizens of the United States.

[Coe Collection.]

307 LONG, CHARLES L'HOMMEDIEU

Diary of an overland journey from Cincinnati, Ohio, to California, March 10 to August 14, 1849, with an entry, September 1, 1850, of his sailing from San Francisco for Panama on the steamer *Republic*.

165 pp. Oblong. 9½ x 16 cm.

Long was evidently a man of some education. He describes in detail the organization of the company while in camp at Independence, the characteristics of the country and events on the journey. He was ill after his arrival in California and returned to the East by the Isthmus in 1850.

The diary records the journey from the start, March 10, by boat down the Ohio and overland from Independence, April 23, by the Platte to Fort Laramie, the Sweetwater, Sublette's Cut-off, Fort Hall, Humboldt and Truckee Rivers, until it breaks off August 14 at Johnson's Ranch. The "Table of distances" at the end of the volume is dated November 12, 1849. Preceding the table are a few accounts and a three-page draft or copy of part of a letter to a sister or brother, written after Long's arrival in California, about the trip and his illness.

[Coe No. 114.]

308 LOUISIANA TERRITORY

By the Superintendent of Indian Affairs for the Territory of Louisiana [General James Wilkinson]. Official notice that no person, the citizen or subject of a foreign power, will be permitted to enter the Missouri for the purpose of Indian trade. Dated at the end: "Done at St. Louis August 26, 1805." In French and English, unsigned.

Copy in an unidentified hand. 2 pp. 33½ cm.

Quoted in part in L. A. Tohill, *Robert Dickson, British Fur Trader*, [Ann Arbor] 1926, with date August 25, p. 217.

[Coe No. 128.]

309 LOVE, ALEXANDER, 1810?–

Diary of an overland journey from Leesburg, Pennsylvania, to the California mines, March 20 to August 23, 1849; experiences in California, 1849–1852; and the journey home by Panama, January 15 to March 5, 1852.

235 pp. including 2 maps. 12½–16½ cm. With typewritten transcript.

The diary is made up of four notebooks and various sizes of letter paper sewed together in a homemade calf binding.

The party left Leesburg March 20, 1849, by boat for St. Louis and Independence, and started overland April 27, following the trail along the Platte and Sweetwater Rivers, Sublette's Cut-off to Fort Hall, the California Trail to the Humboldt River and the Truckee River to the Yuba and Bear River Valleys, August 23–28. Love describes the journey west, his prospecting in the Sacramento Valley, troubles with the Indians especially on the Pitt River, and his life at Major P. B. Redding's [Reading's] ranch, April 2, 1851–January, 1852. He had suffered a great deal from chills and fever from October 1849 and at times the diary is a mere record of the weather and his health. In January 1852 he decided to return to the East, left Reading's January 15 for San Francisco, and sailed for Panama February 1, arriving at New York February 18, and finally at Leesburg March 5, 1852.

[Coe No. 116.]

310 LOVEJOY, ASA LAWRENCE, 1808–1882

Letter to the Hon. E. Evans. Portland, November 11, 1867.

8 pp. 20 cm.

Lovejoy came to Oregon in 1842, wintered at Waiilatpu, returned to Bent's Fort with Dr. Whitman in 1843, and came again to Oregon in 1843. He held many public offices in Oregon and died in Portland in 1882.

The letter gives an account of the emigration of 1842 with Dr. Elijah White, the stay at Fort Laramie, the departure of Dr. White at Green River, the arrival at Fort Hall and Waiilatpu.

[Miller Collection.]

311 LUEG, HENRY, 1830–1906

"Von St. Paul, Minn. nach Portland, Oregon." Journal, in German, of an overland journey from Minnesota to Oregon, June 25 to December 6, 1867, and entries on January 12 and February 3, 1868, after his arrival in Portland.

211 pp. 17 cm. Original binding. With typewritten translation.

Henry Lueg came to America from Prussia in 1861, served in the New York Volunteers, 1861–1863, worked in several eastern cities, and in 1867 in St. Paul determined to join a German emigrant train to Oregon. He was a blacksmith in Portland for many years.

Lueg was a well-read man, and the journal is written in a clear, even script. It contains a table of distances from Spokane River to Walla Walla and, at the end, a roster of the emigrant party.

The journal records the events of each day of the journey and describes the settlements through which they passed, the camp sites, distance traveled each day and details of the route. Lueg left St. Paul by train June 19 to join a party led by P. B. Davy which started overland from St. Cloud June 25. At Fort Abercrombie they joined a government train and traveled by Fort Stevenson, Fort Buford, Captain Fisk's route to Fort Benton, and the Mullan Road to Helena and Missoula, the Coeur d'Alene River and Spokane Bridge, where they took the Kentucky Road to the Snake River and Walla Walla. They left Wallula December 3 on the steamboat *Idaho* for the Cascades and there boarded the *Wilson G. Hunt* for Portland, December 6.

Henry Lueg bequeathed his journal, tools and books to Peter Dueber, one of his messmates on the journey, and his descendants.

[Coe Collection.]

312 LYNE, JAMES, *d.* 1850

Letters written by James Lyne of Henderson, Kentucky, to members of his family while en route to California and after his arrival in San Francisco, April 22, 1849 to January 30, 1850; and letters written by James B. Hine and Samuel F. Grubb after Lyne's death, April 17 and July 25, 1850.

12 letters. 48 pp. 25–31 cm. With typewritten transcript.

The letters give "a general history of the tour" from the departure from St. Louis, April 13, to the arrival at Fort Bridger, July 22, 1849, and describe the difficulties of the route, sickness, encounters with the Indians, the attachment to Colonel Wilson's train, the final dissolution of the company at Fort Laramie, and conditions in San Francisco. The letter from Hine describes James Lyne's death by drowning in the Sacramento River, and that from Grubb tells of his association with Lyne in his last months.

LYNE, JAMES. Eight letters to his brother, Henry Lyne. April 22, 1849–January 30, 1850. 36 pp.

—— Letter to his sister-in-law, Mrs. Henry Lyne. May 4, 1849. 4 pp.

—— Letter to his aunt, Mrs. Sarah P. Bibb. May 9, 1849. 4 pp.

HINE, JAMES B. Letter to Henry Lyne. April 17, 1850. 1 p.

GRUBB, SAMUEL F. Letter to Henry Lyne. July 25, 1850. 3 pp.

Laid in the volume are three leaves from the Louisville *Courier-Journal Magazine*, Sunday, January 25, 1948, containing two articles: "A Century of Gold" and "Kentucky Gold-Rusher." The latter is about the Henderson Company and quotes from a journal of the trip kept by T. A. Eastin which is now in the Library of the Filson Club of Louisville. This journal covers the trip from Independence, Mo., to a point west of Salt Lake City.

[Coe No. 117.]

313 LYNE, LAURA RICHARD

"Extracts from E. N. [i.e., T. A.] Eastin's diary. Letters written by James Lyne." Signed by Laura Richard Lyne.

8 pp. 28 cm.

Brief notes on the Henderson Company which started from Kentucky for the gold fields of California in 1849. The names of the members of the company and the extracts, May 6–June 6, were taken from Eastin's diary.

[Coe No. 117a.]

314 LYON, CALEB, 1821–1875

A four-line quotation, autographed by Caleb Lyon of Lyondale, Governor of Idaho, Boise City, December 25, 1865, for Lewis J. Cist.

1 p. 20½ cm.

The autograph is enclosed with a letter from William P. McCall, secretary of Indian affairs for Idaho Territory, to Lewis J. Cist, a collector of autographs, Boise City, December 23, 1865, written on a blank page of a leaflet containing the printed "Thanksgiving Proclamation" of Governor Lyon, dated November 11, 1865.

Caleb Lyon in 1847 was appointed U.S. consul at Shanghai; in 1849 he was in California and served as assistant secretary of the Constitutional Convention; after his return to his home in New York he was elected to the State Assembly and later to Congress. In 1864 he was appointed the second territorial governor of Idaho and served until April 1866.

The quotation autographed by Lyon is from "Posies for a Parlour," by Thomas Tusser, the 16th-century English agricultural writer and poet.

[Coe Collection.]

315 McCANN, THOMAS R.

"Lah-co-tah Lingua. The language Sioux Indn." Vocabulary, "Pawnee Words," and numbers. With a pencil map of the route from Fort Riley to the Platte; and itineraries of routes from Laramie to Taos and Fort Kearney to Fort Laramie.

52 pp. 19 cm.

A man by the name of McCann was employed by Russell, Majors and Waddell, freighters of Leavenworth, in 1857, who may have been Thomas R., the owner of this manuscript.

The vocabularies are neatly printed by hand with some additions in pencil. The Pawnee vocabulary is dated at the beginning, Fort Kearney, N.T., July 4, 1856; the full-page map is dated Fort Kearney, N.T., July 4, 1856, and the itinerary from Fort Kearney to Fort Laramie is dated Fort Kearney, June 24, 1856. The handwriting of the vocabularies is probably the same as that of the dates, map, and itinerary from Fort Kearney to Fort Laramie and differs from that of the route from Laramie to Taos.

The book belonged to Thos. R. McCann, whose name appears on the inside of the back cover, with the date: "Fort Kearney, N. Territory, July 7, 1856." It had probably belonged previously to R. T. Ackley, since on the inside front cover there is a record of some transactions signed in 1855 by M. S. Winter, Lacompton, Kansas, with the note: "Memorandums made by my order. R. T. Ackley."

[Coe No. 118.]

316 McCONAHA, GEORGE N., d. 1854

Letter to the Hon. J. W. Wiley. Steilacoom City, February 16, 1853.

4 pp. 25 cm.

McConaha, an able lawyer, settled in Seattle and was a delegate at the Monticello Convention in October 1852, when he was elected president. He was also president of the council of the first legislature. He was drowned in May, 1854, on his way to Seattle after the session.

The letter is confidential, concerns the election of delegates to the Democratic Convention to be held at Salem in April 1853, and discusses especially I. N. Ebey and D. R. Bigelow.

[Coe Collection.]

317 McFADDEN, OBADIAH B., 1817–1875

Letter to Messrs. Littlejohn, Harper, and Cornell, Election Board at Tum Water. July 11, 1859.

1 p. 25 cm.

Copy in Elwood Evans' hand, with an added note certifying that it is a true copy, signed by Ira Ward, Jr., clerk, and Thomas J. Harper, judge.

McFadden was appointed one of the associate justices when Washington Territory was established. He filled many public offices, and in 1872 was elected delegate to Congress.

The letter instructs the Election Board that it may accept votes from residents of 20 days provided they have been residents of the Territory for six months.

[Miller Collection.]

318 McKEEBY, LEMUEL CLARKE, 1825–1915

"Memoirs of L. C. McKeeby." 1909.

196 pp. 28½ cm.

Typewritten manuscript, written when the author was over 80 years of age for his "own immediate family."

The memoirs include a brief history of the family and the author's youth, his removal to Detroit, his service with the Michigan Volunteers during the Mexican War, 1847–1848, his settlement in Milwaukee with his family, and decision in 1850 to go with his brother-in-law, George Wright, to California; followed by a transcription of his diary of the journey, May 13–August 3, 1850; an account of his life in the mines and a summary of his later career in Carson City, Nev., and San Buenaventura, Calif., where he was active in political and civic affairs, in business and in the practice of law.

The journal of the overland trip describes in detail the country, daily occurrences, and the route from Council Bluffs by the Platte and Sweetwater Rivers, Fort Bridger and Salt Lake City, across the desert to Goose Creek, the Humboldt and Carson Rivers to Hangtown.

The manuscript belonged formerly to the late Judge Grant Jackson of Los Angeles who died April 2, 1925; it was sold by the executors of his estate. The account of the overland journey has been edited by Mr. Henry R. Wagner and published with title: "The Memoirs of Lemuel Clarke McKeeby," *California Historical Society Quarterly*, 1924, III, 45–72, 126–170.

[Coe No. 119.]

319 McLOUGHLIN, JOHN, 1784–1857

Letter to A. C. Anderson. Vancouver, June 15, 1841. Signature only.

2 pp. 31 cm.

Dr. John McLoughlin, born in the Province of Quebec, was educated in the medical profession in Scotland, and returned to Canada to become a partner in the North West Fur Company. After the union of the North West Fur Company and the Hudson's Bay Company he remained in the service and in 1824 was chief factor of the Columbia District with headquarters at Vancouver, Wash. He retired from the company in 1846 and settled in Oregon City.

The letter directs Anderson, in charge of the Hudson's Bay post at Nisqually, to extend assistance to the U.S. Exploring Expedition and to Dr. Richmond of the Nisqually Mission.

[Miller Collection.]

320 McLOUGHLIN, JOHN, 1784–1857

Letter to Mr. Peter Ogden. Oregon, February 20, 1850.

1 p. 22 cm.

With a letter from William Seton Ogden, sending McLoughlin's letter to Elwood Evans. Portland, October 27, 1865. 1 p.

McLoughlin asks Ogden if he knows of anyone to build a sawmill at Port Discovery.

[Miller Collection.]

321 McLOUGHLIN, JOHN, 1784–1857

Deed for land in Oregon City sold to James Winston, signed October 1, 1850, by John McLoughlin and A. A. Rinearson. Witnessed by J. R. Ralston and A. A. Rinearson.

Printed broadside. 23½ cm.

Congress invalidated McLoughlin's claim to property at Oregon City in 1850 under the Donation Land Law.

The deed is endorsed with the following assignments:

To Noyes Smith, Treasurer, Oregon City. October 24, 1850, signed by James Winston, witness, Wm. K. Kilborn.

To James Fruit, Oregon City, November 26, 1850, signed by N. Smith.

To Egbert Olcott, September 27, 1856,

signed by James H. Fruit, witnesses, A. E. Wait, W. C. Johnson.

To Aaron E. Wait, October 4, 1856, signed by E. Olcott, witnesses, Wm. A. Cason, Jos. N. Prescott.

Noyes Smith settled in Oregon about 1844 and had become a prosperous citizen when he was recognized by an army officer as an Albany bank official who had, years before, embezzled funds and disappeared. His real name was said to be Egbert Olcott.

[Coe No. III, 1770.]

322 McMILLEN, JAMES H., 1823–

Account of the organization of the first military company in Oregon Territory, 1886.

24 pp. 25 cm.

James H. McMillen, a pioneer of 1845, was employed in Abernethy's mills in Oregon City when news was received of the massacre of the Whitmans. The Legislature immediately passed a resolution requiring the governor to raise a company

of riflemen to be sent to The Dalles. The company was organized with Cornelius Gilman, Colonel, H. A. G. Lee, Captain, and J. H. McMillen, 1st Duty Sergeant. They left for The Dalles December 9, 1847.

The account of the organization of the company, the journey to The Dalles and stay there, and McMillen's return to the mills at Oregon City was written in response to a resolution adopted at a meeting held on February 20, 1886, of the Indian War Veterans of the North Pacific Coast, Camp No. 2, Multnomah Co., Ore.

The account was published in the Portland *Oregonian*, at least in part, April 1, 1886, and an extract is quoted by Elwood Evans in his *History of the Pacific Northwest* [1889], I, 286.

[Miller Collection.]

323 MADISON, JAMES, 1750/51–1836

Letter to Rufus King, Esqr. Department of State, January 29, 1803, signed in Madison's hand: "I have the honor to be . . . James Madison."

4 pp. 25 cm. With typewritten transcript.

James Madison's letter of instructions to Rufus King, U.S. Minister to Great Britain, on American rights to the Mississippi, Spain's cession of Louisiana to France, Jefferson's consequent appointment of a Commission Extraordinary to negotiate with France thereon, and his own negotiations with the British Government, assuring Great Britain free and common navigation of the Mississippi but warning her of America's determination to maintain her rights against any who may not respect them.

The letter is printed in U.S. Department of State, *State Papers and Correspondence Bearing upon the Purchase of the Territory of Louisiana*, Washington, 1903, pp. 92–93; and in *The Writings of James Madison*, ed. by Gaillard Hunt, New York, 1900–1910, VII, 7–9.

[Coe No. 120.]

324 MALEY, JOHN

Journal of John Maley's wanderings in the Red River country of the Southwest, 1811–1813.

2 vols. [i.e., 182 pp.] 20½ x 16½ cm.

John Maley, an adventurer with some knowledge of minerals and mines, made three expeditions from Natchitoches up the Red River, first in December 1811, second March 5–November 10, 1812, and third March 3–October 10, 1813, to trade with the Indians, to look for mineral deposits, and if possible to secure a specimen of the native iron about which he had heard in Natchitoches.

The author calls the manuscript, which is unsigned and lacks the first page, his "journal," but it is a narrative account of his adventures written after 1814. He mentions on page 18 the British attack on New Orleans, December 23, 1814. He describes in detail New Orleans, life in Natchitoches, the physical aspects of the country, its mineral resources, the customs of the Kashotoos, Hietans, Pawnees and other tribes he encountered, their relations with the Spaniards of Texas, and the discovery and transportation of the native iron from Texas to New Orleans.

This manuscript was brought to the attention of Professor Benjamin Silliman of Yale College in 1821 by Judge William Johnson, of Charleston, S.C.; in 1824 he published extracts from it and from Captain Anthony Glass' journal (q.v.) in "Notice of the Malleable Iron of Louisiana," *American Journal of Science*, 1824, VIII, 218–225.

[Silliman Family Collection, Historical Manuscripts.]

325 MANBY, THOMAS, 1769–1834

Journal of the voyage of H.M.S. *Discovery* and *Chatham*, under the command of Captain George Vancouver, to the Northwest Coast of America, February 10, 1791 to June 30, 1793.

163 pp. 33 cm.

The greater part of the journal is a copy in a fine, clear hand, but the last few pages appear to be in the handwriting of the author.

Rear Admiral Thos. Manby entered the Royal Navy in 1783, and accompanied Captain Vancouver on his voyage of discovery to the North Pacific Ocean and around the world, 1790–1795, first as a mate on the *Discovery* and later as master of the *Chatham*.

The journal, which was not written every day, is in two parts. The first part [67 pp.] covers the voyage from Deptford around the Cape of Good Hope to Australia, New Zealand, the Sandwich Islands, and the coast of America, February 10, 1791–April 19, 1792. The second part [96 pp.] includes the explorations along the coast in search of a Northwest Passage, the Straits of Juan de Fuca, Nootka Sound, the Columbia River, San Francisco and Monterey, the winter in the Sandwich Islands and the return to the American coast and Nootka Sound. The last entry is dated June 30, 1793, when the *Discovery* was exploring the coast in the neighborhood of Latitude 53° N.

The journal describes events of the voyage, lands visited, negotiations with the Spaniards, ships spoken, and customs of the Indians.

A copy of a letter from Manby to a friend, John Lees, of Dublin, headed "A trip to the Eastward," and dated December 10, 1790, occupies the first page of the journal. In it he tells his friend that he has accepted an offer from Captain Vancouver to accompany him on the expedition.

Mounted in the journal are the following letters:

MANBY, THOMAS. Letter to his brother, George William Manby. Yarmouth, December 1, 1827. 2 pp. 25 cm.

—— Letter in the third person, requesting Mr. Robinson to send to Major General Barnard a copy of Captain Vancouver's *Voyage*, Bedford Street, Friday August 24 [1821]. 1 p. 17 cm.

The journal was formerly in the library of Sir Thomas Phillipps. Phillipps MS. 14823.

[Coe Collection.]

326 MANNING, GEORGE A.

Letters to George A. Manning, a letter about Manning, and others of Idaho interest, 1867–1883.

13 letters. 27 pp. 20½–25 cm.

George A. Manning went to Idaho from Milford, Me., after 1867. In 1879 he represented Nez Percé County in the Legislature.

BOWNESS, GEORGE. Letter to his cousin. October 22, 1883. 3 pp.

CARLTON, CHARLES. Two letters to his brother Steven [Fenderson]. [n.d.], February 19, 1869. 6 pp.

CARLTON, JACK. Letter to brother George [Manning]. August 26, 1877. 4 pp.

GRANGER, ELLA C. Letter to Colonel Manning. July 25, 1879. 2 pp.

KESTER, JOHN. Two letters to G. A. Manning. January 21, May 7, 1877. 4 pp.

LOGAN, JOHN ALEXANDER. Letter to G. A. Manning. April 13, 1886. 1 p.

MONTEITH, JOHN B., Indian Agent. Letter to G. A. Manning. November 25, 1872. 1 p.

MORRIS, BENJAMIN F. Letter to G. A. Manning. August 29 [n.y.]. 1 p.

SEWALL, GEORGE P. Letter to His Excellency, Joshua L. Chamberlain, Governor of Maine. March 18, 1867, recommending Captain Manning. 1 p.

SLATER, SETH S., and MONROE, RICHARD J. Letter to G. A. Manning. February 6, 1873. 1 p.

STEPHENS, W. J. Letter to Charles Carlton. May 9, 1878, with a copy of General Howard's order to Carlton of August 8, 1872, endorsed by Carlton appointing Drouillard his agent. 4 pp.

Gift of Robert G. Bailey, author of *Hell's Canyon* and *River of No Return*.

327 "MANTI HERALD, AND SANPETE ADVERTISER," F. C. Robinson, Editor and Publisher. Manti, May 4, 1867. No. 13, Vol. I.

1 p. 19½ x 30½ cm.

A handwritten newspaper, each issue of one page divided into three columns, issued only to subscribers. Each edition, written entirely by the editor, contained local news, brief items received by telegraph, and some business cards and advertisements. Fifteen numbers of Vol. I were issued, January 31–May 18, 1867. A complete file is preserved in the Salt Lake City Public Library.

This copy has been folded and is inscribed on the back: "To M. A. Musser. A token of esteem and not intended as anything great from your sincere friend & Bro. F. C. Robinson."

A facsimile of this copy is printed, with a history of the early paper, in J. C. Alter, *Early Utah Journalism*, Salt Lake City, 1938, pp. 103, 108, 110.

[Coe No. I, 1240.]

328 MARKER, J. P.

"Map of the 'Great Blue-Gravel Lead' of Northern California." Scale, 2 inches = 1 mile. J. P. Marker, Ashland, Oregon [n.d.].

Manuscript map. 62 x 52 cm.

The map shows the Klamath River and Cottonwood Creek mining district in Siskiyou County, Calif., Hornbrook and Klamath City, and indicates the routes of the Yreka and Ashland stage road and the California and Oregon Railroad. The railroad was incorporated in 1865 but had not reached the Oregon state line before 1886–1887, when it was completed to connect with the Oregon line at Ashland.

[Coe Collection.]

329 MARSHALL, WILLIAM ISAAC, 1840–1906

"Acquisition of Oregon and the long-suppressed evidence about Marcus Whitman."

2 vols. in 4. [i.e., 1,420 pp.] 27 cm.

William Isaac Marshall was born in 1840 in Fitchburg, Mass. He attended high school for only one year but at 18 was teaching school. He taught in a number of towns in the United States and Canada, and in Montana while working his gold mines there. He later returned to the East and lectured on the West. For 29 years he made a study of the acquisition of Oregon Territory.

Carbon copy of the typewritten manuscript with notes and corrections in the author's hand, copyrighted in 1905, the year before the author's death. It was pub-lished about 1911, through contributions from citizens of Oregon and Washington, by Lowman & Hanford Co., Seattle, in two volumes.

The manuscript passed into the posses-sion of Clarence B. Bagley after the au-thor's death, and was given by Mr. Bag-ley to Winlock W. Miller, Jr.

[Miller Collection.]

330 MARSHALL, WILLIAM ISAAC, 1840–1906

"Fremont and Whitman and the discovery of the South Pass. A criticism of Von Holst and Winsor and a demolition of the Whitman saved Oregon fic-tion." Chicago, copyright, 1900.

239 pp. 28 cm.

Typewritten manuscript with insertions and corrections.

The author quotes extensively from the letters of Marcus Whitman and his as-sociates to the American Board and other original and printed material on the Ore-gon Missions and Whitman's journey east. It is evidently one of the manuscripts which were copied by his daughter for dis-tribution among historians for criticism when he was financially unable to publish the results of his research.

Much of the material in "Fremont" is incorporated in his *Acquisition of Oregon*, copyrighted in 1905 but not published until after his death [1911?]—especially in Vol. I, chap. 5.

[Coe No. 121.]

331 MARSHALL, WILLIAM ISAAC, 1840–1906

Original typewritten manuscripts of William I. Marshall regarding the Whitman controversy.

5 portfolios. [i.e., 462 pp.] 28½ cm. With typewritten transcripts.

The manuscripts include "Why his search (?) for the truth of history was a failure, Being a review of Rev. Myron Eells' 'Reply to Prof. Bourne.' Copyright 1903"; "Strange treatment of original sources. A review of 'Marcus Whitman and the Early Days of Oregon,' by W. A. Mowry . . . 1901. Copyright 1902"; "Review of 'Marcus Whitman and the Early Days of Oregon' by W. A. Mowry, . . . 1901. Copyright, 1902" [second, re-vised, and expanded review]; transcripts of letters and documents of the Oregon Mission from the archives of the Ameri-can Board of Commissioners for Foreign Missions, with some comments; and "The authorship and value of the account of the migration of 1843 to Oregon which was published as part two of George Wilkes' *History of Oregon*, New York, 1845" [written in 1903].

The first three manuscripts are carbon copies with manuscript additions and al-terations. The fourth contains copies of 44 letters and documents concerning Whit-man and the Oregon Mission, and includes letters of Cushing Eells, W. H. Gray, H. H. Spalding, Elkanah Walker and Marcus Whitman of the Mission, and Archibald McKinlay and John McLough-lin of the Hudson's Bay Company.

After the death of William I. Marshall his private library, letters, notebooks and manuscripts passed into the possession of

Clarence B. Bagley of Seattle, who also had been collecting material for a book on the Whitman controversy but abandoned his project when he became acquainted with Mr. Marshall and his work on the subject. Marshall used all of this material in preparing his *Acquisition of Oregon* [1911 ?], and quoted extensively from the letters and "Authorship." The first and third manuscripts, "Why his search" and "Strange treatment," were published in his *History vs. The Whitman Saved Oregon Story*, Chicago, 1904.

[Coe No. 122.]

332 MASON, CHARLES H., 1830–1859

Correspondence of Charles H. Mason, Secretary of Washington Territory, 1853–1859, and Acting Governor, 1855–1856, 1858–1859.

34 letters. 77 pp. 20–33 cm.

Charles H. Mason was appointed at the age of 23 the first secretary of Washington Territory, and served under Governors Stevens and McMullin until his death in 1859. He served as acting governor while Stevens was in the Indian country and after McMullin returned to the East in 1858 until Governor Gholson arrived in 1859.

The majority of the letters relate to the beginnings of Indian hostilities in 1855; others to McMullin's attack on Mason's character in 1858. They include the following:

MASON, CHARLES H. Letter to G. Blanchet. December 14, 1855. Signed copy. 1 p.

—— Letter to Lewis Cass, Secretary of State. June 21, 1858. Signed copy. 10 pp.

—— Letter to Governor Curry. October 20, 1855. Signed copy. 3 pp.

—— Three letters to James Douglas. November 10–23, 1855. Signed copies. 5 pp.

—— Six letters to George Gibbs. September 14 [1855]–January 30, 1856. 15 pp.

—— Letter to Father Ricard. December 4, 1855. Copy. 1 p.

—— Two letters to General Wool. August 30, October 20, 1855. Copies. 3 pp.

BLANCHET, GEORGES. Letter to Governor Mason. December 7, 1855, and a copy by Blanchet of the "Commission officielle donnée au P. Pandosy pour être transmise aux soldats." 4 pp.

CROSBIE, HENRY R. Letter to Acting Governor Mason, resigning as aide to the Governor. November 1, 1855. 1 p.

CURRY, GEORGE LAW, Governor of Oregon Territory. Three letters to Acting Governor Mason. April 1, 1854–October 25, 1855. Signature only of the second and third in his hand. 7 pp.

The letter of October 22, 1855 is endorsed in Elwood Evans' hand: "Advising as to movements &c. of the Oregon Mounted Volunteers."

GIBBS, GEORGE. Letter to Governor Mason. November 14, 1855. 7 pp.

McMULLIN, FAYETTE. Letter about Mason to Lewis Cass, Secretary of State. April 16, 1858. Copy. With a brief note in Evans' hand. 3 pp.

—— Letter to U. E. Hicks. April 27, 1858. Copy. 1 p.

—— Letter to W. W. Miller. April 29, 1858. Copy. 1 p.

—— Two letters to R. M. Walker. April 3, 29, 1858. 2 pp.

OLYMPIA, W. T. CITIZENS. Petition to R. M. Walker, Acting Secretary of the Territory of Washington, for the use of the Capitol for musical concerts and a ball, dated, Olympia, April 26, 1858, and signed by 31 citizens of Olympia. 1 p.

RAINS, GABRIEL JONES. Letter to Acting Governor Mason. October 9, 1855. Signature only. 2 pp.

RICARD, PASCAL. Three letters to Acting Governor Mason. October 12–December 1, 1855. 7 pp. With English translations in an unidentified hand; and a copy of Mason's letter to Ricard, December 4, 1855. 1 p.

TOLMIE, WILLIAM FRASER. Letter to C. H. Mason. October 23, 1855. 2 pp.

WALKER, RUDOLPH M. Letter to Fayette McMullin, Governor of Washington Territory. April 29, 1858. Copy. 1 p.

Governor Curry's letter of October 22, 1855, is printed in Evans, *History of the Pacific Northwest* [1889], I, 551–552; Mason's letters to Douglas, November 23, 1855 and Wool, October 20, 1855, and Rains to Mason, October 9, 1855, are printed in *Message of the Governor of Washington Territory* [I. I. Stevens], Olympia, 1857, pp. 103, 130, 160. Mason's letter to Douglas, November 23, 1855, is also printed in C. B. Bagley, "Attitude of the Hudson's Bay Company during the Indian War of 1855–1856," *Washington Historical Quarterly*, 1917, VIII, 299–300. An extract from Ricard's letter of December 1, 1855, is quoted in English by Denys Nelson in "Yakima Days," *idem*, 1928, XIX, 128.

[Miller Collection.]

333 MASON, LEONARD, 1804–1851

Journal of a voyage from New York to California and a year in the mines, February 12, 1849 to December 26, 1850; and correspondence with his family, February 25, 1849 to February 22, 1851.

77 pp. 18½ cm. Original binding. 10 letters. 31 pp. 24½–27 cm.

Colonel Leonard Mason left his home near Syracuse, N.Y., February 12, 1849 for the California gold field. He met with little success, and mortified and discouraged he left San Francisco in November 1850 for Panama and home. When he arrived in New York he was suffering from California fever and died there, January 7, 1851.

The journal was not kept up every day except during the voyage around Cape Horn, and some entries record the latitude only. The journal describes the election of officers of the Cayuga Joint Stock Company, events of the voyage on the bark *Belvedere* from New York to San Francisco, February 28–October 12, 1849; the departure for the mines, October 26, and the stay at the Mariposa Diggings until January 3, 1850, when the party started back to San Francisco arriving January 25. The journal is resumed April 25 when Mason, Mark Herring and Charles Moss

left San Francisco for the Trinity River mines where they spent the summer prospecting and mining. On October 28 Mason sailed on the sloop *Crescent City* from Humboldt Bay for San Francisco; he left San Francisco, November 12, 1850, on the steamship *Antelope*, crossed the Isthmus and sailed for Norfolk, arriving in Philadelphia December 26, 1850.

In the volume with the journal are 13 pages of records of gold dug and accounts for 1849–1850; and 28 pages of memoranda in various hands dated from 1863 to 1876, on the genealogy of the Mason and Hill families, business transactions, mortgages, and bonds relating chiefly to the estate of Isaac Hill, Mrs. Mason's father.

The letters from Mason to his wife and daughter tell of his plans, and his life in San Francisco and at the mines. The first letter was written from New York, the last from Trinity River, and the others from San Francisco. The two letters to Mrs. Mason from the Rev. Mr. Wellington and Dr. Shew describe the illness and death of Colonel Mason.

MASON, LEONARD. Six letters to his wife, Eliza Hill Mason. February 25, 1849– June 30, 1850. 20 pp.

——Letter to his daughter, Henrietta Mason. February 26, 1850. 3 pp.

MASON, ELIZA HILL. Letter to her husband. Canton, N.Y., December 25, 1849. 4 pp.

SHEW, DR. JOEL. Letter to Mrs. Mason. [New York, February 22, 1851.] 1 p.

WELLINGTON, O. H. Letter to Mrs. Mason. New York, February 22, 1851. 3 pp. (On the sheet with Dr. Shew's letter.)

[Coe Collection.]

334 MASSACHUSETTS. GOVERNOR, 1843–1851 (GEORGE NIXON BRIGGS)

Passport issued by the Commonwealth of Massachusetts to Amory Holbrook, Esq., of Marblehead, going to Oregon and elsewhere, signed, and the seal of the Commonwealth affixed, December 8, 1849, by George N. Briggs, Governor, W. B. Calhoun, Secretary of the Commonwealth.

Printed form filled in by hand. 1 p. 41 cm.

In the fall of 1849 Amory Holbrook was appointed U.S. Attorney for Oregon Territory; he arrived by the Isthmus in May 1850, and practiced law in Oregon until his death.

Gift of Mary C. Withington.

335 MATHEWS, E. J.

Quitclaim deed to Adolph Sutro for mining ground in the Virginia district, signed March 28, 1860, by E. J. Mathews of Virginia City, Carson County, Utah Territory. Witnessed by S. D. Levinson and Theophilus Scheuner.

Broadside, 19¼ x 30½ cm.

Endorsed: "Filed March 28, 1860. Recorded in Book C. page 154 & 155, Virginia mining records. Wm. C. Campbell, Recorder."

Form "Printed at the 'Territorial Enterprise' Office, Carson City, N.T." and filled in by hand.

[Coe No. I, 676.]

336 THE MAURY-DRAKE PAPERS

Private and official records and reports of the 1st Cavalry, Oregon Volunteers from its organization to its muster out, 1861–1865, including the Drake-Maury correspondence, Drake's original journal of the Dalles Expedition into the Indian country, 1864, and his history of the Oregon Cavalry.

5 portfolios. 675 pieces. 17–28½ cm. With typewritten transcripts.

DRAKE, JOHN M. "Private journal, Expedition from Fort Dalles Oregon into the Indian country" and the campaign against the Snake Indians April 20, 1864 to October 10, 1864. 212 pp. 17 cm. Original binding.

The journal is written in a diary for 1863, with three leaves of accounts, a list of captured horses, etc.

—— "The Oregon Cavalry." History of the Cavalry in manuscript in Drake's hand. January 17, 1906. 22 pp. 25½ cm.

—— Correspondence: Reports, orders and letters, written by the officers of the regular army, of the Oregon Cavalry and others, in general addressed to Captain Drake, February 23, 1864–October 8, 1866. 138 letters and documents.

MAURY, REUBEN F. Correspondence concerning the raising of the six volunteer companies of the 1st Oregon Cavalry and the Indian campaigns, addressed chiefly to Colonel Reuben F. Maury, November 8, 1861–July 3, 1862. 59 letters.

OREGON VOLUNTEERS, 1st Cavalry, 2d Battalion. Letter book. April 12–June 29, 1862. Official letter book with index and copies of 18 letters signed by Lieutenant Colonel R. F. Maury or Captain John M. Drake, Acting Adjutant. 14 pp.

—— Official returns, reports, inventories and other documents of the 1st Cavalry Oregon Volunteers, 1863–1865, written in the hands of the commanding officers, including detailed reports of the Dalles Expedition. 458 pieces.

[Coe No. 123.]

337 MEACHAM, ALFRED BENJAMIN, 1826–1882

The Meacham papers. Letter books and correspondence of Alfred B. Meacham as superintendent of Indian affairs in Oregon, 1869–1872, and as chairman of a peace commission to the Modocs in 1873.

5 volumes. 27½–30½ cm. With typewritten transcripts.

—— Three letter books, May 15, 1869–April 2, 1872. 1,036 letters.

—— Letters received by Meacham, November 19, 1870–December 28, 1873. 411 letters.

The correspondence deals in detail with the routine work of the superintendent of Indian affairs, the Government's policy in administering the Indian problem, the Indian Wars, and his own removal from office. The principal correspondents are the Commissioners of Indian Affairs in Washington, E. S. Parker, H. R. Clum, and F. A. Walker; and the agents of the various Oregon agencies, W. H. Boyle and N. A. Cornoyer of the Umatilla Agency, John Smith of Warm Springs, Charles Lafollett of Grande Ronde, Joel Palmer of Siletz, I. D. Applegate, L. S. Dyar and O. C. Knapp of Klamath. Most of the letters from these agents and others, dated after March 13, 1872, are addressed to T. B. Odeneal, who succeeded Meacham as superintendent in Oregon.

Meacham's report to Commissioner E. S. Parker, September 21, 1870, is printed in the *Report* of the Office of Indian Affairs for 1870, pp. 48–55; and his report to Acting Commissioner Clum, October 25, 1871, in the *Report* for 1871, pp. 297–309. Commissioner Parker's letter to Meacham, June 28, 1871, is printed in Meacham, *Wigwam and Warpath*, Boston, 1875, pp. 695–697.

[Coe No. 124.]

338 MEDARY, CHARLES STUART

"Voucher no. 6. Abstract D, to property return. Issues to Indians by Charles S. Medary, Indian agent at Flathead Indian Agency . . . Mch. 25th, 1875."

1 sheet. 21 x 52 cm.

Printed form filled in by hand with issues to the Indians by Charles S. Medary and signed by him; L. E. Manning, witness; Lorette Pablo, interpreter; and by marks of Eneas, Chief of Kootenais; Arlee, Chief of Flatheads; Michelle, Chief of the Pend d'Oreilles; Abraham, Lassà, Louisore, and Antoine; and certified by L. E. Manning, F. B. Decker, and Charles S. Medary.

[Coe No. 125.]

339 MERCER, K. B.

Diary of a member of Company A, 1st Regiment of Oregon Mounted Volunteers, during the Yakima War, from November 22, 1855 to March 16, 1856.

102 pp. 14½ cm. Original binding.

Note in pencil on inside front cover, in a late hand: "Diary of K. B. Mercer (Indian War 55/56) from Nov. 22, 1855 to March 16, 1856 inclusive."

The name of the writer of the diary is not mentioned in the manuscript, but it is evidently written by a private or noncommissioned officer of Company A. There is no Mercer in the roster of Company A, and no K. B. Mercer in the muster rolls of the regiment as printed in Victor, *Early Indian Wars of Oregon*, Salem, 1894.

The diary, undoubtedly original, describes the march from The Dalles to the support of Major Chinn on the Umatilla and the campaign in the Walla Walla Country, and gives details of the country, the movements of the regiment and the death of Peu-Peu-Mox-Mox. It breaks off in March, 1856.

[Coe No. 126.]

340 MERRILL, THOMAS G.

Letter to the Hon. Milton DeLano, Washington, D.C. Helena, Montana, May 10, 1888, from Thos. G. Merrill, Chairman, Citizens' Executive Committee, enclosing a printed copy of that part of the Act of Congress, which in granting lands to the Northern Pacific Railroad reserves all mineral lands except coal and iron lands.

Typewritten copy. 2 pp. 32½ cm., and printed broadside 16½ x 24 cm.

The broadside is entitled: "An Act granting lands to aid in the construction of a railroad and telegraph line from Lake Superior to Puget's Sound, on the Pacific Coast, by the Northern Route, approved July 2, 1864." 1 p.

Thomas G. Merrill was chairman of a Citizens' Executive Committee appointed at a convention held in Helena, Mont., February 7 and 8, 1888, regarding the preservation of the mineral lands of Montana. DeLano at the time was a member of Congress from New York.

[Coe No. I, 497.]

341 MILLER, ALFRED JACOB, 1810–1874

"Portfolio of original paintings by Alfred J. Miller."

15 paintings, mounted and bound. Oblong. 41½ x 35 cm.

Leather label on front cover: "Miller's Paintings—William Drummond Stewart Expedition. 1837–38."

Alfred Jacob Miller, born in Baltimore in 1810, was asked to accompany Captain William Drummond Stewart to the West in the summer of 1837, to sketch the scenery and the Indians. Captain Stewart wanted the sketches to be made on the spot, and later to be copied and enlarged to hang in his home in Scotland. Stewart, Miller, and Antoine Clement left New Orleans for St. Louis in the spring, joined the caravan of the American Fur Company, under Thomas Fitzpatrick, on its journey to the Rendezvous of 1837 in the Green River Valley, visited the Wind River Mountains, the Tetons, and the eastern part of Oregon Territory, and returned to St. Louis in November.

Miller made over 150 sketches on the western journey. On his return to Baltimore and in Scotland where he accompanied Stewart in 1840, he painted the large canvases for his patron. The portfolio contains the following:

"River scenery en route—Rocky Mountains." Oil. 17 x 12 cm.

"Oregon Lake Scene." Oil. 25 x 17 cm.

"Indian Woman 'en grande tenue.'" Watercolor. 13½ x 11 cm.

"Throwing the lasso." Watercolor. 15½ x 13 cm.

"Making moccasins." Watercolor. 14 x 16 cm.

"Sioux Indian." Watercolor. 13 x 15½ cm.

"Shoshonee—Wind River." Watercolor. 11 x 12 cm.

"Dakota Squaw & Papoose." Watercolor. 10 x 12 cm.

"Shoshonee Girl with Dog." Watercolor. 11 x 14 cm.

"Nez Perces." Watercolor. 12½ x 15 cm.

"Shooting the Prairie Dog." Watercolor. 12 x 16 cm.

"Kansas Indian." Watercolor. 14 x 17 cm.

"In-ca-tash-a-pa (Red Elk) Snake Warrior." Oval. Oil. 19½ x 23½ cm.

"Chinook Maiden—Columbia River." The head, in oil, oval 15½ x 18½ cm., is evidently older and is mounted on a later watercolor background. 21½ x 27½ cm.

"Wounded Buffalo." 32 x 26 cm. The buffalo, in oil, has been cut out, mounted on a later background and retouched in watercolor.

In 1935 a large collection of 100 "spot" sketches of Miller's were in the Peale Museum in Baltimore, unmounted watercolor sketches of various sizes, used as preliminary sketches for the oils painted for and at Murthly Castle. A number of the oils were later brought to America and purchased by Mr. E. D. Graff of Winnetka. In his Baltimore studio Miller painted many Indian scenes based on his sketches. The original sketches were later purchased by Mrs. Mae Reed Porter and placed in the Nelson Gallery of Art in Kansas City. Miller also made 200 copies of his Indian sketches for W. T. Walters in 1858–1859. All but a few of the surviving watercolor sketches are now owned by Mrs. Porter and members of the Miller family.

[Coe No. V, 26.]

342 MILLER, ALFRED JACOB, 1810–1874

Paintings of the Far West in oil, watercolor and sepia, painted by Alfred Jacob Miller, artist of the William Drummond Stewart Expedition, 1837–1838.

22 paintings. Framed or matted. 36 x 29½–42 x 33½ cm.

"Giving drink to a thirsty trapper."
Watercolor. 18½ x 20½ cm.

"Auguste watering his horse." Sepia.
18½ x 25 cm.

"Capt. Stewart giving signal to hunters—
Buffalo in sight." Sepia. 19 x 20½ cm.

"[Two] Shoshone Indian girls." Watercolor. 20¼ x 28½ cm.

"Pawnee Indians watching the caravan.
'War ground.'" Sepia. 22¾ x 28 cm.

"Shoshonee slicing meat." Watercolor.
11½ x 12 cm.

"Loading on horseback—Buffalo swimming the Platte." Sepia. 29½ x 20½
cm.

"Return from hunting." Oil. 19½ x 16¼
cm.

"Auguste thrown by the blooded stallion
—Fort Laramie." Sepia. 22½ x 14 cm.

"Lake Damala—Wind River Range."
Watercolor. 18½ x 13 cm.

"Indian beating a retreat." Watercolor.
33½ x 23 cm.

"Capt. Stewart, Antoine, Pierre & Indians." Watercolor. 26 x 15¾ cm.

"Trapper making escape from Blackfeet."
Watercolor. 22 x 19¼ cm.

[Sunset campfires at Rendezvous.] Oil.
23 x 34 cm.

[Trappers hunting deer—Oregon 1838.]
Oil. ca. 25 x 19½ cm.

"Fort Laramie. From nature by A. J. Miller 1836 & 7." Watercolor. 29½ x 19
cm.

"Trappers making their escape from hostile Blackfeet." Watercolor. 24 x 17½
cm.

"Wounded buffalo." Watercolor. 24½ x
17½ cm.

"Sunrise, Voyageurs at breakfast."
Watercolor. 23½ x 15½ cm.

"Snake girl swinging." Watercolor. 21 x
27½ cm.

"Starting the caravan at sunrise." Sepia.
37½ x 19½ cm.

"Migration of Pawnees." Sepia. 31 x 17½
cm.

One of the three oils and one watercolor
are framed, the other watercolors and
sepias matted; the majority of the paintings are signed.

[Coe No. V, 24–25.]

343 MILLER, WILLIAM WINLOCK, d. 1876

List of articles sold by W. W. Miller, administrator of the late General I. I.
Stevens, July 13–14, [1863]; his account with the Immigrant Aid Society,
1870–1874; and other accounts and records kept in a ledger that was used
from 1845 to 1856 by A. E. Woodson, Olympia, Washington Territory.

74 pp. 31 cm. Original binding.

—— Lists of merchandise purchased in San Francisco in February and
March 1850, for shipment to M. T. Simmons of Olympia, probably on the
brig *Orbit;* and in April on the *George Emery;* an account of the stock in
M. T. Simmons' store, February 12, 1852; and accounts of W. W. Miller,
1852–1859.

97 pp. 26 cm. Original binding.

A four-page Introduction by Winlock W. Miller, Jr., August 4, 1926, is laid in the latter volume.

General William Winlock Miller was appointed surveyor of customs at Port Nisqually in 1851, traveled overland from Illinois to Oregon and arrived at Puget Sound in October. He settled in Olympia, was twice elected mayor, and during the Indian Wars of 1856–1857 was appointed quartermaster general by Acting Governor Mason.

The record of purchases includes the names of the merchants and the method of payment by cash or by notes payable at the office of Endicott, Green, and Oakes of San Francisco. Mr. Miller's accounts are both official and personal and include the names of many of the prominent settlers of the Territory, among them Thomas J. Dryer, Isaac N. Ebey, Edward Lander, and Richard H. Lansdale.

[Miller Collection.]

344 MILLER, WINLOCK WILLIAM, JR., 1906–1939

"The Olympia Narrow Gauge Railroad," signed: "Winlock Miller, Jr. September 1925."

Typewritten manuscript. 12 pp. 28 cm.

An account of Olympia's effort to secure railroad communication with the rest of the Territory after the Northern Pacific decided on Tacoma for its terminus.

Published in the *Washington Historical Quarterly*, 1925, XVI, 243–250.

[Miller Collection.]

345 MISSOURI FUR COMPANY

Missouri Fur Company letter book kept by Thomas Hempstead, acting partner, June 27, 1821 to February 12, 1823; and [at the other end of the volume] the official letter book kept by Thomas Hempstead as U.S. military store keeper for St. Louis, March 1819 to March 21, 1822.

151 pp. 33 cm. Original binding.

The majority of the letters relating to the Missouri Fur Company are to Joshua Pilcher, acting partner of the company; others are to Charles Billon, Louis Bompart, O. N. Bostwick, J. C. Calhoun, Henry Clay, James Monroe, Andrew Woods, and others.

The letters copied as U.S. military store keeper are mainly to George Gibson, Commissary General of Subsistence at Washington. Others are to Colonel Henry Atkinson; Lieutenant N. Clark; Peter Hagner, auditor; Thomas T. Tucker, Treasurer of the United States; firms providing supplies; and officers commanding posts in the district.

Formerly in the library of George H. Hart of New York. Sold at auction at the Anderson Galleries, October 17, 1922.

[Coe No. 127.]

346 MITCHELL, FREDERICK WILLIAM

The correspondence of Frederick W. Mitchell relating to his mining enterprises in California and Idaho, 1865–1866, and other papers.

12 letters and documents. 74 pp. 13–32 cm. With typewritten transcript.

Frederick William Mitchell, after serving as lieutenant and captain of Co. I, 12th Illinois Cavalry, went to California in 1865 as representative of a group of men of Hudson, N.Y., to invest in mines. After several unsuccessful ventures in the Excelsior district of Nevada County, Calif., in 1866 he moved on through the Humboldt mines to Idaho and became interested in mines there. Here too he did not meet with success and soon returned to his home in Hudson, N.Y.

The letters describe life in the mines and comment on family affairs. They include:

—— Four letters to his father. September 9, 1865–December 14, 1866. 33 pp.

—— Draft of a letter or report. October 15, 1866. 8 pp.

—— Letter to his mother. December 16, 1866. 6 pp.

—— Draft of a deposition by F. W. Mitchell asserting that he had never received double pay for September and October 1863, for service as 1st Lieutenant, I Company, 12th Ill. Cavalry, and asking that the charge be removed, 1881. Unsigned. 3 pp.

FAIRFIELD, GEORGE B. Letter to Fred W. Mitchell. July 12, 1866. Signed also by S. A. DuBois and Theodore Miller. 7 pp.

HEALD, MRS., "Auntie Heald." Letter to Fred. April 28, 1865. 10 pp.

MITCHELL, HOWARD. Letter to his brother Fred. August 18, 1879. 4 pp.

MUNN & Co., New York. Receipt for $341.25 from F. W. Mitchell for English patent on [Motz's] expansive pivot, July 5, 1872. Engraved form filled in by hand. 1 p.

UNITED STATES PATENT OFFICE. Specifications forming part of Letters Patent No. 208,917. October 15, 1878, to Frederick W. Mitchell of Hudson, N.Y. Printed. 2 pp.

The four letters to his father, the draft of October 15, 1866, and the letter to Mitchell from Fairfield, DuBois, and Miller are printed under "Notes and Documents" in the *Pacific Northwest Quarterly*, 1948, XXXIX, 133–151.

[Coe No. 129.]

347 MONROE, JAMES, 1758–1831

Letter to Robert R. Livingston, Minister Plenipotentiary at Paris. Paris, June 4, 1803.

1 p. 34 cm.

In 1803 Monroe was sent to Paris by Jefferson to cooperate with Livingston in negotiating a treaty with France to secure free navigation of the Mississippi. He arrived in time to take an active part in the negotiations for the purchase of Louisiana.

The letter deals with the relations with Spain and information to be sent to Mr. Pinckney, American Minister to Spain.

[Coe Collection.]

348 MONROE, JAMES M., *d.* 1851

Diary September 1841 to June 1842; a record of attendance of his pupils in Nauvoo, 1842–1844; and his journal kept while tutoring the children of Joseph Smith and Brigham Young, 1845. Copied by W. M. Egan.

52 pp. 32 cm.

At the conference of the Church of Jesus Christ of Latter-day Saints at Utica, June 13, 1842, James M. Monroe was ordained an elder and acted as clerk of the conference for James Blakeslee, president. He was soon to leave for Nauvoo, probably with the party leaving Batavia August 15 under the leadership of Moses Martin. He was killed in 1851 by Howard Egan.

The diary was not written day by day, but summarizes events from September 4, 1841 through June 13, 1842, covering his conversion to the Mormon faith, his work for the church in northern New York under Elder Blakeslee, up to his ordination as an elder. Six pages contain a record of attendance of pupils at school, August 22, 1842–January 1843, and November 1843–March 1844 at Nauvoo. The third part contains the "Journal kept during private tuition of the Prophet Joseph's children and also Bro. Taylors [and Brigham Young's]," April 22–May 31, 1845, at Nauvoo.

The journal records Monroe's daily life and struggles with the children, and his own studies, especially in phrenology.

[Coe No. IV, 431.]

349 MONTANA TERRITORY

Three documents certifying that Sidney Edgerton has filed claims in the mines of Montana.

3 printed forms filled in by hand. 18½ x 8–19 x 8½ cm.

—— Beaver Head County. Recorder's Office. Document, dated Bannock City, July 12, 1864, certifying that Sidney Edgerton has recorded claim No. seven, North East from Discovery on the Kearsarge lode. Signed by Amos W. Hall, recorder.

—— Jefferson County. Recorder's Office. Document, Montana City, December 8, 1864, certifying that Sidney Edgerton has recorded claim No. one N. East from Discovery on the Van Dyke lode. Signed by T. G. Merrill, recorder.

—— Deer Lodge County. Recorder's Office. Document certifying that Sidney Edgerton has recorded claim No. . . . Being Discovery on . . . the Lomas lode. Silver Bow City, July 8, 1865. Signed by C. E. Irvine, county recorder.

Sidney Edgerton was the first governor of Montana Territory.

The first document was printed by F. M. Thompson, Printer, Bannock, 1864; and the third by Montana Post Print, Virginia City, 1865.

[Coe No. I, 548, 550, 552.]

350 MONTGOMERY, JOHN ELLIOTT, 1830–1846

Letter to his mother, Mrs. Mary Montgomery. U.S. Ship *Portsmouth*, Yerba Buena Bay of San Francisco, California, July 25, 1846.

4 pp. 27 cm.

In the upper left-hand corner of the sheet is a drawing, in color, of the Bear Flag, "Californian Republic."

John E. Montgomery was, at the time this letter was written, private secretary to his father, Commander John Berrien Montgomery, in command of the U.S.S. *Portsmouth*. In November 1846 he accompanied his brother, William Henry Montgomery, Passed Midshipman, on an expedition up the Sacramento River carrying money to U.S. forces on land. None of the party was ever heard of afterward.

The letter describes the Bear Flag revolution of the American settlers against the Mexican authorities, the capture of

Sonoma and General Vallejo, the appointment of William B. Ide captain and the raising of the Bear Flag. When Commander Montgomery ordered Lieutenant Misroon to Sonoma, John E. Montgomery accompanied him. He describes the flag,

having the original in his possession, the hospitality of Mrs. Vallejo, and Lieutenant Ford's victory over Joaquin de la Torre.

[Coe Collection.]

351 MOONLIGHT, THOMAS, 1833–1899

Papers of Colonel Thomas Moonlight. 1864–1870.

15 documents and letters. 68 pp. 20½–32 cm.

Thomas Moonlight was born in Scotland, ran away to America, enlisted in the 4th U.S. Artillery in 1853, served in Florida and in the campaign against the Mormons. In 1860 he bought a farm in Kansas, served in the 11th Kansas Cavalry, 1861–1865, was secretary of state, 1868; was nominated for governor in 1886 and defeated. President Cleveland appointed him governor of Wyoming Territory, 1886–1889, and minister to Bolivia, 1893–1897.

The manuscripts record Colonel Moonlight's experiences during the years 1861–1865 and the controversy with General Connor over the hanging of Two Face and Blackfoot, Sioux Chiefs. They include General Orders, No. 3, Headquarters, 2d Brigade, District of South Kansas, August 1, 1864, T. Moonlight, Colonel 11th Kan. Cav., relinquishing his command of the Brigade [printed, unsigned. 1 p.]; General Field Order, No. 2, Headquarters, 2d Brigade, 1st Division, Army of the Border, December 15, 1864, Thomas Moonlight, Colonel 11th Kan. Cav. Commanding, signed by Ira I. Taber, 1st Lieut. and A.A.A.G., congratulating the officers and men of the Brigade for their gallant service [printed. 3 pp.]; General Orders No. 63, Headquarters, Department of Kansas, Fort Leavenworth, December 21, 1864, C. S. Charlot, Assistant Adjutant General, signed by John Williams, Assistant Adjutant General, relieving Colonel Moonlight from duty in Kansas and ordering him to proceed to Denver City [printed.

1 p.]; and General Order No. 10 to the Hon. Samuel H. Elbert, Secretary of Colorado Territory, to call for 360 mounted men for service, signed by T. Moonlight and Ira I. Taber, and the call for six companies of cavalry, signed by Samuel H. Elbert, Acting Governor [a clipping from the *Rocky Mountain News*, February 6, 1865]; and the following letters and papers:

—— Account of his military service from 1861 to 1865, and of the service of the 11th Kan. Cav., of which he was colonel, prepared for the Hon. T. J. Anderson, Adjutant General of the State of Kansas. Signed: "T. Moonlight, Col. 11 Ks. Cavy." At end: "Respectfully submitted to the Adgt. Genl. of the State of Kansas." 38 pp.

The manuscript is signed by Moonlight but is not written in his hand. It was evidently written between July 17, 1865, when he was mustered out, and Colonel Anderson's resignation as adjutant general in 1866.

TABER, IRA I. "How Buckeye *didn't* describe the hanging of the Indian Chiefs Two-face and Black-foot. And *how* he *did* describe other things." Signed at the end: "I. I. T." [9 pp.] Accompanied by a letter from Ira I. Taber to Colonel Moonlight, August 5, 1870 [2 pp.], and a photograph taken from a pencil sketch of the hanging. 10 x 6 cm.

The manuscript is a review and correction of an article that appeared in the

State Record, July 13, 1870, based on an article signed "Buckeye" in the *Kansas City Bulletin*. Four clippings from the *Record* are pasted in the manuscript. The review was written and sent to Colonel Moonlight at his request for publication in the *Kansas Commonwealth* [Topeka].

WHARTON, J. E. Two letters to Thomas Moonlight. July 22, 27, 1870. The former endorses Moonlight's statements, saying that at the time of the hanging he [Wharton] was editor of the *Rocky Mountain News* and has the report of it that appeared in the *News*, June 27, 1865, having been previously published in the Cincinnati *Commercial*. 4 pp.

—— Letter to the editors, *Commonwealth*, enclosing the account of the execution clipped from the *Rocky Mountain News* and sent to Colonel Moonlight. August 13, 1870. 3 pp.

WILCOX, JOHN A. Letter to Colonel Moonlight. July 15, 1865, enclosing a telegram from George F. Price, by command of General Connor, to John A. Wilcox, A.S.M., Fort Laramie, July 14, 1865, regarding mustering out of Colonel Moonlight. At end: "Official copy. John A. Wilcox, Capt., 4th U.S. Cavalry." 3 pp.

WILDER, ABEL CARTER. Telegram to General Moonlight. February 27, 186[5], notifying him that he has been breveted and confirmed. 1 p.

Manuscript copy of the article in the Cincinnati *Commercial*, June 10, 1865, "War on the Frontier . . ." Signed: "A true copy. B.M." 3 pp.

There is a pencil note on p. [4] of General Field Order No. 2 to "Friend Goldrick" [O. J., pioneer reporter on the *Rocky Mountain News*] in Moonlight's hand, sending the "congratulatory order" for him "to read, publish, and comment on," and asking that it be returned.

[Coe No. 130.]

MOONLIGHT, THOMAS. "Extracts from life of Thomas Moonlight written by himself. To be published by William H. Murray." Typewritten transcript. 49 pp. 20½ cm.

The transcript includes the papers with the exception of the first 35 pages of the "Account of his Military Service," General Orders No. 3, and General Field Orders No. 2.

The Moonlight papers are from the collection of the Rt. Rev. Nathaniel Seymour Thomas, Bishop of Wyoming.

[Coe No. 131.]

352 MOORE, HENRY MILES, 1826–1909

Journals of H. Miles Moore; his personal papers and documents; and records of the Free State Legislature, Kansas, and the Leavenworth Association. 1852–1880.

43 vols., 11 documents, letters, etc., 2 maps. [i.e., over 8,100 pp.] 12½–33 cm.

Henry Miles Moore was born in Brockport, N.Y., was admitted to the bar in 1848, and spent 1848–1850 in Louisiana. Intending to go west, he went up the Mississippi and Missouri to Weston, Mo., in 1850, arriving too late to cross the Plains before spring. He became associated with O. Diefendorf, a lawyer of Weston, and decided to remain there; practiced law and was on the editorial staff of the Weston *Reporter*. He was one of the original proprietors of Leavenworth, Kan., and moved there in 1854. From that time he was identified with the development and growth of Leavenworth. He was a delegate to the Topeka Constitutional Convention in 1855, was elected attorney general under that Constitution, and represented Leavenworth in the Territorial Legislature of 1857 and again in the State Legislature in 1868. He took an active part in the Free State War, served in the Union Army in the Civil War, and for 20 years was secretary of the Democratic State Central Committee. He served as city attorney for several terms and continued his law practice until his death.

—— Journals, January 1, 1852–October 13, 1880. 37 vols. 12½–22 cm. Original bindings.

The journals give details of his family life, marriages, birth of his son, social life, theaters and other entertainments, the weather, cases tried in court and fees received, household and personal expenses, church activities, steamboat arrivals and departures, emigrant trains, discovery of gold at Pikes Peak and the Pike's Peak Express, the struggle for railroads, political conventions, Shannon's Potato War, the Ladies' "Whiskey War," the murder of Malcolm Clark and tarring and feathering of William Phillips, and national and world events as reported in Kansas.

Moore evidently kept small pocket diaries in which he noted his cases, receipts and expenditures and daily happenings both in his home and elsewhere, and later wrote up more detailed journals. This series contains a few of the brief diaries.

—— Notebook containing records of cases in the Circuit Court and Court of Common Pleas, Weston, December 1852–June 1854. 51 pp. 13 cm. Original binding.

—— Miscellaneous personal papers and documents, 1858–1894. 19 pp.

The papers include 8 pages from a family Bible, one inscribed, with records of marriages, births, deaths; 2 leaves from an album with 8 small family photographs; draft of the minutes of the first meeting of the Old Settlers of Leavenworth County, August 8, 1874, Moore, secretary; photograph of Amos Rees,

signed by Mary M. Rees; and 7 printed forms filled in by hand: 3 deeds for property in Leavenworth County, 1858, 1861 and 1866; 3 licenses to practice law granted to H. Miles Moore, 1862 and 1873, and his commission as notary public, Topeka, 1894.

—— Free State War, 1857. 74 pp.

Record of action on bills by the Legislature, January–February 1857; autographs of 56 of the members with addresses; and a list of commissions issued, July 18–September 16, 1857, in the Kansas Volunteers for the Protection of the Ballot Box; commission of H. Miles Moore as superintendent of enrollment, 5th Brigade, Headquarters Kansas Volunteers, Lawrence, August 2, 1857, signed by J. H. Lane, Organizing, and M. F. Conway, Adjutant General [printed form]; and autograph document to General Whitman certifying that H. Miles Moore is appointed brigadier general of this Brigade, Leavenworth, September 22, 1857, and signed: "J. H. Lane, Organizing."

Warrant No. 604 on the Auditor's Office, Lecompton, Kansas, for $730 for the payment of a claim for damages received during the Free State War of 1856. Signed by H. J. Strickler, auditor, September 1, 1859 [printed form], with Strickler's letter to Moore, September 17, 1859, enclosing the warrant; and the "Claim of H. Miles Moore," petition for the recovery of the amount of the warrant, which, with Mr. Strickler's letter, he had sent to the Territorial Treasurer in 1859. The warrant was not paid or returned to him and no trace of it was found until it was returned in 1906 by the agent of the Rock Island Railroad. 4 pp.

LEAVENWORTH ASSOCIATION [Articles of association of the City of Leavenworth]. Signed by the 32 founders at Weston, Mo., June 20, 1854, in the handwriting of H. Miles Moore. 5 pp. 33 cm. With a preliminary draft in ink, in Judge L. D. Bird's hand (see Moore's *History of Leavenworth*, p. 19), with corrections and alterations in ink and pencil, some of them in Moore's hand. 4 pp.

—— Constitution and amendments, signed by 72 members, followed by the minutes of meetings, July 1, 1854–December 6, 1856, signed by the president and secretary; accounts and assessments; and a preliminary draft in pencil of the minutes of meetings, August 11–October 28, 1854. 74 pp. 32 cm.

The Constitution and minutes through October 17, 1854, are in the handwriting of H. Miles Moore, secretary.

—— Account book of the Leavenworth Association, 1854–1856, including accounts of all shares, owners' assessments, transfers, and lots sold or drawn. 246 pp. 32½ cm. Original binding.

The earlier accounts are in the handwriting of H. Miles Moore, and the following statement is on p. [1]: "Leavenworth Association. Composed of 32 members, 5 shares each & 15 shares to be disposed of by the Trustees for the benefit of the Association. Whole number of shares one hundred and seventy-five."

—— First map of Leavenworth, Kan., from which the first sale of lots was made by General George W. McLane, auctioneer [77 x 52 cm.]; and a list of the lots sold, kept by H. Miles Moore, secretary, on the first and second day, October 9 and 10, 1854, on the town site with a list of all lot owners, by blocks. 103 pp. 30½ cm.

—— Map of Rees' addition to Leavenworth City [47½ x 36 cm.] with a blank book containing lists of lots drawn in South Leavenworth and Clark & Rees' addition, and miscellaneous notes. 38 pp. 18½ cm. Original binding.

The Moore journals and manuscripts were sold at the Anderson Galleries, May 2, 1928, sale No. 2268. Extracts from the journals have been quoted in Moore, *Early History of Leavenworth*, Leavenworth, 1906, and many of the details are taken from the journals.

[Coe No. 132.]

353 MORAN, PETER, 1841–1914

Shoshone Reservation, August 1890.

Wash drawing. 27 x 20 cm.

Original drawing titled and signed: "Shoshone Res— August /90. P. Moran," inscribed on the verso: "Shoshone Agency. Wyoming. Slaughter house at Agency."

[Coe Collection.]

354 MUNGER, JAMES F., 1830–1852

Journal of a whaling expedition from New Bedford on the ship *St. George*, Captain Hawes, sailing September 2, 1850 to Cape Horn, the Sandwich Islands, Bering Straits and Hong Kong, where Munger left the ship February 23, 1852. After a stay of some weeks at Whampoa, China, he shipped again April 13, 1852, on the *Annie Bucknam*, Captain Barber, bound from Whampoa to New York by Cape of Good Hope with a cargo of tea.

152 pp. 33½ cm. Original binding. With printed version.

The first entry in the journal, following a list of the crew of the *St. George*, is July 10, 1850, when Munger set out from Verona, N.Y. The number of whales caught and the number that escaped are indicated by drawings in the margin. There is also a drawing of a ship in full sail on the inside of the flyleaf. The account of his stay in China includes a brief list of Chinese words with their meaning. The journal of the voyage home on the *Annie Bucknam* begins with a list of the crew and ends with a brief entry on July 22, 1852, the day before he met with an accident and was drowned.

Laid in the journal are the following letters, which, with three earlier ones, are included in the printed version (pp. 57–71):

—— Letter to his father, William H. Munger. April 4, 1851. 3 pp.

—— Two letters to his parents. October 19, 1851, February 25, 1852. 13 pp.

—— Two letters to Charles Harrison. April 6, October 29, 1851. 6 pp.

—— *Two years in the Pacific and Arctic Oceans and China, Being a Journal of Everyday Life on Board Ship, Interesting Information in Regard to the Inhabitants of Different Countries and the Exciting Events Peculiar to a Whaling Voyage,* Vernon: J. R. Howlett, Printer, 1852.

The printed version is preceded by a biography of James F. Munger by L. H. Stanley.

[Coe No. 137.]

355 MURO, FRAY ANTONIO DE SAN JOSÉ

"Al Plan de Conquista, y Población de lo Reconocido en el Sur el año de 1779 se añade algunas Reflexiones, por la noticia cierta de los Establecimientos Rusos; y de haber subido nrōs descubridores asta los 68 g̃. de Latt. Norte."

11 pp. 31 cm. With typewritten translation.

Fray Antonio Muro, a member of the Bethlehemite Community of Mexico, fearing the danger to both church and state from the Russian settlements on the Pacific Coast, has prepared a plan for the conquest and colonization by Spain of the coast north to the 68th parallel that had been explored in 1779. He describes the Russian attitude toward the Catholic Church, the richness of the country's natural resources, and recommends to the Spanish Ministry his plan to expel the Russians from North America and to extend the Spanish colonies.

The document is dated February 22, 1789 and is signed with rubric: "Fr. Antonio de S. Jose Muro." With an added note that it was dispatched by sea on the 24th of the same month and year.

[Coe Collection.]

356 MURRAY, ALEXANDER HUNTER, 1818–1874

Journal of an expedition to build a Hudson's Bay Company post on the Yukon, by A. H. Murray, written in the form of a letter to Murdo McPherson, Esqr., Fort Simpson. Youcon, May 1848 and continued to June 23 at Lapiers House.

86 pp. 32 cm. With the printed version.

A. H. Murray was born in Scotland, emigrated to the United States as a young man, and joined the American Fur Company. In 1846 he entered the service of the Hudson's Bay Company and was appointed to the Mackenzie River district, under Murdock McPherson.

The letter covers the journey from June

11, 1847, when he left Fort McPherson, until his return to Lapiers House, June 23 [1848]; describes in detail the route down Bell River and the Porcupine to the Yukon, the building of the fort, the characteristics and customs of the natives, the Russian fur traders on the Yukon; and includes a Kutchin vocabulary, meteorological journal for July 1847–May 1848, and 15 original drawings, all of them reproduced in the printed edition.

The printed version has the following title: *Journal of the Yukon, 1847–48*, By Alexander Hunter Murray. Edited with notes by L. J. Burpee, Ottawa, Government Printing Bureau, 1910 (Publications of the Canadian Archives, No. 4).

The original manuscript journal was at Fort Simpson in 1848 where it was made available to Sir John Richardson by Murdock McPherson, Chief Factor of the Hudson's Bay Company. The copy of the journal reproduced by the Canadian Archives was obtained by Dr. James Hannay for the Dominion Archives from E. O. S. Schoefield, Legislative Librarian, Victoria, B.C. L. J. Burpee, editor, notes a number of words that are illegible in the manuscript and one passage with several words missing. In the Coe manuscript there are no words missing, and words noted as illegible are quite clear. There are also variations in the underlining of words. The Coe manuscript is probably the original which was badly copied for the Dominion Archives.

[Coe No. 138.]

357 NAUVOO LEGION

"Record of Orders, Returns, & Courts Martial &.c. of 2nd Brigade, 1st Division, Nauvoo Legion, Headquarters, 14th Ward G.S.L. City. July 1857" to October 28, 1868.

202 pp. 31½ cm. Original binding.

The Nauvoo Legion was originally organized in Nauvoo in 1840, was reorganized in July 1857 in two divisions, and included the entire militia force of the Territory. After service in the "Mormon War," 1857–1858, the Legion was active in campaigns against hostile Indians, especially in 1865–1867.

Orders, reports and muster rolls of the 2d Brigade, 1st Division of the Nauvoo Legion, Brigadier General F. D. Richards commanding, June 13, 1857–July 2, 1864, October 28, 1868, copied in various hands. The signatures are in the hand of the copyist. The last entry, October 28, 1868, and the muster roll of the field and staff, October 30, 1862, are loose and laid in the volume. The complete muster roll of the Division, July 4 to September 19, 1857, begins at the back of the volume.

[Coe No. IV, 440.]

358 NEVADA MINING DISTRICT, JEFFERSON TERRITORY

Constitution and By-Laws of the Nevada Mining District; Minutes, November and December meetings; and Miners' Laws of Nevada [1860–1861].

62 pp. 20 cm. Original binding. With typewritten transcript.

The manuscript is made up of three parts: the preamble, constitution and by-laws; minutes and resolutions, November and December meetings; and the miners' laws. It is badly stained by water and worn, but is still legible. It is in the handwriting of William Muir, who was elected judge of the Miners' Court, January 21,

1861. R. D. Darlington was secretary, February 4, 1860–1861.

A note at the end, in an unidentified hand reads: "In the handwriting of William Muir, 1832–1867. This book was sent to his sister Marion Muir Bellman on his death in 1867. He was said to have been clerk of the first Miners' Court because of his legal training in a law office in Glasgow Scotland in 1852–55."

The original "Manuscript Proceedings of the Miners' Meetings of Nevada District in Gilpin County, from January 21, A.D. 1860, to Sept. 28, A.D. 1861," is now owned by the State Historical and Natural History Society in Denver. It has been published in T. M. Marshall, "Early Records of Gilpin County Colorado," *Colorado Historical Collections*, 1920, II, 122–145.

[Coe No. 35.]

359 NEWCOMB, SILAS, 1822–

Journal, April 1, 1850 to March 31, 1851, of his overland journey from Darien, Walworth County, Wisconsin, to Hangtown, California, his stay at the mines, and his travels in Oregon Territory.

231 pp. 31½ cm. Original binding.

Mounted on page 30 is the printed broadside of the resolutions of the Beloit Company, Kanesville, May 7, 1850, with Newcomb's name added in manuscript and the other members of Captain Clark's mess marked, Frontier Guardian Print. 17½ x 27½ cm.

In 1849 Silas Newcomb, of Madison, Wis., lost his property through a business partner, and determined to take this overland trip.

The diary describes in detail the journey from Darien, April 1, by stage and steamboat to St. Louis, St. Joseph, and Kanesville, where on May 7 he joined the Beloit Company camped nearby; the overland journey by the Platte and Sweetwater Rivers, Fort Bridger, Salt Lake City, Weber River and the Mormon Route to the California Trail, and the Humboldt and Carson Rivers to Hangtown, May 13–September 5; and work in the mines, Sep-

tember 7–19, when the writer decides to go to Oregon. He resumes his diary on January 1, 1851, summarizing the events since his departure from Sacramento for San Francisco, his voyage up the coast to the Umpqua River and his adventures in Oregon until he accepted a position as teacher to the children of John Trapp of Benton County for three months, January 1–March 31, 1851.

The journal is preceded by a table of contents and "Prefatory and Explanatory to the Reader," Minneapolis, Minn., February 13, 1895.

The journal was sold at the American Art Association in January 1924. The Beloit Company broadside with Newcomb's name added is reproduced by D. C. McMurtrie, "Two Early Issues of the Council Bluffs Press," *Annals of Iowa*, 1931, 3d ser., XVIII, 82–86 (see No. 235).

[Coe No. 139.]

360 NEWMAN, ORSON N., 1830–

"Memoranda of O. N. Newman," March 22 to December 30, 1869, diary of a journey from Montana to California.

109 pp. 17 cm. Original binding. With typewritten transcript.

The entries are in pencil in a *Daily Pocket Diary for the Year 1864* . . . *New York, Kiggins & Kellogg*, with the name Gabriel Morris on title page.

Newman traveled by wagon from Madison Valley, Mont. Ter., to San Diego, Calif., taking with him his wife and two sons, by way of Virginia City, Pocatello Station, Great Salt Lake, Elko Station, Ruby Valley, and Austin, Nev.; Walker's Pass, Bakersfield, Los Angeles, and San Luis Rey, Calif.,—a total distance of 1,688 miles at a cost of $476.68. The entries are terse, giving facts only about the route, weather, purchases, mileage, condition of the land for grazing and hunting, etc. The diary is followed by a complete cash account of the trip, and other accounts and memoranda.

[Coe No. 140.]

361 NICHOLS, HENRY K.

"*Private*. Journal. Construction of Ft. Kearney, South Pass and Honey Lake Wagon Road. Henry K. Nichols. 1857." [Added at a later date] "Pottsville, Penna."

94 pp. 25½ cm. Original binding.

Henry K. Nichols was first assistant engineer of the expedition under William M. Magraw, under the direction of the Department of the Interior, to construct that portion of the Pacific Wagon Road from Fort Kearney through South Pass to Honey Lake on the border of California. Mr. Nichols was assigned to the Eastern Division, under F. W. Lander, chief engineer, covering the road from Fort Kearney to Independence Rock.

The journal, probably begun about June 1, covers the journey from Philadelphia, May 13, to Independence, May 23, 1857, and from June 1 gives a daily account of the expedition until September 17, at Fort Laramie, where he left the train under Magraw and was awaiting instructions from Lander, who was with an advance party. A plan of the camp [6 x 3 cm.] is drawn on page 14, June 20.

Laid in the manuscript is a letter from Samuel M. Magraw to M. P. O'Hern, Baltimore, July [changed to June] 20, 1856, with a note added in pencil from M. P. O'Hern to an unnamed person. Endorsed: "July 9, 1856 Saml. Magraw Relative to purchase of Potomac Furnace."

[Coe No. 141.]

362 OATMAN, LORENZO and OLIVE

Daguerreotypes of Lorenzo D. Oatman and Olive Ann Oatman. [San Francisco, 1857.]

Original double folding case. 8½ x 10 cm.

Roys Oatman, his wife and seven children left Independence, Mo., in August 1850 with a company of some 50. From the Pima Villages the Oatmans continued alone and in February 1851, while encamped on the Gila, were attacked by Indians and killed, except for Lorenzo, who was left for dead, and two daughters, Olive and Mary, who were taken captive. Lorenzo recovered and made his way back to Pima Village, and later to Fort Yuma and San Francisco. Mary died after a year or two in captivity; Olive was finally ransomed in 1857, and joined her brother.

The daguerreotype of Olive shows her chin tattooed. It was reproduced as a wood engraving, signed Herrick, S. F., by R. B. Stratton in his *Life among the Indians; Being an Interesting Narrative of the Captivity of the Oatman Girls, among the Apache and Mohave Indians*, San Francisco, 1857.

[Coe No. II, 956.]

363 O'FALLON, BENJAMIN, 1793–1842

Letter to His Excellency William Clark. Fort Crawford, November 29, 1817.

7 pp. 25½ cm.

Endorsed on fourth page: "St. Peters Prairie du chien. Benjn O'Fallon relative to British traders."

The letter reports to General Clark, Governor of Missouri Territory, the activities of British traders under Robert Dickson from the Red River Settlement; and describes the situation in his own agency.

From the library of Guthrie Y. Barber of New York, sold by Parke-Bernet, Sale No. 304, Oct. 22–23, 1941.

[Coe No. 142.]

364 OLNEY, OLIVER H.

The Olney papers, records of Mormon affairs and events at Nauvoo in 1842–1843.

49 documents. 457 pp. 15½–32½ cm. With typewritten foreword and calendar of the documents by Dale L. Morgan.

Oliver H. Olney was the brother of Jesse Olney (1798–1872), author of textbooks, and the son of Ezekiel Olney. He moved to Ohio and in 1831 became a Mormon. After his denunciation by Joseph Smith in an editorial in the *Times and Seasons*, April 1, 1842, and being "disfellowshipped because he would not have his writings tested by the word of God," he began keeping the record contained in the Olney papers. He also received revelations from "the Antient of Days" and planned to establish his own church. In 1843 he was convicted of robbing Moses Smith's store and was committed to jail.

Many of the documents record chronologically the events in Nauvoo from April 6, 1842 through January 23, 1843, with criticisms of the Nauvoo authorities and the Nauvoo Legion and his plans to publish a pamphlet expressing his views. He records also the early plans of Joseph Smith to move west, the John Cook Bennett scandal, the beginnings of polygamy. Other documents contain accounts of sessions with the "Antient of Days," and directions for the establishment of a new church; plans for the publication of his pamphlet, "The Absurdities of Mormonism Portrayed," drafts of the introduction and digests of letters—some of them for quotation; drafts of letters to Elias and Malena Chapman, to the church authorities, to Lucinda White, to Eliza Snow, to Joseph Smith, to Oliver Snow, to Orson Hyde; draft of an article for the Quincy *Whig*, and of a proposed lecture before the Nauvoo Lyceum Exchange; "An Epitaph on the Life of General A. Jackson" in verse; autograph letters to Olney from William Clayton as Joseph Smith's clerk, Nauvoo, July 15, 1842; from Phebe M. Wheeler, later his wife, Knoxville, August 21, 1842; and last, a letter, unsigned, from Phebe M. Wheeler Olney, Nauvoo, January 24, 1844, to her Uncle and Aunt Dunning in Connecticut, telling of her marriage and describing her husband.

Olney wrote in an obscure style with many inversions of phrases and words, and many of the manuscripts are written in lines of varying length as if they were in blank verse.

[Coe Collection.]

365 OLYMPIA, WASHINGTON TERRITORY

"A plan of the town of Olympia," with a pencil annotation in the handwriting of Winlock W. Miller, Jr.: "Drawn prior to 1859."

90 x 54 cm.

Notes on the plan give the width of the streets and alleys, the size of lots, and the latitude and longitude of the town.

The names of the owners have been written in many of the lots.

[Miller Collection.]

366 OREGON GOVERNORS AND UNITED STATES SENATORS

Collection of letters, documents, autographs and portraits of governors of Oregon and United States senators from Oregon.

44 pieces. 18½–35 cm.

ABERNETHY, GEORGE, Governor under the provisional government of Oregon, 1845–1849. Letter to L. J. Cist. March 9, 1855. 1 p.

BAKER, EDWARD DICKINSON, U.S. Senator, 1861. Portrait engraved by A. H. Ritchie. 16 x 25 cm.

CHADWICK, STEPHEN FOWLER, Secretary of State, Acting Governor, 1877–1878. Letter to Ben W. Austin. November 17, 1886. 3 pp. With a photograph [12½ x 19 cm.] mounted on a sheet with the official seal of the State of Oregon.

CHAMBERLAIN, GEORGE EARLE, Governor of Oregon, 1903–1909, U.S. Senator, 1909–1915. Letter to Lawrence F. Bower. May 11, 1903. 1 p. With an autographed photograph. 12 x 20 cm.

CORBETT, HENRY WINSLOW, U.S. Senator, 1867–1873. Portrait, engraved by G. E. Perine. 17½ x 25 cm.

DOLPH, JOSEPH NORTON, U.S. Senator, 1883–1895. Letter to Lawrence F. Bower. October 30, 1893. 1 p. With a photograph. 10½ x 16½ cm.

GAINES, JOHN POLLARD, Territorial Governor, 1850–1853. Letter to Major General Worth. April 18, 1848. 4 pp.

GROVER, LAFAYETTE, Governor of Oregon, 1870–1877, U.S. Senator, 1877–1883.

Letter to Lawrence F. Bower. June 12, 1891. 1 p.

—— Letter to Master Lawrence F. Bower. August 11, 1891. 1 p.

—— Document signed as Governor, appointing James B. Bell Commissioner of Deeds for Oregon. January 17, 1874. Signed also by S. F. Chadwick, Secretary of State. 1 p. With an engraved view of the Oregon State House. 22½ x 14 cm.

HARDING, BENJAMIN F., U.S. Senator, 1862–1865. Letter to Ben W. Austin. October 24, 1894. 1 p.

KELLY, JAMES KERR, U.S. Senator, 1871–1877. Letter to L. D. Merchant. September 28, 1872. 1 p. With a portrait engraved by W. H. Barnes & Co. 18 x 25½ cm.

LANE, JOSEPH, Territorial Governor, 1849–1850, Senator, 1859–1861. Letter to Isaac Toucey, Secretary of the Navy. February 28, 1858. Signed also by Delazon Smith and LaFayette Grover. 1 p. With a portrait engraved by J. C. Buttre from a photograph. 14 x 21 cm.

LORD, WILLIAM PAINE, Governor of Oregon, 1895–1899. Receipt signed April 27, 1895, for money received from J. M. Bermingham, general treasurer, National Home for Disabled Volunteer Soldiers. Signed also by Bermingham and W. B. Franklin, president. 1 p.

MCBRIDE, GEORGE W., U.S. Senator, 1895–1901. Letter to Lawrence F. Bower. September 14, 1896. 1 p.

MITCHELL, JOHN HIPPLE, U.S. Senator, 1873–1879, 1885–1897, 1901–1905. Letter, signed, to Mr. Merchant. April 15, 1873. 1 p. With a portrait engraved by H. B. Hall & Sons. 17½ x 24½ cm.

MOODY, ZENAS FERRY, Governor of Oregon, 1882–1887. Letter, signed, to Geo. F. Edmunds. June 12, 1883. 1 p.

NESMITH, JAMES WILLIS, U.S. Senator, 1861–1867. Letter to Ben Perley Poor [n.d.]. 1 p.

PENNOYER, SYLVESTER, Governor of Oregon, 1887–1895. Letter to General William B. Franklin. April 8, 1897. 1 p.

SIMON, JOSEPH, U.S. Senator, 1898–1903. Typewritten letter to Lawrence F. Bower. February 6, 1900. 1 p.

SLATER, JAMES HARVEY, U.S. Senator, 1879–1885. Note to Ben Perley Poor. December 3, 1872. 1 p.

SMITH, DELAZON, U.S. Senator, 1859. Signature on a letter to Isaac Toucey. February 28, 1858. Signed also by Joseph Lane and LaFayette Grover.

STARK, BENJAMIN, U.S. Senator, 1861–

1862. Letter to an unidentified correspondent. October 18, 1890. 1 p.

THAYER, WILLIAM WALLACE, Governor of Oregon, 1878–1882. Letter to Ben W. Austin. October 10, 1888. 1 p.

WHITEAKER, JOHN, Governor of Oregon, 1859–1862. Letter to D. S. Walker. August 7, 1879. 1 p.

WILLIAMS, GEORGE HENRY, U.S. Senator, 1865–1871. Letter, signed, to L. J. Cist. June 28, 1873. 1 p. With a portrait engraved by Bureau of Engraving & Printing. 9 x 12½ cm.

WOODS, GEORGE L., Governor of Oregon, 1866–1870. Document, signed, appointing James B. Bell Commissioner of Deeds. January 17, 1870. Signed also by Samuel E. May, Secretary of State. 1 p.

A number of the letters are accompanied by clippings and biographical notes not listed above. Only two of the letters have special interest, Chadwick to Austin accepting honorary membership in the Northwestern Literary and Historical Society, Sioux City; and Gaines to General Worth about conditions in the Mexican War.

A number of these letters and documents at one time belonged to the Rev. Lawrence F. Bower.

[Coe No. 143.]

367 ORVIS, ANDREW M., 1819–1895

Journal of an overland trip from Lake Maria, Marquette County, Wisconsin, to California, and life in the mines. March 12, 1849 to June 8, 1850.

87 pp. 12 cm. Original binding. With typewritten transcript.

—— Letter to his wife, Mrs. Caroline Orvis. Sacramento City, February 15, 1850.

4 pp. 25½ cm.

The journal records briefly the journey from Wisconsin, March 12, 1849 across Illinois and Iowa to Council Bluffs, the north bank of the Platte and Sweetwater Rivers to South Pass, Fort Bridger and Salt Lake City, July 7–9, 1849. From July

10, when Orvis started on alone, no entries were made until November 30, when he wrote briefly of his sufferings on the journey from Salt Lake over the Mormon Route to the Humboldt and Truckee Rivers and the Diggings, August 12, and experiences in the mines and in Sacramento. On December 1 he again made entries almost daily until they break off on June 8, 1850, when he was in the Redwood country.

The journal is followed by 43 pages of memoranda, accounts and records of employment of helpers showing that Orvis in 1858 was back on his farm in Wisconsin.

[Coe No. 145.]

368 OWEN, JOHN, 1818–1889

Letter book of Major John Owen, containing copies in his hand of 124 letters and documents relating to his work as Indian Agent to the Flatheads, the purchase of St. Mary's Mission, 1852, the relations between the Catholic Missions and the Indians and white settlers, the Hudson's Bay Company, Indian Wars, and Fort Owen. 1856–1865, 1875–1881.

198 pp. 32½ cm. Original binding.

John Owen came to the Northwest in 1849 with the "Oregon Rifles," and was sutler during their stay at Cantonment Loring. The following year he settled as a trader in the Bitter Root Valley and became one of the outstanding pioneers of the region. He purchased St. Mary's Mission where he built Fort Owen. From 1856 to 1862 Owen was special agent to the Flatheads. After 1871 his mental powers began to fail and he was for a number of years in a hospital in Helena, Mont. In 1877 he was sent east to his relatives in Philadelphia, where he died in 1889.

Owen lists on page 148 "letters & official Papers taken East by Jno. Owen Fall, 1863," with a notation of the pages in the letter book where copies may be found.

All of the letters and documents have been printed in full (with the exception of the Fort Owen Mills accounts) in *The Journals and Letters of Major John Owen . . . 1850–1871*. Transcribed and edited by Seymour Dunbar: and with notes to Owen's texts by Paul C. Phillips. New York, Edward Eberstadt, 1927. 2 vols.

[Coe No. 146.]

369 OWEN, JOHN, 1818–1889

"Suttler, For Rifle Regiment, Cantonment Loring, September, 1849." Account book.

69 pp. 31 cm. Original binding.

John Owen was sutler for the regiment but left the service to become a trader soon after Cantonment Loring was abandoned.

The accounts cover the period September 30, 1849–May 6, 1850, soon after the post was officially abandoned. They are followed by two pages of pencil sketches of heads of contemporaries.

This is evidently the second volume, as some of the entries are headed "carried over from Journal I."

Colonel William W. Loring was in command of the Mounted Rifle Regiment, provided by Act of Congress, May 19, 1846, for service in Oregon Territory and to establish military posts to protect the emigrants on the trail. The Mexican War interfered with the plans and it was not until May 10, 1849, that the regiment left Fort Leavenworth. Posts were established at Fort Laramie and at Cantonment Lor- ing near Fort Hall. The latter was abandoned the following spring.

[Coe No. IV, 441.]

370 PALMER, JOEL, 1810–1881

Four letters to John Flett, October 1, 1855 to a date after January 8, 1856; a letter to Flett from Berryman Jennings, November 23, 1855, and one from P. D. Blanchard, April 3, 1856.

6 letters. 11 pp. 25 cm.

General Joel Palmer was appointed the first superintendent of Indian affairs for Oregon Territory, under Governor Lane.

Enclosed with the letter of October 19, 1855 is a copy of the broadside, "Regulations for the guidance of agents in the Oregon Indian Superintendency pending existing hostilities." Dayton, O.T., October 13, 1855, Joel Palmer, Superintendent of Indian Affairs, O.T. 25 x 39 cm.

John Flett was special sub-Indian agent at Wapato Lake. The letters request information about the Indians in his neighborhood and their attitude toward the hostile Indians, and give instructions regarding the gathering of the Indians in encampments. Berryman Jennings was special sub-Indian agent, Willamette Valley.

The regulations are printed in 34th Congress, 1st Session, House Ex. Doc. No. 93, 1857, pp. 72–74.

[Miller Collection.]

371 PARKER, SAMUEL J.

"Article written by Samuel J. Parker, M.D., son of Rev. Samuel Parker, the original projector of the missions of the American Board of Commissioners for Foreign Missions to Oregon." Original article written at Ithaca, New York, in 1878–1879.

74 pp. 32 cm.

Copied by the author with alterations and remarks "for some Historical Society in some part of the country once 'Oregon,'" and sent to Elwood Evans, September 17, 1882.

The article was originally written as a reply to J. Ross Browne's report, *Indian Wars in Oregon and Washington Territories* (35th Congress, 1st Session, House Ex. Doc. No. 38, 1858); and gives a sketch of his father's life and the part he played in establishing the mission in Oregon, and extracts from the correspondence and records of the American Board relating to its establishment.

[Miller Collection.]

372 PATTEN, GEORGE WASHINGTON, 1808–1882

"Over the prairie, By Brevet Major G. W. Patten, U.S. Army."

155 pp. 31 cm.

Accompanied by 21 original drawings and watercolors by Captain Alfred Sully to illustrate Major Patten's manuscript. Various sizes. Mounted 25 x 22½ cm.

In May 1856 Company K, 2d Infantry was ordered to march from Fort Ripley, Minn., to Fort Pierre. The march started June 13, going first to Fort Snelling, where they parted with their families, then to Fort Ridgely, by steamer, where they joined Colonel Abercrombie. After a long delay caused by the lack of any transportation, the command broke camp at Fort Ridgely on August 25 for the march across the bad lands to Fort Pierre, arriving September 24, where Major Patten learned they were to proceed to Fort Lookout, arriving October 2.

The narrative describes in detail the forts and the country through which they traveled and records with much humor the incidents of army life on the prairie and in frontier posts. The manuscript is endorsed on the back of page two: "Over the Prairie. Father's original." There are a few corrections in the manuscript that may be in a different hand. "Directions to Compositor" in the manuscript indicate where the plates are to be inserted, and a note on page 66 reads: "Our talented friend Capt. Sully, son to the eminent artist of that name delineated the above sketch [View of Upper Sioux Agency] . . . To the kindness of Capt. Sully we are indebted for all our sketches."

The manuscript evidently belonged at one time to Colonel Patten's son or one of his daughters. This manuscript or another copy was sent to a magazine for publication. A statement in "Dakota in the Fifties" (*South Dakota Historical Collections*, 1920, Vol. X), says it was printed in *Harper's Magazine*. A careful checking has failed to find it.

[Coe No. IV, 442.]

373 PATTEN, JAMES IRVING

"Reminiscences and Recollections." Accompanied by an undated letter to Bishop [Thomas], signed: "Jas. I. Patten."

24 pp. 28 cm. With typewritten transcript.

The reminiscences describe the settlement of the Shoshones on the Wind River Reservation, Dr. James Irwin, agent, the distribution of "ammities" and the visits of the Missionary Bishop of Colorado and Wyoming from 1871 to 1874 while Patten was teacher and lay reader at the agency.

Formerly in the library of the Rt. Rev. Nathaniel S. Thomas, Bishop of Wyoming, with his bookplate.

[Coe No. 147.]

374 PAUL, CHARLES RODMAN, *d.* 1901

Diary kept by Charles Rodman Paul on the Milk River expedition, January 14 to February 2, 1881.

21 pp. 17 cm. Original binding. With typewritten transcript and 44 photographs 16½ x 11–20½ x 13 cm.

On January 14, 1881, Captain R. L. Morris, with two troops of the 2d Cavalry and four companies of the 18th Infantry, left Fort Assiniboine, Mont., for the Milk River to intercept the retreat to Canada of Sitting Bull's band of hostile Indians. The troops had reached Medicine Lodge, January 22, and on the 24th received orders to return to Fort Assiniboine as word had been received at headquarters that Sitting Bull and most of his band had escaped into Canada.

The diary, written in pencil, gives a detailed account of the journey to Medicine Lodge and back and the difficulties of the march with the temperature usually ranging from 10° to 38° below zero.

The diary is accompanied by 19 photographs of Sioux Indians and scenes and 25 photographs of views of Forts Assiniboine and Maginnis and of the officers and men stationed there.

[Coe Collection.]

375 PEABODY, PUTNAM BURTON, 1856–1937

"Coming back. A missionary experience. Rev. P B Peabody, Wyoming." [1918.]

Typewritten manuscript. 41 pp. 20 cm.

The Rev. P. B. Peabody was the Episcopal missionary at Newcastle and Sundance, Wyo., under Bishop Graves, 1903–1906. The manuscript recounts some of his experiences and ends with the following statement: "All publication rights rigidly reserved (Ultimately intended for the *Spirit of Missions*)."

Formerly the property of the Rt. Rev. Nathaniel S. Thomas, S.T.D., with his bookplate.

[Coe No. 148.]

376 PECK, SIMON L., 1844–

Notes of travel on a journey from Helena, Montana, and the gold fields, down the Missouri River to St. Louis, August 25 to October 13, 1867, with accounts and expenses kept while in Montana and on the route. April to October, 1867.

28 pp. 17 cm. With typewritten transcript and printed version.

After a winter of school teaching in Wallingford, Vt., Simon L. Peck, in the spring of 1866, set out for the gold fields of Montana in company with his lawyer brother and some 150 others whom he joined in Minnesota. The present diary begins on August 25, 1867, when Peck began his return journey to Vermont, and continues to October 13 of the same year when he took the train at Cleveland for home. He traveled by small boat and steamer on the Missouri and overland on foot by Forts Benton, Union, Buford, Berthold, Rice, Sully, Randall; Sioux City, Omaha, St. Joseph, and finally St. Louis.

The diary is brief but includes interesting details of life at the forts and miscellaneous facts about towns along the way. The expense accounts range from April, before Peck left Montana, to October 11, and his arrival at St. Louis.

Published in an altered version in the author's *History of Ira, Vermont . . . to which is added the Author's Early Experiences upon the Plains and the Rockies of the Great West during the Years 1866–1867, from His Diary of the Period*, Rutland, Vt., 1896. Pp. 75–83.

[Coe No. 149.]

377 PECK, WILLIAM R.

Letter to his brother, Robert G. Peck, Midshipman, U.S. Naval School, Annapolis, Md. Post Hospital, Fort Laramie, D.T., November 11, 1866.

4 pp. 25 cm. With original cover postmarked Fort Laramie, Daka. [Territory], November 15, 1866.

The letter describes his life at the fort, the unsettled conditions of the Indians and plans for the future after his discharge. [Coe No. IV, 448.]

378 PEÑA SARAVIA, FRAY TOMÁS DE LA

Diario hecho por el P[adr]e P[redicato]r Fr. Tomás de la Peña de la expedicion de mar que fue al Reconocim[ien]to de la costa hasta los 60. grad[o]s de latitud en el Año de 1774.

31 pp. 30½ cm. With a printed text and translation.

Diary of the voyage of the *Santiago*, or *Nueva Galicia*, kept by Fray Tomás de la Peña, who, with Fray Crespi, by order of Fray Junípero Serra, president of the missions of California, served as chaplain and diarist of the expedition. The *Santiago*, commanded by Don Juan Pérez, was ordered by Bucareli, Viceroy of Mexico, to explore the coast from Monterey north to 60 degrees latitude. It sailed June 6, 1774 but failed to carry out its orders, turning south at 55 degrees (by their own observation) July 22, arriving at Monterey, August 27, 1774.

Testifying to the truth of the diary, it is signed: "Y para q[u]e conste ser verdad lo q[u]e en este Diario tengo escrito, lo firmo en esta Mission de Sn. Carlos de Monterrey, día 28 de Agosto del Año de 1774. Fr. Thomas de la Peña" [with rubric].

Father Peña's diary was sent overland to Mexico on arrival at Monterey; the original diaries kept by Pérez and Martínez are in the Archivo General de la Nación [Mexico] Historical Section, Vol. 61. The diary kept by Crespi has been published by Griffin.

The printed text and translation are extracted from "Documents from the Sutro Collection, translated, annotated and edited by Geo. Butler Griffin" in Historical Society of Southern California, *Publications*, 1891, II, [5]–6, 83–143, Document 18. The Spanish text has been printed from a copy made for Mr. Alfred Sutro of California in 1883–1884 of the original in the Archivo General de Indias in Seville. The text, as printed from the Sutro copies, differs from the Coe manuscript in spelling, order of words, and phrasing in many instances although the account does not vary. Two long passages that are omitted in the printed text are checked in the margin of the Coe manuscript, which also has some marginal notes and annotations in another hand. The Coe manuscript seems to be an earlier draft of the report than that sent to Spain.

The manuscript was secured from Mexico for Adolph Hafer of the Cadmus Book Shop, New York. It is endorsed: "Car. 5, Leg. 6, n. 6," and probably belonged to the College of San Fernando at San Blas (see note under No. 12).

[Coe No. 150.]

379 PÉREZ HERNÁNDEZ, JUAN JOSÉ

Brief account in Spanish of the two voyages of Juan Pérez to explore the coast of California to the northwest in the frigate *Santiago*, or *Nueva Galicia*, the first in 1774, the second, under the command of Bruno de Hezeta, in 1775; followed by a statement of the conditions in the missions of Monterey, December 31, 1774, in an unidentified hand.

4 pp. 30 cm.

The manuscript, beginning: "Segun el diario de la expedición que por mar se hizo el año de 74 con destino de reconocer las costas de la California septentrional h[as]ta la altura de 60g de latitud al norte . . . en el mes de Junio salio del P[or]ta de Sn. Carlos de Monterrey la fragata de S.M. nombrada Santiaga, alias la nueva Galicia . . ." continues: "A mediades del mes de Marzo de este año de 75 salio del P[or]to de San Blas segunda vez d[ic]ha fragata, y una galeota [Sonora] con el mismo destino . . ." and ends with a statement about the missions giving the date of founding, the number of baptisms, marriages, and deaths, and an inventory of the stock in the missions of San Diego, San Gabriel, San Luis [Obispo], San Antonio [de Padua], and San Carlos.

The manuscript summarizes very briefly the voyage of the *Santiago* sent out by Bucareli under the command of Juan Pérez. (For a complete account of this voyage see the diary kept by Fray Tomás de la Peña. No. 378.)

On the second voyage the *Santiago*, under the command of Bruno de Hezeta, with Juan Pérez second in command, and the schooner *Sonora* with Juan de Ayala

in command (later replaced by Juan Francisco de la Bodega y Quadra) sailed March 16, 1775 from San Blas to explore the coast to 65 degrees, accompanied by the *San Carlos*, commanded by Ayala, with supplies for the California missions and orders to explore San Francisco Bay. The *Santiago* turned back at 49 degrees 17 minutes on August 10, arriving at Monterey August 29.

This brief report deals mainly with the "gentiles" and adds details about the missions. It may have been prepared by one of the chaplains for the guardian of the College of San Fernando.

Four diaries of the first expedition are extant, that of Fray Juan Crespi in the Archivo General de Indias, Seville, and those of Fray Peña Saravia, Juan Pérez, and Estéban Martínez in the Archivo General de la Nación, Mexico. Of the second expedition there are six, Bodega y Quadra's in the Museo Naval, Spain; Hezeta's, Pérez', and Campa Cos' in the Archivo General de la Nación, Mexico; Mourelle's in the Archivo General de Indias, Seville, and Fray Serra's, formerly in the library of the College of San Fernando.

[Coe No. 151.]

380 PERPETUAL EMIGRATING FUND COMPANY

Bill of expenses, Brigham Young, President, P. E. Fund Compy. in a/c with Daniel Spencer, Great Salt Lake City, U.T., January 29, 1857.

2 pp. 26½ cm.

The Perpetual Emigrating Fund Company was founded in October 1849 for the purpose of aiding poor to remove from Europe and the United States, with Brigham Young president and Willard Richards secretary. The emigrants signed notes promising to repay the amounts received in supplies and transportation after arriving at Salt Lake City. In September 1852 the first company of emigrants arrived in Salt Lake City with A. O. Smoot in charge. The first handcart companies arrived in September 1856, under Captains Edmund

Ellsworth and Daniel McArthur, followed by companies under Captains James G. Willie and Edward Martin. The last two companies suffered great hardship and many died on the way, those surviving reaching Salt Lake City in November. The catastrophe was due to the late start from Iowa City.

The accounts include items for J. G. Willie's Co., E. Martin's Co., and Jesse Haven's Co., of the disastrous handcart migration of 1856. A note is appended:

"The President told me Feb. 10, 1859 to not settle one dime of this acct." Signed by Thomas W. Ellerbeck. Daniel Spencer was in charge of emigration at the headquarters at Iowa City.

[Coe No. 135.]

381 PERPETUAL EMIGRATING FUND COMPANY

Five documents dealing with the handcart companies of 1860.

5 pieces. 12½–20½ cm. With typewritten transcripts.

The documents are three notes promising to pay to George Q. Cannon or order, after arrival in Great Salt Lake City, for provisions and shares in the Hand Cart Company, signed by William Falconbridge, Florence, N.T., June 6, 1860, and Francis Kerby, Florence, N.T., July 6, 1860; an agreement signed by Eric Eliason to deliver a cow to Cannon on arrival in Great Salt Lake City, Florence, N.T., July 18, 1860, witnessed by C. Widerborg; and "Indebtedness by note of 2d Hand Cart Company for 1860," a list of notes, without place or date, which includes the two Kerby notes.

In 1860 George Q. Cannon was in New York and Florence to receive emigrants and send them on their way.

[Coe No. 134.]

382 PERRIN DU LAC, FRANÇOIS-MARIE, 1766–1824

"Lettres à xxxxxxx sur les deux Louisianes; ou, Voyage dans cette Belle Partie du Nouveau Monde, par quelques unes de les Provinces Maritimes des États-Unis; l'Ohio, le Mississipi et les États qui les Bordent; avec un aperçu des Moeurs Usages et Cérémonies des Sauvages du haut Missouri, les moins fréquentés de l'Amérique Septentle. par les peuples Civilisés."

3 vols. [i.e., 409 pp.] 32½–33½ cm.

Perrin du Lac sailed from Bordeaux August 14, 1801, landed in New York, visited Philadelphia and Washington, traveled down the Ohio to the Mississippi, St. Louis, the Upper Missouri, and New Orleans, and sailed for Bordeaux, December 29, 1802.

The manuscript is an early draft of the author's *Voyage dans les deux Louisianes*, written in the form of letters, describing in detail the cities visited, conditions of travel, life and customs in America, and the customs of the Indians. The manuscript has many deletions, insertions, and corrections which appear in the printed text. The printed text shows still more changes and insertions and omits a number of the detailed descriptions, especially of some of the Indian dances and ceremonies. The text as printed is not in letter form but divided into chapters, and the order has been changed in a few instances. A draft of a dedication and two of a preface are in Vol. III, but they are not the ones used in the finished work.

The drawings in Vol. III are a pencil sketch of a small village with a ship at anchor (p. [431]) and an unfinished one of a ship (p. [432]).

The account of the voyage, with alterations, many omissions, and some additions, was published in 1805 in Paris and Lyon with title: *Voyage dans les deux Louisianes, et chez les nations sauvages du Missouri, par les États-Unis, l'Ohio et les provinces qui le bordent, en 1801, 1802 et 1803,* A Lyon, chez Bruyset aîné et Buynand, An XIII—1805.

[Coe No. V, 34.]

383 PICKEL, LEONARD

Eight letters to Leonard Pickel, five from friends who have moved to Nauvoo, Illinois, to join Joseph Smith, and three from E. H. Davis, Mormon missionary in Maryland, New Jersey, and Connecticut. 1841–1844.

24 pp. 24–32½ cm. With typewritten transcript.

Leonard Pickel, a cooper, of Bart Township, Lancaster County, Pa., had evidently become a Mormon and contemplated joining friends at Nauvoo.

The letters from the west give an account of the journey from Pennsylvania to Nauvoo, a description of the rapidly growing settlement and economic conditions there, of the arrest of Joseph Smith and the sorrow over the loss of Joseph and Hyrum Smith, and of the departure of Sidney Rigdon. All the writers urge Pickel to come to Nauvoo where he will prosper in his trade.

BROOKE, HENRY and CATHERINE. Letter to Leonard and Mary Pickel. November 15, 1844. 3 pp.

[BUSHMAN, MARTIN.] Letter to Leonard Pickel. December 18, 1842. 2 pp.

DAVIS, ELISHA H. Three letters to Leonard Pickel. [October 27, 1842]–September 9, 1843. 9 pp.

JENKINS, DAVID. Letter to Leonard Pickel. September 28 [1841 ?]. 4 pp.

KEARNS, HENRY. Letter to Leonard Pickel. December 7, 1842. 3 pp.

WRIGHT, ROBERT and ANN. Letter to Leonard and Mary Pickel. October 19, 1841. 2 pp.

[Coe Collection.]

384 PICKERING, WILLIAM, 1798–1873

Letter to A. M. Poe, public printer of Washington Territory. Executive Office, Olympia, June 29, 1862.

2 pp. 25 cm.

Accompanied by a copy, unsigned and undated, of an answer, not from Poe. 2 pp.

The letter, written soon after Governor Pickering's arrival in Olympia, criticizes Poe's failure to print the laws and journals of the last session of the Legislature more promptly, and asks when he will have them ready for distribution. The answer is insultingly personal. A brief note, in Elwood Evans' hand, implies that the answer was written by Bezaleel F. Kendall.

[Miller Collection.]

385 PIKE, ALBERT, 1809–1891

Letter to "Bro. Hayden" [James R. Hayden]. Washington, February 14, 1885.

1 p. 21½ cm.

In 1859 General Pike was elected grand commander of the Supreme Grand Council, Southern Jurisdiction, of the Scottish Rite, an office which he held for 32 years.

The letter to James R. Hayden, receiver, Land Office, Olympia, and a brother Mason, asks him to send some bear meat and salmon trout to him in Washington for a special occasion.

[Miller Collection.]

386 POPE, GEORGE L.

"Incidents of traveling from Coldwater to Pike's Peak, 1859." March 7 to June 28. Signed at the end by Geo. L. Pope, Cold Water, Michigan.

85 pp. 15 cm. Original binding. With typewritten transcript.

George L. Pope, with a party of Michigan men, left Coldwater, Branch County, March 7, 1859 for the Pikes Peak gold mines. In his diary he records the events of each day's journey, by rail and boat, to St. Joseph and Nebraska City, where they started overland by Fort Kearney and the South Platte to a point about 28 miles west of Bijou Creek. Many of the party had turned back at Beaver Creek discouraged by the reports heard from returning miners met on the trail, and on May 2 Pope and his companions started

back for Bijou Creek and the trail east by Fort Kearney, Iowa City, and Dixon, arriving at Coldwater June 28.

Pope describes briefly the route, camping places, the Pawnee and Sioux Indians they encounter, and mentions the mileage covered each day.

With the diary there is a photostat of a page from the *Nebraska News*, Nebraska City, March 12, 1859, containing an account of the arrival at that town of the Michigan company.

[Coe Collection.]

387 POWERS, MARY L. ROCKWOOD (MRS. AMERICUS WINDSOR), *d.* 1858

"The overland route, leaves from the journal of a California emigrant." 1856. Manuscript copy signed at the end: "Written by A. Field Richmond, 1859."

33 pp. 31½ cm.

Dr. Americus Windsor Powers emigrated from Vermont to Wisconsin in 1841, settled on a farm near Palmyra, and married Mary L. Rockwood whom he had met in Milwaukee. He later sold the farm to Warren Richmond, who had married into the Powers family, and in 1856, with his wife and three children, started overland for California.

The manuscript describes the journey from the start, April 17, 1856, by train for Chicago and Iowa City, and overland by Council Bluffs, the Platte, Fort Laramie, Malade River, Humboldt River, Lassen's Cut-off to the Sacramento Valley, with all its hardship and suffering, and the friendliness of the Mormon women and fellow travelers, but gives few details about the route. They spent almost seven months on the journey and finally settled in San Leandro, California.

A note in pencil at the end reads: "Mrs. Mary L. Powers died on May 1, '58."

The manuscript is preceded by a note addressed to the editors of the *North Western Home Journal*, published in Chicago, 1856–1862. The manuscript was published in full in *The Amateur Book Collector*, September 1950–January 1951, Vol. I, Nos. 1–5. The editor, W. B. Thorsen, has expanded the account by inserting passages from letters of Mary Powers written to her mother during the journey and stay in California, which he quoted from *Some Annals of the Powers Family*, Compiled by W. P. Powers, Los Angeles, 1924. Mr. Thorsen was unable to find that the manuscript was printed in the *North Western Home Journal*.

[Coe Collection.]

388 PRATT, ORVILLE C., 1819–1891

Diary of an overland journey from Fort Leavenworth to Los Angeles, June 9 to October 25, 1848.

2 vols. [i.e., 157 pp.] 18 cm. Original binding.

Orville C. Pratt, a lawyer of Rochester, N.Y., and Galena, Ill., was appointed associate justice of the Second District, Oregon Territory, and gave distinguished service. In 1856 he moved to San Francisco, where he was later elected judge of the Twelfth District.

Vol. I contains the diary of the trip from Fort Leavenworth to Santa Fé, August 1, over the old Santa Fé Trail, a brief record of the stay there, the distances west of Santa Fé, and notes on the route, grass, water, camping places, etc. Vol. II contains the diary of the trip from Santa Fé to Los Angeles, August 27–October 25, 1848, by the San Juan, Grand, Green, and Sevier Rivers; a brief account of his stay at Los Angeles, his trip to San Francisco by Monterey and San José and his voyage to Oregon on the *Undine*, where he entered his official duty as associate justice on June 1, 1849.

The diary describes in detail events of the journey, the country, encounters with Indians, etc.

[Coe No. V, 35.]

389 PRESTON, JOHN B.

Document signed by John B. Preston, Surveyor General of Oregon, Oregon City, September 22, 1851, acknowledging the receipt from James H. Burt of papers pertaining to lots in the Oregon City claim sold or granted by Doctor John McLoughlin previous to the fourth day of March, 1849.

Broadside filled in and signed by Preston. 19½ x 24½ cm.

The papers are not with the document but are described in it as a quitclaim, James D. Holman and Woodford Holman to Burt, and the same to Noyes Smith, September 17, 1850. The document provides that if the title is found correct and proper it is to be certified and forwarded to the General Land Office in Washington, so that a patent may be issued.

[Coe No. III, 1774.]

390 PUGET SOUND AGRICULTURAL COMPANY

Papers relating to the case of the Puget Sound Agricultural Company vs. Pierce County, and Pierce County vs. George B. Roberts of Cowlitz. 1861–1863.

11 papers. 18 pp. 20½–32 cm.

The commissioners of Pierce County in 1859 ordered that the property claimed by the Puget Sound Agricultural Company be assessed and taxes paid, which the company refused to do, and the case was appealed to the Supreme Court of the Territory and to the Supreme Court of the United States, where it was dismissed in 1867 on a technicality. Two years later the British and American Joint Commission for the settlement of the claims of the Hudson's Bay and Puget Sound Agricultural Companies agreed on a purchase price, and the companies withdrew from the Territory.

PUGET SOUND AGRICULTURAL COMPANY vs. the County of Pierce. Supreme Court, Territory of Washington, December Term 1861. Brief, signed by "Chenoweth & Kendall, of Counsel for P. Sd. A. Co." in an unidentified hand. 3 pp.

U.S. DISTRICT COURT, Third Judicial District of W.T. Summons to the County of Pierce to appear before the U.S. District Court, September 8, 1862. Signed: "C. C. Hewitt, Chief Justice, August 16, 1862. Andrew J. Moses, Clerk." Endorsed: "Served the within process . . . on James M. Bachelder, Auditor, Pierce Co. W.T. this 18th day of August, 1862, Wm. Huntington, U.S. Marshal, per F. C. Seaman, depy." 1 p.

—— September Term, 1863. Motion to dismiss the complaint, Frank Clark, Attorney for Defendant. Endorsed: "Filed Sept. 18, 1862 Andrew J. Moses, Clerk." 1 p.

—— Brief, unsigned and undated, in the handwriting of William W. Miller. 1 p.

—— "Memo," in an unidentified hand. Endorsed: "PSA Co. vs Pierce. Brief on tax lien" in W. W. Miller's hand.

[WASHINGTON] TERRITORY vs. Roberts. Brief. Criminal Law. Unsigned and undated. 1 p.

HUNTINGTON, WILLIAM, U.S. Marshal. Letter to Messrs. Kendall and McGill, October 7, 1862. 1 p.

McGILL, HENRY M., Deputy U.S. District Attorney. Letter to William Huntington. October 4, 1862. Copy. 2 pp.

ROBERTS, GEORGE B. vs. Judson, Chambers, Kincaid and Bitting, in District Court for Pierce County, April Term, 1863. Motion to amend complaint, Edward Lander, Attorney for Defendants. 1 p.

TUCKER, EGBERT H., Sheriff of Pierce Co. Letter to Edward Huggins. February 10, 1862. Copy. 1 p.

List of names of men and women associated with the Puget Sound Agricultural Company, in an unidentified hand. 4 pp.
[Miller Collection.]

391 PURVIANCE, M. C.

Journal of an overland trip from Morristown, Henry County, Illinois, to California, April 13 to August 29, 1863.

2 vols. [i.e., 208 pp.] 15 cm. Original binding.

M. C. Purviance, the writer, his brother, Marsh J. Purviance, and Jonus Houghton set out from Illinois for Pikes Peak, by Des Moines, Council Bluffs, Omaha, the south side of the Platte and the South Fork, Julesburg to Denver, arriving May 25. From Denver they traveled by Fort Hallock and Fort Bridger to Salt Lake City, by Box Elder, Weber River and west to the Humboldt and Truckee to Vir-ginia City, Carson City, the Big Trees, and Sacramento, June 11–August 29.

The journal appears to have been written at intervals on the journey and not every day. It is in pencil and some passages are rubbed or very faint. He records his observations on the Mormons, the Indians encountered, and the characteristics of the country.
[Coe No. 152.]

392 RAINIER, PETER, 1741?–1808

Order for an inspection of the boatswain's stores on *La Sybille*. By Peter Rainier, Vice Admiral of the Blue, and Commander in Chief of H.M. ships and vessels in the East Indies. H.M.S. *Suffolk*, Madras Road, June 24, 1800. Signed by Peter Rainier.

3 pp. 32 cm.

George Vancouver named Mt. Rainier after Admiral Peter Rainier, who was not on the expedition to the Northwest Coast.

The order, addressed to the Masters of H.M.S. *Intrepid, Braave, Daedalus*, and *Centurion*, or any three of them, and signed by John Brouncker, required that

the report of the inspection be made on the same sheet and returned. The report is dated: "On Board H.M.S. *La Sybille*, Madras Roads, June 26, 1800," and signed by W. J. Davis, *Intrepid*, W. Blake, *Centurion*, Wm. Lugg, *Braave*.

[Miller Collection.]

393 RAYNOLDS, WILLIAM FRANKLIN, 1820–1894

Journals, account book, sketches and photographs of the expedition under Captain W. F. Raynolds to explore the Yellowstone River and the headwaters of the Missouri; to ascertain the numbers, habits and disposition of the Indians, agricultural and mineral resources, climate, and topographical features. Captain Raynolds was also to distribute to the Dakotas (Sioux) the clothing etc. granted them by the treaty made by General Harney, 1859–1860.

7 portfolios of manuscripts and one of paintings, sketches, and photographs.

—— Journal, Yellowstone and Missouri Exploring Expedition, from its arrival at Fort Pierre to its return to Omaha. June 18, 1859–October 4, 1860. 4 vols. [i.e., 552 pp.] 2 drawings. 19 cm. Original bindings.

In the front of the fourth volume there is a note: "My field journal is only intended to refresh my memory as to the incidents of the trip. Should my life be spared I expect to rewrite it all as in the field I could only write in haste . . ."

These journals were the basis of the report of the exploration submitted on July 1, 1867 to Brevet Major General Humphreys, Chief of Engineers, U.S. Army, with the reports of other members of the expedition, and printed in 1868, by resolution of the Senate, with the map but without the illustrations, 40th Congress, 2d Session, Senate Ex. Doc. No. 77, 1868.

—— Draft of a letter, probably to General Humphreys. Omaha, N.T., October 4, 1860, giving a summary report of the expedition and saying that as soon

as the party can be disbanded and the equipment disposed of, he will report to Washington and prepare the full report. 12 pp. 19 cm.

The outbreak of the Civil War interrupted the preparation of the report.

—— Account book containing copies of 13 letters to members of the party, notifying them of their appointment and giving instructions; and accounts of the expedition. *ca.* 120 pp. Original binding. With two bundles of loose papers.

The papers include a bill of lading for shipping goods for the Indians on the *Spread Eagle*, invoices for dry goods, hardware, guns, and food for distribution to the Indians (Ogalallas, Oncpapas, Brulés, Minniconjoux, Blackfeet, Sioux); invoices of equipment for the expedition, bills of sale, account of stock and animals, and account of sale of public property at Omaha October 8, 1860. 42 pieces.

MAYNADIER, HENRY E. "Report of a reconnoisance made by Lieut. Henry E.

Maynadier, 10th Infantry, in the country about the Yellowstone River in the summer of 1860." Signed at the end: "Henry E. Maynadier, Capt. 10th Inf. Washington, April 1, 1861." 107 pp. 21½ cm. Original binding.

The report covers the period from May 10 to October 3, 1860 and includes an account of a Mandan ceremony that Lieutenant Maynadier witnessed. It is printed in full in the official report except for the entry for June 13, which is omitted and June 14 wrongly dated June 13.

SNOWDEN, J. HUDSON. "Journal, J. Hudson Snowden 1860." 159 pp. 19 cm. Original binding.

The journal covers the exploration from the breaking of winter quarters, May 10, to the arrival at Omaha, October 3, 1860. Mr. Snowden was topographer of the expedition and accompanied Lieutenant Maynadier. His journal covers the same ground as Maynadier's but gives more details about the Indians, physical aspects of the country, etc.

—— "Yellowstone Survey, J. H. Snow-den, 1859." 15 pp., including 6 original maps. 19 cm. Original binding.

—— Observations made at various camps from August 16 to September 2, 1859. 7 pp.

—— "The Indian sign language—as obtained at Winter Quarters 1860." 13 pp. 18 cm. Original binding.

SCHONBORN, ANTOIN, and HUTTON, J. D. Original paintings, sketches, and photographs of scenes on the journey. 59 pictures mounted on 36 leaves. 43 x 31½ cm.

The album contains 3 watercolors, 6 pen and ink sketches, 3 pencil sketches, 41 photographs of paintings and sketches, and 6 photographs.

Raynolds' official report was published as U.S. Engineer Department, *Report on the Exploration of the Yellowstone River*, by Bvt. Brig. Gen. W. F. Raynolds. Communicated by the Secretary of War in compliance with a resolution of Senate, February 13, 1866 (40th Congress, 1st Session, Senate Ex. Doc. No. 77, Washington, 1868).

[Coe No. IV, 443.]

394 RAYNOR, JAMES O.

Two letters to Governor Pickering of the same date. Drew, June 26, 1863.

8 pp. 20 cm.

James O. Raynor was a Methodist preacher, a pioneer of 1847, and a candidate for delegate to Congress in 1863, running against G. E. Cole who won the election and L. J. S. Turney.

The letters are about the campaign, the Knights of the Golden Circle, and his opponents.

[Miller Collection.]

395 RECTOR, WILLIAM HENRY, *ca.* 1806–

Biographical sketches of the life of William Henry Rector. Written by himself.

Photostat. 91 pp. 34 cm.

The narrative, written for the benefit of his posterity after 1869, covers his boyhood, the move from Virginia to Ohio and later to Indiana; his marriage, the move to Independence, Mo. in 1839, and Oregon in 1845; life in Oregon and development of the woolen industry; his removal to California in 1865, and journey to England and Scotland in 1868.

The last five leaves of the manuscript were written by Volney Rector in 1911, at the age of 75, correcting an error in his father's narrative.

The manuscript, except Volney Rector's

addition, was published by Mr. Lockley in his *History of the Columbia River Valley*, 1928, I, 1060–1094, from a photostat that he secured of the original journal, which, in 1929, was in the possession of Daniel Waldo Bass of Seattle.

[Coe No. 153.]

396 RED RIVER SETTLEMENT

Documents relating to the founding and early history of Lord Selkirk's Colony and the Red River Settlement. 1817–1833.

6 documents. 28–32 cm.

SELKIRK, THOMAS DOUGLAS, *5th earl of*. Grant of land and agreement on terms between Lord Selkirk and the Scotch settlers, signed by Lord Selkirk and 19 of the settlers. Fort Douglas, August 1817. 4 pp.

—— Grant of land and agreement on terms between Lord Selkirk and the settlers of De Meuron's and Watteville's regiments, signed by Lord Selkirk and 13 of the settlers. Fort Douglas, August 30, 1817. 2 pp.

—— Receipt for payment of goods from the executors of Lord Selkirk, through Robert Parker Pelly, to the Indian chiefs, for rent under the deed of July 18, 1817. Signed at Fort Douglas, October 9, 1823, by D. Mackenzie and the chiefs, L'Homme Noir, Robe Noire, and Pigwiss, with their marks and totems. 1 p.

GALE, SAMUEL. Memorandum of instructions for Mr. McDonell, sheriff, with orders that he recommend no interference with servants of the North West

Company and avoid all intercourse. Undated, but endorsed: "Memorandum from Mr. Gale. 1817." 1 p.

McDOUGALL, GEORGE. Letter to John Rowand, Chief Factor, Hudson's Bay Company, about François Gardepie. Lesser Slave Lake, April 24, 1833. Endorsed: "Received May 16, 1833. This letter contains some accounts of Master Gardepie's travels to the north of the Saskatchewan Sumr. 1832 & fall also." 4 pp.

Statement of the case of François Gardepie, undated and unsigned, but evidently written by a Hudson's Bay Company factor of 1833/34. 3 pp.

These documents were discovered by Miss Agnes Laut and were secured from her by Lathrop C. Harper by private sale. The original grant to the settlers is published in part in Alexander Ross, *Red River Settlement*, London, 1856, pp. 43–44, and Archer Martin, *The Hudson Bay Company's Land Tenures*, London, 1898, pp. 11–12.

[Coe No. 154.]

397 REDFIELD, ALEXANDER H.

Reports of Alexander H. Redfield, U.S. Indian Agent for the Upper Missouri Agency, to Colonel A. M. Robinson, Superintendent of Indian Affairs, St. Louis, Missouri. Upper Missouri Agency, Fort Union, September 1, 1858, and Sioux City, Iowa, October 12, 1858.

28 pp. 31 cm. With typewritten transcript.

Endorsed on last leaf: "Alexr. H. Redfield U.S. Indn. Agt. for the Upper Missouri Agency—Reports, 1858."

The reports cover his voyage from St. Louis up the Missouri and Yellowstone Rivers to Forts Benton and Sarpy distributing annuities and presents to the Arikarees, Assiniboines, Crees, Crows, Gros Ventres, Mandans and Yanctons, from May 22 to October 12, 1858; his observations regarding the attitude of the Indians toward the provisions of the Treaty of Fort Laramie, and recommendations for a peaceful settlement.

These reports are printed in full, except for one paragraph, in the *Report of the Commissioner of Indian Affairs . . . for the Year 1858*, pp. 83–94.

[Coe No. 155.]

398 REED, SAMUEL B.

Letter to the Rev. J. W. Cook. Salt Lake City, August 15, 1868.

2 pp. 20 cm.

Mr. Reed, general superintendent of construction of the Union Pacific Railroad, was among the first to meet the Rev. J. W. Cook on his arrival in Cheyenne, and was active in establishing St. Mark's Episcopal Church, served on the vestry and was a member of the building committee.

The letter, written while Mr. Reed was temporarily in Salt Lake City, concerns the location and building of the church.

[Coe Collection.]

399 REED, SILAS, 1807–1886

Diaries, correspondence, business and family papers, 1833–1886.

16 vols. 2,000 letters and papers, maps and diagrams. 10½–36 cm.

Silas Reed was born in Ohio in 1807, received a diploma from the Medical College of Ohio, and lived in Cincinnati for several years. About 1838 he moved to Rock Island, Ill., and in 1841 was appointed by President Harrison surveyor general of Illinois and Missouri. This appointment was not confirmed by the Senate, but after the presentation by Dr. Reed of letters and memorials to President Tyler and the Senate, it was brought up again and approved. Dr. Reed served as surveyor general from March 17, 1841 to May 12, 1845, and continued to make his headquarters in St. Louis until he was appointed the first surveyor general of Wyoming Territory in 1870 by President Grant. Due in part to political intrigue he resigned in 1875 and devoted his remaining years to his mining interests in Utah and the promotion of the Dallas and Wichita Railroad Company in Texas. In 1876 he appeared before the Congressional Committee on Expenditures in the Interior Department in its investigation of surveys in the Territory of Wyoming. During the Civil War Dr. Reed served as acting assistant surgeon in army hospitals in Tennessee and Missouri. He died in Utah October 1 or 2, 1886.

—— Diaries, January 1, 1872–August 29, 1874; January 1, 1877–January 31, 1881. 11 vols. [i.e., *ca.* 1,895 pp.] 14½–19½ cm. Original bindings.

The diaries record Dr. Reed's travels to and from Boston and Washington and the West, letters and telegrams received and sent, and brief references to business and family affairs.

REED, SILAS. Correspondence and business papers. *ca.* 6,000 pp. 10½–36 cm.

Dr. Reed's letters to his wife, written almost daily when they were separated, and especially in 1872 and 1880–1886, and to other members of the family have been preserved. The letters to others are usually drafts or copies. He also obtained by permission of the Senate the original memorials and letters sent to Congress in his favor in 1841.

The letters to his family give details of his business transactions and record the names of people he meets and political and local affairs, especially in Missouri and Wyoming. The business papers include deeds (some of them forged), tax lists and receipts, and other documents relating to property in St. Louis and other parts of Missouri; notes on mines and mining claims in Missouri and Utah; papers dealing with the Missouri Smelting and Mineral Lands Company; maps and diagrams, canceled drafts and notes, accounts, bills, and receipts.

The family correspondence also includes letters to members of the Reed and Anthony families from friends and relatives in the East and letters of the Anthony family written between 1890 and 1893, after the death of Dr. Reed.

The letters and papers of western interest include the following:

REED, SILAS. 718 letters to his wife, Henrietta Maria Rogers. February 28, 1856–August 27, 1886. 2,602 pp., 67 postcards.

—— Letter to Beverly Allen. October 12, 1841. Draft. 1 p.

—— Letter to J. G. Anderson. February 21, 1873. Draft. 1 p.

—— Letter to W. J. Andrews. November 3, 1883. Draft. 2 pp.

—— 15 letters to his grandson, Arthur Cox Anthony. January 23, 1878–May 30, 1886. 54 pp.

—— 86 letters to his daughter, Clara James Reed (Mrs. Nathan Anthony). October 12, 1856–[June 23?] 1886. 322 pp.

—— 14 letters to his son-in-law, Nathan Anthony. December 3, 1866–September 25, 1880. 47 pp.

—— Eight letters to his grandson, Silas Reed Anthony. August 14, 1875–July 11, 1886. 33 pp.

—— Two letters to John Atkinson. May 19, October 11, 1881. Copies. 4 pp.

—— Letter to George Barry. May 13, 1886. Draft. 1 p.

—— Letter to Edward Bates. September 12, 1862. Draft. 1 p.

—— Letter to James G. Blaine. June 16, 1876. Draft. 1 p.

—— Letter to George Bliss. January 25, 1867. Draft. 2 pp.

—— Letter to George Sewel Boutwell. November 27, 1872. Copy. 4 pp.

—— Letter to Arthur Brown. March 25, 1881. Copy. 2 pp.

—— Letter to C. C. Cady. November 25, 1841. Copy. 3 pp.

—— Two letters to J. G. Cameron. October 30, November 8, 1841. Copies. 2 pp.

—— Letter to Grover Cleveland. March 26, 1886. Draft. 2 pp.

—— Letter to James D. Cleveland. June 15, 1869. Draft. 2 pp.

—— Four letters to Henry I. Coe. April 5, 1866–September 26, 1877, and a release, March 1, 1874. Copies. 7 pp.

—— Letter to J. B. Cooke. January 17, 1881. Copy. 1 p.

—— Letter to W. W. Curtis. May 25, 1874. Copy. 1 p.

—— Letter to Caleb Cushing. December 7, 1870. Copy. 2 pp.

—— Letter to John F. Darby. October 18, 1841. Copy. 1 p.

—— Letter to George C. Davis. October 29, 1872. Copy. 1 p.

—— Five letters and two telegrams to Columbus Delano. March 21, 1873–May 11, 1876. Copies. 9 pp.

—— Letter to J. S. Delano. June 14 [1873]. Copy. 2 pp.

—— Letter to Richard S. Dement. July 24, 1886. Copy. 2 pp.

—— Letter to Stephen W. Downey. April 22, 1873. Copy. 2 pp.

—— Eight letters and a telegram to Willis Drummond. March 27, 1873–November 14, 1881. Copies and drafts. 12 pp.

—— Letter to Cyrus Edwards. October 30, 1841. Copy. 1 p.

—— Letter to A. Eurgens. December 1, 1875. Draft. 1 p.

—— Letter to Thomas Ewing. August 22, 1841. Copy. 1 p.

—— Letter to the Rev. J. P. Farley. May 28, 1866. Copy. 2 pp.

—— Letter to Alpheus Felch. May 29, 1852. Copy. 4 pp.

—— Letter to Thomas W. Ferry. February 26, 1882. Copy. 5 pp.

—— Letter to George D. Foglesong. April 22, 1873. Copy. 2 pp.

—— Letter to J. O. Friend. February 3, 1870. Copy. 2 pp.

—— Letter to T. M. Fulton. July 6, 1875. Copy. 1 p.

—— Letter to J. E. Gallagher. January 12, 1882. Copy. 2 pp.

—— Letter to Hamilton R. Gamble. October 18, 1841. Copy. 1 p.

—— Two letters to his brother-in-law, Mason Gibbs. September 27, 1841 [June 4, 1843]. 3 pp.

—— Letter to H. Glafcke, January 29, 1876. Copy. 1 p.

—— Letter to Miss Nellie Grant. August 23, 1873. Copy. 2 pp.

—— Telegram and letter to Orville L. Grant. March 23, 25, 1873. Copies. 4 pp.

—— Letter to J. P. Green. November 17, 1875. Copy. 2 pp.

—— Letter to J. Wesley Hammond. July 17, 1874. Copy. 1 p.

—— Letter to Fred Hartje. May 31, 1871. Copy. 2 pp.

—— Letter to J. W. Haskins. September 9, 1881. Copy. 2 pp.

—— Three letters to Henry G. Hay. February 26, 1871–June 8, 1885. Copies. 15 pp.

—— Letter to George Hearst. October 19, 1874. Copy. 2 pp.

—— Letter to Nathaniel P. Hill. January 28, 1882. Draft. 2 pp.

—— Two letters to Hill and Hammill, St. Louis. May 8, 1874, October 17 [1885?]. Copies. 3 pp.

—— Letter to E. F. Honey. May 8, 1871. Copy. 2 pp.

—— Letter to H. H. Houghton. August 15, 1872. Copy. 1 p.

—— Letter to Andrew J. Houston. March 4, 1882. Copy. 1 p.

—— Letter to Andrew A. Humphreys. February 1, 1881. Copy. 2 pp.

—— Two letters to Frank Johnston. May 28, 1881, April 7, 1882. Copies. 6 pp.

—— Letter to Pat Kerwin. May 28, 1881. Copy. 2 pp.

REED, SILAS. Letter to Thomas L. Kimball. May 17, 1885. Copy. 2 pp.

—— Letter to John W. Kingman. June 14, 1874. Copy. 2 pp.

—— Three letters to Webster B. Lanphere. December 3, 1872–September 24, 1874. Drafts. 3 pp.

—— Two letters to Hiram Leffingwell. September 26, October 13, 1856, and a receipt, June 1, 1856, witnessed by C. S. Carpenter. Copies. 3 pp.

—— Letter to President Lincoln. April 11, 1861. Draft. 1 p.

—— Letter to [E.] Livigneur. September 28, 1877. Copy. 1 p.

—— Letter to J. F. Long. April 1, 1875. Draft. 3 pp.

—— Six letters to Frank G. Macomber. March 28, 1880–August 2, 1884. Copies. 22 pp.

—— Four letters to James Morrissey. June 20–July 23, 1874. Copies. 8 pp.

—— Letter to Henry A. Morrow. June 20, 1874. Copy. 1 p.

—— Five letters to Edward Page. September 30, 1881–July 2, 1886. Copies. 8 pp.

—— Letter to George Pierson. June 7, 1881. Copy. 2 pp.

—— Letter to William G. Provines. May 20, 1874. Copy. 1 p.

—— Letter to his father, Charles Reed. June 4, 1843. 2 pp.

—— Letter to his brother, Charles Reed, Jr. February 2 [–8], 1833. 4 pp.

—— Letter and telegram to his nephew Charles J. Reed. February 25, 1871, April 29, 1875. 2 pp.

—— Letter to his nephew, Alfred M. Rogers. June 25, 1886. Copy. 1 p.

—— Four letters to his nephew, Henry Munro Rogers. January 6, 1872–January 3, 1884. 17 pp.

—— Three letters to his brother-in-law, John H. Rogers. July 21–October 4, 1860. 8 pp.

—— Letter to his niece, Lucy Rogers. August 26, 1886. 4 pp.

—— Letter to Frederick Salomon. January [1881?]. Draft. 1 p.

—— Letter to Thomas A. Scott. January 27, 1881. Draft. 1 p.

—— Two letters to Seay and Kiskaddon. August 9, September 1, 1874. Drafts. 4 pp.

—— Letter to James Shields. July 12, 1845. Draft. 1 p.

—— Letter to D. K. Sickles. November 2, 1883. Draft. 3 pp.

—— Letter to Sickles and Randall. October 8, 1883. Draft. 2 pp.

—— Order on Dr. R. P. Simmons. November 18, 1841. 1 p.

—— Three letters to Oliver H. Smith. December 6, 1841–January 17, 1842. Copies. 4 pp.

—— Letter to W. R. Steele. April 22, 1873. Copy. 2 pp.

—— Letter to L. C. Stevens. February 26, 1871. Copy. 2 pp.

—— Letter to Charles H. Thirlwell. February 7, 1882. Copy. 1 p.

—— Letter to Lyon G. Tyler. April 21, 1886. Draft. 6 pp.

—— Letter to U.S. Congress, Judiciary Committee. April 22 [1886]. Draft. 2 pp.

—— Nine letters to President Grant. May 20, 1873–June 7, 1885. Drafts or copies. 16 pp.

—— Six letters to President Tyler. November 18, 1841–February 28, 1842. Drafts. 13 pp.

—— Letter to the U.S. Senate. December 15, 1841. Endorsed: "27 Cong. 2 Sess. Ex. Memorial of Silas Reed, with memorials from sundry persons of Illinois, Missouri & Iowa praying that injunction of secrecy be removed from his nomination, documents on file, &c. 1841, Dec. 20. read and ordered to lie on the table. Dec. 30 resumed & referred to select committee . . . Jan 25, report made & ordered to be printed in confidence for the use of the senate. Feb. 8. report & resolutions considered and agreed to, which grants leave to withdraw these memorials. Rec. Dec. 20." 1 p.

—— Memorials to the Senate of the United States. 9 printed forms signed by citizens of Davenport, Iowa; Hancock and Henderson Counties, Mo.; Madison County, Ill.; Peoria, Ill.; Rock Island, Ill.; Winnebago & Lee Counties, Ill.; St. Louis, Mo.; and by editors and proprietors of newspapers of St. Louis. 9 pp.

—— Memorandum of the memorials of July 8 to September 25 [1841] with a list of the signers in Reed's hand. 5 pp. With two copies of the printed report of the Senatorial Committee, *Report: The Select Committee to Whom Were Referred the Memorials of Silas Reed, with Memorials from Sundry Persons . . . Have Had the Same under Consideration, and Submit the Following Report . . .* (27th Congress, 2d Session, Confidential, Executive, No. 1, January 25, 1842). 5 pp.

—— Draft of a memorial "To the Honorable, the Senate and House of Representatives of the U.S. of America, in Congress Assembled," presenting his claim for compensation for the condemnation, in 1872, of his Olive Street property in St. Louis for a site for a post office and custom house, with memoranda and notes concerning the case [1874]. 29 pp.

—— Letter to Judge Robert Wash. October 18, 1841. Copy. 1 p. With a two-page draft of a letter about Judge Wash intended for publication in a newspaper.

—— Letter to Daniel Webster. August 20, 1841. Copy. 1 p.

—— Letter to L. B. Woodsides. August 8, 1874. Copy. 2 pp.

[ALLEN, WILLIAM S.] Extract from a letter from the editor of the St. Louis *Evening Gazette*, January 3, 1842. Copy by Reed. 1 p.

ANTHONY, ARTHUR COX. Seven letters to his mother. June 30, 1884–August 7, 1886. 29 pp.

—— 42 letters to his grandfather, Silas Reed. January 4, 1878–July 7, 1886. 169 pp.

ANTHONY, CLARA JAMES REED (MRS. NATHAN). Three letters to her husband. May 9, 1870–February 6, 1880. 18 pp.

—— 13 letters to her father, Silas Reed. June 21, 1870–May 27, 1886. 42 pp.

—— 24 letters to her mother. [August 22? 1863]–November 16, 1885. 82 pp., 7 postcards.

ANTHONY, NATHAN. 14 letters to his wife. August 11, 1864–February 6, 1880. 53 pp.

—— 56 letters and a telegram to his father-in-law, Dr. Reed. October 10, 1866–August 20, 1880. 153 pp.

—— Seven letters to Mrs. Reed. August 31, 1872–September 11, 1874. 15 pp.

ANTHONY, NATHAN, JR. Five letters to his grandfather, Dr. Reed. March 24, 1878–January 10, 1885. 11 pp.

ANTHONY, SILAS REED. Three letters and a postcard to his mother. August 5, 1881–November 15, 1885. 13 pp.

—— 49 letters to his grandfather, Dr. Reed. April 26, 1868–August 31, 1886. 209 pp.

—— 33 letters to his grandmother. January 21, 1871–October 2, 1886. 56 pp.

BABSON, JOHN JAMES. Letter to his brother-in-law, Dr. Reed. October 22, 1873. 4 pp.

BAILEY, F. C. Letter to James Moffat. January 4, 1886. Copy. 1 p.

BARNES, JOSEPH K. Circular No. 21. Instructions, Washington, October 1, 1863. Signed by Joseph K. Barnes, A.S.G. 3 pp.

BETTS, THOMAS. Two letters to Reed. May [2,] 18, 1872. Copies. 3 pp.

BISER, CHARLES T. Agreement, signed also by Reed. May 26, 1882. 2 pp.

BLAIR, MONTGOMERY. Letter to Thomas H. Benton. November 18, 1841. Copy. 1 p.

BROWN, ARTHUR. Letter to Reed. November 21, 1884. Copy. 2 pp.

BROWN, WALTER C. Letter to John C. New. September 24, 1875. Copy. 2 pp.

BURDETT, SAMUEL S. Letter to Reed. October 8, 1875. Signature only. 1 p.

CADY, C. C. Letter to Thomas Ewing. August 20, 1841. Copy. 1 p.

—— Two letters to the President of the United States. August 20, November 18, 1841. Copies. 2 pp.

—— Letter to Daniel Webster. August 20, 1841. Copy. 1 p.

CHAMBERS, WILLIAM. Letter to Thomas H. Benton. November 9, 1841. Copy. 1 p.

CLARK, JOHN B. Letter to Reed. July 23, 1841. 1 p.

COE, HENRY I. Letter to Reed. June 12, 1874. Copy. 2 pp.

CUSHING, CALEB. Letter to Reed. December 17, 1841. 1 p.

DALLAS COUNTY, TEXAS, DISTRICT COURT. Summons to Reed to appear in court, June 9, 1878, to answer petition of Francis Fox. Signed May 31, 1878, by W. A. Harwood, Clerk. Printed form.

DAUGHERTY, JOHN M. Letter to Reed. November 15, 1869. 1 p.

DELANO, COLUMBUS. Three letters to Reed. June 19, 1873–September 5, 1875. 5 pp.

DELANO, JOHN S. Letter to Reed. October 14, 1872. Signature only. 1 p.

DEMENT, P. B. Letter to Reed. December 18, 1885. Signature only. 1 p.

DINNIES, J. C. Letter to Thomas Ewing. August 20, 1841. Copy. 2 pp.

DROGER, HENRY C. Letter to Reed. February 1, 1873. 1 p.

DRUMMOND, WILLIS. Order to Reed to turn over the surveyor general's office to Hiram Latham. March 29, 1873. Printed form. 1 p.

—— Instructions to registers and receivers. June 30, 1873. Printed form. 1 p.

—— Letter to Dr. Reed. February 2, 1881. 1 p.

EADS, JAMES B. Letter to Edward Bates. March 28, 1861. Copy by Eads. 2 pp.

EITZEN, CHARLES D. Letter to Reed. November 25, 1874. 1 p.

ELLIOTT, RICHARD S. Letter to Reed, with Olive Street property account. November 2, 1856. 4 pp.

ERVIN, W. C. Agreement with Mrs. Reed about the Carrie Shields mine, signed by Ervin and Mrs. Reed. August 30, 1871. 3 pp.

EWING, THOMAS. Letter to Reed. August 30, 1841. Signature only. 1 p.

FARRAR, BENJAMIN. Letter to F. P. Blair, Jr. March 25, 1861. 2 pp.

FERGUSON, DANIEL. Letter to Reed. December 1, 1841. 1 p.

FIELD, A. P. Letter to Caleb Cushing. October 29, 1841. Copy. 1 p.

—— Letter to Daniel Webster. October 29, 1841. 1 p.

FIELD, KATE. Letter to Reed. May 18, 1886. 2 pp.

FLETCHER, THOMAS C. Letter to W. H. Austin. December 23, 1876. 1 p.

FOGLESONG, GEORGE D. Two letters to Reed. April 22, 23, 1873. 4 pp.

GARNSEY, C. A. Letter to Reed. October [25] 1841. 3 pp.

GARNSEY, DANIEL G. Letter to Reed. October 30, 1841. 3 pp.

GLAFCKE, HERMAN. Two letters to Reed. January 2, April 23, 1873. 3 pp.

GORLINSKI, ROBERT. Letter to Reed. September 2, 1886. 1 p.

GOULD, PHILANDER. Letter to Thomas Ewing. August 21, 1841. Copy. 2 pp.

HALL, J. W. Letter to J. T. Moorehead. August 20, 1841. Copy with note to Thomas Ewing added by Reed. 2 pp.

HAMMOND, J. WESLEY. Letter to Reed. December 29, 1873. 4 pp.

—— Memorandum of understanding between Hammond and Mr. Marion. May 1874. 1 p.

HARLOW, LEWIS D. Letter to Reed. December 10, 1863. 1 p.

HARRISON, C. R. Letter to Reed. June 20, 1884. 2 pp.

HARRISON, GEORGE W. Letter to Reed. July 8, 1841. 2 pp.

HAY, HENRY G. 27 letters to Reed. November 14, 1864–August 19, 1886. 58 pp.

—— Two letters to Mrs. Reed. November 10 [1872], November 2, 1885. 7 pp.

—— Letter to H. M. Rogers. June 27, 1882. 3 pp.

HEARST, GEORGE. Power of attorney to Reed, February 1, 1873, witnessed by James Mason, F. I. Thibault, Henry C. Droger, with affidavit by Thibault. Recorded, March 5, 1873, by Michael Bauer. 3 pp.

HEARST, PHOEBE APPERSON (MRS. GEORGE). Letter to Clara Anthony. [May ? 1886.] 3 pp.

—— Letter to Dr. Reed. May 15, 1886. 2 pp.

—— Ten letters to Mrs. Reed. March 21, 1872–[June ? 1886]. 55 pp.

HENDERSON, D. R. Letter to Reed. September 11, 1867. 1 p.

HENDERSON, MALCOLM. Letter to Allen & Gaston. August 30, 1877. Endorsed: "Accepted, W. H. Gaston, Pres. D. & W. R.R. Co." 1 p.

—— Contract for financing the construction of the Dallas and Wichita Railroad, September 12, 1878. Signed by Henderson and Reed. 2 pp.

—— Agreement, July 3, 1879. Signed by Henderson and Reed. 4 pp.

—— Statement of claims and expenditures covered by the contract of September 12, 1878. Draft by Reed. 5 pp.

HERRICK, H. J. Letter to Reed. September 22, 1883. With note added by Josephine Steffens. 1 p.

HERRON, J. H. Letter to Reed. April 3, 1873. 1 p.

HOUGHTON, H. H. Letter to Reed. April 9, 1872. 3 pp.

HOUSTON, ANDREW JACKSON. Letter to H. M. Rogers. December 31, 1881. 2 pp.

—— Two receipts to Reed for payments in cases of Allen & Nettleton vs. Dallas and Wichita Railroad, and Reed vs. Harris. November 18, 1880. 2 pp.

HUNTINGTON, E. M. Three letters to Reed. July 27–November 22, 1841. 4 pp.

HUSSEY, J. B. Two letters to Reed. October 11, 13, 1879. Copies in Reed's letters to his wife, October 14, 15.

JAMES, CLARA ROGERS (MRS. EDWIN). Letter to her sister, Mrs. Reed. April 28, 1838. With note added by Mr. James. 1 p.

JAMES, EDWIN. Three letters to his sister-in-law, Mrs. Reed. January 13, 1859–September 18, 1860. 12 pp.

JOHNSTON, ALEX. Letter to Reed. March 22, 1871. 1 p.

JOHNSTON, FRANK. Three letters and a postcard to Reed. September 21, 1882–August 11, 1886. One a copy. 3 pp.

KIMBALL, NATHAN. Letter to Reed. June 6, 1874. 1 p.

KINGMAN, JOHN W. Three letters to Reed. April 22–June 5, 1873. One a copy. 13 pp.

KINNEY, GEORGE N. Letter to Reed. December 12, 1841. 1 p.

KISKADDON, J. C. Letter to A. J. Seay. February 5, 1881. Copy. 4 pp.

KRONE, WILLIAM. Letter to Reed. December 6, 1871. 1 p.

LANPHERE, WEBSTER B. 21 letters to Reed. August 15, 1873–October 16, 1874. 90 pp.

LATHAM, HIRAM. Letter to Reed. April 14, 1873. 1 p.

LAWLESS, L. E. Letter to Colonel T. H. Benton. November 15, 1841. Copy. 1 p.

LEFFINGWELL, HIRAM W., U.S. Marshal. Notices of bankruptcy of Henry I. Coe. June 18, 1878. Copy. 1 p.

LIGHTNER, J. H. Letter to Montgomery Blair. March 26, 1861. 1 p.

McDERMONT, C. Letter to Reed. December 10, 1863. 1 p.

McFARLAND, N. C. Letter to Reed. April [26] 1882, signature only, enclosing a copy of a letter to him from A. Bell, acting secretary, Department of the Interior. August 8, 1880. 12 pp.

McKEE, WILLIAM. Letter to Reed. April 10, 1873. 2 pp.

—— Letter to the President of the United States. May 2, 1873. Signed by William McKee, Henry T. Blow, C. W. Ford. Copy. 2 pp.

MACOMBER, CLARA ELIZABETH ROBISON (MRS. F. G.) "Belle." Eight letters to her grandfather, Dr. Reed. October 30, 1867–June 27 [1886]. 39 pp.

MALLORY, THOMAS H. Letter to Reed. February 24, 1875. 1 p.

MATTHEWS, LEONARD, and WHITTAKER, EDWARDS. Judgment vs. Silas Reed, Circuit Court, City of St. Louis, February 17, 1879. With assignments to James L. Blair by Matthews and Whittaker, August 1, 1879; and to Hugh A. Crawford by Blair, October 2, 1879. Certified, a true copy, by Charles F. Vogel, Clerk, with seal, October 3, 1879. Recorded, October 4, 1879, W. L. Lyles, Clerk. 2 pp.

MILLER, JOHN G. Letter to Governor Gilmer. January 7, 1841 [i.e., 1842]. Copy. 1 p.

—— Letter to Reed. February 1, 1842. 4 pp.

MISSOURI LAND COMPANY. Letter to George K. Budd. January 10, 1866. Signed by T. S. Rutherfurd, Thomas E. Souper, H. I. Coe. Copy. 2 pp.

—— Agreement to sell land to Reed. December 29, 1865. Signed by Rutherfurd, Souper and Coe. 2 pp.

MISSOURI SMELTING AND MINERAL LANDS COMPANY. Mr. Coe's statement of assets and liabilities, August 27, 1869. 2 pp.

—— List of stockholders. St. Louis, May 11, 1875. Copy. 1 p.

—— Agreement, Silas Reed with William A. Shepard, August 4, 1876. Signed before J. L. Harrison, and continued to March 10, 1877. 3 pp.

—— Agreement to purchase land from Reed, March 7, 1877, signed by Shepard. 1 p.

—— Agreement regarding price for land in Dent and Phelps Counties, March 10, 1877, signed by Shepard. 1 p.

MOORE, JOHN M. Letter to Reed. October 23, 1841. 2 pp.

MORROW, HENRY A. Letter to Reed. April 29, 1873. 2 pp.

NEWBERRY, J. S. Letter to Reed. April 8, 1881. 3 pp.

O'CONNOR, W. F. Letter to Isaac S. Coe. April 17, 1872, with added note to Reed from Thomas Betts. Copy. 2 pp.

PAGE, EDWARD. Four letters to Reed. September 16, 1883–August 20, 1886. One a copy. 4 pp.

—— Agreement with William F. James, November 5, 1881, signed by Page and George W. Emery, attorney for James. Copy. 2 pp.

PAGE, HENRY. Letter to Reed. November 2, 1882. 3 pp.

PASCHALL, NATHANIEL. Letter to President Tyler. August 19, 1841. Copy. 2 pp.

POST, M. HAYWARD. Letter to Reed. October 12, 1872, with note added by T. M. Post. 3 pp.

POST, T. M. Letter to Reed. September 25, 1872. Signature only. 3 pp.

PROVINES, WILLIAM G. Letter to Reed. January 18, 1875. 3 pp.

RAY, JAMES M. Letter to Reed. April 2, 1873. 1 p.

REAMS, JOHN T. Agreement to sell land in Franklin County, Mo., September 20, 1859. Signed by Reams and Reed. 2 pp.

REED, HENRIETTA M. ROGERS (MRS. SILAS). 25 letters to her husband. [Summer, 1859]–September 3, 1886. 86 pp., 2 postcards.

—— 12 letters to her daughter, Clara Anthony. July 29, 1859–August 21, 1875. 49 pp.

RICHARDS, JOHN F. Letter to Reed. January 4, 1884. 1 p.

RICHARDSON, W. Letter to Reed. December 16, 1873, enclosing "Resolution of Council" November 24, 1873, to send to Reed in Washington a copy of Joint Resolution No. 7, signed by F. E. Warren. 2 pp. With a printed copy of the Joint Resolution, signed: "A true copy of the original memorial as passed by the two Houses of the 3d Legislative Assembly, Wyoming Ter., W. Richardson, Secretary." 3 pp.

ROBISON, BELLE REED (MRS. JOSEPH). Letter to her father, Silas Reed. November 24 [1857?]. 2 pp.

—— 13 letters to her mother. March 21, 1854–January 29, 1863. 48 pp.

ROGERS, ALFRED M. Letter to his uncle, Dr. Reed. June 7, 1878. 6 pp.

ROGERS, HENRY M. Four letters to Clara Anthony. June 22, 1872–July 3, 1882. 10 pp.

—— Letter to Nathan Anthony. July 27, 1871, with note on verso from Anthony to Reed. 1 p.

—— Letter to Henry G. Hay. [July 3, 1882.] Copy. 1 p.

Rogers, Henry M. Letter to Mr. Hayward. [July 3, 1882.] Copy. 1 p.

——25 letters to his uncle, Silas Reed. June 13, 1871–June 28, 1886. 87 pp.

—— Two letters to Mrs. Reed. March 12, October 30, 1872. 6 pp.

—— Letter to Alex. White of White and Plowman. January 13, 1882. Letter press copy. 2 pp.

Rogers, John Hicks. Letter to his brother-in-law, Silas Reed. May 12, 1885. 2 pp.

Russell, J. Letter to Reed. December 25, 1841. 3 pp.

Scott, Thomas A. Letter to Reed. March 3, 1875. 1 p.

Seay and Kiskaddon. Letter to Reed. July 19, 1873. 1 p.

Seay and Woodside. Agreement to try the case of Reed vs. Greenman, Salem, Mo., April 12, 1875. 2 pp.

Sheldon and Waterman. Letter to H. M. Rogers. June 12, 1872. Copy. 4 pp.

Shy, A. H. Letter to Reed. January 12, 1876. 1 p.

Simmons, R. P. Letter to O. K. Smith. November 18, 1841. 1 p.

Simmons, S. Letter to Reed. November 24, 1872. Copy. 2 pp.

Simpson, James B. Letter to Colonel M. Henderson. August 5, 1881, enclosing a notice from the U.S. Circuit Court, Dallas, Texas, August 4, 1881, in the judgment Reed vs. Ira Harris to Jos. G. Graves or J. B. Simpson, his solicitor, signed by A. J. Houston. 4 pp.

Smith, Amos. Letter to Reed. September 2, 1875. 2 pp.

Smith, Charles H. Letter to Reed. November 10, 1841. 1 p.

Smith, Oliver H. Two letters to Reed. December 6, 9, 1841. Signatures only. 3 pp.

—— Letter to Reed. February 9, 1842, with notes added by S. Prentiss, J. O. Balis, and N. P. Tallmadge. 2 pp.

—— Copy of the letter of February 9, 1842, with added note by R. J. Walker. 3 pp.

Snake Creek Mining District, By-laws in operation to November 1885, signed by S. H. Epperson, chairman, R. B. Ross, secretary. Certified a true copy by N. C. Springer, recorder, C. H. Miller, deputy. October 22, 1881. Copy. 2 pp.

—— Map, in pencil, of part of Parley's Park mines, showing mines in Snake Creek District. 38 x 50 cm.

Souper, Thomas E. Letter to Reed. August 29, 1863. 1 p.

Steele, William R. Letter to Reed. April 22, 1873. 3 pp.

Steffens, Josephine (Mrs. D. J.). Letter to Reed. August 25, 1881. 1 p.

Stevens, Leverett C. Five letters to Reed. January 15, 1873–June 1, 1874. 12 pp.

Thirlwell, Charles H. Letter to Reed. January 31, 1882. 2 pp.

—— Agreement, May 22, 1882, signed by Reed and Thirlwell. 2 pp.

Thomas, John B. Six letters to Reed. November 14, 1869–June 17, 1886. 15 pp.

Tighe, John. Letter to Reed. October 23, 1872. Copy. 1 p.

Tutt, Henry. Letter to Senator Rives. June 23, 1841. 2 pp.

Tweed, W. N. Memorandum of agreement, Tweed mines. December 19, 1882, signed by Reed and Tweed. 3 pp.

TYLER, JOHN. Letter to Reed. March 31, 1873. 3 pp.

TYLER, LYON G. Three letters to Reed. March 31, 1885–May 20, 1886. 10 pp.

U.S. CIRCUIT COURT, Eastern District of Missouri. Notice to take depositions in Boston in the case of George Hearst against James Halligan and others. Signed January 2, 1874, by Seay & Kiskaddon and Knox, attorneys for plaintiff. T. von B. Crews, attorney for defendants. Printed form. 1 p.

U.S. PRESIDENT, 1841–1845 (John Tyler). Note signed J. T. on Reed's letter to the President. February 22, 1842.

U.S. PRESIDENT, 1869–1877 (U. S. Grant). Letter to Reed. August 7, 1875. Copy. 2 pp.

U.S. SENATE. Select Committee to whom were referred the memorials of Silas Reed. *Report. In Senate of the United States, January 25, 1842. Ordered to be Printed in Confidence, for the Use of the Senate* (27th Congress, 2d Session, Confidential, Executive No. 1). 5 pp.

—— Extract of so much of the Executive proceedings of the Senate as relates to the nomination of Silas Reed. In Senate of the United States, June 17, 1842. 3 pp.

U.S. SENATE. Committee on Public Lands. Draft of a letter [to the President] framed by Colonel Birch for the signatures of the Committee, February 1842. Copy on the sheet with Caleb Cushing's letter of December 17, 1841. 1 p.

URBAN, D. Order No. 4, to A. A. Surgeon Silas Reed. June 29, 1863. Signature only. 1 p.

WARD, GEORGE L. Two letters to Reed. December 6, 1841, March 30, 1842. The letter of March 30 a copy. 5 pp.

WARREN, WINSLOW. Letter to Reed. June 18 [n.y.]. 1 p.

WASH, ROBERT. Letter to Reed. October 31, 1841. 2 pp. With draft of a letter about Wash written by Reed. 2 pp.

WASHBURNE, ELIHU B. Letter to Reed. November 15, 1879. 1 p.

WATSON, THOMAS. Letter to Thomas H. Benton. November 17, 1841. Copy. 1 p.

WETMORE, GEORGE P. Letter to Reed. August 12, 1869. 2 pp.

WETMORE, HENRY. Three letters to Mrs. Reed. August 23, 1869–October 13, 1886. 10 pp.

WHEELER, WILLIAM S. Letter to Reed. January 7, 1861. 1 p.

WHITE, ALEXANDER. Three letters to Reed. October 16, 1879–May 18, 1882. Two are copies. 8 pp.

WHITE, RODGERS. Letter to H. M. Rogers. December 23, 1881. 1 p.

WHITE AND PLOWMAN. Two letters to H. M. Rogers. December 5 [i.e., January 5], January 23, 1882. 4 pp.

WHITTLESEY, ELISHA. Letter to Thomas Ewing. March 24, 1841. Copy. 1 p.

—— Letter to Edwin M. Stanton. August 28, 1862. Copy. 2 pp.

WILSON, JOSEPH S. Notification to Reed of his appointment as surveyor general of Wyoming. March 5, 1870, signed by J. S. Wilson. Printed form. 1 p.

—— Letter to Reed. January 11, 1871. 1 p.

WOOD, R. C. Letter to Reed. November 19, 1863. Copy. 1 p.

WOOD, WILLIAM. Letter to Reed. January 24, 1837. 1 p.

WYOMING TERRITORY. COUNCIL. A bill to increase the number of members of the Territorial Council and House. Printed, and certified a true copy by Jason B. Brown, Secretary, January 2, 1874. 1 p.

ZANE, ORLOFF A. Letter to Reed. May 19, 1875. Copy. 1 p.

REED, SILAS. Cipher, for use with Ward. [n.d.] 1 p.

—— Reed vs. Greenman. Notes on the case over the Densmore property. [April 1875.] 6 pp.

—— "Minutes of Salem, Mo., Suit, &c." Memoranda on the Densmore property and forged deeds. [1875?] 3 pp.

—— "Memorial to Congress" Draft of a letter in defense of Secretary Delano. [1876?] 9 pp.

—— Trial testimony, 1876. Dr. Reed's statement of the Jno. Delano contract. 16 pp.

—— Copy in pencil by Reed of L. C. Stevens' testimony. Pages 96–150 and 2 unnumbered [i.e., 57 pp.].

U.S. CONGRESS. Committee on Expenditures in the Interior Department. *Surveys in the Territory of Wyoming* (44th Congress, 1st Session, House Report No. 792, August 2, 1878). Proof sheets. 7 pp.

REED, SILAS. Will, February 5, 1866, witnessed by Henry Wetmore and George P. Wetmore. 3 pp.

"Map of mining claims in Parley's Park, Utah. Compiled from Government & location surveys, by Jos. Gorlinski, C.A. and U.S. Mineral Surveys, 1882." New York, Lehmaier & Brother. 118 x 76 cm.

"Map of the property of the Uinta Mining Company, Ontario Mining Company . . . Parley's Park, Utah Territory." New York, Lehmaier & Brother. Endorsed by Reed: "Dec. 18, 83." 32 x 23½ cm.

"Free Missouri State Board of Immigration." St. Louis, L. Gast Bro. & Co. Lith. [n.d.] With estimates of lands and values by Reed on the same sheet. 26½ x 20 cm.

"Yellowstone National Park, from surveys made under the direction of F. V. Hayden . . . 1871." Compiled and drawn by E. Hergesheimer, J. Bien, photolith. [n.p., n.d.] 28 x 30 cm.

REED, SILAS. Cash accounts, March 18, 1870–January 16, 1871. 28 pp. 14½ cm. Original binding.

—— "Copies of telegrams & correspondence between Dr. Silas Reed and Henry M. Rogers about the Reward Mine." November 13–December 25, 1882. Copied by Clara Anthony. 41 pp. 21 cm. Original binding.

—— "Lands of M.S. and M.L. Co. in Jefferson Co., Mo." 7 pp. 14½ cm. Original binding.

—— Park City, Utah, mine book. "Cash received for mining purposes in Utah." May 3, 1874–August 1875. 30 pp. 16½ cm. Original binding.

—— Scrapbook of newspaper clippings 1837–1886. 25 cm.

The clippings are chiefly about Reed's appointment as surveyor general of Missouri and Illinois in 1841, its rejection by the Senate and final confirmation, the investigation of his administration of the office, and the libel suit of the United States and James S. Conway (his successor as surveyor general) against Reed, editor of the St. Louis *Morning Post*, 1841–1848.

[Coe Collection.]

400 *RELIANCE* (U.S. Revenue Cutter)

"Journal of the U.S. Revenue Cutter *Reliance* from Baltimore, Maryland, to San Francisco, California. Capt. John A. Henriques, Commanding. Copied

from the Ship's Log and Respectfully tendered, by John C. Carter, Surgeon."
1867–1869, followed by "the journal of the Revenue Steamer *Lincoln* in
Alaska." 1869.

372 pp., 8 folded maps, 1 drawing. 32 cm. Original binding.

In August 1867 Captain John A. Hen-riques was ordered to the *Reliance*, then at Baltimore, to proceed to the Pacific Station; he sailed August 17, 1867, arriving at San Francisco January 27, 1868. While at anchor in San Francisco Harbor, February 6, Dr. J. C. Carter was discharged at his own request. The *Reliance* sailed for San Diego February 14, and while there Captain Henriques received orders to return to San Francisco and refit the *Reliance* for a cruise to Sitka. He sailed on October 30, 1868, arriving off Sitka November 16, but was forced by storms to put to sea again until November 23, when he anchored in Sitka Harbor.

The Revenue Steamer *Lincoln* left San Francisco for Alaska April 12, 1869, Captain James M. Selden in command, to visit Forts Wrangle, Sitka, and Kodiak, and then the Islands of St. George and St. Paul. On May 4, 1869 Captain Henriques relieved Captain Selden as commander of the *Lincoln* and the journal is resumed, covering the cruise of the *Lincoln*, May 5–August 12, 1869, to St. Paul's, Kodiak Island, Unalaska, St. George's Island, and Sitka, and short cruises out of Sitka, where, September 10, Captain David Evans relieved Captain Henriques of the command of the *Lincoln*.

The manuscript is in four parts: Journal of the U.S. Revenue Cutter *Reliance* from Baltimore to San Francisco, August 17, 1867–January 27, 1868; while on her station from San Francisco to San Diego, Calif., January 28–March 20, 1868; "Log of *Reliance* from San Francisco to Sitka, Alaska," October 30–December 7, 1868; and journal of the U.S. Revenue Steamer *Lincoln*, John A. Henriques, Captain, May 4–September 10, 1869.

The maps and drawing are: plans of track of U.S. Revenue Cutter *Reliance* from Baltimore across the Equator in the Atlantic Ocean, on the passage to San Francisco [42½ x 31 cm.]; from parallel of 8 degrees south around Cape Horn [58 x 36 cm.]; from the vicinity of Cape Horn to Valparaiso, thence to Equator [51 x 37 cm.]; from Equator in Pacific Ocean to San Francisco [40 x 34 cm.]; from San Francisco to Sitka, Alaska [29 x 42 cm.]; off Sitka Sound and Cape Edgecombe [108 x 29½ cm.]; plans of track of U.S. Revenue Steamer *Lincoln*, May 5–June 16, 1869 [66½ x 25½ cm.]; July 15–August 11, 1869 [46½ x 20 cm.]; and a pencil sketch of Kodiak, Alaska, with buildings identified in ink, by Benjamin Woche, Esq., Kodiak [56 x 33½ cm.].

Only the first part was copied by Dr. John C. Carter, who left the *Reliance* at San Francisco. The handwriting of Parts II and III seems to be the same but it has not been identified. The original journals were kept and signed by various officers on the ships.

[Coe No. 26.]

401 RENO, MARCUS ALBERT, COURT OF INQUIRY

"Proceedings of a Court of Inquiry in the case of Major Marcus A. Reno, concerning his conduct at the battle of the Little Big Horn River, June 25–26, 1876. Q.Q. 979."

696 pp. bound in 5 vols. 33½ cm.

Typewritten transcript (carbon) of the official report, now in the office of the Judge Advocate General, of the proceedings of the Court of Inquiry in the case of

Major Reno, convened in Chicago, January 13, 1879, by Special Orders No. 255, November 25, 1878, by command of General Sherman, E. D. Townsend, Adjutant General.

The copy of the "Proceedings" is preceded by copies of two letters from Colonel W. A. Graham, Chief, Military Affairs Section, to Major General Blanton Winship, Judge Advocate General, November 29, 1933, citing the condition of the original records and the need of copying them. The transcript includes photostats of two maps, "Custer's Battle-field [June 25, 1876] surveyed and drawn . . . by Sargeant Charles Becker" [40 x 36 cm.], and [Sketch Map—showing positions of Calhoun, Crittendon, Keogh and Custer] Exhibit No. 7 [19 x 17 cm.] ; and, at the end, an affidavit, certifying that it is a true and correct copy of the original, signed by Oliver C. Hinkle and William J. Mould, before N. Curtis Lammond, Notary Public, District of Columbia, October 1933.

The following additional reports accompany the proceedings:

"The Reno Court of Inquiry. Stenographic reports of the testimony, editorials and miscellaneous articles from the *Chicago Times*, January 14–February 12, 1879." 693 pp. bound in 2 volumes. 28½ cm.

The transcript has caption title, "Massacre memories. Revived by the Military Court of Inquiry now convened in this city" with some explanatory notes by W. J. G[hent]. It includes also Appendix A. Findings of the Court, March 11, 1879; Appendix B. Benteen's Official Report, July 4, 1876; Appendix C. Indian Scouts in the Battle, by W. J. G[hent] ; and an index.

"The Reno Court of Inquiry. Photostatic copies of articles and editorials in the *Chicago Times*, January 14–February 12, 1879." 109 leaves. 28½ cm.

Negative photostats of columns of the *Chicago Times* covering the account of and evidence at the Court of Inquiry, mounted on 109 leaves, with some passages supplied by typewriter.

The transcripts were made from the original Graham copy, especially for Dr. Francis R. Hagner of Washington, D.C., in 1933, and with the photostats were sold at auction by G. A. Baker, January 20–21, 1941. Reports of the Court of Inquiry were printed in the *Army and Navy Journal*, November 30, 1878–March 22, 1879, Vol. XVI. The testimony is quoted in part in E. A. Brininstool, *A Trooper with Custer*, Columbus, 1925, chapter 3, and W. A. Graham, *The Story of the Little Big Horn*, Harrisburg [1945].

[Coe No. 50.]

402 REVILLA GIGEDO, JUAN VICENTE GÜÉMEZ PACHECHO DE PADILLA HORCASITAS Y AGUAYO, CONDE DE, 1740–1799

Two letters to Sr. Dn. Alejandro Malaspina. Mexico, 3, de Dic[iembr] e de 1790, signed, with rubric, "El Conde Revilla Gigedo."

5 pp. 29½ cm. With typewritten translations by Professor Jacques Walskin.

The signatures only are in the hand of Revilla Gigedo.

These two letters from the Conde de Revilla Gigedo, Viceroy of Mexico, to Alejandro Malaspina, were written on the same day, December 3, 1790. Malaspina had sailed from Cádiz, July 30, on the *Descubierta* in command of a round-the-world scientific expedition, accompanied by José Bustamante y Guerra in command of the *Atrevida*. The expedition was to cover the West Coast of the Americas, and later orders were to examine the Northwest Coast at 60 degrees for a passage to the Atlantic. Bustamante arrived at San Blas March 30, 1791, and sailed again for

Acapulco on hearing of Malaspina's belated arrival there on March 27.

The first of these letters enclosed a transcript of news received from Baron de Carondelet, Intendant of San Salvador, Guatemala, of some strange ships recently seen in a sheltered port near Osolutan, which aroused suspicion and should be investigated. As most of the Spanish ships on the coast were at San Blas, some of them engaged in the Nootka expedition and in carrying supplies to the missions and garrisons in California, the Viceroy asked Malaspina to have one of his corvettes carry out this reconnaissance. For this purpose he sent a map of the coast, and instructions. The transcript of news, the map and instructions are no longer enclosed with the letter.

The second letter is in answer to one received from Malaspina, saying that he will reach Realejo about next February. The Viceroy answers that he has forwarded all papers concerning the expedition to Acapulco to await his arrival, and that he will send any further communications to San Blas where Malaspina will find the supplies he has requested for the corvettes.

[Coe No. 156.]

403 RICE'S SECTIONAL MAP OF DAKOTA TERRITORY

Draughted by Fred Sturnegh, St. Paul, Minnesota, 1872, with dates of camps on the route from Fort Rice along the Heart River indicated in ink. June 20–26 [n.y.].

Map. Scale 15 miles = 1 inch. 87½ x 69 cm.

This is possibly a map used on the Yellowstone Expedition in the summer of 1873 under the command of General David S. Stanley, which left Fort Rice June 20, 1873.

[Coe No. III, 815.]

404 RICH, CHARLES COULSON, 1809–1883

"Charles Rich. His Day Book. An account of my traveling up to the Land of Zion." May 29 to July 1, 1834.

13 pp. 16 cm. With typewritten transcript.

After the expulsion of the Mormons from Jackson County to Clay County, Mo., they appealed to Governor Dunklin for his help in reinstating and protecting them in their homes. He declared that he had not the power to reinstate them but would provide arms for them to protect themselves after their return. In May 1834 a military company was raised in Kirtland and set out for Missouri. At this time Charles Rich was engaged in missionary work near his home in Tazewell County, Ill., and determined to join the expedition. While in camp at Salt River, Mo., word was received that the governor had changed his mind and would not help them, and that negotiations for a peaceful settlement with the citizens of Jackson County had failed. The army advanced to the neighborhood of Liberty, Mo., and was disbanded June 26.

The daybook records briefly the journey from Tazewell County, Ill., with Lyman Wight and Hyrum Smith across the Mississippi to Mormon camp on Salt River where they were organized in companies and drilled. Rich was elected captain of a company and Lyman Wight commanding general. On June 25 cholera broke out in the camp and there were a number of deaths.

John H. Evans, in his *Charles Coulson*

Rich, New York, 1936, quotes from a journal covering this expedition. The brief quotation does not agree exactly with this text.   [Coe Collection.]

405 RICHARDS, FRANKLIN DEWEY, 1821–1899

Letter to his father and mother, Phineas and Wealthy Dewey Richards. Illinois Town, January 1, 1839. Unsigned.

4 pp. crossed. [i.e., 8 pp.] 32 cm. With typewritten transcript.

Franklin D. Richards joined the Church of Jesus Christ of Latter-day Saints, was baptised by his father in 1838, and a few months later left his home in Richmond, Mass., for Far West. He led a company of emigrants to Salt Lake City in 1848 and was a member of the Council of the Twelve Apostles of the Church from 1849 to 1898.

The letter addressed to: "Mr. Phineas Richards, West Stockbridge, Berk. Co., Mass." is written in black ink on four folio pages. It has been continued in red ink across the four pages. A note at the be- ginning reads: "Read the black & then the red."

In the letter Richards describes his arrival in St. Louis, the journey on foot to Far West, the hostility of the settlers, the arrival at Haun's Mill, where he learned of the massacre that had taken place on October 30 when his brother George was killed, and his short stay in Far West. He writes of the Mormon War, news of relatives in Far West, his strengthened faith in the Church, the fertility of the country, and his return to Illinois Town where he was employed cutting timber.

[Coe Collection.]

406 RICHARDSON, WILLIAM P., *d.* 1857

Copy of a letter to Nathaniel Pascall. Lecompton, February 10, 1857. Certified an accurate copy of a letter written for publication by General Richardson immediately previous to his death, by John W. Forman, Seventh Council District, Lecompton, February 14, 1857.

3 pp. 32½ cm.

Endorsed: "The original letter was furnished Governor Geary by Mr. Foreman the confidential friend of General Richardson. Copy taken Feby. 14, 1857."

William P. Richardson was major general of the Kansas Territorial Militia, and member of the Council of the Territorial Legislature. He died February 14, 1857. After his death the original letter came into the possession of his colleague, John W. Forman, who retained it and forwarded a copy to Nathaniel Pascall of St. Louis, asking him to publish it in his paper.

The letter gives an eyewitness account of the insult offered Governor John W. Geary by William T. Sherrard as the Governor was leaving the House of Representatives, February 9, 1857.

The letter is published, with Forman's letter of the same date, on pages 286–287 of "Governor Geary's Administration. Correspondence." Kansas State Historical Society, *Transactions*, 1896, V, 264–289.

[Coe Collection.]

407 RIEGEL, R.

Letter in German to "Geehrter Herr General." Fort Laramie, D.T. May, 1867. Signed: "R. Riegel C— 2 U.S. Cav."

6 pp. 32½ cm.

Riegel was evidently a private or non-commissioned officer in the 2d U.S. Cavalry.

The letter, written in ink in a careful hand, describes conditions at Fort Laramie, the failure of the Indian commissioners to reach an agreement with the Indians at Fort McPherson, preparations for a campaign against the Indians; and criticizes the conduct of the officers, mentioning especially General [Lt. Col.] Palmer, Captains Ball and Thompson, and Lieutenants Bates, Gregg, and Norton.

The place, date, and salutation have been crossed out and a heading added in a different hand: "*Indianer-Krieg* und '*irregulärer*' *Unfug*. Einem Privatbrief aus einem der westlichen Forts entnehmen wir folgende interessante Stellen." Some of the more severe criticisms have been crossed out and other alterations have been made in the same hand, apparently editing the manuscript for publication in some newspaper.

[Coe No. 203.]

408 ROSS, ALEXANDER, 1783–1856

"The Fur Hunters of the Far West. A Narrative of Adventures in the Oregon and Rocky Mountains." Original manuscript in two parts, accompanied by drafts of the dedication and preface, the manuscript of a vocabulary of the Nez Percés and the table of the weather at Fort Nez Percés, 1822.

440 pp. 25½ cm.

The drafts of the dedication and preface differ widely in phraseology from the text as printed. The manuscript of the text shows many deletions and alterations, and there are other minor variations from the printed text.

Published in full with title: *The Fur Hunters of the Far West; A Narrative of Adventures in the Oregon and Rocky Mountains . . .* In two volumes, London, 1855.

[Coe No. 157.]

409 ROTHWELL, WILLIAM RENFRO

Journal of an overland trip from Missouri to California in 1850; letters written en route and from the mines; and a manuscript guide.

3 vols. [i.e., 289 pp.] 25 cm. With typewritten transcript.

After his stay in California Rothwell returned to his home in Missouri and became a member of the faculty of William Jewell College in Liberty, Mo. With his letter to his father and mother, November 23, 1850, which he sent by his uncle, W. E. Stephens, who was returning to the East, he sent his "Notes of a journey" and "Guide" for safekeeping with the thought that they might be helpful to future emigrants to California, and possibly worth publishing.

—— "Notes of a journey to California in the spring and summer of 1850, by Wm. R. Rothwell of Callaway County, Missouri." April 8–August 28, 1850. 140 pp.

Rothwell, W. R. Four letters to his father, Dr. John Rothwell. April 13–September 15, 1850. 19 pp.

—— 11 letters to his father and mother. April 18–November 23, 1850. 46 pp.

—— Four letters to his brother Thomas. April 19–October 27, 1850. 20 pp.

—— Letter to his sister Polly (Mrs. J. Pemberton Gibbs). April 30, 1850. 3 pp.

—— Letter to his brother Gideon. May 24, 1850. 2 pp.

—— Letter to his mother. October 25, 1850. 4 pp.

—— "The Californian's Guide. A minute description of the most direct over land route from the States to Sacramento City in California, in which all the various rivers, creeks, lakes, springs, wooding places, mountains, deserts, poisonous waters, and other notable objects upon the road with the distances from point to point are mentioned with such remarks as may convey useful informa-

tion to the emigrant. By Wm. R. Rothwell, 1850." 55 pp.

The last five pages are dated September 1, 1850 [not included in the transcript]. They contain notes on "Mining operations," "Placerville," "Weber Creek," "Our location," and "Our mining."

The journal, letters, and guide give a detailed description of the journey across the Plains from Fulton, Mo., to Weber Creek, Calif., in company with his uncles, Dr. William E. Stephens and Captain Joseph Price, and his brother-in-law J. Pemberton Gibbs, who was not well and turned back on April 17. The party reached St. Joseph April 27, crossed the Missouri May 1 and camped near St. Joseph until May 9, started west along the trail to Fort Kearney and the north bank of the Platte to Fort Laramie, through South Pass to Sublette's Cut-off, Hudspeth's Cut-off, Humboldt and Carson Rivers to Hangtown, August 28, and to the mines on Weber Creek.

[Coe No. 158.]

410 RUSLING, JAMES FOWLER, 1834–1918

"Memoranda of Inspections from Fort Leavenworth, Ks. to Great Salt Lake City U.T. 1866."

95 pp. 14½ cm. Original binding. With typewritten transcript.

A notebook kept while on a tour of inspection, ordered by the Quartermaster General, to examine into the condition of the military posts from Fort Leavenworth to the Pacific Coast, including especially Denver and Salt Lake City, with a view to reducing the great expenditures that prevailed. General Rusling was to return by Panama and report in person to the Quartermaster General.

The notebook records conditions at Fort Leavenworth, which he reached August 1, 1866, Fort Riley, Kans., Fort Kearney, N.T., Fort McPherson, Neb., Fort Sedgwick, C.T., Fort Morgan, C.T.,

Denver, Fort Bridger, U.T., and Camp Douglas, U.T., near Salt Lake City, November 2, 1866, and ends with notes on the navigability of the Colorado River.

All of these notes were incorporated in the full reports submitted by Rusling to the Quartermaster General and published in *Inspection by Generals Rusling and Hazen. Letter from the Secretary of War Transmitting Reports of Inspection Made by Generals Rusling and Hazen* (39th Congress, 2d Session, House Ex. Doc. No. 45, 1867).

[Coe Collection.]

411 RUSSELL, OSBORNE, 1814–*ca.* 1865

"Journal of a trapper, or, Nine years residence among the Rocky Mountains between the years of 1834 and 1843 . . . by Osborne Russell."

190 pp. 25½ cm. Original binding.

The manuscript journal comprises "a general description of the country, climate, rivers, lakes, mountains, &c., the nature and habits of animals, manners and customs of Indians and a complete view of the life led by a hunter in those regions."

The manuscript includes, in the Appendix [34 pp.], descriptions of the animals of the region and of the Snake and Crow Indians, and is accompanied by the following letters:

—— Three letters to his sister, Mrs. Eleanor Read. April 4, 1848–August 26, 1855[?]. 10 pp.

—— Letter to his sister, Martha A. Russell. April 3, 1848. 3 pp.

The letter contains an account of the Whitman Massacre. It was published in the *Journal*, 1921, pp. xii–xvi.

RUSSELL, REBECCA A. Letter to her aunt, Mrs. Eleanor Read. August 5, 1850;

and, on the same sheet, notes from Daniel Russell and Martha Russell, August 5, 1850.

RUSSELL, OSBORNE. "Journal of a Trapper, or; Nine Years in the Rocky Mountains 1834–1843 . . ." Galley proof of the journal and the appendix, which did not appear in the 1914 edition, with manuscript corrections, and both galley and page proof of the publisher's note, copyrighted in 1921. 40 galleys. 61 cm. 16 pp. 24½ cm.

In 1918 the journal was the property of L. A. York, Boise, Ida., grand nephew of the author. It was published by the family in a limited edition in 1914 with title: *Journal of a Trapper, or, Nine Years in the Rocky Mountains, 1834–1843* [Boise, 1914]; and reissued with a revised Publisher's Note and Appendix in 1921.

[Coe Nos. 159, 160.]

412 RYDER, SIR DUDLEY, 1691–1756

Report "To the Right Honble. the Lords of a Committee of his Majesties most honourable Privy Council" on the petition of Arthur Dobbs and others for finding a passage to the Western and Southern Ocean of America; and for a grant of all lands they may discover and settle adjacent to Hudson's Bay not already occupied by the Company of Adventurers trading to Hudson's Bay. Signed by D. Ryder and W. Murray. August 10, 1748.

5 pp. 31 cm.

Endorsed: "10th August 1748 Dobbs Esqr ad Hudson's bay Company. The attorney & Solicitor Generall's Report."

The opinion of the Attorney General, Sir Dudley Ryder, and the Solicitor General, Lord Murray, was opposed to

granting a charter to the petitioners which must break in upon that of the Hudson's Bay Company.

Both signatures seem to be in the same hand as the text of the report. The manuscript has some alterations in a different hand and is probably an early draft. The printed copy varies slightly and follows some of the alterations.

Printed in *House of Commons. Papers Presented to the Committee Appointed to*

Inquire into the State and Condition of the Countries Adjoining to Hudson's Bay . . . [London] 1749.

[Coe No. 161.]

413 SAC AND FOX INDIANS

Petition of the Fox Indians of the tribe of Sac and Fox Indians addressed to Governor John W. Geary, requesting that their present agent, Burton A. James, not be reappointed. Centropolis, Kansas Territory, February 16, 1857. Signed by the marks of eight chiefs and braves of the Fox Indians.

1 p. 19½ x 49 cm.

The petition is in the handwriting of Perry Fuller who was authorized to sign the names, and is witnessed by George

Powers who acted as interpreter. (*See also* No. 212.)

[Coe Collection.]

414 SAGE, RUFUS B., 1817–

Correspondence and papers of Rufus B. Sage and members of his family, 1789–1864.

108 letters and papers. 268 pp. 12½–51½ cm.

Rufus B. Sage left his home in Upper Middletown, Conn., in 1836 for Marietta, Ohio, where his sister, Jerusha Sage Gear, lived. He spent the next four years, except for the winter of 1837–1838 when he was in West Virginia and made a voyage down the Ohio and Mississippi to Natchez and Fort Gibson, in Marietta. Circleville, and Columbus, Ohio, engaged most of the time in the printing and newspaper business. In 1840 he decided to go to the Rocky Mountains and Oregon, and with some friends went to Independence to join a fur-trading party. They left Independence September 2, 1841, spent the winter in the mountains, returned to Independence and again started west in 1842. In 1844 he was back in Ohio, editing *The Whig Battering-Ram* from August 9 to October 25 and preparing to write an account of his travels, which was published by Carey & Hart of Philadelphia in 1846 with title: *Scenes in the Rocky Mountains, and in Oregon, California, New Mexico, Texas, and the Grand Prairies.*

The family papers include correspond-

ence of Rufus B. Sage's grandfather Elisha Sage, his father Rufus Sage, and other members of the family, about their personal affairs and life in Connecticut, 1789–1828; and the following letters and papers of Rufus B. Sage about his life in Ohio, his travels in the West and the publication of his book:

SAGE, RUFUS B. 22 letters to his mother, Mrs. Jerusha B. Sage. June 19, 1836–January 1, 1847. 73 pp.

—— Letter to his sister, Mrs. Jerusha S. Gear. May 22, 1837. 4 pp.

—— Letter to his sister, Mrs. Francis S. Gear. November 5, 1837. 2 pp.

—— Letter to Messrs. Paine & Burgess. October 25, 1845. 3 pp.

CAREY & HART. 14 letters to R. B. Sage. April 7, 1846–March 15, 1847. 19 pp.

DOWD, LEWIS B. Letter to R. B. Sage. July 24, 1837. 3 pp.

GEAR, MRS. FRANCES S. Five letters to her

brother, R. B. Sage. May 17, 1837–January 11, 1847. 11 pp.

GEAR, MRS. JERUSHA S. Nine letters to her brother, R. B. Sage. March 2, 1838–January 23, 1847. 25 pp.

HEPBURN, JAMES, Pastor of the Second Baptist Church, Middletown. Certificate that notice of the intended marriage of Mr. Rufus B. Sage and Miss Marietta M. Miller was given publicly before the congregation, November 7, 1847. Upper Middletown, November 29, 1847. 1 p.

MERWIN, WEALTHY SAGE. Letter to her cousin, R. B. Sage. July 25, 1845. 3 pp.

MUNSON [?], THOMAS A. Two letters to R. B. Sage. August 16, 19, 1845. 4 pp.

NASH, SIMEON. Letter to R. B. Sage. December 14, 1846. 2 pp.

PAINE & BURGESS. Letter to R. B. Sage. October 21, 1845. 1 p.

PIERCE, F. N. Letter to R. B. Sage. August 23, 1846. 3 pp.

SAGE, EDMUND. Seven letters to his brother, R. B. Sage. February 28, 1846–May 10, 1847. 13 pp.

SAGE, ELIZABETH MARIA. Three letters to her uncle, R. B. Sage. August 23–November 13, 1844. 9 pp.

SAGE, ELIZABETH WILLIAMS. Letter to her uncle, R. B. Sage. September 18, 1844. 3 pp.

SAGE, GEORGE HUBBARD. Two letters to his uncle, R. B. Sage. August 16, 1863, September 20, 1864. 11 pp.

SAGE, MRS. JERUSHA BUTLER. Five letters to her son, R. B. Sage. July 3 [1836?]–August 25, 1844. 8 pp.

STEWARD, A. W. Letter to R. B. Sage. August 19, 1846. 1 p.

WHITE, HENRY. Letter to R. B. Sage. January 7, 1838. 3 pp.

WOODRUFF, GEORGE R. Letter to his cousin, R. B. Sage. August 23, 1847. 3 pp.

SAGE, RUFUS B. "Description of the remains of an ancient fortification at Selsertown, eleven miles north of Natchez, Miss." 2 pp. 49 cm.

—— Eight poems. 21 pp. 24½–42 cm.

—— Memorandum of accounts with Carey & Hart for the publication of *Scenes in the Rocky Mountains*. 6 pp. 12½ cm.

One of the original poems, "Night on the Prairie," is printed in *Scenes in the Rocky Mountains*.

[Coe Collection.]

415 SÁNCHEZ, FRAY FRANCISCO MIGUEL

"Historio Compuesta de todo lo acaesido en la expediccion hecha al Puerto de Nuca año de 1789."

Contemporary copy. 166 pp. 20 cm.

A note at the end in another hand, signed with rubric by Josef Manuel Gonzáles Cabrada, states that the manuscript was copied in the month of February, 1790, in Guadalajara.

In 1788 Viceroy Manuel de Flóres of Mexico sent an expedition to the Northwest Coast under Estéban Martínez to determine the extent of the Russian settlements and trade, and the trade of other nations. On his return to San Blas Martínez wrote to the Viceroy that Nootka should be garrisoned to establish Spanish control from Nootka to San Francisco. In December the Viceroy ordered Martínez and Lopez de Haro, on the *Princesa* and *San Carlos*, to occupy Nootka. The expedition sailed February 17, 1789. Four

Franciscans from the College of San Fernando at San Blas accompanied the expedition to establish a mission at Nootka, Severo Patero and Francisco Miguel Sánchez on the *Princesa* and José Espi and Lorenzo Sosies on the *San Carlos*.

The manuscript, written in the form of a journal, covers the events of the expedition in detail from April 4 to December 12, 1789, describing the meetings with Captains James Colnett, Robert Gray, William Douglas, and John Kendrick, and the seizure of the British ships *Argonaut* and *Princess Royal* and the Portuguese ship *Iphigenia*. The expedition sailed for San Blas in the autumn, arriving in December.

The journal is followed by a ten-page vocabulary of the Nootka language and a 23-page description of the country around Nootka, the trees, flowers, animals and climate, and the Indians and their customs.

The manuscript formerly belonged to Jose M. Linga, whose name is on the flyleaf. Martínez' diary of the expedition is in the Archivo de Indias, Seville, and a contemporary copy is in the Huntington Library.

[Coe Collection.]

416 SCHAEFFER, LUTHER MELANCHTHON, 1821–

"Private journal of L. M. Schaeffer—who does not write out in extenso as he would wish for [a few words missing] he fears he might fill his book before his journey is accomplished, and because he cannot write as correctly and intelligibly as he would on land. At sea, May 25th, 1849." March 24, 1849 to April 25, 1852.

197 pp. 18 cm.

The journal is written in pencil in a neat, clear hand. The first four leaves and the last leaf are badly worn and have been repaired.

L. M. Schaeffer of Frederick, Md., joined the California Mutual Benefit Association, February 7, 1849, and sailed for California on the ship *Flavius* from New York March 24, arriving in San Francisco September 17, 1849. The journal ends with the entry for April 25, 1852, when Schaeffer left the mines in Grass Valley for San Francisco and his home in Maryland.

The journal describes the weather and events of each day of the voyage, the stops at Rio de Janeiro and Valparaiso, the organization and constitution of the Fraternal Gold Seekers, and the arrival in San Francisco, September 17, 1849; the winter of 1850 in San Francisco; and experiences at the mines on the Tuolumne River in 1849, at Nevada City in 1850, and Grass Valley, 1851–1852.

The journal is accompanied by Schaeffer's *Sketches of Travels in South America, Mexico and California*, New York, James Egbert, Printer, 1860, which is based upon the journal but omits many of the details and incidents in the manuscript.

[Coe Collection.]

417 SEAMAN, WILLIAM VALENTINE

"Journal of a voyage &c. on board Barque Susan from New York to San Francisco around (about as bad as going around the world) Cape Horn via Rio de Janeiro and (one of the greater ports on the Pacific) Talcahuano, or Conception from March 16, to Oct. 14, 1849. W. Valentine Seaman, 1849."

212 pp. 20½ cm. Original binding.

Note on flyleaf: "Dear Parents. You will please keep this journal as I wish to make a copy of it when I return, and oblige your son William."

The *New York Tribune* advertised in March 1849 the sailing of the bark *Susan*, Captain Lothrop, and opportunities to join an "association for California" on payment of $500. W. Valentine Seaman of New York joined the company and sailed March 14.

The journal gives a detailed account of each day of the voyage from New York to San Francisco, March 14 to October 15, 1849; describes their stay in Rio de Janeiro and in Talcahuana and Concepcion; and records the actions taken at the meetings of the Aurelian Association. The last two pages contain a table of the daily temperature from March 13 to October 24, 1849.

Laid in the volume are copies of the following documents:

"Articles of Impeachment" of the president of the Aurelian Association, June 9, 1849. Signed by W. Valentine Seaman, J. Russell Field, John Pattison, M.D., S. B. Lothrop, John R. Dunn, E. R. Green, H. C. Sweetser, Franklin Lothrop, D. Bassett. 2 pp. 20 cm.

Letter to Captain S. B. Lothrop. Atlantic Ocean, June 20, 1849, on board bark *Susan*. Signed by 17 members of the Association and two passengers. 1 p. 19½ cm.

Two designs in color for the flag of the Aurelian Association. 1 p. 19½ cm.
[Coe Collection.]

418 SERRA, FRAY JUNÍPERO, 1713–1784

Diario [de el Viaje para los puertos de San Diego de Monterey] 28 de Marzo–30 Junio 1769.

Photostat. 35 pp. 33½ cm.

Fray Junípero Serra of the College of San Fernando in Mexico was made president of the missions of Lower California in 1768; in 1769, when Don José de Galvéz, Visitador General of New Spain, organized an expedition to San Diego by sea, and overland, Serra was sent with the overland group under the command of Don Gaspar de Portolá.

The diary covers Fray Serra's journey from the mission at Loreto until his arrival at San Diego, describing conditions at the missions visited on the journey north through Lower California, the Indians, and the country.

The original manuscript was formerly in the Ramirez Collection which is now a part of the Edward E. Ayer Collection in the Newberry Library in Chicago. It has been translated by C. F. Lummis and published in *Out West*, 1902, XVI–XVII. The photostat is of the manuscript in the Edward E. Ayer Collection and is inscribed: "To W. R. Coe. Compliments Edward E. Ayer. December 9, 1924."
[Coe No. IV, 137.]

419 SEYMOUR, SAMUEL

"The original views drawn by the artist S. Seymour during the expedition from Pittsburgh to the Rocky Mountains under the command of Major Stephen A. Long. 1819–20."

10 watercolors, mounted. 27 x 21½ cm.

Samuel Seymour was an engraver of portraits in Philadelphia, 1797–1822, when he was appointed artist to accompany Major Long, who was ordered by Secretary of War John C. Calhoun to explore the country between the Mississippi and the Rocky Mountains, beginning with the Missouri, Red River, Arkansas River, and the Mississippi above the mouth of the Missouri. The party included Mr. Peale, assistant naturalist, and Mr. Seymour, painter. The expedition went up the Missouri and wintered near Council Bluffs. The next spring the original plan to explore the Yellowstone was canceled. The expedition was ordered to ascend the Platte to its source and return by the Arkansas and Red Rivers. The views are:

"Pawnee Council." Signed. 20½ x 15 cm.

"War dance in the interior of a lodge." 20½ x 14½ cm.

"Kiawa encampment." Signed. 20½ x 14½ cm.

"Hills of trap formation." Initials. 21 x 14½ cm.

"View on the Arkansas near the Rocky Mountains." Initials. 20½ x 13½ cm.

"Cliffs of red sandstone near the Rocky Mts." Signed. 20½ x 14½ cm.

"View paralel [sic] to the base of the mountains at the head of the Platte." Signed. 21 x 14½ cm.

"View near the base of the Rocky Mountains." Initials. 21 x 14½ cm.

"Indian record of a battle between the Pawnees and Konzas, being a Fac Simile of a delineation upon a bison robe." By T. R. Peale. 18½ x 14 cm.

Three portraits "Kaskaia, Shienne Chief, Arrappaho." Initialed. 15 x 12½ cm.

Dr. James, physician on the expedition, edited an *Account of an Expedition from Pittsburgh to the Rocky Mountains, Performed in the Years 1819 and '20 . . . under the Command of Major Stephen H. Long*, Philadelphia, 1823. 2 vols. and atlas, 1822. The atlas contained 2 maps, 1 chart, 6 plates by Seymour and 2 by Peale.

James' *Account* was also published in London in 1823 in three volumes, with some slight variations in the text. Most of the plates were re-engraved. Three additional ones by Seymour and one substitution were included. The Peale and four of the Seymour views are reproduced in the London edition.

[Coe No. 162.]

420 SHARPE, JAMES M.

"J. M. Sharpe. Private journal from March 1 1843 to" February 10, 1848.

63 pp. 20½ cm. Original binding.

James M. Sharpe, brother of Thomas H. Sharpe, banker of Indianapolis, Ind., left home to seek his fortune as a traveling merchant, buying chiefly in Cincinnati, trading first in Indiana and Louisville and later in St. Louis, Independence, Keokuk, Nauvoo, and other towns on the Mississippi and Missouri Rivers, and New Orleans and the Red River. He also traded in lands and was interested in the "Half Breed Tract." When the journal ends in

1848, he was teaching in Yellow Creek, Linn Co., Mo., and studying law.

The journal was written daily from time to time with the intervals summarized briefly. The periods covered in most detail are 1843 and September–October 1844. The journal describes the places he visits and the people he sees, especially Nauvoo and Joseph Smith.

[Coe No. 163.]

421 SHEPARD, CYRUS, 1799–1840

The journal of Cyrus Shepard's trip across the Plains with the Wyeth Expedition in 1834 and his life and labors among the Indians of Oregon Territory, March 3, 1834 to December 20, 1835.

213 pp. 19½ cm. Original binding. With typewritten transcript.

Cyrus Shepard was selected by the Board of Foreign Missions of the Methodist Episcopal Church and the Rev. Jason Lee to accompany him to Oregon. The party consisted of Jason Lee, his nephew Daniel Lee, Courtney M. Walker, Philip L. Edwards, and Shepard. They joined Captain Nathaniel J. Wyeth on his second expedition, to cross the Plains and Rockies, meeting his party near Independence April 27 and traveling with him until July 30, when they left him near the site of Fort Hall, and continued accompanied by Mr. McKay of the Hudson's Bay Company until August 16. They arrived at Vancouver Monday, September 15, 1834, where Shepard remained when the rest of the party went on to the Willamette to found their mission. He took care of the school until March 2, 1835, when he joined his associates at the mission.

The journal is carefully written in ink and opens with Shepard's departure from Massachusetts March 4, 1834. A note on the flyleaf reads: "Cyrus Shepard—Book purchased at St. Louis, Missouri, 3d April 1834. Price 62½ cts." There is a rough index in pencil on the flyleaf and back cover in a different hand.

A large part of Shepard's journal is printed in Z. A. Mudge, *The Missionary Teacher, A Memoir of Cyrus Shepard*, New York, 1848.

[Coe No. 164.]

422 SHEPARD, CYRUS, 1799–1840

Letter to "Dear Father in Christ Jesus." Mission House, Walamette [*sic*] River, October 28, 1836.

2 pp. 24 cm.

The letter is written in answer to one received September 12, dated December 21, 1835. He reports on the number of children at the mission school and mentions both Spalding and Lee.

[Coe No. 164 A.]

423 SHIELDS, JAMES G., 1829–

California trip from St. Joseph to Sacramento, California, April 9 to August 13, 1850.

218 pp. 17½ cm. With typewritten transcript.

James G. Shields of Floyd County, Ind., was interested in a number of Ohio River steamers. He served during the war carrying provisions, and after the war was a traveling salesman for a firm in Louisville.

The diary is vividly written with details of the route, camping places and incidents on the way. The party left New Albany March 27, on the *Courtland*. Shields and some companions landed at Liberty and proceeded overland to St. Joseph. They left St. Joseph April 25 following the trail to the Platte and Fort Kearney, along the southern bank to the ford of the South Platte, to Fort Laramie, the Sweetwater, South Pass, Fort Bridger, and Salt Lake City, June 29, the Mormon Route to the Humboldt River by Pilot Springs, the Carson River to Pleasant Valley and Weaverville, August 13.

For a large part of the journey Shields' mess traveled with or near another party from New Albany including James Abbey, whose journal has been published.

[Coe No. III, 656.]

424 SHIPLEY, CELINDA E. HINES (MRS. H. R.)

Diary of Celinda E. Hines (afterward Mrs. H. R. Shipley) from February 16, when the Hines family left Hastings, Oswego County, New York, to October 11, 1853, after their arrival in Portland, Oregon.

3 vols. [i.e., 283 pp.] 12½–15½ cm.

Celinda Hines with her mother, and her father who was drowned on August 26, accompanied her uncles, Gustavus Hines and Harvey K. Hines, and their families to Oregon in 1853. Upon arrival in Portland she and her mother stopped with Mr. and Mrs. Kingley, principal of the Academy, and she undertook to teach. She also attended singing school where Mr. Shipley was the teacher.

The diary was almost destroyed by fire many years ago before it was placed in the custody of George H. Himes, Secretary of the Oregon Pioneer Association. It is published in the *Transactions* of the Oregon Pioneer Association, June 1918, XLVI, 69–125, but breaks off in the entry for September 29.

[Coe No. 165.]

425 SILLIMAN, BENJAMIN, 1816–1885

Letter to Charles Wilkes. New Haven, January 12, 1846, with a note added by James Dwight Dana.

3 pp. 28½ cm.

The letter paper is headed by a half-page engraving of the Yale College library.

The letter is about Silliman's work on the corals brought back from the Exploring Expedition by Mr. Dana, and asking for samples of sea water and to see Dr. Jackson's analysis of Savu water. Mr. Dana's note seconds the request.

[Rare Book Room.]

426 SILLIMAN, BENJAMIN, 1816–1885

Agreement, September 1, 1866, between John Felix De Ville of San Francisco, California, by his attorney-in-fact, Benjamin Silliman, and Lewis M. Hills, of the city of New Haven, for the sale before March 1, 1867 of the Mount Gains gold-bearing vein and mine on Burns Creek, Mariposa County, California.

4 pp. 31½ cm.

The agreement is signed by Silliman and Hills, and witnessed by Mrs. B. Silliman.

[Rare Book Room.]

427 SIMMONS, MICHAEL TRAUTMAN, 1814–1867

Bill in Chancery vs. Nathaniel Crosby, Jr., Lawrence C. Gray, and Clanrick Crosby, September 8, 1851.

9 pp. 25 cm.

Michael T. Simmons emigrated to Oregon in 1844 and in 1845 settled on Puget Sound. He took an active part in the establishment of Washington Territory and was appointed superintendent of Indian affairs by Governor Stevens.

The complaint, addressed to the Honorable William Strong, Judge of the U.S. District Court for the Third Judicial District of the Territory of Oregon, asks an injunction against the defendants to prevent their occupancy of part of Simmons' property as they had not fulfilled their part of the original agreement to purchase it. The complaint is accompanied by a copy of the original agreement and terms of sale, September 26, 1849, in the handwriting of Z. C. Bishop and attested a true copy by him July 10, 1850.

The bill in chancery is signed by M. T. Simmons before Judge William Strong, September 8, 1851, and endorsed: "I allow an injunction as prayed for in the within bill the complainant to give bail in the sum of one thousand dollars. Cathlamet Sept. 8, 1851, Wm. Strong. Judge &c. Filed Sept. 8, A.D. 1851. James C. Strong, Clerk." The manuscript is in two unidentified hands.

[Miller Collection.]

428 SIMPSON, JAMES HERVEY, 1813–1883

Manuscript map in color, showing the route followed by Captain Simpson's expedition from Camp Floyd to Fort Bridger in 1858, and from Camp Floyd across the Great Basin of Utah to Genoa, Nevada, and return in 1859. With autograph inscription, lower right: "To Major Dodge with the compliments of J. H. Simpson, Washington, D.C. Dec. 16, 1859."

Map. *ca.* 58 x 13 cm.

In 1858 Captain Simpson received orders to examine the route from Camp Floyd to Fort Bridger to open a new wagon road by the Timpanagos and White Clay Creek route; and in 1859 to explore the Great Basin of Utah from Camp Floyd to Genoa, Carson Valley, Nev., for a shorter route to California.

The manuscript map has been inlaid and forms the central portion of the "Map of Utah Territory showing the routes connecting it with California and the East. Compiled in the Bureau of Topographical Engineers . . . from the latest and most reliable data, 1858." Lithograph, Ritchie & Dunnavant, Richmond, Va. 115 x 82½ cm.

This map, showing the new routes in relation to earlier explorations, was prepared and presented to Major Frederick Dodge, government agent of the Washoe and Pi-Ute Indians, who gave Simpson much valuable information about the Indians and their languages.

A similar map of Captain Simpson's expeditions was printed with title: "Map of wagon routes in Utah Territory explored & opened by Capt. J. H. Simpson, Topl. Engrs. U.S.A., Assisted by Lieuts. J. L. K. Smith and H. S. Putnam, Topl. Engrs. U.S.A., and Mr. Henry Engelmann, in 1858–59, by authority of Hon. John B. Floyd, Sec. of War, . . . Drawn by J. P. Mechlin," in Simpson, *Report of*

Explorations across the Territory of Utah for a Direct Wagon-route from Camp Floyd to Genoa, in Carson Valley in 1859 (35th Congress, 2d Session, Senate Ex. Doc. No. 40, Washington, 1876).
[Coe No. 166.]

429 SISTIAGA, SEBASTIAN DE, S.J., 1684–1756

Letter in Spanish to the Reverend Padre Provincial Christóbal de Escobár y Llamas, dated at the Mission San Ignacio, September 19, 1743, and signed by Sebn. de Sistiaga.

12 pp. 31 cm.

Father Sistiaga was born in Mexico in 1684 and entered the Society of Jesus as a young man. In 1718, while a professor of literature at San Andrés College, he was selected to accompany Brother Bravo to the California missions where he spent the next 29 years, first at Santa Rosalía and later at San Ignacio. In 1747 his health had failed and he was transferred to Mexico, where he died in 1756.

In the opening paragraph of the letter Father Sistiaga apologizes for not writing it himself on account of a weakness in his right arm. He then acknowledges the receipt of the Provincial's order to turn the control of the garrison over to the captain, but before executing the order he wishes to present the reasons for his grave doubts about the result of the action. He then summarizes the history of the Jesuit missions in Lower California, their relations with the military officials and with the government; and emphasizes the importance of retaining in the hands of the missionaries the privilege of appointing and dismissing the officers protecting their settlements.

[Coe Collection.]

430 SMITH, JOSEPH, 1805–1844

Five letters and documents of Joseph Smith, Hyrum Smith and Mary Fielding Smith, his wife, 1839–1846.

7 pp. 31–33 cm. With typewritten transcripts of the letters.

Joseph Smith, Mormon prophet, left Ohio in 1835 for Missouri where Mormons had settled at Far West and in neighboring counties. By 1838 the hostility of the native Missourians had grown so violent that the Mormons undertook to defend themselves, the state militia was called out to quell the disturbances and finally Far West surrendered to the militia. Joseph Smith, his brother Hyrum Smith, and others were imprisoned for treason, murder, and felony. After six months in jail they were released and went to join the other Far West Mormons in Illinois.

The letters and documents are:

Smith, Joseph. Letter to his wife. Liberty Jail, Clay Co., Mo., April 4, 1839. 3 pp.

The signature has been cut off. The letter is addressed to Mrs. Emma Smith, Quincy, Ill. It was written shortly before the trial was to take place, and is chiefly about his concern for his wife and children.

—— Letter "To all whom it may concern," certifying that Elder Hugh Herringshaw is a member of good standing in the Church of Jesus Christ of Latter-day Saints. Undated. Signed by Joseph Smith, pres., R. B. Thompson, clerk. 1 p.

SMITH, HYRUM. Bond signed by Hyrum Smith, May 30, 1842, to execute a deed for Lot 4, Block 7, in Nauvoo, Ill., to Bingham Bement of New Hampshire on receipt of payment of four notes due May 30, 1843, 1844, 1845, 1846. Printed form. 1 p.

—— Indenture, signed by Hyrum Smith and Mary, his wife, deeding to Bingham Bement Lot 4, Block 7, in Nauvoo for the sum of $150, June 8, 1843. With affidavit of Ebenezer Robinson, J.P., June 9, 1843. Endorsed: "Filed for record June 15, 1843," with certification signed Joseph Smith, recorder, by William Clayton, clerk. Printed form. 1 p.

SMITH, MARY (MRS. HYRUM). Letter to Mr. Warren. Nauvoo, June 8, 1846. Endorsed: "Mrs. Hyrum Smith letter to C. A. Warren June 15/46. Ansd." 1 p.

The letter is about claims made by Mr. Warren of Quincy, Ill., against Hyrum Smith's estate.

[Coe Collection.]

431 SMITH, LEVI LATHROP, *d.* 1848

Diary, May 17 to 23, September 27, 1847 to August 29, 1848.

26 pp. 20–32 cm.

L. L. Smith, with Edmund Sylvester, came to Puget Sound in 1846 and settled on a claim where Olympia now stands. He suffered from epilepsy and spent many days alone on his claim but was respected by his fellow settlers and in 1848 was elected representative to the Oregon Legislature. Before taking his seat he was drowned while returning to his home in a canoe, probably as a result of an epileptic seizure. The claim then became the property of his partner, Edmund Sylvester.

The diary is usually brief but records the visits of his partner and neighbors, the progress of his farm work, his health and attacks of "falling sickness," and his thoughts, which were often melancholy. It is written on loose sheets of different kinds and sizes, sometimes across the sheet and then folded. The entries for May 1847 are on the back of a sheet with notes on Oregon laws.

With the diary there is a draft of a lease, to persons unnamed, by Michael T. Simmons, Ore. Ter., Lewis Co., Newmarket, August 20, 1847, of land for a sawmill, with the names "Michael T. Simmons and L. L. Smith witness" crossed out [in Smith's handwriting, 1 p., 20 x 12½ cm.]; and a memorandum of a bill of lumber received from Thomas W. Glasgow, July 16, 1846, L. L. Smith, proprietor of Smithfield, Oregon Territory [1 p.]. The latter has added notes, some in Chinook, and, on the back, a note about the soil of the country.

[Miller Collection.]

432 SNODGRASS, R. H. P.

"R. H. P. Snodgrass's Journal of the trip from Piqua, Ohio, to Sacramento across the Plains in 1852, with an appendix containing prices current and news of various subjects." March 28 to August 11, 1852.

114 pp. 12½ cm. Original binding. With typewritten transcript.

Snodgrass, according to surviving members of the family, was killed in the Civil War in which he served as a captain of volunteers.

The journal describes briefly the events on the way and the route followed from Piqua, Ohio, March 28, by boat, train, and overland to St. Louis, by the steamer *Alton* to Fort Leavenworth; the departure overland May 4 to Fort Kearney, the south bank of the Platte River to Ash Hollow, Fort Laramie, the Sweetwater, South Pass, Fort Bridger, Salt Lake City, June 23, the Mormon Route to Raft River, the Humboldt and Carson Rivers to Weaverville, the American River to Sacramento, August 7, and to the mines at Auburn, August 11.

It is preceded by a brief preface dated Wyandotte, Butte Co., Calif., March 3, 1854, and a list of the members of the company; and at the end are two pages of notes on what became of the members of the party, also dated March 3, 1854.

[Coe No. 167.]

433 SNOW, LORENZO, 1814–1901

Tribute of respect to the memory of Hon. Joseph A. Young. Council Chamber, City Hall, Salt Lake City, February 17, 1876. Signed: "Lorenzo Snow, President of the Council; John Taylor, Chief Clerk of the Council."

5 pp. 35 cm.

At the time of his death, August 5, 1875, Joseph A. Young was a member of the Territorial Legislative Council. The "Tribute" summarizes the events of his life and services for others.

Parts of the last two pages are quoted in Jenson, *Latter-day Saint Biographical Encyclopedia*, 1901, I, 519.

[Coe No. I, 1229.]

434 SPALDING, ELIZA HART (MRS. HENRY H.), 1807–1851

An unsigned note: "Clear Water August 8, 1843. Beloved Parents, Brothers & Sisters. A package of letters."

19½ x 5 cm.

Endorsed: "My first wife's autograph. Eliza H. Spalding," in the handwriting of Henry Harmon Spalding.

[Miller Collection.]

435 SPALDING, HENRY HARMON, 1803–1874

Letter to Archibald McKinlay, Esq., Fort Walla Walla. Clear Water, January 9, 1843.

4 pp. 25½ cm.

Henry Harmon Spalding and his wife accompanied Elkanah and Mary Walker to Oregon in 1836 to join Whitman, and established a mission at Clearwater among the Nez Percés (see also Nos. 501–504).

The letter speaks of the arrival of Mr. and Mrs. Littlejohn, and of the order from the American Board to recall Mr. Spalding because of reports received from members of the Mission, and asks Mr. McKinlay to write to the Board in his behalf. An added note signed "A McK" says that the "member" was William H. Gray.

[Miller Collection.]

436 SPALDING, HENRY HARMON, 1803–1874

"Narrative of an overland journey to Fort Vancouver and Lapwai in 1836. Together with an account of the beginning of the American Protestant Missions beyond the Rockies." By H. H. Spalding.

Typewritten copy. 107 pp. 28 cm.

This manuscript, evidently prepared for publication with a few directions to the printer in pencil, was written sometime after the journey, in narrative form.

Mr. Spalding quotes from his wife's diary from time to time.

[Miller Collection.]

437 SPALDING, HENRY HARMON, 1803–1874

Selections from the Scriptures, mainly from the Acts of the Apostles, the Gospel of Matthew, and the Books of Moses, translated into the Nez-Percé language by Henry H. Spalding, 1839–1846.

2 vols. [i.e., 180 pp.] 16½ cm. Original bindings.

The first manuscript, bound in hide, contains chapters 1 through 11:3 of the Acts with a few omissions, and selections from the Books of Moses. The second volume contains a few extracts from Acts 16:28–31, Matthew 10:1–7 and 1:1–3, and selections from the Books of Moses.

Laid in the second volume is a Hospital Tax receipt—a form printed by Idaho Signal Print, Lewiston, dated June 21, 1874 and signed by J. B. King, tax collector, W. P. Hunt, auditor. 15 x 7 cm.

These manuscripts are printed by hand, very neatly for the most part. The handwriting varies because Spalding had others helping him with the translating and writing of the selections.

At the annual meeting of the Oregon Mission in September 1839 it was voted that Mr. H. H. Spalding prepare a book of religious instruction from the Old Testament (Howard Malcolm Ballou, "The History of the Oregon Press," *Oregon Historical Quarterly*, 1922, XXIII, 48). According to Mr. Ballou the seventh book printed on the Mission Press at Lapwai was to have been a book of select portions of the Scriptures, but no copy is known to exist. In August 1843 Mr. Spalding wrote that he had commenced setting the type. At the annual meeting in May 1845 Mr. Spalding was requested to translate the Acts of the Apostles. He was still engaged on the translation in 1846.

Neither of these translations was printed at the Lapwai Press and they may never have been completed. It is possible that these manuscripts are the ones Spalding was preparing for the Mission Press.

[Coe No. V, 40.]

438 SPERRY, MRS. L.

Letter to her son, Anson Sperry. Fort Laramie, September 19, 1849.

2 pp. 25 cm.

Mrs. Sperry writes of another son, Pierpont, at Fort Laramie, the news of the fort and business affairs. Anson Sperry was an attorney in Marengo, McHenry Co., Ill.

[Coe Collection.]

439 STANLEY, JOHN MIX, 1814–1872

Letter to Messrs. Walker and Eells. Fort Wallawalla, December [2, 1847].

1 p. 29½ cm.

John Mix Stanley began painting Indians in 1838–1839. In 1846 he was with General Kearny's expedition into California; in 1847–1848 he toured the Pacific Northwest, reaching Oregon in July 1847, and in October was at Tshimakain and on his way to Waiilatpu when he heard of the massacre of the Whitmans. In 1853 he was artist of Governor Stevens' expedition to survey a northern route for a Pacific railroad.

This letter brought to Tshimakain the first news of the Whitman Massacre.

Formerly owned by the late F. W. Skiff of Portland, Ore., and published in his *Adventures in Americana*, 1935, pp. 197–198, and in N. B. Pipes, "John Mix Stanley," *Oregon Historical Quarterly*, 1932, XXXIII, 252–253.

[Coe No. III, 1708.]

440 STANLEY, JOHN MIX, 1814–1872

Portrait of the Rev. Elkanah Walker, signed: [J.] "M. Stanley, Oregon—1847."

Oil on paper. Oval. 22 x 18 cm.

Stanley began the portrait of Walker November 19, completing it on the 22d. The next day he set out for the Whitman mission but before reaching his destination received word of the massacre the preceding evening, November 29. He succeeded in reaching Walla Walla in safety December 2.

Formerly in the possession of Frederick W. Skiff of Portland, Ore. The portrait is reproduced as frontispiece in Drury, *Elkanah and Mary Walker*, Caldwell, Idaho, 1940.

[Coe No. III, 1709.]

441 STEELE, FLETCHER, 1885–

"Wyoming. Cheyenne to Dubois by automobile, Dubois to Moran by wagon. Being observations made on a trip with the Bishop of Wyoming, Nathaniel Seymour Thomas, and his guests . . ." August, 1914.

Typewritten manuscript (carbon). 51 pp. 27 cm.

Fletcher Steele was a landscape architect of Boston, Mass.

From the library of the Rt. Rev. Na-

thaniel Seymour Thomas, Bishop of Wyoming, with his bookplate.

[Coe No. 168.]

442 STEVENS, ISAAC INGALLS, 1818–1862

Correspondence and other papers relating to Governor Stevens' proclamation of martial law in Washington Territory.

57 letters and papers. 144 pp. 20–34 cm.

General Stevens, after graduating from the U.S. Military Academy at West Point, served in the Engineer Corps of the Army until 1853, when he resigned to accept the governorship of Washington Territory. He was also appointed director of the survey of a northern route for a Pacific railroad.

Early in 1856 Indian hostilities began, several massacres occurred in supposedly peaceful districts, and Governor Stevens ordered the settlers to leave their claims and go to the towns for protection. When some of these settlers, former employees of the Hudson's Bay Company, disregarded his order and remained unmolested by the Indians the Governor, believing that they were assisting the enemy, had them removed to the custody of Colonel Casey at Fort Steilacoom, and to insure their trial by a military tribunal issued his proclamation of martial law in Pierce County, April 3, 1856, later extended to Thurston County (see also Nos. 187, 509).

The letters from Stevens and Tilton are the file copies in the writers' hands or signed by them. The correspondence and papers include the following:

STEVENS, ISAAC INGALLS. Three letters to Colonel Casey. March 31–April 7, 1856. 4 pp.

—— Letter to Hon. F. A. Chenoweth. May 28, 1856. 2 pp.

—— Letter to Elwood Evans. June 3, 1856. 1 p.

—— Letter to Lieutenant Colonel Lander. May 4, 1856. 1 p.

—— Letter to Hon. Victor Monroe. May 28, 1856. 1 p.

—— Four letters to Lieutenant Colonel Shaw. May 4–22, 1856. Signed by Stevens. 5 pp.

—— Copies of two letters to the President of the United States [Franklin Pierce]. May 23, August 18, 1856. 9 pp.

—— Letter to William F. Tolmie. March 8, 1856. 1 p.

—— Copy of a few lines of Governor Stevens' answer to alleged cause of complaint, in the case of the U.S. vs. Isaac I. Stevens [July? 1856]. In the handwriting of Judge Strong. 1 p.

BROOKS, QUINCY ADAMS. Letter to Governor Stevens. May 27, 1856. 1 p.

CASEY, SILAS. Two letters to Stevens. March 31, April 3, 1856. 2 pp.

CHENOWETH, FRANCIS A. Two letters to Stevens. May 29, November 15, 1856. 3 pp.

—— Letter to Elwood Evans. May 30, 1856. 2 pp.

—— Two letters to Judge Lander. April 30 [copy in handwriting of W. W. Miller], May 29, 1856. 2 pp.

—— Draft of the appointment of Elwood Evans to prosecute Charles Wren and others. May 29, 1856, in Judge Chenoweth's hand, and, on the same page, a copy of Elwood Evans' letter to Stevens notifying him of the fact, May 30, 1856. 1 p.

—— Draft of a letter to Messrs. Ed[ito]rs [1856]. In Judge Chenoweth's hand. 4 pp.

EVANS, ELWOOD. Draft of a letter to the Hon. William Bigler. May 19, 1856. 3 pp.

—— Two letters to George Gibbs, about the posting of the proclamation abrogating martial law. May 26, 1856. 3 pp.

GIBBS, GEORGE. Letter to Evans. Monday 12 [May 1856]. 2 pp.

—— Drafts of three letters from Gibbs and Goldsborough to the Secretary of State, William L. Marcy. May [11]–June [6] 1856. 22 pp.

—— Draft of his opinion on martial law. Undated. 5 pp.

—— Drafts of two papers on martial law in Washington Territory, undated, the second written in answer to an article in a newspaper, probably the *Pioneer and Democrat*. 10 pp.

—— Draft of a letter to the editor of the *Oregonian* on martial law in Washington Territory. Unsigned. 8 pp.

KENDALL, BEZALEEL FREEMAN. Letter to George Gibbs. May 10, 1856. 2 pp.

LANDER, EDWARD. Two letters to Stevens. May 4, 5, 1856, with a draft of the latter. 5 pp.

—— Draft of a writ of *habeas corpus* and a writ of attachment, Charles Wren, et al. [vs. I. I. Stevens]. May 15, 1856, Edward Lander, To the clerk of the Thurston U.S. District Court, Wm. W. Miller. 1 p.

MARCY, WILLIAM LEARNED, Secretary of State. Letter to Stevens. September 12, 1856. Signature only. 3 pp.

[MILLER, WILLIAM WINLOCK]. Summary in the handwriting of William W. Miller of the action taken against Governor Stevens. [n.d.] 3 pp.

MONROE, VICTOR, Judge Advocate. Letter to Colonel B. F. Shaw. May 2 [i.e., 22], 1856. Signature only. 1 p.

—— Letter to Stevens. May 27, 1856, written by Quincy A. Brooks and signed also by Judge Monroe. 2 pp.

SHAW, BENJAMIN F. Letter to Stevens. May 5, 1856. 2 pp.

TILTON, JAMES, Adjutant General, W.T.V. Letter to the Commanding Officer at Fort Steilacoom, W.T. [Lt. Col. Casey]. April 2, 1856. 1 p.

—— Copy of letter to President Pierce. August 18, 1856. 5 pp.

—— Letter to Stevens. August 18, 1856. 3 pp.

—— Charges and specification of charges against Charles Wren. Certified copy signed by J. M. Bachelder, J.P. [1856.] 1 p.

WASHINGTON TERRITORY. GOVERNOR (Isaac I. Stevens). Draft of the proclamation of martial law in Pierce County, W. T. [April 3, 1856]. 1 p.

—— Proclamation of martial law in Thurston County, May 13, 1856. Signed by Isaac I. Stevens. 1 p.

—— Copy of the proclamation abrogating martial law in Pierce and Thurston Counties, May 24, 1856, with a deposition regarding the proclamation, signed by Simpson P. Moses, May 26, 1856. 2 pp.

—— Draft of a respite issued by Governor Stevens to himself as defendant against the charge of contempt of court, in the handwriting of Judge Strong [July 10, 1856]. 1 p.

WASHINGTON TERRITORY. MILITARY COMMISSION. Memorandum of the charges against the defendants, in the court martial [Lyon A. Smith, Charles Wren, and John McLeod], in the handwriting of Q. A. Brooks. 1 p.

—— "Proceedings of a General Court Martial or Military Commission convened at Camp Montgomery by virtue of an order from Isaac I. Stevens, Governor of the Territory of Washington, and Commander-in-Chief of the Volunteer Forces thereof," May 20–29, 1856. 16 pp.

The manuscript is in the handwriting of Quincy A. Brooks, recorder. The commission consisted of Lieutenant Colonel J. S. Hurd, Major H. J. G. Maxon, Captain C. W. Swindal, Captain W. W. DeLacy, Lieutenant A. Shepherd; Lieutenant S. B. Curtis, supernumerary, Victor Monroe, Judge Advocate. The proceedings are signed at the end by the members of the court, and approved, May 29, 1856 by Governor Stevens.

Casey's letters and Stevens' letters to Casey, except that of April 7, Chenoweth's letter to Stevens, Lander's two letters to Stevens, Monroe's letter to Shaw, Shaw's letter to Stevens and Stevens' letters to Shaw, Stevens' letters to Lander and Tolmie, the proclamation abrogating martial law, and the proceedings of the court martial are printed in Washington Territory Council, 4th Session, 1856–1857, *Martial Law—Minority Report* [Olympia, 1857]. Chenoweth's letter to Lander, April 30, Gibbs' and Goldsborough's letter to the Secretary of State, June 6, the Secretary of State to Stevens, Stevens to Chenoweth, and the proclamation abrogating martial law are printed in 34th Congress, 3d Session, Senate Ex. Doc. No. 41, 1857. Gibbs' and Goldsborough's letters of May 11 and 19, and the proclamations of martial law in Pierce and Thurston Counties are in 34th Congress, 1st Session, Senate Ex. Doc. No. 98, 1857. The "respite" is printed in S. F. Cohn, "Martial Law in Washington Territory," *Pacific Northwest Quarterly*, 1936, XXVII, 195–218; and in the *Oregon Historical Quarterly*, 1924, XXV, 228–229.

[Miller Collection.]

443 STEVENS, ISAAC INGALLS, 1818–1862

Correspondence of Isaac I. Stevens, Governor of Washington Territory, during the years 1848 to 1857.

206 letters and papers. 541 pp. Map. 18½–37 cm.

The correspondence deals chiefly with the Indian hostilities of 1856 and relations with the U.S. Army; but also with the political affairs of the Territory under Governor Stevens; the relations with the Hudson's Bay Company and Puget Sound Agricultural Company; Mullan's explorations in 1853–1854; the murder of White and Northcraft; the trial of Leschi; etc.

The majority of the letters to Stevens are the originals, while those from Stevens are in most cases copies or drafts preserved by the writer for his files. The correspondence includes the following letters and papers:

—— Copies of 37 letters to Colonel Casey. February 2–December 1, 1857. 77 pp.

—— Copy of letter to Colonel Sam Cooper. February 16, 1855. 1 p.

—— Drafts and copies of 16 letters to Jefferson Davis, Secretary of War. February 19–December 6, 1856. 78 pp.

—— Copies of three letters to Sir James Douglas. February 17–March 8, 1856. 3 pp.

—— Three letters to George Gibbs. August 30, 1855–February 6, 1856. 3 pp.

—— Copies of two letters to Captain Jordan. August 3, December 4, 1856. 3 pp.

—— Copy of letter to Major Lugenbeel. August 3, 1856. 2 pp.

—— Letter to G. N. McConaha. March 9, 1854. 2 pp. Endorsed: "Received March 9, 1854 and referred to Committee on Roads and Highways. Elwood Evans, Chf. Clerk."

—— Copy of letter to O. B. McFadden. February 16, 1855. 1 p.

—— Letter to Captain M. Malony. March 16, 1857. 1 p.

—— Two letters to C. H. Mason. January 29, November 14, 1856. 2 pp.

STEVENS, I. I. Letter to Hon. D. J. Pearce, enclosing some observations on the Military Academy at West Point, June 5, 1848; and a letter to Pearce from William H. C. Bartlett commenting on Stevens' observations. 10 pp.

—— Copies of four letters to the President of the United States [Franklin Pierce]. January 29–July 12, 1856. 6 pp.

—— Copies of two letters to Captain D. A. Russell. August 31, September 4, 1856. 2 pp.

—— Copies of two letters to Lieutenant Colonel Shaw. May 21, November 5, 1856. 3 pp.

—— Copy of letter to J. S. Smith. January 23, 1857. 2 pp.

—— Copies of five letters to Lieutenant Colonel Steptoe. August 25–November 22, 1856. 9 pp.

—— Copy of letter to James C. Strong. February 16, 1855. 1 p.

—— Copies of two letters to Dr. W. F. Tolmie. March 26, May 15, 1856. 2 pp.

—— Copy of letter to R. M. Walker. May 4, 1855. 1 p.

—— Copy of letter to James G. Wood. February 22, 1855. 1 p.

—— Drafts or copies of five letters to General Wool. May 22, 1855–May 12, 1856. 32 pp.

—— Drafts or copies of 13 letters to Colonel Wright, January 30–November 22, 1856. 26 pp.

ALLEN, EDWARD JAY. Letter to Stevens. January 29, 1856. 2 pp.

BACHE, ALEXANDER DALLAS. Circular letter to Stevens, signed by A. D. Bache. September 26, 1856. 1 p.

CASEY, SILAS. 22 letters to Stevens. January 31–November 12, 1856. 34 pp.

Casey's letter to Stevens, April 28, encloses a copy of a letter from Gibbs to Casey, April 20, 1856; and that of November 12 encloses a copy of a letter from Lieutenant D. B. McKibben to Lieutenant John Nugen, November 8, 1856.

—— Two letters to Adjutant General Tilton, February 19, March 12, 1856. 2 pp.

CLARK, FRANK. Letter to an unnamed correspondent. June 4, 1856. 1 p.

DeLACY, WALTER WASHINGTON. "Itinerary of the march of the Right Wing of the Second Regiment of the W.T. Vols. under command of Lieutenant Colonel Shaw, from Montgomery's to Grande Ronde," June 12–August 29, 1856. To Governor I. I. Stevens. 49 pp. Map, "Plan of the battle of Grande Ronde fought July 17, 1856." 18½ x 22 cm.

DOTY, JAMES. Letter to Stevens, with information on the crossings of the Snake River, etc. December 21, 1855. 3 pp.

—— "Itineraries of routes from 'Whitman's Station' in the Walla Walla Valley to 'Craig's,' in the Nez Percé country, the Coeur d'Alene Mission and Spokane Prairie at Antoine Plantes." 8 pp.

DOUGLAS, SIR JAMES. Five letters to Stevens. January 22, 1855–March 14, 1856. Signatures only. 13 pp.

DOYLE, REUBEN L. Forwarding to Stevens a resolution of the House of Representatives requesting information about the survey of Grays Harbor. January 23, 1857. 1 p.

FITZHUGH, EDMUND C. Three letters to Stevens. December 23, 1854–March 27, 1855. 3 pp.

HALLER, GRANVILLE OWEN. Letter to Stevens. April 20, with postscripts, May 3, 5, 1857, enclosing copies of extracts from letters to Captain Maloney, April 5, Major Mackall, April 7, and Governor James Douglas, April 15, 1857. 6 pp.

JORDAN, THOMAS. Three letters to Stevens. June 24–October 4, 1856. 5 pp. Letters of September 4 and October 4 have signature only in Jordan's hand.

McCURDY, SAMUEL. Two letters to Stevens. April 25, 1855, December 16, 1856. 3 pp.

MARCY, WILLIAM LEARNED. Letter of instructions to Stevens. June 3, 1853. Signature only. 7 pp.

MULLAN, JOHN. "Copy of reports and communications on affairs of Blackfeet & Selish Indians, and explorations from Nov. 1853 to Jan. 1854, from Lieutenant Mullan, U.S.A. to Governor Stevens," November 18, 1853–January 25, 1854. 26 pp.

NUGEN, JOHN. Letter to James Tilton. March 3, 1856. Signature only. 1 p.

—— Letter to Lieutenant Colonel Shaw. June 1, 1856. Copy. 1 p.

—— Letter to Stevens. December 3, 1856. Signature and postscript in his hand. 2 pp.

OGDEN, PETER SKENE. Letter to Stevens. January 16, 1854. Signed also by Dugald Mactavish. 3 pp.

PACKARD, J. A. Letter to Stevens. October 20 [1856]. 1 p.

PIERCE COUNTY, W. T. VIGILANCE COMMITTEE. Draft of compact, June 1, 1856. Unsigned. 2 pp.

RICARD, PASCAL. Letter to Stevens. January 29, 1856. 1 p.

RUSSELL, CHARLES J. W. Letter to Stevens on the fisheries of the coast. February 6, 1856. 4 pp.

RUSSELL, DAVID ALLEN. Letter to Stevens. September 2, 1856. 3 pp.

SHAW, BENJAMIN F. Letter to Stevens. January 17, 1856. 3 pp.

SIMPSON, SIR GEORGE. Letter to Stevens. regarding the rights of the Hudson's Bay Company and the Puget Sound Agricultural Company. March 22, 1854. 8 pp.

STEPTOE, EDWARD JENNER. Seven letters to Stevens. August 28–November 2, 1856. 9 pp.

SWARTWOUT, SAMUEL. Letter to Stevens containing his report of the attack on the northern Indians near Port Gamble. November 23, 1856. 9 pp.

TILTON, JAMES. Four letters to Colonel Casey. January 31–March 15, 1856. 5 pp.

TOLMIE, WILLIAM FRASER. Four letters to Stevens. December 27, 1853–May 22, 1856. 11 pp.

WASHINGTON TERRITORY. GOVERNOR (I. I. Stevens). Seven certificates of election to the first Legislative Council of the Territory. Executive Office, Olympia, February 25, 1854, signed by Isaac I. Stevens, Governor, and issued to Lafayette Balch, Daniel R. Bigelow, D. F. Bradford, Seth Catlin, Henry Miles, William H. Tappan, and B. F. Yantis. 7 pp.

—— A proclamation organizing the Territorial Government of Washington Territory. November 28, 1853, with additional proclamations dated December 1 and 3, 1853. Signed by Isaac I. Stevens, Governor, and C. H. Mason, Secretary. 6 pp.

WOOL, JOHN ELLIS. Five letters to Stevens. February 19, 1855–February 12, 1856. 13 pp.

WRIGHT, GEORGE. Six letters to Stevens. February 3–October 4, 1856. 13 pp.

—— Copy of letter to Colonel Shaw. February 21, 1856, with note to Governor

Stevens added by Lieutenant Brackett, Q.M. Clerk. 1 p.

—— Copy of letter to Colonel Shaw. May 27, 1856. 1 p.

—— Copy of letter to J. F. Noble. July 15, 1856. 2 pp.

—— Copy of letter to Lieutenant Colonel T. Morris. July 26, 1856. 1 p.

The majority of the letters in the Casey, Steptoe, Wool and Wright correspondence; Stevens' letters to Secretary of War Davis and to Captain D. A. Russell; Nugen's letter to Lieutenant Colonel

Shaw, and Captain Swartwout's letter are published in Washington Territory, *Message of the Governor . . . Also, the Correspondence with the Secretary of War, Major General Wool*, Olympia, 1857, pp. 62–96, 124–151, 164–180, 196–221. The proclamation as signed November 28, 1853, was printed as a broadside, and has been published from that broadside in the *Washington Historical Quarterly*, 1930, XXI, 138–141. Captain DeLacy's Report to Governor Stevens, edited by James R. Tanis, is published in the *Yale University Library Gazette*, 1951, XXVI, 53–72.

[Miller Collection.]

444 STEVENS, ISAAC INGALLS, 1818–1862

Letter to M[?] F. Schmidt. St. Nicholas, New York, March 18, 1859.

1 p. 24½ cm.

The letter contains instructions as to the chapter headings in the "Geographical Memoir," which is part of Stevens' *Narrative and Final Report of Explorations for a Pacific Railroad*, Washington, 1860

(U.S. War Dept. Reports of Explorations and Surveys, 1860, Vols. XII–XIII).

Gift of James R. Tanis.

[Miller Collection.]

445 STEVENS, ISAAC INGALLS, 1818–1862

"Prepared in the Office of Explorations & Surveys, War Department, from a Map of the Indian Nations and Tribes of the Territorys of Washington and Nebraska west of the mouth of the Yellowstone. Made under the direction of Isaac I. Stevens, Gov. of Wash. Terrt. & Supt. of Ind. Affairs" [April, 1857].

Map. 125 x 63 cm. Mounted on linen and folded. Original leather binding stamped in gold, "Indian tribes of Washington and Nebraska. Secretary of War."

The map consists of the engraved map of the region from the Rocky Mountains to Puget Sound, prepared by Governor Stevens for his report on the survey for a Pacific railroad, with information added in manuscript about the Indian tribes and reservations, settlements, and military posts [90 x 63 cm.]; a manuscript extension east of the Rocky Mountains to the Yellowstone River to show the more eastern tribes; and, inserted in the lower left corner in place of the original caption and part of Oregon, two tabular statements of

the Indians west and east of the Cascades, showing "tribes, population, parties to the several treaties, reservations provided in the treaties, and temporary encampments"; and "Notes of the Indians of the Territory of Nebraska between the Rocky Mountains and the mouth of the Yellowstone."

A month before Governor Stevens was relieved as superintendent of Indian affairs by Colonel James W. Nesmith, he sent to George W. Manypenny, Commissioner of Indian Affairs, April 30, 1857, a letter and map of the Indian nations and tribes of the Territory of Washington and of the Territory of Nebraska, with tabular statements and notes. The region from the Cascades to Fort Benton has been printed on a reduced scale, with much less detail, in Hazard Stevens, *Life of Isaac* *Ingalls Stevens*, 1900, I, facing p. 16, and the "Tabular Statements" and "Notes" as the Appendix to Vol. I, pp. 503–505, from the original on file in the Indian Bureau. The Miller map is a copy made for the Secretary of War.

[Miller Collection.]

446 STIEFFEL, HERMAN, 1827–

"Attack on Gen. Marcy's Train, escorted by Comp. K, 5th U.S. Infantry, Br. Major Brotherton commanding,—near Powne-Fort Kansas, September 23, 1867." Signed, lower right, "H. Stieffel, Co. K 5th U.S. Infy."

Watercolor drawing. 51 x 29 cm.

According to the pension records of the Veterans' Administration in the National Archives, Herman Steiffel [i.e., Stieffel] was born in Germany, was a painter and soldier and served as private in Company K, 5th U.S. Infantry. A letter from the War Records Branch of the General Services Administration states: "A discharge certificate dated October 16, 1868, indicates that Pvt. Herman Stieffel was engaged in action with the Indians near 'Cimmaron Crossing' on the Arkansas River on September 23, 1867."

From September 28, 1866 to March 8, 1869 General Marcy was inspector general of the Department of Missouri. In September 1867 Company K, 5th U.S. Infantry was stationed at Fort Harker, Kansas.

Acquired through the Jared Eliot Associates.

447 STRANG, JAMES JESSE, 1813–1856

Correspondence and papers of James Jesse Strang, founder of the Church of Jesus Christ of Latter Day Saints (Strangite), and correspondence and notes collected by his biographer, Milo M. Quaife.

709 letters and papers. *ca.* 2,040 pp. 13½–40 cm. With a typewritten calendar of the manuscripts.

Strang, born in Scipio, N.Y., had little formal education but read widely. He taught school a year or two, studied law, and was admitted to the bar in 1836. In 1843 he moved to Wisconsin with his family to settle near his wife's family, and through her brother-in-law, Moses Smith, became interested in the Mormon religion. In 1844 he visited Nauvoo and became an ardent convert. On the day of the murder of Joseph Smith, Strang received a revelation that he was ordained to succeed the prophet, and in support of his claim produced a letter supposedly from Smith, naming Strang as his successor. Brigham Young, with the support of the Apostles at Nauvoo, succeeded Smith, but Strang gathered a number of followers at Voree, Wis. They later moved to the Beaver Islands in Lake Michigan, and in 1850, after the establishment of the City of St. James, Strang was crowned king. Trouble with his gentile neighbors and dissension among his followers eventually caused his death. He was shot on June 16, 1856 as he was about to board the *Michigan* in answer to a summons from the captain. He was removed to Voree and died there July 9, 1856.

Dale L. Morgan, historian and bibliographer of the Mormons, has examined the Strang papers in detail, identified the handwriting of many unsigned manuscripts, and assigned approximate dates to undated letters and documents. The collection consists of manuscripts relating to Strang's conversion to Mormonism, his relations with the church at Nauvoo, and conditions at Nauvoo; Strang's personal writings, drafts of his letters, and family correspondence; documents and letters relating to the establishment of the Church of Jesus Christ of Latter Day Saints (Strangite), the Order of the Illuminati, the Associated Order of Enoch, and the Kingdom of St. James; Strang's general correspondence; and notes and correspondence collected by Milo M. Quaife in writing *The Kingdom of Saint James*, New Haven, Yale University Press, 1930.

The miscellaneous Strang manuscripts include accounts; drafts of patriarchal blessings; plan and diagrams for the Temple at Voree; notes for sermons, lectures, and debates; and notes on subjects connected with the church and its progress, many of them for publication in the *Voree Herald*.

The manuscripts collected by Mr. Quaife include copies of articles in newspapers, some typewritten, others copied by Charles J. Strang; correspondence with Strang's descendants; notes collected by Charles J. Strang; and notes on Strang collected by Mr. Quaife.

The following documents and letters are included:

STRANG, JAMES JESSE. Diary [November 11, 1832]–June 24, 1835. Fragment. 20 pp. 20½ cm.

—— Diary. May 29 [1831]–May 29, 1836. Transcript of the portion formerly owned by Henry Denio (now lost), with a note signed M.M.Q. 30 pp. 21½ x 13½ cm.

—— "Letter of appointment." Letter to James J. Strang. Nauvoo, June 18, 1844. Signed: "Joseph Smith." 3 pp. 31½ cm.

This letter, supposed to have been written by Joseph Smith shortly before his death, bears the Nauvoo postmark of June 19. It was used by Strang to support his claim that he had been ordained to succeed Joseph Smith in a visitation by the Angel of God.

—— Letter to George J. Adams. May 5, 1846. Draft. 2 pp.

—— Letter to John C. Bennett. May 5, 1846. Draft. 1 p.

—— Letter to the Rev. Mr. Cook. January 16, 1850. Draft. 1 p.

—— Letter to Frank [Cooper?]. September 1, 1849. Draft. 2 pp.

—— Letter to E. B. Fairfield. August 11, 1849. Draft. 2 pp.

—— Letter to Andrew J. Graham. November 19, 1849. Draft. 3 pp.

—— Two letters to Peter Hess. November 20, 23, 1849. Drafts. 5 pp.

—— Letter to L. D. Hickey. December 10, 1849. Draft. 2 pp.

—— Letter to [I. A. Hopkins]. December 21, 1846. Draft. 1 p.

—— Letter to M. Lindley. November 19, 1849. Draft. 2 pp.

—— Letter to [Amos Lowen]. November 21, 1849. Draft. 4 pp.

—— Letter to James Smith. April 22, 1846. Draft. 2 pp.

—— Two letters to his wife, Mary Perce Strang. January 25, 1850 [May 19, 1851]. Drafts. 3 pp.

—— Letter to his parents. May 19, 1851. 2 pp.

—— Letter to M. Stroper. June 27, 1843. Draft. 1 p.

—— Letter to the Twelve, summoning them to report at Voree. January 13, 1846. Copy in Strang's hand, signed by him as "Pres. Ch. J.C.L.D.S." with a list of the ten Apostles to whom the summons was to be sent. 2 pp.

—— Letter to John Ursbruck. November 20, 1849. Draft. 4 pp.

—— Letter to B. G. Wright. June 13, 1850. With Wright's answer on same sheet, June 15, 1850. 3 pp.

—— Autobiography, covering his childhood from his birth to his twelfth year, written in 1855. 7 pp.

The manuscript breaks off in the middle of a sentence. A note at the end, unsigned but written by his son Charles, says Strang commenced to write this autobiography the year preceding his death.

—— Article for the Plymouth, Mass., *Old Colony Memorial*. Letter to General J. C. Bennett. January 25, 1850. Incomplete. 4 pp.

—— Contract with James Beardsley, January 13, 1842, covering the sale of oxen by Strang in exchange for a cow and clearing some land by Beardsley. 2 pp.

—— "Covenant." Strang's secret covenant, copied June 1920, from the manuscript owned by Henry Denio of Lamoni, Iowa. Typewritten. 11 pp.

—— Poem in three stanzas, with an unsigned note by Strang saying that the poem is in his hand, "regularly school boy." It is endorsed: "A very important Poem of the Prophet James—which showeth that when he wrote love ditties he was very spiritually minded & somewhat dangerous." 1 p.

—— "Reubenism." A brief note answering Reuben Miller's pamphlet, *James J. Strang, Weighed in the Balance of Truth, and Found Wanting*, Burlington, Wis., 1846, for publication in the *Herald*, October 1846. 1 p.

—— Opening paragraph of an article on the "State of Deseret." Draft in the hand of "Charles Douglass" [i.e., Elvira Field]. Possibly written in Baltimore in January 1850. 1 p.

ABBOTT, SAMUEL. Letter to Strang. May 2, 1850. 1 p.

ACKERT, G. V. Four letters to Strang. March 28, 1850–July 29, 1851. 7 pp.

ADAMS, DANIEL M. Letter to Strang. [n.d., 1846?] 1 p.

ADAMS, GEORGE J. 18 letters to Strang. March 27, 1846–[August 1, 1850]. 56 pp.

—— Letter to his wife Louisa Isibella [*sic*]. August 1 [1850]. 6 pp.

—— Letter "To the Saints Scattered abroad in all the World." July 6, 1846. Addressed to Strang "for the Voree Herrald." 4 pp.

—— Address to "King James" about the Kingdom on Beaver Island. Unsigned but in Adams' hand, probably written between July and October 1850. 3 pp.

—— Accounts of Adams with E. J. Moore and Eli Steele. 1848. 1 p.

ADAMS, LOUISA I. Letter to her husband, George J. Adams. [1850?] With endorsement in Adams' hand. 2 pp.

ALDRICH, HAZEN. Letter to Strang. April [14?] 1846, enclosing some notes for the *Herald*. 6 pp.

ALDRICH, MARVIN M. Letter to Samuel Graham. November 23, 1849. Copy apparently in the hand of Elvira Field. 1 p.

ALEXANDER, S. Two letters to Strang. November 22, 1854, April 6, 1855. 2 pp.

ALVORD, NAOMI. Letter to Strang. April 20, 1846. 2 pp.

APPLETON, C. W. Letter to Strang. December 17, 1849. 3 pp.

APPLETON, MARY (MRS. C. W.). Letter to Strang. November 22, 1849. 2 pp.

ASSOCIATED ORDER OF ENOCH. Depositions by Finley Page, Spaulding Deloss Lewis, Andrew J. Parrish, Asa C. Field, Joseph R. Ketchum, and Walter Ostrander, in suit of Archer vs. Strang and John Cole, before W. P. Lyon, J.P., Mackinac Co., Mich. [ca. 1850.] 14 pp.

—— Minutes of the Order of Enoch. December 26, 1849. 1 p.

—— Minutes of the second meeting. April 30, 1850, on the same sheet as the preceding, with the names of those present. 1 p.

—— Order adopted September 23, 1848 about clothing, and vote removing Lyman Reynolds from the Association. Signed by J. J. Strang. 1 p.

—— Report of the building committee on receipts and expenditures for the year October 6, 1847 to October 5, 1848, with names of contributors and report on the progress of the building of the Temple. 4 pp.

—— Report of the "Committee on Accountabilities" and stewardships, September 23, 1848; and resolution to purchase nothing from enemies. 2 pp.

—— Report of the committee on clothing. September 23, 1848, signed by Gilbert Watson, B. G. Wright, John Porter. 2 pp.

—— Resolution against contracting debts. Passed June 10, 1848. Signed by J. J. Strang, patriarch, B. G. Wright, steward, Anson W. Prindle, asst. 1 p.

—— Resolution that all members of a family labor faithfully according to their ability. Adopted September 8 [changed to 9], 1848. Signed by James J. Strang, Benjamin G. Wright, Anson W. Prindle. 1 p.

AUSTIN, LOIS L. Letter to Samuel Graham. November 20, 1849. With an unsigned note added in Graham's hand forwarding the letter to Strang. 4 pp.

BACON, J. N. Letter to Strang. April 13, 1848, enclosing a letter from J. Williams. April 12, 1848. 2 pp.

BARNES, CALEB P. "C. P. Barnes vs. J. J. Strang." A joke accusing Strang of taking a pair of mittens, February 16, 1849. Signed: "I Snort Atty for Plff." 1 p.

BARTHOLF, JAMES W. Letter to George Thompson and Brethren at Batavia, N.Y., introducing Strang. July 27, 1846. 1 p.

BARTON, ELISHA. Letter to Strang. November 11, 1850. 1 p.

BATES, GEORGE C. Extract from " 'King' Strang, The Beaver Island Prophet's Trial in this City in 1851. A statement from a prominent actor in that noted case." Letter to the editor of the Detroit Tribune, 1877. Copied by Charles J. Strang. 7 pp.

BENEDICT, DAVID. Letter to B. Pearce [Perce?]. March 10, 1843. 1 p.

BENEDICT, GEORGE H. Letter to Strang. May 15, 1846. 1 p.

BENNETT, JOHN COOK. 24 letters to Strang. [ca. March 1846]–March 31, 1851. 39 pp.

The letter of September 3, 1846 is written on the verso of a broadside advertisement, "Practice of Medicine. Dr. Bennett, Professor of the Principles and Practice of Midwifery." Burlington, Racine Co., Wis., July 4th, A.D. 1846. 21 x 33½ cm.

—— Letter to James Arlington Bennet. July 29, 1846. 1 p.

—— "From the 'Times and Seasons' of June 15, 1842, page 380. Notice." Withdrawal of the hand of fellowship from General John C. Bennett, May 11, 1842. Signed by members of the First Presidency, the Quorum, and Bishops. Copied by Bennett, probably for publication in Voree Herald, October 1846. 1 p.

BENNETT, SAMUEL. Two letters to Strang. December 11, 1849, March 12, 1850. 4 pp.

BENNETT, SILAS. Letter to Strang. April 28, 1846. 1 p.

BLAKESLEE, JAMES. Letter to Strang. October 4, 1850. 3 pp.

BLANCHARD, JAMES L. Letter to William Smith. November 6, 1846. 3 pp.

BOARDMAN, H. Letter to Strang. September 16, 1850. 1 p.

BONNEY, ALFRED. Letter to Strang. April 11, 1846. 2 pp.

BOTSFORD, DANIEL F. Four letters to Strang. January 9–May 20, 1847. 10 pp.

BOTSFORD, DANIEL F., NANCY BOTSFORD and JOHN ALSTON. Deposition [ca. January 1847?] that they had heard Peltyre [?] Barten[?] state in public that he knew by the spirit that Strang was a prophet of God. 1 p.

BOUTIKER, SAMUEL. Letter to Strang. May 10, 1847. 1 p.

BRAIDWOOD, THOMAS W. Six letters to Strang. December 3, 1849–January 24, 1850. 11 pp.

BREWSTER, JAMES C. Letter to Strang. March 15, 1846. 2 pp.

BROOKS, LESTER. Four letters to Strang. [May 8, 1846]–March 20, 1850. 6 pp.

—— Letter to J. M. Adams. January 12, 1847. 4 pp.

BROWN, HIRAM P. Four letters to Strang. January 19–August 29, 1850. 13 pp.

—— Letter to Mrs. Mary Strang. August 6, 1851. 1 p.

BROWN, SAMUEL A. Letter to Henry Brown. August 16, 1843. 2 pp.

BROWNSON, GEORGE. Six letters to Strang. March 27, 1849–July 19, 1851. 13 pp.

BULKLEY, JULIA. Letter to Strang. August 19, 1850. 1 p.

BURLINGHAM, JANNETTE. Two letters to Quaife. January 16, 22, 1923. Typewritten. 6 pp.

BUTTERFIELD, ZIMRI. Letter to Strang. August 8, 1851. 1 p.

CAHOON, THOMAS. Letter to Strang. May 7, 1849. 2 pp.

CALHOON, ANDREW. Power of attorney to Strang to act for him against Joseph Peirse [?]. February 16, 1849. Witnessed by C. P. Barnes and Lewis Razee and certified by C. P. Barnes. 1 p.

CALKINS, A. B. Letter to Strang. February 25, 185[0?]. 3 pp.

CANNY, JAMES. Two letters to Strang. June 16, November 18, 1850. 4 pp.

CHANEY, HENRY A. "The Mormons of Beaver." Extracts from a paper read by H. A. Chaney before the October Club of Detroit. [n.d.] Copied by Charles J. Strang [?]. 13 pp.

CHAPMAN, BENJAMIN. Letter to Strang. March 24, 1846. 3 pp.

CHEESEMAN, ALONZO. Letter to Strang. July 28, 1851. 1 p.

CHEREVOY, GEORGE H. Letter to Strang. January 17, 1850. 1 p.

CHIDESTER, DENNIS. Five letters to Strang. March 13, 1846–November 12, 1850. 11 pp.

CHILD, MRS. ALPHA. Letter to Quaife. June 21, 1920. 1 p.

CHILDS, CALVIN B. Letter to Strang. April 26, 1846. 3 pp.

CHURCH OF JESUS CHRIST OF LATTER DAY SAINTS (STRANGITE). Financial report by John W. Crane as bishop for the October 4, 1847 conference, with a letter of transmittal to Strang. September 26, 1847. 3 pp.

—— Minutes of conference at Voree [October, 1846] receiving John Greenhow as apostle, appointing Strang Trustee-in-Trust, and other actions. [Bennett's hand?] 1 p.

—— Minutes of discourses at the conference at Beaver Island, July 2–3, 1850, including remarks of G. J. Adams, J. J. Strang, and Elder Wright. 7 pp.

—— Report by the presiding officers [ca. October 1846] on the members of the Quorum of the Twelve. Signed by J. J. Strang, William Marks, John C. Bennett, and William Smith. 2 pp.

—— Subscription lists for building the Temple and Tower of Strength. [n.d. 1847?] 1 p. 20½ x 53 cm.

—— Ground plans [at Voree?]. 2 diagrams. 2 pp. 30 cm.

—— Testimony of witnesses to "the organization of the Kingdom of God . . . July 8, 1850." With 234 signatures. 8 pp.

A note on the first leaf, signed by Clement James Strang, says that the book from which these pages were cut was given to him by Anson W. Prindle at Black River Falls, Wis., in the year 1890 [i.e., 1880?].

—— HIGH COUNCIL. Minutes of the meeting at Voree, October 4, 1846 to investigate charges against J. C. Bennett. Testimony by Moses Smith, Willard Griffith, Hazen Aldrich, and Collins Pemberton. 4 pp.

—— Proceedings of the trial of Collins Pemberton at Voree, October 25, 1846 and his excommunication. Signed by J. J. Strang, pres., James M. Adams and A. B. Fuller, assts., Gilbert Watson, general church clerk and recorder, Daniel Avery, John L. Bartholf, Uriel H. C. Nickerson. 2 pp.

—— Testimony, Stephen Bartholf vs. B. Young and others, relative to the crimes and heresies of the Twelve at Nauvoo [April 6, 1846]. 10 pp.

Includes the testimony of John E. Page, Isaac Cleveland, Geo. J. Adams, T. S. Edwards, Jehiel Savage, Charles B. Thompson, Samuel Shaw, Moses Smith, Increase Van Deusen.

—— BOSTON BRANCH. Resolutions, February 1, 1847, protesting the introduction of secret societies in the church and condemning George J. Adams for his conduct, signed by David Brown, presiding elder. Copy by Jacob Phelps, clerk, sent to Strang. 3 pp.

—— CHATHAM BRANCH, Litchfield, Medina County, Ohio. Record, September 3, 1843–March 12, 1846, including minutes of meetings, ordinations, baptisms, blessings of members before the organization of the Strangite Church. Signed by H. Edwards, clerk. 4 pp.

—— CHICAGO BRANCH. Record of organization with list of members and resolutions passed. John Alston, clerk. May 10, 1846. 3 pp.

—— NEW YORK BRANCH. Proceedings cutting off Increase Van Deusen and disfellowshiping L. D. Hickey. Samuel Bennett, pres., Jacob W. Jenks, clerk. [ca. September 1849.] 5 pp.

—— PHILADELPHIA BRANCH. Record of organization. September 2–6, 1846. Signed by John Greenhow, presiding elder, and Charles Greenwood, clerk, with a list of 33 members and a note from Greenwood transmitting the record to Strang. 3 pp.

CLARK, MRS. LURENA. Letter to Strang. June 26, 1846. 1 p.

CLARK, R. B. Bill for Strang's account, February 11, 1843, with interest to May 20, 1853. Endorsed: "Rd. Randolph,

May 20, 1853 on the within his note for one year. R. B. Clark." 1 p.

COLE, ANNA. Letter to Strang. April 3, 1851. 1 p.

COLE, JOHN. Two letters to Strang. December 3, 1849, January 10, 1850. 4 pp.

COMSTOCK, JOHN S. Four letters to Strang. March 3–November 28, 1849. 12 pp.

COOLEY, D. Letter to Strang. May 23, 1846. 1 p.

COPELAND, REUBEN. Letter to Strang. April 3, 1849. 2 pp.

COWLES, AUSTIN. Letter to Strang. [n.d.] Endorsed by Strang: "Recved in Conference meeting August 10th, 1846 during ordinations . . . by the hand of Mr. Milliken." 1 p.

CRANE, JOHN W. Letter to Strang. January 9, 1847. 3 pp.

CRAWFORD, SARAH T. Letter to Strang. November 30, 1846. 1 p.

CURTIS, ASA. Letter to Strang. April 20, 1846. 1 p.

CURTIS, THEODORE. Letter to John Greenhow. March 14, 1847. 1 p.

DEMARY, MARY. Letter to Strang. [ca. 1849 or 1850.] 1 p.

DENNISON, JOHN. Two letters to Strang. March 13, 1846, July 11, 1849. 5 pp.

DENSMORE, JAMES. Letter to Strang. [July 24, 1846?] 1 p.

DERROUGH, A. Two letters to Strang. July 4, August 20, 1846. 3 pp.

DIXON, WILLIAM R. Letter to Strang. June 15, 1846. 2 pp.

DOUGLAS, BENJAMIN W. Two letters to Quaife. October 27, November 1, 1919. Typewritten. 2 pp. With carbon copy, unsigned, of Quaife's answer, October 29, 1919. 1 p.

DRAPER, JOEL. Letter to Strang. March 14, 1846. 2 pp.

DUNCAN, GEORGE W. Letter to Strang. March 31, 1850. 3 pp.

DURKEE, CHARLES. Four letters to Strang. December 25, 1849–January 31, 1850. 6 pp.

A letter to Durkee from E[?] E. Habicht, Acting Consul General, Swedish Consulate, New York, January 11, 1850, is enclosed in the letter of January 13, 1850. 3 pp.

ELMORE, D. W. Letter to Strang. May 21, 1846. 3 pp.

ENGLEBRACHT, CHARLES A. Four letters to Quaife. March 25–May 30, 1919. With carbon copies unsigned, of Quaife's answers, March 31–June 3, 1919. 11 pp.

ENGLAND, GEORGE. Letter to Strang. January 15, 1849. 2 pp.

EWING, A. E. Letter to Quaife. April 9, 1919. Typewritten. 2 pp. With a carbon copy, unsigned, of Quaife's answer, April 15, 1919; a signed copy of a typewritten letter from Lena McNutt to Ewing, May 18, 1910; and 14 letters to Ewing from George Sage [i.e., Gabriel J. Strang], January 1, 1910–March 31, 1913. 29 pp.

FAIRFIELD, EDMUND BURKE. Letter to Strang. July 30, 1849. 1 p.

FLAGG, SAMUEL G. Letter to Strang. February 4, 1850. 2 pp.

FOSTER, NATHAN. Letter to Strang. November 26, 1849. 2 pp.

FOX, GEORGE R. Two letters to Quaife. February 13, March 29, 1919. Typewritten. With a typewritten letter to "Friend Brown," January 7, 1919; and unsigned carbon copies of Quaife's answers, February 7, 18, 1919. 8 pp.

FREEMAN, FREDERIC. Letter to Strang. March 3, 1849. With endorsement by John S. Comstock. 3 pp.

FULLER, GEORGE N. Letter to Quaife. January 4, 1918. Typewritten. 4 pp. With unsigned carbon copy of Quaife's answer, February 3, 1919. 1 p.

GEORGE, JOSEPH. Letter to G. J. Adams. January 15, 1850. 3 pp.

GIBBS, DANIEL S. Letter to [Strang?]. May 25, 1846. 2 pp.

GIBSON, JACOB. Two letters to Strang. April 10, June 25, 1846. 3 pp.

GILLETT, M. M. Letter to Strang. August 6, 1851. 1 p.

GOODRICH, ENOS. Letter to Charles E. Stuart. March 7, 1853. 1 p.

GOSSICK, J. D. Letter to Strang. March 23, 1853. 1 p.

GRAHAM, ANDREW J. Letter to Strang. January 22, 1850. 2 pp.

GRAHAM, MARIETTA. Two letters to Strang. August 11, October 18, 1849. 3 pp.

GRAHAM, SAMUEL. 30 letters to Strang, January 13, 1848–August 24, 1851. 81 pp.

—— Letter to Miss Elisabeth McNutt. July 30, 1851. 2 pp.

GRANT, HENRY D. Decision in judging a debate on the veto power of the president before the Ellington Lyceum, November 6, 1841, in favor of the negative [Strang?]. 4 pp.

GREENHOW, JOHN. Statement about John C. Bennett. Written for and printed in the *Voree Herald*, October 1846. 1 p.

GREENWOOD, CHARLES. Two letters to Strang. July 1, 1849, September 5, 1850. 7 pp.

The letter of July 1 is signed also for W. Skimmins, David Brown, and Joseph Ball.

GREIG, JAMES M. Five letters to Strang. December 29, 1846–August 26 [1850?]. 16 pp.

GRIERSON, JOHN W. Two letters to Strang. January 22, 1850, April 30, 1851. 6 pp.

GRIFFITH, STEPHEN. Letter to the Church of Latter Day Saints. November 11, 1849. Addressed to Strang. 1 p.

GRIFFITH, WILLARD. Statement about the controversy over the "covenant," October 23, 1846, in an unidentified hand [Strang's?] and a note by Strang that Griffith dictated the statement and then refused to sign it. 1 p.

HALE, ALDEN. Seven letters to Strang. May 13, 1848–December 31, 1849. 19 pp.

—— Letter to William Skimmins. March 7, 1850. 2 pp.

HALL, J. C. Letter to Strang. September 23, 1850. 2 pp.

HANNAMAN, MANNING J. Letter to Strang. February 25, 1847. 3 pp.

HARVEY, O. H. Letter to Strang. April 28, 1846. 1 p.

HEATH, DAVID. Letter to Strang. July 22, 1851. 3 pp.

HERRON, HENRY P. Letter to J. E. Page (or Jehiel Savage). May 31, 1846. 1 p.

HESS, PETER. 13 letters to Strang. December 14, 1846–April 3, 1850. 33 pp.

—— Letter to Bro. Hosmer. January 17, 1850, forwarding request from Thomas Gale. 2 pp.

HICKEY, LORENZO DOW. Six letters to Strang. September 26, 1846–August 14, 1850. 16 pp.

HICKS, THOMAS R. Letter to Strang. January 16, 1847. 2 pp.

HOLMES, ABIGAIL. Letter to Strang. October 6, 1850. 4 pp.

HOPKINS, I. A. Three letters to Strang. November 28, 1846–July 26, 1849. 4 pp.

HUBBARD, LYDIA. Letter to Strang. August 14, 1850. 2 pp.

HUBBELL, LEN. Letter to Strang. July 12, 1849. 1 p.

HUGHEY, WILLIAM L. Letter to J. E. Page. June 28, 1846. 1 p.

HUNT & BUTLER. Letter to Strang. April 27, 1847. 1 p.

HYDE, ORSON. "Will Mr. Strang answer this question?" Argument against Strang's claims [January 1846]. Unsigned but apparently in Hyde's hand. 1 p.

JACKSON, ANDREW G. Four letters to Strang. November 22, 1849–March 15, 1850. 10 pp.

—— Letter to Thomas Braidwood. January 3, 1850. 2 pp.

—— Letter to Peter Hess. January 3, 1850. 4 pp.

JAMES, J. N. Letter to Strang. January 8, 1851. 3 pp.

JAMES, POLLY (MRS. J. N.). Letter to Strang. August 26, 1849. Endorsed by F. Cooper apologizing for delay in forwarding. With draft of Strang's answer on the same sheet, December 24, 1849. 4 pp.

JENKS, J. W. Two letters to Strang. April [16], October 24, 1846. 5 pp.

JOHNSON, NELSON R. and LEVENNA. Depositions about Benjamin Ellsworth, November 3, 1846, signed by N. R. and Levenna Johnson. 1 p.

JORDAN, JOHN. Letter to Strang. November 30, 1846. 2 pp.

KETCHUM, ANDREW I. Letter to Strang. August 18, 1850. 1 p.

KETCHUM, JOSEPH R. Letter to Strang. November 8, 1846. 1 p.

KUYDENDALL, ABSALOM. Letter to E. & E. Strang. February 5, 1860. 2 pp.

LAKE, ANSEL. Letter to Strang. June 11, 1851. 1 p.

—— Letter to Bro. Chidester. May 30, 1850. 1 p.

LEARNED, EDWARD. Two letters to Strang. April 9, 1848, April 1, 1850. 2 pp.

LEATHERBURY, MARY. Letter to Strang. April 23, 1849. 2 pp.

LINDLEY, M. Letter to G. J. Adams. November 15, 1849. 2 pp.

LOCKWOOD, M. L. Letter to Strang. June 30, 1851. 3 pp.

LOSEE, MYRAETTE A. STRANG (MRS. ARAD). Letter to Strang. July 29, 1845, sending formal demission from the Baptist Church at Randolph of Mary and James Strang, May 4, July 20, 1845. Signed by R. D. Gould, clerk. With postscript by David Strang. 4 pp.

—— Five letters to Strang. May 5, 1846–November 20, 1850. 14 pp.

—— Copy of a letter to "Friend Dennison," February 7, 1878, prepared for Charles K. Backus. The original was signed Myraette A. Losee per A. Losee. 4 pp.

LOWEN, AMOS. Seven letters to Strang. October 22, 1849–June 15, 1851. 18 pp.

MACAULEY, JOHN. Two letters to Strang. June 24, July 15, 1849. 5 pp.

—— Letter to Francis Cooper. June 21, 1850. 3 pp.

McCLELLAND, ROBERT. Letter to Strang. June 29, 1855. 1 p.

McCULLOCH, HEZEKIAH D. Letter to Strang. November 13, 1855. 1 p.

McNutt, James Oscar. Four letters to Quaife. October 31–December 22, 1920. 8 pp.

Marks, William. Letter to Strang. May 23, 1847. 1 p.

Matteson, P. Letter to Strang. April 2, 1846. 1 p.

Merryweather, F. Three letters to Strang. October 11–November 29, 1846. With two pages of thoughts on the kingdom of God and a note from Strang to Greenhow suggesting that he print them, without the letter, in his paper [*Zion's Reveille*]. 7 pp.

Meyers, Isaac B. Letter to Strang. December 23, 1849. 2 pp.

Miller, Mark. Three letters to Strang. September 2–December 23, 1850. 3 pp.

Miller, Reuben. Three letters to Strang. February 15, 1845 [i.e., 1846]–December 23, 1846. 6 pp.

—— Notes in an unidentified hand of a discourse against Strang. Voree, July 24, 1846. 3 pp. With Strang's answers, point by point. 3 pp.

Moore, Eri J. Letter to S. Graham. October 6, 1849. 4 pp.

—— Letter to A. Wadsworth. June 20, 1850. 1 p.

Murray, Joel [?]. Letter to Strang. July 22, 1849. 1 p.

Nash, Eben. Letter to Strang. September 23, 1850. 1 p.

Neal, R. B. Letter to C. J. Strang. November 3, 1906. 1 p.

Nichols, Jesse W. Four letters to Strang. March 4, 1847–January 3, 1850. 9 pp.

Nichols, Reuben T. Two letters to Strang. July 22, December 15, 1846. 2 pp.

Nickerson, Uriel C. H. Letter to Reuben Miller. March 27, 1846. 2 pp.

Nixon, James D. Letter to C. J. Douglass [Elvira Field]. January 9, 1850. 4 pp.

Nixon, T. Letter to Strang. May 1, 1846. 2 pp.

Northrup, Samuel. Letter to Strang. March 9, 1846. 2 pp.

O'Malley, Charles M. Two letters to Strang. April 25, 1850. 3 pp.

O'Malley, Tully. Letter to Strang. May 2, 1850. 1 p.

Order of the Illuminati. Part of the ritual of the Order, its origin, the address to be made to candidates, in the handwriting of J. C. Bennett. [*ca.* July 6, 1846.] 2 pp.

Ormsby, Esther. Letter to Strang. May 17, 1846. 3 pp.

Paden, Isaac. Letter to Strang. February 19, 1847. 4 pp.

—— Letter to James M. Adams. April [1] 1846. 2 pp.

—— Report to Strang of a meeting of the Knoxville Branch, with a list of members, signed by Isaac Paden and Jones L. Dunkin, clerk. May 17, 1846. 2 pp.

Page, Angeline (Mrs. F.). Argument that "the Holy Spirit was specially given before the day of Pentecost," June 6, 1856. 3 pp.

Page, Ebenezer. Four letters to Strang. [October 17, 1846]–March 7, 1850. 12 pp.

—— Report to Strang of a conference of the church in the Black River district, held at Antwerp, N.Y. November 3, 1846. 2 pp.

Page, John E. Three letters to Strang. February 1, 1846–January 1, 1847. 11 pp.

—— Letter to Greenhow. June 23, 1847. With annotations by Greenhow which were printed with the letter in *Zion's Reveille*. February 11, 1847. 4 pp.

—— Four "objections to points of doctrine taught by J. J. Strang" for a debate. Voree, August 26, 1849. 2 pp.

PATTEN, IRA J. Letter to Strang. December 3, 1849. 1 p.

PEIRCE, JOHN C. Two letters to Strang. November 7, 1850, May 10, 1851. 2 pp.

PENHOLLOW, REUBEN. Assignment to James J. Strang of judgment in Justice's Court of Penhollow vs. William L. Perce. June 2, 1841. Discharged September 20, 1845. 2 pp.

PERCE, L. Letter to her daughter, Mary P. Strang. September 20, 1846. 1 p.

PERCE, SAMUEL G. Three letters to Strang. February 10–June 6, 1850. 3 pp.

PERCE, W. E. Letter to Strang. September 18, 1849. 1 p.

PERCE, W. L. Two letters to Strang. January 18, 1849, June 3, 1850. 2 pp.

PERCE, W. L., JR. Two letters to Strang. June 3, November 10, 1850. 3 pp.

PERSONS, ELISHA. Letter to Strang. April 18, 1849. 3 pp.

PHILLIPS, EUGENIA J. STRANG (Mrs. Thomas H.). Two letters to Quaife. July 15, August 26, 1920. 8 pp. With unsigned carbon copy of Quaife's answer, August 11, 1920. 2 pp.

PIERCE, B [?]. Letter to L. D. Hickey. August 9, 1861. With note on verso signed I. Pierce, August 16, 1861. 2 pp.

PIERCE, ISAAC. Letter to Strang. November 6, 1849. 2 pp.

PORTER, ANDREW J. Letter to Strang. December 26, 1849. 1 p.

POST, STEPHEN. Five letters to Strang. April 20, 1849–June 7, 1850. 6 pp.

PRESTON, EDWARD. Three letters to Strang. November 19, 1849–November 12, 1850. 6 pp.

PRINDLE, ANSON W. Two letters to Strang. November 14, December 26, 1849. 5 pp.

PUGH, JAMES W. Letter to Strang. March 23, 1846. 2 pp.

QUAIFE, MILO MILTON. Letter to John Flanders. November 19, 1919. Unsigned carbon. 1 p.

RACINE COUNTY, TERRITORY OF WISCONSIN, DISTRICT COURT. Certificate that Elder James J. Strang has filed a copy of his credentials of ordinations. August 18, 1843. Albert G. Knight, clerk, by Isaiah G. Parker, deputy. Endorsed: "Authority to solemnize marriage, Racine Co., W.T." 1 p.

RANSOM, E. D. Letter to Strang. June 30, 1849. 1 p.

RAUNSEILER [?], WILLIAM. Letter to Strang. January 4, 1847. 1 p.

REEVE, SAMUEL MOORE. Letter to Strang. July 12, 1846. 3 pp.

REFORMED TEMPERANCE SOCIETY. Constitution. [*ca.* December 1849?] 2 pp.

RIDLON, CHARLES. Letter to Strang. October 21, 1850. 1 p.

ROGERS, CHARLES A. Letter to Strang. March 27, 1850. 1 p.

ROGERS, STRATTEN. Letter to Strang. April 3, 1851. 1 p.

ROSE, PHILIP S. Letter to Quaife. December 3, 1919. Typewritten. 1 p. With unsigned carbon copy of Quaife's answer, December 6, 1919. 1 p.

ROSE, WILLIAM. Letter to Strang. October 5, 1846. 1 p.

ROUTZEN, D. Letter to Strang. March 13, 1847. 1 p.

[SANGER?], LOUISA. Four letters to

Strang. July 15 [1846]–April 18, 185[0?]. 12 pp.

SAVAGE, CATHERINE. Letter to Strang. January 8, 1849. 1 p.

SAVAGE, JEHIEL. "Charges preferred against Brigham Yong, Heber Cimble [*sic*], Parley Pratt" in conference at Voree. April 6, 1846. 1 p.

SCOTT, SAM. Letter to Bro. Gosline. [n.d.] Typewritten copy unsigned. 2 pp.

SEAMAN, MURRY. Letter to Strang. July 20, 1851. 2 pp.

—— Letter to J. M. Wait and H. G. Hall. November 11, 1859. 4 pp.

SEELYE, JESSE. Letter to Strang. December 6, 1846. 1 p.

SEGAR, WILLIAM S. Letter to Strang. December 30, 1846. 1 p.

SHAW, SAMUEL. Letter to Strang. June 1, 1846. 2 pp.

SHIPPEN, GEORGE M. Letter to Strang. March 31, 1846. 1 p.

SHOOK, DAVID. Letter to Strang. May 26, 1856. 1 p.

SIAS, A., JR. Letter to Strang [?]. February 23, 1849. 1 p.

SMALL, JOHN. Letter to Strang. April 8, 1847. 1 p.

SMITH, HEMAN C. Two letters to Quaife. January 27, February 12, 1919. Typewritten. 3 pp. With unsigned carbon copies of three letters from Quaife, January 7–February 18, 1919. 5 pp.

SMITH, HEMAN HALE. Four letters to Quaife. June 7–July 14, 1920. 7 pp. Enclosed with the letter of June 23 is a copy of a letter from Lyman Wight to the editor of the *Northern Islander*, July 1855. 8 pp.

SMITH, JAMES. Letter to Strang. May 16, 1846. 3 pp.

SMITH, LUCY (MRS. JOSEPH). Letter of March 22, 1846, in reply to Babbitt, Heywood and Tulmer [i.e., Fullmer]. Copy, with a copy of their letter to her. 4 pp.

SMITH, WEALTHY. Letter to Strang. November 1, 1846. 3 pp.

SMITH, WILLIAM. Six letters to Strang. March 17–Christmas Day, 1846. 23 pp.

—— Trial before the first Presidency on charges of adultery, John C. Gaylord accuser [*ca.* April 23, 1847]. Adjourned to June 1, 1847. 1 p.

—— Testimony of Sarah Ellsworth in trial of Gaylord vs. William Smith, taken by J. J. Strang. April 23, 1847. 2 pp.

—— Copy of questions put to B. C. Ellsworth by John C. Gaylord and William Smith [*ca.* April 23, 1847]. 2 pp.

SOMERS, A. N. Three letters to Quaife. January 13–May 30, 1920. 7 pp.

—— "Mysterious Relics of Mormon Impostures." Typewritten 9 pp.

—— "The Origin of Mormonism." Typewritten. 4 pp.

—— "Some Relics of Early Mormon Impostures." Typewritten. 11 pp.

SOUTHWORTH, H. L. Letter to J. J. Strang. November 18, 1846. Written on the blank leaf of a printed *Prospectus of the Independent Inquirer and Journal of the Times*, a proposed weekly newspaper, November 20, 1846. 2 pp.

SQUIRE, FREDERIC. Letter to Strang. April 3, 1850. 2 pp.

STEPHENS, RICHARD. Letter to Strang. March [8, 1846]. 1 p.

—— Letter to W. L. Perce. March 16, 1847. 1 p.

STONE, ROYAL. Letter to Strang. August 19, 1849. 2 pp.

STRANG, ABIGAIL (MRS. CLEMENT). Three letters to Strang. [May? 1850–June 23, 1851?] With additions by Arad Losee and M. S. Losee. 12 pp.

STRANG, CHARLES J. "Outline Copy of Sketch of James J. Strang written for C. K. Backus, Detroit, in summer of 1878, by Chas. J. Strang." Copy made in 1882. 9 pp.

—— Miscellaneous manuscript notes. 29 pp.

STRANG, CLEMENT J. Ten letters to Quaife. July 25, 1920–December 3, 1921. 21 pp. With a carbon copy of Quaife's answer, September 14, 1920. 2 pp.

STRANG, DAVID. Three letters to his brother. May 28, 1848–August 11, 1850. 9 pp.

STRÁNG, ELVIRA FIELD (MRS. JAMES JESSE), "Charles J. Douglass." Two letters to Strang. February 4[–6], February 7, 1850. 3 pp.

—— Biographical sketch of J. J. Strang by his wife and their son Charles J. Strang. Typewritten, with manuscript annotations. 12 pp.

STRANG, MARY PERCE (MRS. JAMES JESSE). Four letters to Strang. November 4, 1849–January 9, 1850. 6 pp.

TEWKSBURY, ABIJAH A. Letter to Strang. April 3, 1847. 2 pp.

THOMPSON, SAMUEL E. Letter to Strang. September 23, 1846. 3 pp.

TUBBS, LORENZO. Letter to Strang. May 3, 1849. 2 pp.

TUCKER, HIRAM. Letter to Strang. May 15, 1846. 1 p.

URSBRUCK, JOHN. Two letters to Strang. August 13, November 17, 1849. 4 pp.

UTTER, F. A. Letter to Strang. May 16, 1846. 1 p.

VAN BÜREN, LEWIS. Two letters to Strang. March 14, May 6, 1846. 5 pp.

VAN DEUSEN, INCREASE MCGEE. Two letters to Strang. June 18, [December 21, 1849]. 6 pp.

—— Letter to J. B. Wheeland. January 3, 1847. 4 pp.

WAIT, JAMES M. Letter to Strang. December 1, 1855. 1 p.

WALKER, MOORE. Letter to Strang. February 2, 1850. 2 pp.

WALTER, GEORGE. Letter to Strang. July 11, 1847. 1 p.

WALWORTH COUNTY, WIS. TER., DISTRICT COURT. Certificate that James J. Strang filed a copy of his credentials as minister of the Gospel on December 30, 1845. Signed by LeGrand Rockwell, clerk, at Elkhorn, June 13, 1846. 1 p.

WATSON, GILBERT. Eight letters to Strang. September 19, 1849–April 16, 1850. 19 pp.

WATSON, WINGFIELD. Letter to Gilbert Watson. February 16, 1862. Incomplete. 2 pp.

—— 11 letters to Quaife. January 2, 1919–July 18, 1925[?]. 80 pp. With carbon copies of Quaife's letters of February 4, April 5, May 1, 1919. 5 pp.

WHIPPLE, D. R. Four letters to Strang. November 21, 1849–April 10, 1850. 5 pp.

—— Letter to George J. Adams. November 29, 1849. 1 p.

—— Letter to A. N. Hosmer. December 28[and 31], 1849. 3 pp.

—— Letter to a sister [in the church]. March 29, 1869. 4 pp.

WILCOX, DAVID. Letter to Strang. April 14, 1846. 2 pp.

WILKIE, C. Letter to Strang. June 15, 1856. 1 p.

WILLIAMS, G. Letter to Strang. December 3, 1849. 1 p.

WILLIAMS, SAMUEL. Letter to Strang. January 26, 1851. 1 p.

WILSON, JOHN [?] H. Letter to Strang. December 26, 1849. 1 p.

WING, MRS. SARAH A. WRIGHT (formerly Mrs. J. J. Strang). Three letters to Quaife. [Spring 1920]–January 20, 1921. 18 pp.

WINSOR, ALONZO. Two letters to Strang. April 29, June 13, 1846. 2 pp.

WOODRUFF, WILFORD. Letter to J. W. Grierson. January 11, 1850. 2 pp.

WORKMAN, HENRY. Letter to Strang. February 12, 1850. 1 p.

WRIGHT, BENJAMIN G. Ten letters to Strang. September 13, 1849–August 1, 1850. 17 pp.

WRIGHT, PHINEAS. Two letters to Strang. August 7, 23, 1850. 3 pp.

WRIGHT, MRS. ZENOS H. Six letters to Quaife. September 15, 1920–October 16, 1921. 10 pp. With a photograph of Phoebe Wright Strang.

YARRINGTON, ALVAH. Letter to Strang. May 11, 1849, with postscript by Stephen Post. 2 pp.

YOUNG, BRIGHAM. Letter "To the branches of the church in the neighborhood of Ottawa, Ill." denouncing Strang. January 24, 1846. In the handwriting of Orson Hyde and signed by Young as president, and Hyde as clerk. 4 pp.

The Strang manuscripts were collected by Charles J. Strang, son of the Prophet and Elvira Field, and after his death became the property of his brother, Clement J. Strang, who was planning to write a biography of his father. He gave up his project however and turned the material over to Mr. Quaife for his use in writing *The Kingdom of Saint James*. The diary, except for the fragment in this collection, and the original "Covenant" were some years ago in the possession of Henry Denio of Lamoni, Iowa, grandson of Strang and Betsy McNutt.

Many of Strang's manuscripts and some of the letters were printed in the *Voree Herald*, 1846–1850. Mr. Quaife quoted extensively from them in his book and printed in full the diary (pp. 195–234), Brigham Young's letter (p. 23), the "Letter of Appointment" (pp. 235–237), the "Summons to the Twelve" (pp. 241–242), Lester Brooks' letter to Adams (pp. 243–245), and Mrs. Lucy Smith's letter (pp. 246–248); the autobiography was published by Henry E. Legler, "A Moses of the Mormons," Michigan Pioneer and Historical Society, *Historical Collections*, 1903, XXXII, 201–206.

[Coe Collection.]

448–452 STUART, GRANVILLE and JAMES

The journals of James and Granville Stuart, describing their life in California, their journey from California to Montana, the discovery of gold in Montana, and the early settlement of the Territory; with the contemporary journals of F. H. Burr and A. B. Henderson, 1854 to 1880.

14 volumes in 12 portfolios. With typewritten "Catalogue of the Stuart papers, 1854–1880." 16 pp. 12½–33 cm.

James and Granville Stuart were early settlers of Montana and their journals are important sources for the history of the Territory. James died in 1873 but Granville continued to take a prominent part in the development of the Territory until his death in 1918. He served on the Territorial Council and in the Legislature, was president of the Board of Stock Commissioners, the Historical Society of Montana, and the Society of Montana Pioneers. In 1894 President Cleveland appointed him Minister to Uruguay and Paraguay, and in 1916 the State Legislature commissioned him to write a history of Montana, on which he was engaged at the time of his death.

448 STUART, JAMES, 1832–1873

Diary, January 28 [1854] to June 27, 1855, and June 14 to July 17, 1857, describing his experiences in California and during the journeys northward to the Oregon boundary in 1854 and 1855, and eastward in 1857 across the Plains to northern Utah. With a table of distances and a Snake Indian vocabulary. 1854–1857.

82 pp. 12½ cm. With typewritten transcript.

The first part of the diary, to June 27, 1855, while James is on a prospecting journey, is written in code with a key inserted. It was resumed June 14, 1857, when with Anderson and others the Stuarts started east, and ends July 17 at Malade Creek when Granville was too ill to travel and James and Anderson stayed with him while the rest of the party continued on its way. The rest of the volume contains accounts, recipes, etc.

—— "Fort Browning, Montana Territory. The private memoranda and record of current events of James Stuart, Deer Lodge, Montana, commencing October 12, 1871" to April 20, 1873. 3 vols. [i.e., 174 pp.] 25 cm.

James Stuart was appointed post trader in 1871 at Fort Browning, Agency for Assiniboine and Upper Sioux Indians. It was abandoned in 1873 and the Sioux Agency was moved to Fort Peck. Stuart died at Fort Peck September 30, 1873.

The journal records daily events at the post, Stuart's trip to Fort Benton and Helena, November 1871–January 1872; a flood in Milk River, February 17, 1872; illnesses that he treated; the accident, May 14, when the roof fell on him; and his trip to Helena, July–November, 1872. The entries from January 3, 1873, are brief records of the weather, until February 11, when his thermometer was stolen and broken.

449 STUART, JAMES and GRANVILLE

Diary of James and Granville Stuart of events in Montana Territory. May 1, 1861 to November 17, 1862, March 15, 1863 to May 31, 1864, and occasionally to April 19, 1866.

2 vols. [i.e., 147 pp.] 33 cm.

This diary, kept jointly by Granville and James Stuart, describes life in Montana during the gold rush and the days of the road agents and Vigilantes. The latter part is written in a more narrative form.

450 STUART, GRANVILLE, 1834–1918

Diary kept on the overland journey from California to Malade Creek, Utah, in 1857. A fragment.

9 pp. 12½ cm. Original binding. With typewritten transcript.

The first entry of the diary is July 6, 1857 on the Humboldt, and the last July 14, three days before Granville is ill at Malade with mountain fever. The diary includes a list of the party that left Yreka in 1857, and is followed by an itinerary of the journey from Montana to Salt Lake in 1858 and vocabularies of the Snake and Shoshone languages. 54 pp.

—— Diary, January 6–June 8, 1866, of his overland journey from Montana to Iowa and back to Fort Benton by way of the Missouri River. With a table of distances and a record of steamboats arriving at the Fort, 1866. 45 pp. 19 cm. Original binding.

Stuart left Deer Lodge January 6, 1866 and Virginia City on the 17th by the Overland Mail coach for Salt Lake, Denver, and Atchison, and the North Missouri Railroad to St. Louis and West Liberty, Iowa. He returned March 26, by Chicago and St. Louis by train, and St. Louis to Fort Benton by steamer. The diary describes the journey on the *Walter B. Dance* in detail and the country passed through.

—— Journal of a hunting and fishing excursion in the Deer Lodge country in 1867, with a series of pencil sketches drawn from nature, 1867–1872. 36 pp. 16 cm. Original binding.

The journal describes a hunting trip with his brother James, August 30–September 10 or 11, 1867; records altitudes November 19, 1867, temperature of hot springs, and record of weather, September 10–18, 1869, January 7–18, 1870, and includes a few accounts, some dated 1872. The ten drawings are scenes in Montana dated September 1, 1867–June 1872.

—— Journal of a trip to the National Park. The Yellowstone Expedition of 1873. 39 pp. Map. 21½ cm. Original binding.

The journal is in pencil, badly rubbed. Newspaper clippings about Yellowstone Park trails are pasted on inside covers, dated "Deer Lodge, August 12, 1873," and signed "M," from the *New North-West*. There is a small sketch map of the trail on Fire Hole River at the entry for August 27. The party, consisting of W. W. Dixon, W. B. Judd, D. P. Newcomer, Charles A. McCabe, N. Dickinson, Pat Ryan, W. Egbert Smith, Thomas Frazier, Robert Miller, Charles Aspling, and Granville Stuart, left Deer Lodge August 18, 1873. The journal breaks off September 12.

—— Journal of a trip to the Yellowstone country to look for a cattle range. April 11–June 29, 1880. 152 pp. 19½ cm. Original binding.

The journal is followed by accounts and a table of distances, Indian Creek to Martinsdale. In the text are small outline sketches, "Little Snowie Mountains" and "Black Butte" [p. 63].

In 1879 Granville Stuart formed a partnership with A. J. Davis, Erwin Davis, and Samuel T. Hauser, under the firm name of Davis, Hauser & Co., to engage in the cattle raising business.

451 BURR, FREDERICK H.

Diary kept in the Bitterroot country and during his journeys from Fort Owen to Salt Lake and return and to the gold diggings in 1857. January 1, 1857 to January 4, 1858.

96 pp. 15½ cm. Original binding.

The journal occupies the first 63 pages and is followed by accounts, records of cattle and other memoranda. Accompanying the diary are letters from F. H. Burr to James Stuart, October 12, 1868 and to Granville Stuart, May 16, 1895. 6 pp.

Burr came to Montana in 1853 with Lieutenant Mullan's party; in 1856 he settled in Bitter Root and married a sister of Granville Stuart's wife Aubony. This diary supplements the diary of John Owen for the same period. Burr was associated with Owen and John Grant, and later with the Stuart brothers.

452 HENDERSON, A. B. ("BART")

Journal of the Yellowstone Expedition of 1866 under Captain Jeff Standifer, by A. B. Henderson, Lieutenant of the Company, with the diaries kept by Henderson during his prospecting journeys in the Snake, Wind River, and Yellowstone country during the years 1867–1873. Transcribed from the four original journals into one volume by Granville Stuart.

101 pp. 32½ cm. Original binding.

The journal of the Yellowstone Expedition of 1866 under Captain Standifer, July 31, 1866–April 12, 1867, is followed by narratives of prospecting trips in the summers of 1867, 1870, 1871, 1872, and 1873.

The first expedition prospected east and south to the Big Horn, Yellowstone, Wind, and Snake Rivers, south through Wyoming to Utah, and the journal describes the country in detail, the stay in Salt Lake City, experiences with the Mormons, and an encounter with the Apaches. After recovering from his wounds Henderson traveled by stage to Dixie County and Yuma, to join a party from California for Mexico.

All the Stuart journals were used by Granville Stuart in preparing his *Forty Years on the Frontier as Seen in the Journals and Reminiscences of Granville Stuart*, Cleveland, 1925. 2 vols. Edited after his death by Paul C. Phillips. The printed version of the Stuart journals is much more detailed than the originals. Parts of the joint journal of James and Granville are printed verbatim, but others are expanded and some entries omitted. Some dates differ in the printed version.

[Coe No. 169.]

453 STUART, GRANVILLE and JAMES

Correspondence between Granville and James Stuart, 1864–1873, and letters to them from friends and business acquaintances, 1865–1873.

98 letters. 220 pp. 18–30 cm.

The letters of the brothers discuss their business affairs, mines, troubles with the Indians, local politics, and family news. Those written to them are in general on business or local politics.

STUART, GRANVILLE. 27 letters to his brother James. October 7, 1864–September 17, 1873. 81 pp.

—— Letter to Reece Anderson. October 14, 1873. 2 pp.

—— Letter to Mary Stewart. December 5, 1878. 1 p.

STUART, JAMES. 23 letters to his brother Granville. February 15, 1866–September 18, 1873. 53 pp.

—— Letter to Major A. J. Simmons. April 23, 1872. 3 pp.

—— Letter to Frank L. Worden. April 11, 1865. 2 pp.

STUART, J. Three letters and a telegram to Dance, Stuart & Co. December 24, 1866–March 25, 1867. 9 pp.

STUART, THOMAS. Letter to his brother James. November 14, 1871. With note added by Granville Stuart. 3 pp.

ADAMS, THOMAS. Two letters to Granville Stuart. June 10, 1865, December 29, 1867. 7 pp.

ATCHISON, JOHN S. Letter to Granville Stuart. December 24, 1867. 1 p.

BARBER, S. W. Letter to Granville Stuart. August 10, 1868. 1 p.

BROWNE, JOSEPH ALOYSIUS. Letter to James Stuart. April 12, 1863. 3 pp.

BUCK, D. V. Letter to James Stuart. September 17, 1872. 1 p.

CAMPBELL, C. C. Letter to Granville Stuart. December 2, 1867. 1 p.

CAMPBELL, ROBERT. Letter to Granville Stuart. September 28, 1872. 1 p.

CAVANAUGH, JAMES M. Letter to Granville Stuart. March 2, 1868. 2 pp.

CULBERTSON, R. S. Letter to Granville Stuart. September 28, 1873. With note added from James Stuart. 2 pp.

DANCE, WALTER B. Letter to Granville Stuart. July 5, 1865. 1 p.

—— Letter to James Stuart. July 7, 1865. 3 pp.

DANCE, STUART & COMPANY. Bill to Deer Lodge County. February 3, 1868. 1 p.

EDWARDS, W. R. H. Letter to Dance, Stuart and others. November 28, 1867. 2 pp.

GRANT, AGGIE. Letter to Granville Stuart. October 9, 1867. 1 p.

HARRIS, THOMAS W. Letter to "Friend Stewart." December 5, 1865. 1 p.

HAUSER, SAMUEL THOMAS. Telegram to James Stuart. October 26, 1870. 1 p.

KENNETT, FERD. Two letters to Granville Stuart. September 2, 1868, May 31, 1872. 5 pp.

MAILLET, LOUIS R. Two letters to Granville Stuart. August 31, September 3, 1868. 4 pp.

MORRISON, ARTHUR. Letter to James Stuart. September 20, 1872. 2 pp.

PINNEY, GEORGE M., & Co. Letter to Granville Stuart. October 23, 1867. Signed: "per Busain." 1 p.

REED, MARY EBEY (MRS. CHARLES B.). Invitation to Granville Stuart and Lady. October 26, 1866. 1 p.

RITCHIE, J. D. Letter to James Stuart. June 25, 1871. Enclosed in letter from Granville to James, July 12, 1871. 2 pp.

SAUNDERS, COLE. Letter to Granville Stuart. August 5, 1868. 1 p.

SIMMONS, ANDREW J. Two letters to James Stuart. January 7, 1873 [undated 1873]. 4 pp.

THUM, M. C. Letter to James Stuart. March 11, 1872. 2 pp.

TUTTLE, DANIEL SYLVESTER. Letter to Granville Stuart. September 5, 1868. 1 p.

WADE, THOMAS B. Letter to Granville Stuart. March 30, 1868. 2 pp.

WARE, GEORGE W. Three letters to Granville Stuart. November 29, 1867–June 24, 1868. 6 pp.

WOODY, FRANK H. Two letters to Granville Stuart. November 11, 1867, September 4 [1868]. 3 pp.

WORDEN, FRANK LYMAN. Two letters to James Stuart. June 15, 20, 1867. 2 pp.

—— Letter to Granville Stuart. September 4, 1868. 1 p.

[Coe Collection.]

454 STUART, GRANVILLE, 1834–1918

Letter books for the years 1880–1887.

4 vols. [i.e., 2,623 letters] 31½–30½ cm. Original binding.

The letters cover the period from February 10, 1880 to April 11, 1887. Each volume is indexed.

These letters represent the business correspondence of Granville Stuart with a few personal letters included, in general from Helena and Fort Maginnis. He writes as superintendent and manager of Davis, Hauser & Co., and later for Stuart, Kohrs & Co. and the Pioneer Cattle Co.; as president of the Territorial Board of Stock Commissioners and of the Montana Stock Growers Association; as chairman of the Board of Trustees, School District No. 19; and as a member of the Territorial Council and House of Representatives.

The letters deal with the development of the cattle industry in Montana, the Indian policy, and political questions of the day, and include letters to editors of various journals and papers.

[Coe No. IV, 444.]

455 STUART, JAMES EWELL BROWN ("JEB"), 1833–1864

"Journal of the march of Companies F, G, H, & K, 1st Cavalry, commanded by Major John Sedgwick, 1st Cavalry, from Fort Riley, K.T., on an expedition against the hostile Kiawas and Comanches; pursuant to Special Orders, No. 34, Headquarters, Department of the West, St. Louis, Mo., April 3d, 1860."

54 pp. 18½ cm. Original binding. With typewritten transcript.

Note in pencil inside front cover: "Journal of J. E. B. Stuart on Indian campaign of 1860. Not in his hand."

General Stuart was born in Virginia in 1833, entered West Point in 1850, and spent the years following his graduation on the southern and western borders, first in the Mounted Rifles. In 1855 he was transferred to the 1st Cavalry. As soon as Virginia seceded he resigned from the army and enlisted in the Virginia militia.

Seven pages of printed instructions, General Orders No. 12, signed by S. Cooper, Adjutant General, April 1860, are pasted in the front of the notebook.

The journal, in accordance with these instructions, is written across facing pages, giving the date, hour, weather, distance, route and remarks. Under "route" are over 90 carefully drawn maps indicating all remarkable features passed, hills, streams, fords, camps, etc. At the end of the march the journal was to be copied, the copy kept at the station and the original forwarded to the headquarters of the Department. A note at the end states: "This journal has been very accurately kept by Lieut. J. E. B. Stuart, 1st Cavalry, from notes taken during the day, and copied every evening . . . Fort Wise, Big Timbers, Sept. 12, 1860."

The journal records the expedition against the Kiowas and Comanches from Fort Riley, May 15–September 12, 1860.

A note at the end is signed by H. Sedgwick. The journal may therefore be the copy retained by Major Sedgwick.

[Coe No. 170.]

456 STUART, LEVI B., 1829–

Journal of a voyage to California in 1849, and the return by Panama in 1850–1851.

67 pp., incl. 5 drawings. 20 cm. Original binding.

Levi B. Stuart of Southville, Conn., left Bridgwater, March 6, 1849, for New Haven where he joined the New Haven and California Joint Stock Company, which chartered the bark *Anna Reynolds*, John Bottom, Captain, and sailed March 12 from New Haven for California. The journal describes the trip from Bridgwater, and the voyage around the Horn to the bay of Talchuana [i.e., Talcahuano, Chile], where it breaks off, March 6–September 14, 1849. Stuart resumes his journal March 23–30, 1850, when the New Haven and California Company broke up

at Sacramento and he set out for the mines at Negro Bar on the American River; and on November 3 [1850], in San Francisco, when he takes passage on the ship *Talma* for Realejo, sailing November 8. The last entry is on January 18, 1851, south of Realejo, en route to Panama.

The journal is followed by a table of latitude and longitude from March 18 to November 21, 1849, and contains five pencil sketches of the mountainous shoreline, with volcanoes, of Guatemala and Salvador.

457 STUART, ROBERT, 1785–1848

"Journal of a voyage across the continent of North America from Astoria, the Pacific Fur Company's principal establishment on the Columbia, to the City of New York, kept by Robert Stuart." June 29, 1812 to May 24, 1813.

135 pp. 21 cm. Original binding.

——Travelling Memoranda.

212 pp. 25 cm. Original binding.

Robert Stuart left his home in Scotland as a young man of 22 to join his uncle, David Stuart, an agent of the North West Fur Company, and entered the service of that company. He later became a partner in John Jacob Astor's Pacific Fur Company. He sailed from New York for the Columbia in 1810 on the *Tonquin*, and it is his return journey with despatches for Astor in 1812 that is recorded in the journal. He was later head of Astor's American Fur Company for the upper Lake region, with headquarters at Michilimackinac, and became active in civic, religious and political affairs. In 1835 he moved to Detroit.

The journal, written on the road, covers

the journey from June 29, 1812, when Stuart and his companions left Astoria, to April 30, 1813, when he arrived in St. Louis; and contains at the end an account of Stuart's trip from St. Louis, May 16, until it breaks off after his arrival at Green River, Kentucky, May 24, 1813. The "Travelling Memoranda," evidently written at a later date, is a transcript of the journal, with some variations and amplifications, prepared for Mr. Astor and by him made available for publication in French in *Nouvelles annales des voyages* . . . Paris, 1821. It bears the following note on the flyleaf: "Retour de l'embouchure de la Columbia jusques au Missouri par—& six personnes." The volume was later used by Irving in writing *Astoria*.

The journal remained in the possession of members of Stuart's family until it came into the possession of Frederick S. Dellenbaugh, from whom it was acquired by Mr. Coe. The "Travelling Memoranda" bought by Mr. Coe at a sale at the American Art Association–Anderson Galleries, Inc., according to the sale catalogue, was found in a cupboard at Sunnyside by

E. M. Grinnell, grandnephew of Washington Irving, and remained in the possession of the family until the time of the sale. The journal has been published in full under the title: *The Discovery of the Oregon Trail. Robert Stuart's Narratives of His Overland Trip Eastward from Astoria in 1812–13*. Edited by Philip Ashton Rollins, New York, London, 1935.

[Coe Nos. 171–172.]

458 STUART, ROBERT, 1785–1848

[The Discovery of the Oregon Trail. Robert Stuart's Narratives.] Typewritten copy of his journal and travelling memoranda, edited by Philip Ashton Rollins, with notes and supplementary material.

588 pp. 28–31 cm.

The typewritten manuscript includes all of the text of Mr. Rollins' edition except chapter 11, "Postscripts to various entries in journal," the Biographical Note and Foreword, and Appendix A.

The text is accompanied by the following letters and papers:

ROLLINS, PHILIP ASHTON. Six letters to Edward Eberstadt. January 17–August 15, 1933. Typewritten. 11 pp.

EBERSTADT, EDWARD. Letter to W. R. Coe. October 10, 1933. Typewritten. 1 p.

—— "Basis of my argument on the deletion of the travelling memoranda. Differences or additional material found in travelling memoranda in comparison with the journal." Typewritten manuscript. 28 pp.

—— "My suggested changes in Mr. Rollins' text and notes." Typewritten and in pencil. 658 pp.

In general Mr. Eberstadt's suggestions were incorporated in Mr. Rollins' final manuscript.

[Coe Collection.]

459 STUART, ROBERT, 1785–1848

Circuit Court of the United States in and for the County of Michilimackinac, Territory of Michigan, of the term of July 1825. Indictment of Nay-náu-ahbee, of the Chippewa Nation, for the murder of Eli Ractier, signed by Henry S. Cole, Prosecuting Attorney.

4 pp. 32 cm.

Endorsed: "A true bill, Robert Stuart, Foreman. Filed in court July 19, 1825, J. P. King, Clk. Witnesses: Lyman N. Warren, John B. Corbin, Louis Corbin."

At this time Robert Stuart was a prominent citizen of Michilimackinac and dur-

ing 1825 served as judge of the County Court.

The indictment by the Grand Jury, Robert Stuart, Foreman, finds Nay-náu-ah-bee of Muddy Lake Village guilty of shooting Eli Ractier on May 5, 1824.

[Coe No. 173.]

460 STUART, ROBERT, 1785–1848

Printed token [or order] filled in by hand and signed by Robert Stuart, Agent, American Fur Company. "No. 38 Good to Wm. McGulpin for the baking of 100 loaves bread for retail store Michilimackinac, July 5th, 1882." 13½ x 4½ cm.

[Coe No. IV, 105.]

461 SUCKLEY, GEORGE, 1830–1869

Letters of George Suckley, naturalist of the Stevens expedition to survey a northern route for a Pacific railroad, describing the organization of the expedition and the transcontinental journey of 1853; life and adventures on the coast, 1854–1856; Indian Wars of the Northwest, 1854–1858; overland journey to Utah with the troops, 1859; and the controversy with Stevens over the publication of his work on the natural history of Washington Territory.

34 letters and papers. 106 pp. 15½–31½ cm. With typewritten transcripts.

Dr. George Suckley was born in New York in 1830. He was graduated from the College of Physicians and Surgeons in New York, and in 1853 joined the Isaac I. Stevens railway survey as surgeon and naturalist; was appointed assistant surgeon in the Army and served in the Indian Wars and at Fort Steilacoom until 1858. In 1859, again in the East, he crossed the Plains with recruits for the Utah regiment.

Laid in the volume with the letters are four leaves [pp. 161–168] from Stevens' *Narrative and Final Report*, 1860, covering the account of Dr. Suckley's trip from Fort Owen to Vancouver.

—— Ten letters to his brother, John H. Suckley. May 12, 1853–October 15, 1854. 34 pp.

—— Seven letters to his aunt, Mary Suckley. June 6, 1853–July 1, 1859. 26 pp.

—— Drafts of four letters to Governor Stevens. August 26, 1853–July 19, 1860. 6 pp.

—— Two letters to his uncle, Rutsen Suckley. December 9, 1853, including a copy of Governor Stevens' instruc-

tions to proceed by canoe, St. Mary's, October 2, 1853; January 13, 1855. 10 pp.

—— Letter to his sister, Miss F. M. Josephine Price. March 31, 1854. 2 pp.

—— Draft of a letter to Will A. Slaughter. April 12, 1854. 3 pp.

—— Letter to his "Uncle" [neither Rutsen nor Tom]. May 20, 1854. 4 pp.

—— Letter to his uncle [Thomas H. Suckley?]. January 24, 1855. 2 pp.

—— Letter to Brigadier General Thomas Lawson. September 12, 1859. Copy. 4 pp.

—— Letter to editors, Silliman's *Journal*. July 31, 1860. Copy. 1 p.

—— Draft of a letter to Brigadier General J. W. Turner. January 3, 1865. 2 pp.

COOPER, JAMES GRAHAM. Letter to Dr. Suckley. September 5, 1860, enclosing a copy of Cooper's letter to Governor Stevens, September 5, 1860, and the corrected proof of Bailliere Brothers' announcement of the publication of *The Natural History and Physical Geography of Washington Territory and Oregon . . .* By Dr. Geo. Suckley . . . and J. G. Cooper. 7 pp.

GIBBS, GEORGE. Letter to Wolcott Gibbs, introducing Suckley. June 24, 1855. 1 p.

[Unidentified writer.] Letter to Suckley, discussing the Leschi case, mines, affairs on the Sound. August 29, 1858, evidently from one of his fellow officers at Fort Steilacoom. 4 pp.

The draft of the letter to Governor Stevens, August 26, 1853, is printed from another copy in the Huntington Library in "Sidelights on the Stevens Railway Survey," *Pacific Northwest Quarterly,* 1945, XXXVI, 238–239.

[Coe No. 174.]

462 SULLIVAN, W. W.

"Crossing the Plains in 1862 by W. W. Sullivan, uncle of William L. Simpson, Esq., of Cody, Wyoming."

Typewritten manuscript. 23 pp. 21 cm.

A brief account, written in later years, of the journey of W. W. Sullivan with his father, James Sullivan, and family from Eden, Iowa, to Colorado, where they settled in Pleasant Park, now Bergen's Park. He was one of seven children. The manuscript includes a short statement about the secret Vigilance Committee in Colorado, and a few facts about Sullivan's later life.

The typescript was formerly in the collection of the Rt. Rev. Nathaniel S. Thomas, and contains his bookplate.

[Coe No. 175.]

463 SUMMERS, JOSEPH

Letter to his "Esteemed Companion." Dry Town, October 30, 1850. Followed by an open letter describing briefly the overland route and the mines, written "for the benefit of those who have got the California fever."

43 pp. 13¼ cm. With typewritten transcript.

The letters are written across two pages in a small notebook with glazed paper covers: *Miners' and Travellers' Pocket Letter Book. Designed Expressly for the Convenience of Miners and Travellers to the Mines.* By Jos. W. Gregory. New York, San Francisco, 1850.

The letter, probably to his wife [18 pp.], tells of his health, his move from the diggings on the middle fork of the American River to Dry Town where he has formed a partnership with John Catherwood of Guernsey County, Ohio.

The second letter [25 pp.], of the same date, is for publication if the recipient thinks best. It describes briefly Summers' overland journey from Fort Kearney, May 6, to Salt Lake City, the Humboldt and Carson Rivers, the George Town Cutoff and the middle fork of the American River, July 22, and conditions in the mines.

[Coe No. 176.]

464 SURÍA, TOMÁS DE, 1761–

"Quaderno q[u]e contiene el ramo de historia natural y diario de la Espedicion del circulo del Globo. Reservado. Original Año de 1791," with a note added much later and signed Tomas de Suría.

92 pp. 30 cm. Original binding. With the printed text, edited and translated by Henry R. Wagner, 1936.

Malaspina sailed from Cádiz in the *Descubierta*, July 30, 1791, as commander of a round-the-world scientific expedition. At Acapulco, as the two painters of the expedition had fallen ill, the Viceroy appointed Tomás de Suría to accompany Malaspina in his exploration of the Northwest Coast.

The diary covers the period from Suría's arrival in Acapulco, February 16–August 17, 1791, at Nootka Sound, and contains 5 small sketches and a map in the text, and 13 pages of drawings.

Suría, who in later years was losing his eyesight, has added notes on some of the pages and drawings, many of them illegible, and in one case he has written over almost the entire page.

Translated and edited by Henry R. Wagner with the title: "Journal of Tomás de Suría of His Voyage with Malaspina to the Northwest Coast of America in 1791," *Pacific Historical Review*, 1936, V, 234–276, with 8 plates. Also reprinted and issued separately, Glendale, Calif., 1936.
[Coe No. 177.]

465 SUTRO TUNNEL COMPANY

Certificate No. 176 for fifty shares of stock issued to Adolf Sutro, San Francisco, February 3, 1870, signed by W. K. Van Alen, Secretary, Samuel Merritt, President [with seal]. Lithograph by Britton & Rey, San Francisco.

Broadside. 31 x 19 cm.

Endorsed by Adolph Sutro: "17 shares to Robert C. Kammerer, 17 to Lucy Kammerer, 16 to Adelheid Liebert"; and "17 shares assigned to Lucy Luhman, December 18, 1914." Signed by Chas. H. Liebert and Edward Steiner, Executors of Robert C. Kammerer, deceased, in the presence of August L. Martin.

Gift of Herman W. Liebert, grandson of Charles H. Liebert.

466 SWAIN, WILLIAM, 1821–1904

Journal of an overland trip from Youngstown, N.Y., to Feather River Valley, California, April 11 to October 31, 1849; and letters written to members of the family while en route, at the diggings, and on the return journey by Panama to New York, April 11, 1849 to January 31, 1851.

2 vols. [i.e., 168 pp.] and 33 letters and documents, 113 pp. 15–17 cm.

William Swain, with his friends Frederick A. Bailey, Michael Hutchinson, and John Root, left his home in Youngstown, N.Y. to join the emigration to the gold mines of California. After a few months at the mines, where he met with some success but suffered hardships and ill health, he returned to New York by Panama. He later developed his farm, specializing in peaches, and became prominent in local politics. The letters include the following:

—— 12 letters to his wife, Mrs. Sabrina Swain. April 11, 1849–January 28, 1851. 44 pp.

—— 11 letters to his brother, George Swain. April 13 [1849]–November 14, 1850. 41 pp.

—— Five letters to his mother, Mrs. Patience Swain. April 22, 1849–August 17, 1850. 18 pp.

—— Letter to all the family. November 6, 1850. 3 pp.

—— Letter to Daniel W. Currier. September 9, 1850, in Swain's hand, signed by Curnelious Kelley and James B. McMennomy, regarding Swain's work at Taylor's Bar and Mr. Currier's indebtedness to him. 1 p.

—— Statement dictated by William Swain to his daughter, Sara Sabrina Swain, regarding his activities in California during October 1850 [ca. 1897]. 2 pp.

SWAIN, GEORGE. Letter to his mother and sister. January 31, 1850. 3 pp.

The journal and letters written en route describe in detail the journey from Youngstown by the Lakes to Chicago, St. Louis, and Independence; the preparations for the overland journey, and the start with the Wolverine Rangers, May 15, by Fort Kearney, the Platte, Fort Laramie, South Pass, Sublette's Cut-off, Humboldt River, and Lassen's Cut-off to the Feather River Valley, when the journal breaks off on October 31. The letters from California describe the rest of the journey to Lassen's, November 8, life in the mines; and his return voyage and illness [Chagres fever].

Laid in the journal [Vol. II] is a typewritten letter to Edward Eberstadt from Elihu Root [New York], April 17, 1935, saying that John Root, son of Benjamin Root, is his second cousin, both great-grandsons of James Root. 1 p.

The journals and letters written on the way to California are at present being edited by J. S. Holliday, and will be published shortly. Mr. Holliday plans to publish a second volume containing the letters written from California and on the return voyage.

[Coe No. 178.]

467 TABEAU, PIERRE ANTOINE, 1755–1820

"Voyage dans Le Haut-Missouri, en 1803, 1804 & 1805. Par Pre. Antne. Tabeaux."

117 pp. 25 cm. Original binding. With the published version of Tabeau's journal.

—— Tabeau's Narrative of Loisel's Expedition to the Upper Missouri. Edited by Annie Heloise Abel. Translated from the French by Rose Abel Wright. Norman, University of Oklahoma Press, 1939.

Tabeau was born at Lachine, 1755, attended the Seminary at Quebec [now Laval University] 1771–1773, and in 1776 went west. He was at one time associated with the North West Company and in 1803 accompanied Régis Loisel on his expedition, under a commission from Lieutenant Governor de Lassus to investigate British intrusions in the territory, its resources, and the Indians. When Loisel returned to St. Louis in 1804, Tabeau lived with the Arikaree Indians, and while there met Lewis and Clark who had been referred to him for information about the country.

The narrative summarizes the voyage up the Missouri, describes the native fruits, animals, and birds; hunting; the Indian tribes, the Sioux, Indian warriors, the Arikarees, the Cheyennes, the Mandans and Gros Ventres; their trading, manners and customs, religion, superstitions, ceremonies and warfare.

The text of the edition of 1939 is translated from a manuscript found among the papers of Jean N. Nicollet in the Topographical Bureau of the U.S. War Department, now in the Library of Congress. A second manuscript, the "Montreal" version, was in the Archepiscopal Ar-

chives in Montreal but its present location is unknown. The Coe manuscript is written in a fine, clear hand and contains the letter to A. D. and the section on hunting; it follows the arrangement and text of the "Montreal" version. It appears to be in the same handwriting and may be a copy, with some punctuation and accents added, spellings corrected, and proper names capitalized.

[Coe No. 179.]

468 TAYLOR, HOWARD P.

"A thrilling experience."

Typewritten manuscript. 12 pp. 28½ cm.

The manuscript, without date or signature, is a narrative, written some 40 years later, of the attempt of 50 men from Virginia City, Nev. Ter., to drive off the hostile Piute Indians who were threatening the city and neighboring settlers; their march into the Indian country, where they were ambushed and many of

them killed, and the escape of Taylor and one companion by plunging into a stream. These events probably took place early in 1860. Published accounts of the Piute War differ from the manuscript, which recounts recollections of one incident.

[Coe No. 180.]

469 TAYLOR, JOHN Y.

"Sketch book. Dr. J. Y. Taylor, U.S.N. 1854."

37 pp. Oblong. 34½ x 27½ cm. Original binding.

—— Album of mounted sketches by Taylor and two printed woodcuts.

40 pp. 34 cm. Original binding.

John Y. Taylor was assistant surgeon on the U.S. Sloop *Decatur* attached to the Pacific Squadron, 1854–1857. The 36 drawings in the sketch book, each carefully titled, include scenes on the voyage through the Straits of Magellan, Tierra del Fuego, Patagonia, the Sandwich Islands, California, Oregon, and Washington, and a number of sketches of the Indians of the Northwest Coast. The *Decatur* was on the beach at Seattle in December 1855, during the attack by the Indians.

The Album contains 39 original draw-

ings and two mounted woodcuts. These include a view of Port Townsend, W.T., in 1855; two of Seattle, and several sketches of Indians. Most of the sketches are of the sea and South America, and a few are dated 1858, 1859, and 1860, when Dr. Taylor was attached to the Sloop *Preble* and later, 1860, to the Brig *Dolphin*, both in the Brazil Squadron.

These sketches were formerly the property of Frederick W. Skiff of Portland, Ore.

[Coe No. 181.]

470 TAYLOR, WILLIAM O., 1856–

"Notes for 'With Custer on the Little Big Horn,' by W. O. Taylor, 7th U.S. Cavalry." [1921?]

108 pp. 2 maps. 25½ cm.

The maps are a blueprint map of the Custer battlefield [37 x 20 cm.] and a pencil sketch map of the battlefield by the Superintendent of the National Cemetery, 1921. 20½ x 17 cm.

William O. Taylor of Orange, Mass., served in Troop A, 7th U.S. Cavalry, under Major Reno from January 17, 1872 to January 17, 1877. He planned to write a book "With Custer on the Little Big Horn" and collected material through the years to 1921. The book was never written. In addition to the book of manuscript notes there are in the Coe Collection four scrap-books of pictures and articles clipped from magazines and newspapers, some of the articles and poems contributed by Taylor himself.

The "Notes" consist of articles copied from newspapers about Custer and the battle of the Little Big Horn and the Custer Battlefield National Cemetery, and extracts copied from official reports, books and articles, and from unpublished letters written to Taylor; with annotations and two original poems signed W. O. T.

[Coe No. 182.]

471 TELLER, WOOLSEY

Letters from Woolsey Teller to his brother, Daniel W. Teller, in New York, written on the trail to California and from San Francisco, March 22, 1849, to May 31, 1850.

14 letters. 82 pp. 24½ cm.

Teller was a member of the Havilah Mining Association that left New York March 19, 1849, traveling by train, stage, and boat to Fort Smith, Ark., April 9. After some weeks in camp near Fort Smith the party set out again May 2 for the overland journey to Santa Fé and California. The letters give vivid descriptions of the route and incidents as far as Santa Fé. On July 2 Teller was elected secretary of the company. The letters from San Francisco describe life in the city and his hopes and plans to import, with his brother's help, scarce articles of food, to open a restaurant, to visit the mines, etc.

[Coe No. IV, 445.]

472 THOMAS, H. K.

Diary of H. K. Thomas, kept at Laramie [City], Wyoming, September 23, 1870 to September 27, 1871.

129 pp. 19½ cm. Original binding.

The diary is written in ink, in a very careful, rather elaborate hand, by the station master [?] of the Union Pacific Railroad at Laramie, Wyo., and records the events of each day, the train schedules, amount of travel, important people pass-ing through, accidents on the railroad, news of neighboring mines, the weather, the establishment of the local lodge, and events in the town and neighborhood.

[Coe No. IV, 446.]

473 THOMPSON, WILLIAM P.

"W. P. Thompson. Diary 1850," of an overland journey from St. Joseph, April 30, to Sacramento, September 24, 1850; and his return journey from Nevada City to the East by the Isthmus and New Orleans, December 22, 1851 to April 12, 1852.

50 pp. 14½ cm. Original binding. With typewritten transcript.

The entries are brief, giving the distance traveled each day and camps. The party followed the regular trail to South Pass, Sublette's Cut-off to Fort Hall, the California Trail to the Humboldt River and the Truckee to Nevada City. Returning, Thompson left Nevada City December 22, 1851, sailed from San Francisco February 8 on the *Olive Branch* for Panama, and from Chagres on the *North America* March 29 for New Orleans, reaching Lagrange [Mo.?] on April 13, 1852.

[Coe No. 183.]

474 TIFFANY, P. C., 1809–

Diary of a journey from Mount Pleasant, Iowa, overland to California, April 17 to August 29, 1849; experiences at the mines, January 1 to December 5, 1850; and the voyage home by the Isthmus, December 8, 1850 to March 13, 1851.

3 vols. [i.e., 533 pp.] 14½ cm. Original binding. With typewritten transcript.

P. C. Tiffany with his wife and father-in-law, Pennel Cheney, migrated to Iowa from Massachusetts, settling in Mount Pleasant in 1838. He opened a tavern, which Mrs. Tiffany ran during his absence in California. He later engaged in the jewelry business, was justice of the peace, postmaster, and one of the early trustees of Iowa Wesleyan College.

The diary records in vivid detail the route he followed from Mount Pleasant, Iowa, to California, April 7–August 25, 1849, and incidents on the journey; experiences at the mines, December 31, 1849–December 5, 1850; and his voyage home as far as Chagres when it breaks off, March 13, 1851, on board the *Falcon*. The company, with Presley Saunders as captain, went by boat from Burlington, Iowa, to St. Louis and St. Joseph, followed the usual trail by Sublette's Cut-off, Fort Hall, the Humboldt and Carson Rivers to Hangtown and the mines. During the stay in the mines and the return voyage Tiffany did not make daily entries in his journal. On December 31 he copied the entries for November 20–December 31, 1849 from Mr. Grantham's diary, and usually summarized the interesting events when he resumed his writing.

[Coe No. 184.]

475 TILTON, JAMES

Correspondence of Adjutant General James Tilton with Governor Douglas of Vancouver Island, Dr. William F. Tolmie of the Hudson's Bay Company, General George Gibbs, and others, 1855–1857.

24 letters. 48 pp. 20–33 cm.

James Tilton was surveyor general of Washington Territory, 1854–1861, and adjutant general during the Indian War of 1855–1856.

The letters of Sir James Douglas and Dr. Tolmie are chiefly about the assistance given by Governor Douglas and the Hudson's Bay Company to the Washington Territorial Government in the Indian War of 1855–1856. The following letters are included:

—— Copies of two letters to the Hon. James Douglas, November 1, 1855, March 9, 1856. 5 pp.

—— Six letters to General George Gibbs. [October 15]–December 15, 1855. 14 pp.

—— Letter to Judge Lander. March 10, 1861, with a short note signed E. E. explaining how the letter came into the possession of Elwood Evans. 2 pp.

—— Letter to Colonel Ripley, Chief of Ordnance Dept., Pacific Division. February 4, 1856. 1 p.

—— Copies of five letters to Dr. Tolmie. October 31, 1855–March 31, 1856. 8 pp.

DOUGLAS, SIR JAMES. Two letters to James Tilton. November 6, 19, 1855, the former enclosing three invoices of ammunition and supplies shipped to Dr. Tolmie for the use of the Washington Volunteers. Signature only. 7 pp.

MILES, HENRY. Letter to James Tilton. January 6, 1857, with note from Tilton to Governor Stevens added in pencil. 1 p.

TOLMIE, WILLIAM FRASER. Five letters to James Tilton. October 30, 1855–March 9, 1856. 9 pp.

WILSON, JOSEPH S. Letter to James Tilton. September 2, 1855. 1 p.

Tilton's letter to Tolmie of March 2, 1856 and Tolmie's answer of March 9 are printed in Council of Washington Territory, 4th Session, 1856–1857, *Martial Law—Minority Report*, pp. 11, 14; the correspondence with the Hon. James Douglas, November 1–19, 1855, is published in *Message of the Governor of Washington Territory*, Olympia, 1857, pp. 100–102. Tilton's letters to Tolmie, October 31, 1855 and March 2, 1856; and to Sir James Douglas, November 1, 1855; and Douglas' letters to Tilton, November 6 and 19, 1855, are published in Clarence B. Bagley, "Attitude of the Hudson's Bay Company during the Indian War of 1855–1856," *Washington Historical Quarterly*, 1917, VIII, 291–307.

[Miller Collection.]

476 TOLMIE, WILLIAM FRASER, 1812–1886

Three letters to John Bradley, William Dougherty, and Mr. Smith. Fort Nisqually, May 5, 1851. Signatures only.

3 pp. 31 cm.

Dr. Tolmie, a graduate of the Medical College of Edinburgh, joined the service of the Hudson's Bay Company arriving at Fort Vancouver in 1833. He was later chief trader at Fort Nisqually and agent of the Puget Sound Agricultural Company. In 1859 he moved to Vancouver Island and continued in the service of the Hudson's Bay Company until 1870.

The three letters are identical in contents, written under advice of the U.S. District Attorney for the Territory, warning the addressees that they are occupying land that belongs to the Puget Sound Agricultural Company under the treaty of 1846, and giving them notice to remove from the premises they occupy without unnecessary delay. The recipients were Mr. John Bradley and Mr. William Dougherty, Round Plain by Steilacoom, and Mr. Lyon A. Smith, Douglas River, Nisqually.

[Miller Collection.]

477 TOLMIE, WILLIAM FRASER, 1812–1886

Copy of a letter from Tolmie to Elwood Evans, Esq. Victoria, B.C., January 16, 1881, with a note at the end in Evans' hand: "Original MS. returned to him by request. E.E."

15 pp. 20½ cm. Original binding.

The letter contains an account of the attack by Snoqualmie Indians on Fort Nisqually in May 1849, and the murder of L. C. Wallace. It has been copied into a blank book which also contains on one page some brief notes in Evans' hand.

Laid in the book is a one-page autograph note from W. F. Tolmie to Archibald McKinlay, Victoria, November 27, 1884.

This volume was formerly among the Elwood Evans papers.

[Miller Collection.]

478 TOLMIE, WILLIAM FRASER, 1812–1886

"Mem. in reference to Japanese Junk, wrecked at Cape Flattery, W.T. in winter of 1834–5, Communicated by Dr. W. F. Tolmie, Victoria, B.C."

Manuscript copy. 3 pp. 25 cm.

The original was received May 24, 1872 from Dr. Tolmie, and sent to Professor George Davidson, astronomer and associated for many years with the U.S. Coast Survey. The copy is signed I. G. L.

The manuscript gives a brief account of the wreck and the final rescue of the three survivors from the Makah Indians by Captain McNeill of the Hudson's Bay Company brig *Llama*.

[Miller Collection.]

479 TOPEKA ASSOCIATION

Constitution, by-laws, and minutes of the Topeka Association, December 5, 1854 to May 7, 1858, with the names of the founders, lists of the members, and records of lots drawn.

151 pp. 26 cm. Original binding. With the papers and journals of H. Miles Moore (see No. 352).

The Constitution and by-laws are probably in the handwriting of C. K. Holliday, chairman, and the minutes are signed by the successive secretaries.

Notes on the inside of front cover: "Presented to Wm. Hall Jenkins by Cyrus K. Holliday, President of Association of Town Site of Topeka, Kansas, December 21, 1871," and "Sold to George Hampe this 27th day of Dec. 1916. P. W. Griggs,

Administrator for the Wm. Hall Jenkins Estate." The manuscript was again sold May 2, 1928 at the Anderson Galleries, Catalogue 2268.

F. W. Giles, in his *Thirty Years in Topeka*, Topeka, 1886, quotes the original agreement, which is incorporated in the Constitution in the manuscript (p. 21), and two resolutions (pp. 62 and 403).

[Coe No. 132.]

480 UNDERWOOD, JOSEPH A., *d.* 1840

"Journal of a cruise in the U.S.S. *Relief*, Lt. Commdg. A. K. Long, on a Surveying and Exploring Expedition in the years 1838, 1839, 1840. By Joseph

A. Underwood, Lieut. U.S. Navy. Continued in the U.S.S. *Vincennes*, Charles Wilkes, Esqr. Commdg. Exg. Exd."

147 pp. 31½ cm.

Joseph A. Underwood, Passed Midshipman, was serving on the Store Ship *Relief* as lieutenant on the Exploring Expedition commanded by Charles Wilkes. He was transferred at Callao, Peru, June 21, 1839, to the U.S.S. *Vincennes;* served on the *Vincennes* until July 24, 1840, when he, with Midshipman Wilkes Henry, was murdered by the natives at Malolo, Fiji Islands.

The journal covers the voyage of the *Relief* from Norfolk, August 18, 1838, to Porto Praya, Rio de Janeiro, Tierra del Fuego, Valparaiso, and Callao; continues with the voyage of the *Vincennes* to the Coral Islands, Tahiti, New South Wales; and ends February 14, 1840, during the exploration of the coast of the land in the Antarctic.

From August 1838 through August 1839 the daily reckonings and meteorological observations are tabulated with a note that these observations "are taken partly from the different journals."

[Coe No. III, 264.]

481 U.S. ARMY. DEPARTMENT OF UTAH

General Orders of the Department of Utah, 1857.

3 pp. 17½ x 16 cm. and 17½ x 32 cm.

HEAD QUARTERS TROOPS OF THE U.S. IN UTAH. Camp Winfield . . . October 5, 1857. General Orders No. 1A, announcing that the undersigned has assumed command of the troops of the Army for Utah. The signature is partly torn off, but it was signed by Colonel E. B. Alexander. 1 p.

—— ARMY FOR UTAH, Camp Winfield October 7, 1857. General Orders No. 2A giving the order of march. Signed: "Henry E. Maynadier, 1st Lt. & Adjt 10th Infy. Act. Asst. Adjt. Gen. Official. James Deshler 2d Lieut. & Act. Adjt. 10th Inf." 2 pp.

These orders, entirely in manuscript, are bound in a volume of General Orders for 1857–1859, which were delivered to Company F, 10th Infantry, Captain Cuvier Grover, who took part in the Utah Expedition and was later provost marshal of the Territory.

Note on flyleaf in ink: "Bound at Salt Lake City. January 1860," and in pencil the autograph of Charles William.

This volume formed part of the Auerbach Collection, No. 843.

[Coe No. IV, 954.]

482 U.S. ARMY. 4th U.S. VOLUNTEERS.

Records of the Quartermaster Department of the 4th U.S. Volunteers, November 5, 1863 to July 6, 1866.

1,467 documents. *ca.* 2,100 pp. 7½ x 25–42½ x 72 cm.

In 1863 and 1864 the 2d U.S. Volunteers served in the Department of Virginia, near Norfolk, and on March 30, 1865, by special orders, its designation was changed to the 4th U.S. Volunteers. In the spring of 1865 it was transferred to the Department of Missouri, with Lieutenant Colonel Charles C. G. Thornton in command and 1st Lieutenant William H. Blyton, Regimental Quartermaster and Acting Assistant Quartermaster at Fort Sully until September 30, 1865 and then at Fort Randall. The regiment was mustered out of service by companies June 18, 19, and July 6, 1866.

The records during the service in Virginia are few, but they are very complete from May 1865 to July 1866, while the regiment was attached to General Sully's command in Dakota Territory and during the Northwestern Indian Expedition of 1865.

The records include copies of general and special orders; proceedings of boards of survey; correspondence with officers at other posts in Dakota about supplies and transportation; official forms covering abstracts, estimates, invoices, monthly returns, receipts, vouchers and reports on clothing, camp and garrison equipment, commissary and subsistence stores, ordnance, fuel and forage; accounts; and lists of officers and employees. These forms are signed by the various officers and are usually signed or docketed by Lieutenant Blyton. The officers whose signatures occur most frequently are Captain F. H. Cooper, 7th Iowa Cav., and Lieutenant C. W. Fogg, 6th Iowa Cav., at Fort Randall; Lieutenant Henry O. Fox, Adjutant, 4th U.S. Vols., and Captain Moses H. Goodridge, Assistant Quartermaster, at Fort Sully; Captain William C. Johnston, 4th U.S. Vols.; Lieutenant John O'Neill, 50th Wis. Vols.; Lieutenant Wallis Pattee, 7th Iowa Cav.; Captain Samuel G. Sewall, 4th U.S. Vols., at Fort Thompson; Lieutenant John F. Shoemaker, Post Adjutant at St. Louis; Lieutenant F. O. Udall, 6th Iowa Cav.; and Lieutenant William H. Vose, 4th U.S. Vols.

[Coe Collection.]

483 U.S. COMMISSION TO NEGOTIATE A TREATY OR TREATIES WITH THE HOSTILE INDIANS OF THE UPPER PLATTE AGENCY

"Proceedings of the Board of Commissioners to negotiate a treaty or treaties with the hostile Indians of the Upper Platte Agency," May 21 to July 17, 1866. E. B. Taylor, President, Chas. E. Bowles, Secretary.

65 pp. 32½ cm.

Endorsed: "Report of Proceedings of the Indian Commission Convened at Fort Laramie, D.T. June 1st, 1866. To go with Up. Platte B[?] 26/66."

The commissioners, E. B. Taylor, president, R. N. McLaren, and Thomas Wistar, met in Omaha, May 21, 1866, organized with Charles E. Bowles, secretary, and Frank Lehmer, assistant secretary, and adjourned to reassemble at Fort Laramie June 1, where they were joined by Colonel H. E. Maynadier. One of the most important conditions in the treaty was that the road up the Powder River Valley to Bozeman, Mont., should be secure from hostilities.

The proceedings record in detail the conferences with the chief men of the Ogalalla and Brulé bands of Sioux, and the treaty signed by them; and the later conferences held with the Cheyennes and Arapahoes.

[Coe Collection.]

484 U.S. PRESIDENT, 1865–1869 (ANDREW JOHNSON)

Authorization to the Secretary of State [William H. Seward] to affix the seal of the United States to President Johnson's proclamation of the treaty between the United States and the [northern] Cheyenne and Arapahoe tribes of Indians, concluded October 28, 1867. Washington, August 19, 1868. Signed by President Andrew Johnson.

Printed form. 1 p. Bound with the printed text of the treaty. 28 cm.

A photograph of President Johnson is mounted on the flyleaf. 6½ x 9½ cm.

The text of the treaty has been extracted from an unidentified source. It is the same as that in Kappler, *Indian Affairs, Laws and Treaties*, Washington, 1904, II, 1012–1015, but the names of the signers are omitted. The text of the treaty as pub-lished on pp. 136–141 of *A Compilation of All the Treaties between the United States and the Indian Tribes Now in Force as Laws*, Washington, 1873, includes the President's proclamation, which is omitted in the later texts.

[Coe No. 100.]

485 U.S. PRESIDENT, 1869–1877 (U. S. GRANT)

Executive Order restoring to the public domain a tract of land in Montana Territory set apart by Executive Order of July 5, 1873 and not included in the tract set apart by Act of Congress, April 15, 1874, for the Gros Ventres and other Indians. Executive Mansion, August 19, 1874. Signature only.

1 p. 31½ cm.

The order fixes the exact boundaries. [Coe Collection.]

486 U.S. WAR DEPARTMENT (WILLIAM W. BELKNAP)

Letter from the Secretary of War to the House of Representatives submitting all the information in his possession relative to the late expedition against the Piegan Indians, April 20, 1870, signed by William W. Belknap.

210 pp. 32 cm.

The letter of transmittal is accompanied by copies of orders, reports, telegrams, and correspondence of the officers and officials concerned in the expedition against the Piegans in Montana in January and February 1870. This is evidently the original letter and report sent to Congress. It is endorsed: "Ho. Ex. Doc. 269. Piegan Indians, May 11, 1870. Referred to Committee . . ." and has in pencil directions to the printer.

The manuscript was formerly in the Auerbach Collection. The complete report was printed in 1870, U.S. War Dept. *Piegan Indians. Letter from the Secretary of War . . . in relation to the Expedition against the Piegan Indians, in the Territory of Montana* (41st Congress, 2d Session, House Ex. Doc. No. 269 [Washington, 1870]).

[Coe No. 180 B.]

487 U.S. WAR DEPARTMENT (W. R. DRINKARD, ACTING SECRETARY)

Extracts from the instructions of the President of the United States to Lieutenant General Scott, War Department, September 16, 1859.

3 pp. 25 cm.

Signed at the end: "Official. Copy respectfully furnished for the information of His Excy. the Governor of Washington Territory. By order of Lt. Gen. Scott. George W. Lay, Lt. Col. A.D.C."

The extracts from a letter from W. R. Drinkard, Acting Secretary of War, to General Scott concerned San Juan Island and the procedure to be followed until definite title had been established.

The letter is published in full in the *Report of the Secretary of War* for 1858/59 (36th Congress, 1st Session, House of Representatives. Ex. Doc. [no no.]).

[Miller Collection.]

488 UPHAM, HIRAM D., 1839–

Two letters from Hiram D. Upham, describing in detail his voyage up the Missouri from St. Louis to Fort Benton and his life in Montana, to his friend, Abner Wood, June 18, 1865, and to Miss Jennie A. Coe [later Mrs. Abner Wood], August 1, 1865.

20 pp. 25½ cm. With the printed edition of the letters.

Hiram D. Upham had obtained a clerkship in the Indian Bureau under Major Gad E. Upson, Blackfoot Agent, and remained in that position until 1871.

The letters remained in the possession of the recipients and their daughter, Virginia Coe Wood, for many years. The printed edition has title: *Historical Reprints. Upham Letters from the Upper Missouri, 1865,* ed. by Paul C. Phillips (Sources of Northwest History No. 19, State University of Montana). Reprinted from the Historical Section of *The Frontier,* 1913, XIII, 311–317.

[Coe No. 185.]

489 UTAH SOUTHERN RAILROAD COMPANY

Draft on the Treasurer to pay $66.60 to Seymour B. Young for grading, signed, "Brigham Young, Pres. George Swan, Sec. Salt Lake City June 29, 1872."

Printed form filled in by George Swan. 20½ x 8½ cm.

The draft is endorsed by S. B. Young.

Ground was broken for the Utah Southern Railroad, May 1, 1871, and the road was completed to Provo by December 1873.

With the draft are the autographs of George Q. Cannon, Joseph F. Smith, and Wilford Woodruff. From the autograph collection of Dr. S. C. G. Watkins of Montclair, N.J.

Gift of Mr. Edward Eberstadt.

490 VAN BOKKELEN, JOHN J. H.

Letter to the Honorable James Douglas, Governor of Vancouver Island. Head Quarters, Co. G. 1st Regiment, W.T.V. Port Townsend, January 17, 1856.

Manuscript copy. 1 p. 28½ cm.

Lieutenant Van Bokkelen was at this time in command at Port Townsend. He was later major, commanding the north- ern battalion of the 2d regiment of Washington Volunteers.

The copy, in an unidentified hand, is

signed, "James Keynes, 2d Lt. in command per Lt. H v B orderly." It has two endorsements: "To James Douglass, Gov. Van Island 17 Jany 1856. From J. J. H. Van Bokkelen, Relative to the Northern Indians coming to Port Townsend &c.," and "Copy. Lt. Keynes to Gov. Douglass, Jan 17, 1856."

The letter requests Governor Douglas to notify the northern Indians that Acting Governor Mason has issued instructions that all northern Indians entering the southern waters are to be stopped and made to return.

[Miller Collection.]

491 VANCOUVER, GEORGE, 1757–1798

Letter to his brother, J. G. Vancouver. Nootka Discovery, September 8, 1794.

2 pp. 22½ cm. Mounted in Vol. I of Vancouver's *Voyage*, 1798.

In the letter Vancouver says he has completed the investigation of the Northwest Coast and is expecting instructions for

negotiating the business of these territories [the Nootka question with the Spaniards].

[Coe No. III, 265.]

492 VANCOUVER, GEORGE, 1757–1798

Letter to Mr. Heath. Petersham, December 10, 1797, signed, Geo. Vancouver.

1 p. 23 cm.

Vancouver is writing to James Heath, the engraver, with regard to the plates for his *Voyage*. Heath engraved two of the plates in Vol. I of the *Voyage of Discovery to the North Pacific Ocean and round the World*, London, 1798. 3 vols. and atlas, and two in Vol. III.

VANCOUVER, JOHN G. Letter to Messrs. Robinsons. Sutton Farm, October 5, 1800. 1 p. 22½ cm.

Vancouver died before completing the last volume of his *Voyage*. It was completed by his brother John. This letter, written to the publishers, G. G. and J. Robinson, Paternoster-Row, requests that one set of the *Voyage* be sent to Mr. John Wright, Felthorpe Hall, near Norwich, and placed to his account.

[Coe No. 186.]

493 VANCOUVER, GEORGE, 1757–1798

"An account of the Expence of Gunners Stores on board His Majestys Sloop *Discovery*, George Vancouver, Esqr. Commander," for August 12 to 23, 1793, and for July, August and September 2 to 7, 1795. Signed by Geo. Vancouver, Captain, Richard Collett, Gunner.

4 pp. 38 x 23 and 38 x 24 cm.

Manuscript record in tabular form of gunner's stores used in firing salutes, signaling to parties on shore, etc. The entry under August 12, 1793, covers powder and shot "fired away in the Boats when employed surveying, Our People Being At-

tackted by A Large Party of Indians" at Traitors Cove. The second account covers the stay at St. Helena in July 1795 and the voyage to England.

[Coe No. 186.]

494 VANCOUVER ISLAND. COLLECTOR OF CUSTOMS

"General sufferance, Port Victoria, Vancouver's Island . . ." Signed and dated: "Victoria, V.I., this 20th day of September, 1858. Alex. C. Anderson, Collector."

Printed document filled in by hand. 2 pp. 26½ cm.

This document grants permission to Captain Burns to proceed to Fraser's River with his steamer *Wilson G. Hunt*, with passengers and mining equipment under the conditions set forth. These conditions are that the owner could carry only goods of the Hudson's Bay Company, could not transport arms except from the United Kingdom, could not transport passengers without a government permit and gold mining license, and could not trade with the Indians.

[Coe No. II, 1294.]

495 VAUGHAN, ALFRED J., 1801–1871

Annual report on the affairs and conditions of the Indian tribes in the Upper Missouri, to Colonel Alfred Cumming, Superintendent of Indian Affairs, Saint Louis. Fort Clark, September 12, 1855, signed by Alfred J. Vaughan, Indian Agent.

13 pp. 31½ cm. With typewritten transcript.

Alfred J. Vaughan was in the Indian service for many years. He was agent for the Iowas, Sacs and Foxes, 1848–1849, and for the Upper Missouri 1853–1857, when he became agent for the Blackfoot Indians at Sun River until 1861.

The manuscript report covers his journey up the Missouri River on the *St.* *Mary's* in the summer of 1855 to distribute annuities to the tribes of the Upper Missouri. He stopped at Forts Pierre, Clark, Berthold and Union, but was unable to continue up the Yellowstone on account of the hostile Sioux, and returned to Fort Clark. He employed Zephyr Rencontre as interpreter for the journey.

[Coe No. 187.]

496 VICTOR, FRANCES FULLER (MRS. HENRY CLAY), 1826–1902

Extensive manuscript annotations and criticisms written on the margins of a large paper edition of William H. Gray, *Did Dr. Whitman Save Oregon?* Circular No. 8. Reprint from the *Daily Astorian* [Astoria, 1881].

19 pp. 25 cm.

Gray's article defends Whitman and answers statements by Mrs. Victor in her *River of the West*, Hartford, 1870. In these manuscript notes she replies to Gray.

Purchased from E. H. Sauer of Los Angeles, September 1922.

[Coe No. III, 1504.]

497 "A VOCABULARY of the language of the natives of the North west coast of America" followed by "A vocabulary of Wahsington [*sic*] & Is-

lands language"; "Latitudes and Longitudes of the Capes and head lands with some of the principal Islands, Harbours and Villages on the North west coast of America, . . ." and, at the end, "Accounts with Sloop *Union*" for money and articles received during the voyage.

26 pp. 19½ cm. With typewritten transcript.

This manuscript evidently belonged to a member of the crew of the sloop *Union*, John Boit in command, that sailed from Newport, R.I., August 1, 1794, for the Northwest Coast and China, returning to Boston in July, 1796.

[Coe No. 188.]

498 VOORHEES, LUKE, 1838–

Typewritten letter to the Rt. Rev. N. S. Thomas. Cheyenne, February 2, 1911, accompanied by transcripts of documents and other original material dealing with the expedition of Lewis and Clark, in the possession, in 1911, of Mrs. Julia Clark Voorhis and Miss Eleanor Glasgow Voorhis.

118 pp. 20½ cm.

Laid in the volume are five clippings from the *Wyoming Tribune*, Cheyenne *State Leader*, *Chicago Blade*, 1913–1914. Three are reminiscences by Luke Voorhees, one is about his appointment as receiver of the U.S. Land Office at Cheyenne, and the fifth (*Chicago Blade*) tells of the finding of a plate on one of the hills near Fort Pierre, placed there in 1743 by Vérendrye, claiming the land for France.

Luke Voorhees was born in New Jersey in 1838. He came to Wyoming in 1859, organized the Cheyenne-Deadwood stage line in 1876, became receiver of public moneys and disbursing agent of the U.S. Land Office at Cheyenne.

The letter summarizes briefly the transcontinental expeditions from 1810/11 to 1869 and the location of the overland trails. The accompanying notes on the journals of the Lewis and Clark Expedition quote from the journals and from correspondence of Lewis and Clark, and letters of Clark to his brother, George Rogers Clark, and Toussaint Charbonneau.

The manuscript is from the library of the Rt. Rev. Nathaniel Seymour Thomas, Bishop of Wyoming, and contains his bookplate. All of the letters and documents quoted are published in full in R. Gold Thwaites' 1904 edition of the *Original Journals of the Lewis and Clark Expedition*, 1904, VII, 226 *passim;* and parts of the text are copied verbatim from the same edition, Vol. I, Introduction, p. xxxvii *passim.*

[Coe No. 189.]

499 WALDO, DANIEL, 1800–1880

"Critiques. Narrative and remarks."

Typewritten copy. 3 pp. 28 cm.

Waldo emigrated from Virginia to Missouri in 1819 and was a neighbor of the Applegates. His health was very poor and, hoping to improve it, he joined the 1843 emigration to Oregon. The manuscript summarizes the events of the journey and expresses critical opinions of W. H. Gray, Whitman, and the missions.

The original manuscript, in the Bancroft Library, was dictated to a stenographer who gave it the title "Critiques" because of Waldo's critical remarks "which abounded in sensible and pertinent suggestions" (see Bancroft, *Oregon*, I, 404).

Two brief extracts from the manuscript are quoted by Bancroft, *History of Oregon*, 1886–1888, I, 403, 405, and by C. M. Drury, *Marcus Whitman*, Caldwell, Ida., 1937, pp. 332, 342.

[Miller Collection.]

500 WALKER, CYRUS HAMLIN, 1838–1921

"Glimpses of Old Oregon, by Cyrus H. Walker, the oldest white man living born West of the Rocky Mountains." Albany, Oregon, October 26, 1909.

7 pp. 25 cm.

This manuscript describes briefly the journey of Elkanah Walker and Cushing Eells, with their families, from Fort Colville, where they had taken refuge after the Whitman Massacre in 1847, to the Willamette Valley in the summer of 1848; Oregon City as it was during the Walkers' stay from 1848 to 1849, and their final settlement at Forest Grove in October 1849.

[Coe Collection.]

501–504 WALKER, ELKANAH, and WHITMAN, MARCUS

Letters and documents of the early missionaries to Oregon from the foundation of the mission to the settlement of the Territory, 1834–1872.

20 portfolios. 533 items. 1,647 pp. 26½ cm.

The Rev. Elkanah Walker and Cushing Eells, with their wives, were sent to Oregon in 1838 by the American Board of Commissioners for Foreign Missions to reinforce the Mission established in 1836 by Dr. Marcus Whitman, the Rev. H. H. Spalding and their wives, and W. H. Gray. They were joined in New York by the Rev. and Mrs. Asa Bowen Smith, and in Cincinnati by Cornelius Rogers, and reached Waiilatpu August 29.

The manuscripts cover the foundation and history of the Oregon Mission; the relations with other religious denominations; the overland emigrations; the administration of Indian affairs and work among the Indians; Marcus Whitman and the purpose of his journey of 1843–1844; the Whitman Massacre, 1847; the establishment of the Lapwai Press; and the final settlement of the Territory.

501 WALKER, ELKANAH, 1805–1877

Drafts or copies of letters written by Elkanah Walker, 1839–1854, many of them unsigned and unfinished; letters to the Walkers, and other family papers.

576 pp. 12–33 cm.

—— Two letters to the editor of *The Christian* [*Mirror?*]. October 6, 1846 [n.d.]. 9 pp.

—— Letter to the members of the Columbia Mission. Chimakine [*sic*], October 27, 1839. Endorsed, in Whitman's hand: "Oct. 1839, Mr. Walker to the members of the Mission." 4 pp.

—— Letter to Chief Factor James Douglas. March 8, 1842. 2 pp.

—— Letter to "My dear friends." October 26, 1847. 2 pp.

—— Eight letters to the Rev. David Greene, Secretary, American Board of Commissioners for Foreign Missions. February 7, 1839–January 18, 1847. 58 pp.

—— Letter to Edwin O. Hall. June 28, 1842. 6 pp.

—— Two letters to the Hudson's Bay Company. March 17, 1847, one enclosing an order for goods. 5 pp.

—— Three letters to John L. Lewes. January 13, 1847–March 9, 1848. 14 pp.

—— Letter to Archibald McDonald. September 22, 1845. 3 pp.

—— Two letters to Dr. John McLoughlin, Chief Factor, Hudson's Bay Company. March 20, 1840. Drafts. 6 pp.

—— Letter to the editors of the *New England Puritan*. February 3, 1846. 7 pp.

—— Two letters to the Rev. H. H. Spalding. March 12, 1840, August 10, 1842. 5 pp.

—— Letter to John Mix Stanley. Undated, probably after November 1847. 7 pp.

—— Letter to Mrs. Walker. June 21, 1847. 8 pp.

—— Letter [or journal] probably to Mrs. Walker, without beginning or end, with entries for Saturday through Tuesday, 12–15 [July 1851], while accompanying Dr. Dart as interpreter on his expedition to the Indians. 7 pp.

—— Letter to "My dear Boy" [Cyrus Walker?]. April 1847. Fragment.

—— Copy of a form letter promising a donation to Pacific University, Tualatin, O.T. August 22, 1854. 2 pp.

—— Oregon Mission meeting, Elkanah Walker, secretary, and later moderator. Draft of minutes and votes at meetings of September 1838, February 1839, and January 1841; and a letter to the members of the Sandwich Island Mission, April 15, 18[?]. 9 pp.

—— Miscellaneous manuscripts; notes for sermons; parts of letters; memoranda; receipts, bills, orders; a notebook containing a table of distances and days crossing the continent, notes on earlier missionaries, the country traversed, the natives and their customs [12 pp.]; certificate of baptism of Michel Ogden, April 21, 1848; account book, 1849–1851 [24 pp.]; statement of Walker's views "written on or near the tenth of March, 1854, at Tualatin Plains during a sitting of a council at this place" [8 pp.]; Commission of the American Home Missionary Society appointing the Rev. Elkanah Walker missionary at the First Congregational Church of Hillsboro, Ore., February 11, 1867, printed form filled in by hand with a note added by Milton Badger, New York, April 22, 1867. 100 pp.

WALKER, MARY RICHARDSON (MRS. ELKANAH). Diary, June 10–December 31, 1838. Typewritten copy. Endorsed: "Copied by J. E. Walker." 34 pp.

—— Part of a letter describing the journey west, arrival at the Whitmans', their arrival and home at Tshimakain, written during the summer of 1839. 4 pp.

—— Letter to the Rev. S. A. McLean. June 7 [1842?]. Draft. 3 pp.

—— Part of a letter to Sister C. [Charlotte Richardson?]. October 26, 1847. Draft. 1 p.

—— Three letters to Mrs. Mercy L. Whitney. July 28, 1839–April 16, 1847. Drafts. 9 pp.

—— Memorandum in pencil, regarding raising money for Sunday school books, May 8 [1836]; manuscript poems, and memoranda. 6 pp.

COLUMBIA MATERNAL ASSOCIATION. Constitution and minutes, September 3, 1838–June 1842. 10 pp.

The Constitution is written in a careful, copperplate hand, possibly Mrs. Walker's, and is evidently the Constitution as drawn up at the first meeting, when Mrs. Spalding was elected president, Mrs. Walker vice-president, and Mrs. Gray recording secretary. It is followed by the minutes of the first meeting, September 3, 1838, in Mrs. Walker's hand, and the records of the meetings she attended through August 26, 1840, and the general meeting of June 1842.

Letters to Elkanah and Mary Richardson Walker, and one to Cornelius Rogers, 1832–1838, include the following:

ALLEN, RUTH C. Letter to Mary Richardson. December 19, 1832. 3 pp.

DOUGLAS, JAMES. Letter to Mr. Walker. February 7, 1849. 2 pp.

ERMATINGER, FRANCIS. Letter to C. Rogers. January 14, 1839. 2 pp.

FLETT, JOHN. Letter to Mr. Walker. April 13, 1857. 1 p.

FLETT, THOMAS. Three letters to Mr. Walker. January 21–April 26, 1845. 3 pp.

FRASER, PAUL. Letter to Mr. Walker. March 18, 1845. 1 p.

GRIFFIN, MRS. DESIRE. Letter to Mrs. Walker. February 15, 1840. 3 pp.

HALE, HORATIO. Two letters to Mr. Walker. October 8, 1841. 5 pp.

HALL, EDWIN O. Three letters to Eells and Walker. May 5, 1839–March 16, 1840. 9 pp.

HATCH, SARAH C. Letter to Mrs. Walker. July 13, 1858. 4 pp.

JOHNSON, ROBERT E. Letter to the Ladies of the Mission [May 1841]. 3 pp.

—— Letter to Eells and Walker. June 27, 1841. 3 pp.

JORDEN, WILLIAM V. Letter to Mr. Walker. October 25, 1846. 3 pp.

LITTLEJOHN, PHILO B. Two letters to Walker and Eells. February 25, September 11, 1843. 5 pp.

LITTLEJOHN, MRS. ADELINE S. Letter to Mrs. Walker. February 1, 1844. 2 pp.

MCLEAN, DONALD. Letter to Mr. Walker. February 1842. 1 p.

MCPHERSON, JOHN. Letter to Mr. Walker. February 17, 1846. 2 pp.

MACTAVISH, DUGALD. Letter to Mr. Walker. April 18, 1845. 1 p.

PELLY, A. E. Letter to Mr. Walker. October 30, 1844. 2 pp.

[RICHARDSON], CHARLOTTE. Two letters to Mr. Walker, one with no date, the first part missing; the other January 2 [1850]. 2 pp.

RODGERS, ANDREW. Two letters to Mrs. Walker. October 8, 1846, June 26, 1847. 5 pp.

TOD, JOHN. Letter to Mr. Walker. July 7, 1844. 3 pp.

WALKER, JOSEPH M. Letter to his uncle, Elkanah Walker. April 22, 1850. 2 pp.

WHITMAN, PERRIN B. Order on Mr. Walker to pay Albion Post $50. Oregon City, August 1, 1851. Endorsed by A. R. Post, March 17, 1852. 1 p.

WALKER, ELKANAH. Manuscript booklets in the Indian tongue; extracts from Matthew, lists of words and phrases, and vocabularies in the Flathead language; an English-Nez Percé dictionary; and a hymnbook for children in English in Mrs. Walker's hand. 20 pieces. 181 pp.

502 WHITMAN, MARCUS, 1802–1847

Letters of Dr. and Mrs. Marcus Whitman to members of their families and of the Mission, and papers dealing with mission affairs, 1838–1847.

286 pp. 19½–31½ cm.

—— Letter to the Metting [*sic*] of the Oregon Mission to convene about the 10th of the month at Tshimakaine, Rev. Elkanah Walker chairman, transmitting a report on the work of his station during the year. February 3, 1846. 7 pp.

—— Letter to the Hon. Stephen Prentiss and Mrs. Prentiss, stating his views on the future of Oregon to his father and mother-in-law. May 16, 1844. 4 pp.

—— 36 letters to Mr. Walker, 8 to Walker and Eells, 2 to Walker, Eells, and Smith, and 1 to Walker, Eells, and Spalding. August 22, 1838–July 26, 1847. 187 pp.

—— Letter to Alvan F. Waller. [1844 or 1845.] First half of sheet missing.

—— Order, undated, on William H. Gray to pay William S. Hibbard $11.36, signed by Marcus Whitman, and a list of notes sent to George Abernethy, March 14, 1845. 3 pp.

WHITMAN, NARCISSA PRENTISS (MRS. MARCUS). Letter to her husband. October 22, 1842. 4 pp.

—— Three letters to her parents, Mr. and Mrs. Prentiss. [March 14, 1838]–August 11, 1843. 10 pp.

—— Letter to her father. October 10, 1840. 4 pp.

—— Letter to her sister, Jane Prentiss. September 18, 1838. 4 pp.

—— Letter to Jane and Edward Prentiss. March 1, 1842. 8 pp.

—— Letter to Mr. Walker. October 8, 1838. 3 pp.

—— 17 letters to Mrs. Walker. July 29, 1839–March 30, 1847. 50 pp.

—— Letter to Mrs. Walker and Mrs. Eells. July 15, 1847. 1 p.

503 —— Correspondence of members of the Oregon Mission, accounts, and other papers.

779 pp. 14½–40 cm.

ABERNETHY, GEORGE. Letter to the Rev. Jason Lee [?]. February 4, 1843. Forwarded to the Revs. Walker and Eells. 3 pp.

EELLS, CUSHING. Seven letters to Mr. Walker. December 27, 1837–July 23, 1872. 14 pp.

—— Letter to Mr. Spalding, written by Walker, and signed by Walker and Eells. August 25, 1842. 1 p.

—— Letter to the Superintendent of the Methodist Episcopal Mission in Oregon

[the Rev. William Roberts ?]. July 19, 1847. Draft written and signed by Walker in the names of Walker and Eells. 4 pp.

EELLS, MYRA FAIRBANK (MRS. CUSHING). Four letters and a note to Mrs. Walker. May 14, 1849–December 21, 1869. 13 pp.

EELLS, EDWIN. Letter to Cyrus Walker. January 18, 1849. Written for Edwin by Mrs. Eells, with a note added by her. 2 pp.

EELLS, EDWIN. Letter to Mrs. Walker. April 22, 1863. 2 pp.

EELLS, MYRON. Letter to [Joseph E. Walker]. January 17, 1869. 4 pp.

GRAY, MARY AUGUSTA DIX (MRS. WILLIAM H.). 17 letters to Mrs. Walker and members of the Mission. April 3 [changed to 4], 1838–August 9, 1849. 48 pp.

GRAY, WILLIAM H. 19 letters to Elkanah Walker and members of the Mission. August 22, 1838–June 27, 1848. 73 pp.

LEWES, JOHN LEE. 22 letters to Mr. Walker. December 7, 1845–March 2, 1849. 50 pp.

—— Letter to Mrs. Walker. October 24, 1846. 1 p.

—— Statement, testifying that he thinks it unsafe for Messrs. Walker and Eells to remain at Tshimakain, May 31, 1848. 1 p.

McDONALD, ARCHIBALD. Letter to Mr. Cushing Eells. January 15, 1841. 3 pp.

—— 47 letters to Mr. Walker. April 18, 1839–October 11 [1844?]. 115 pp.

McDONALD, JANE KLYNE (MRS. ARCHIBALD). Letter to Mrs. Walker. January 15, 1840. 2 pp.

McKINLAY, ARCHIBALD. Six letters to Mr. Walker. June 4, 1841–January 23, 1843. 16 pp.

OGDEN, PETER SKENE. 17 letters to the Rev. Mr. Walker, April 22, 1844–February 18, 1850, and a "List of names of the persons from the Mission of Dr. Whitman," including all those taken captive, the age of each child, and in most cases the county and state from which the family migrated, followed by list [on verso] of those killed. 43 pp.

Peter Skene Ogden was born in Quebec in 1794 and in 1811 entered the service of the North West Company and later of the Hudson's Bay Company, eventually becoming chief factor at Vancouver. It was he who rescued from the Indians the survivors of the Whitman Massacre who had been taken prisoners.

OREGON MISSION. Accounts of the American Board with the Hudson's Bay Company, Harvey Clark, and others; and bills, receipts, etc. of the Rev. Elkanah Walker, 1834–1853. 27 pieces. 60 pp.

PAMBRUN, PIERRE CHRYSOLOGUE. 12 letters to Mr. Walker, and one to Walker and Eells. December 21, 1838–April 20, 1841. 27 pp.

—— Letter to Mrs. Walker. October 4, 1838. 1 p.

PERKINS, ELVIRA JOHNSON (MRS. H. W. K.). 13 letters to Mrs. Walker. [n.d., 1838]–November 8, 1844. 41 pp.

PERKINS, H. W. K. Letter to Mr. and Mrs. Walker. March 7, 1839. 3 pp.

ROGERS, CORNELIUS. Six letters to Mr. Walker. July 8, 1839–December 28, 1842. 21 pp.

SMITH, ASA BOWEN. Six letters to Mr. Walker. March [28, 1839]–October 12, 1840. 27 pp.

SMITH, SARAH GILBERT WHITE (MRS. ASA B.). Two letters to Mrs. Walker. [n.d.] Endorsed June 1839, December 22, 1839. 7 pp.

SPALDING, ELIZA HART (MRS. HENRY HARMON). Nine letters to Mrs. Walker and to Mrs. Eells and Mrs. Walker. [January? 1839]–June 12, 1843. 29 pp.

SPALDING, HENRY HARMON. Letter to the Rev. David Greene. June 7, 1842. Draft, signed by Walker, Eells, and Spalding. 3 pp.

—— Letter to Henry Hill, Treasurer, A.B.C.F.M., March 28, 1843, and two drafts payable to Archibald McKinlay, March 28, 1843. 3 pp.

—— 38 letters to Mr. Walker and Walker and Eells. December 24, 1838–July 16, 1853. 116 pp.

—— Two inventories (copies) of property destroyed in the Waiilatpu massacre, November 29, 1847, followed by the statement of H. H. Spalding, sworn to before John McCoy, September 1, 1849, and affidavits of Horace Hart, P. B. Whitman, and Alvin T. Smith. 26 pp.

—— "Bill of property pertaining to the Mission Station at Wascopam [i.e., The Dalles] and belonging to the A.B.C.F.M." Salem, September 20, 1849, with affidavits of Alvan F. Waller and H. H. Spalding. 8 pp.

STANLEY, JOHN MIX. Two letters to Messrs. Walker and Eells. December 31, 1847, February 24, 1848. 6 pp.

—— Letter to Mr. Walker. November 26, 1853. 1 p.

WHITE, ELIJAH. Letter to Spalding, Walker, and Eells. December 12, 1842. 3 pp.

—— Letter to Walker and Eells. December 26, 1842. 3 pp.

504 SANDWICH ISLANDS MISSION

Letters to the Rev. Elkanah Walker and members of the Oregon Mission from missionaries of the American Board to the Sandwich Islands; six bills of lading, and miscellaneous papers. August 9, 1839 to February 20, 1855.

33 pieces. 100 pp. 25–33 cm.

The letters deal with the business of the missions and include the following:

CASTLE, SAMUEL NORTHRUP. Seven letters to Mr. Walker. February 21, 1840–May 19, 1848. 9 pp.

CHAMBERLAIN, LEVI. Seven letters to Mr. Walker. August 9, 1839–August 21, 1847. 29 pp.

HALL, EDWIN OSCAR. Five letters to Mr. Walker. July 6, 1840–September 14, 1844. 24 pp.

LOCKE, EDWIN. Letter to Mr. Walker. December 24, 1839. 7 pp.

PARIS, JOHN DAVIS. Four letters to Mr. Walker. June 18, 1841–October 25, 1848. 13 pp.

WHITNEY, MERCY PARTRIDGE (MRS. SAMUEL). Three letters to Mrs. Walker. January 28, 1843–June 10, 1851. 12 pp.

The majority of the Walker-Whitman papers belonged to Frederick W. Skiff of Portland, Ore., who describes his discovery of the manuscripts in his *Adventures in Americana*, 1935, p. 153, in the possession of a son of one of the associates of Marcus Whitman, probably Cyrus Walker. Some of the Whitman letters Mr. Skiff secured from other sources.

A number of the letters have been printed in "The Oregon Missions as Shown in the Walker Letters, 1839–1841," *The Frontier*, 1930, XI, 74–89, with a foreword by Paul C. Phillips. These letters were printed from copies made many years earlier by W. S. Lewis from originals then in the possession of Cyrus Walker. Many of the letters in the collection have been quoted extensively in the *Transactions* of the Oregon Pioneer Association and the *Oregon Historical Quarterly;* by Clifford M. Drury in his three volumes on Spalding (1936), Walker (1940), and Whitman (1937); by Arthur B. and Dorothy P. Hulbert in *Marcus Whitman, Crusader* (1936–1941); and by others.

[Coe No. 190.]

505 WALLER, ALVAN F., 1808–1872

"Alvan F. Waller's property bought Batavia Oct. A.D. 1833." Religious and moral thoughts, extracts from books read, occasional entries of events, marriages performed, the weather, and a catalogue of his books. 1833–1854.

95 pp. 20 cm. Original binding. With typewritten transcript.

The Rev. A. F. Waller, his wife and children arrived in Oregon on the *Lausanne*, June 1840, to reinforce the Methodist Episcopal Mission. He was stationed at Willamette Falls, and at The Dalles Indian Mission; and later was managing agent of Willamette University.

The first entries are religious and moral extracts and thoughts, followed by notes of happenings, not written day by day but covering events of 1834–1840; catalogue of his books; and affairs at the missions 1840–1854.

[Coe No. 191.]

506 WASHINGTON TERRITORY

"Territory of Washington vs. Watsersmi, to October Term, 1854, in indictment, murder." Endorsed: "Brief of arguments on motion to discharge deft. at April Term, 1855."

6 pp. 32 cm.

The brief, written by Elwood Evans, outlines the reasons why the defendant should be discharged. A verdict had been rendered by a jury and a warrant issued to hang the defendant; Hon. O. B. McFadden issued a supersedeas on the ground that a writ of error had been taken to the Supreme Court; that court decided that there was no judgment and nothing to review, and the cause was remanded to Jefferson County.

[Miller Collection.]

507 WASHINGTON TERRITORY. CITIZENS

Petition to the Legislature and Council of Washington Territory for permission to construct a railroad from some eligible point on the Columbia River to Puget Sound. Undated. Signed by 43 citizens. [1858 or 1859.]

1 p. 19½ x 60 cm.

The petition, in an unidentified hand, is undated but was written in 1858 or 1859, as one of the signers, S. C. Hale, arrived in Washington in 1858 and another, Charles H. Mason, died in 1859. Among the signers were Rudolph M. Walker, Edward Lander, William Strong, Joseph Cushman, William W. Miller, George A. Barnes, J. Patton Anderson, A. Frankel, H. A. Goldsborough, Simpson P. Moses, and C. H. Hale.

[Miller Collection.]

508 WASHINGTON TERRITORY. CONVENTION, ELLENSBURG [JANUARY 3, 1889]

"Petition to the Honorable the Senate and House of Representatives of the United States of America in Congress Assembled: Your petitioners the people of Washington Territory at the city of Ellensburg . . . , in delegate convention assembled, would respectfully and earnestly petition . . . for the speedy admission of said Territory into the Union as a state . . ." Signed by Watson C. Squire, President, H. C. Wilmarth, Vice-President, Henry L. Wilson, Secretary.

Engrossed on vellum. 2 pp. 32½ x 42½ cm. Ribbon tie.

This petition was drawn up and signed but not dated, and a note has been added in the margin opposite the last paragraph but one: "The language of this paragraph was modified before its transmission to Washington, D.C."

According to Bancroft's *History of Washington, Idaho and Montana*, San Francisco, 1890 [p. 294], Squire was elected president of the statehood convention at Ellensburg in January 1859. He was appointed governor of the Territory in 1884, resigned in 1887, and after the admission of Washington to statehood was elected U.S. senator and served until 1897.

The memorial, dated January 3, 1889, was presented in the Senate January 22, and is printed as 50th Congress, 2d Session, Senate Misc. Doc. No. 48, 1889.

[Coe Collection.]

509 WASHINGTON TERRITORY. GOVERNOR, 1853–1857 (ISAAC INGALLS STEVENS)

Proclamation ending the Indian War of 1859 and repealing the rule of martial law in Washington Territory. Governor Isaac I. Stevens. Olympia, May 24, 1856.

1 p. 25 cm. With typewritten transcript.

The proclamation is in the handwriting of Andrew Jackson Cain, son of the Indian agent John Cain. (See also Nos. 187, 442.)

The proclamation is printed in *Message from the President of the United States,* *Communicating . . . Information respecting the Proclamation of Martial Law in the Territory of Washington* (34th Congress, 3d Session, Senate Ex. Doc. No. 41, 1857, pp. 38–39).

[Coe No. I, 837.]

510 WASHINGTON TERRITORY. GOVERNOR, 1859–1860 (RICHARD DICKERSON GHOLSON)

Proclamation ordering rigid enforcement of the laws excluding the Northern Indians from the Territory, signed, with the seal of the Territory affixed, at Olympia, May 18, 1860, R. D. Gholson, Governor, Henry M. McGill, Secretary of the Territory.

1 p. 25 cm.

Endorsed: "Proclamation vs. Northern Indians." Text may be in McGill's hand.

As the Indians of British Columbia had been entering the southern waters of Puget Sound and robbing settlers, Acting Governor Mason had ordered them stopped and made to return to the north in 1856 (see No. 490).

[Miller Collection.]

511 WASHINGTON TERRITORY. GOVERNOR, 1862–1866 (WILLIAM PICKERING)

"Gentlemen of the Council, and House of Representatives, of the Territory of Washington." Message of the Governor to the Legislative Assembly, Tenth Annual Session, December 17, 1862. Signed: "William Pickering."

17 pp. 31½ cm.

Undated draft or copy, with a few corrections possibly in Pickering's hand, and signed by him, of his first annual message on conditions in the Territory, and his recommendations.

The message was published as a pamphlet by order of the House of Representatives, Olympia, 1862, and is reprinted in *Messages of the Governors of the Territory of Washington to the Legislative Assembly, 1854–1889*, edited by Charles M. Gates (University of Washington Publications in the Social Sciences, 1940, XII, 102–109).

[Miller Collection.]

512 WASHINGTON TERRITORY. LAWS

"Alterations in Militia Act." Rough notes of changes to be made.

5 pp. 25 cm., 18 cm.

The manuscript is in an unidentified hand. The first three pages, in pencil, with many changes, are endorsed: "Amendments to Militia Law—forwarded Nov. 28th [no year]."

Acting Governor Mason, in his message, December 7, 1855, recommended changes in the militia law and Governor Stevens recommended amendments in his message of 1856. Governor McMullin in 1857 recommended amendments to allow the formation of volunteer companies, which seem to be provided for in these notes.

[Miller Collection.]

513 WATERHOUSE, BENJAMIN, 1754–1846

Letter to the Rev. R. Elton. Cambridge, August 4, 1837. Addressed [on verso of second leaf] to the Rev. Professor Elton, Brown University, Providence.

2 pp. 34½ cm.

Dr. Waterhouse, physician of Cambridge and Boston and one of the earliest to use Jenner's vaccinating methods in America, says in this letter to Professor Elton that he is sending him by his son-in-law, the Rev. William Ware, a little book which he wishes him to read, and asks if "you think it worth depositing in the archives of your society, if it should be found that one of its members wrote it, for John Wythe can handle a hammer & file better than a pen. I am the humble editor of my smutty-faced neighbor," thus claiming for himself the responsibility for Wyeth's *Oregon; or, A Short History of a Long Journey . . . Drawn up from the Notes and Oral Information of John B. Wyeth*, Cambridge, 1833, which Waterhouse published to discourage emigration.

[Coe No. II, 230.]

514 WATERS, ABRAHAM

"A Vocabulary of Words in Hancock's Harbor Language, on the North West Coast of N. America. Taken by Abraham Waters, who sailed to that place with Capt. Gray, of Boston (about 20 years ago), whose widow presented the Original, from which this is transcribed, to Elbridge G. Howe." Paxton, December 13, 1828.

Photostat. 14 pp. 20 cm.

Photostat of the original transcript in the library of the American Antiquarian Society.

Abraham Waters was fourth mate on the second voyage of the *Columbia*, 1791.
[Coe No. 192.]

515 WATKINS, WILLIAM HENRY, 1827–1888

Letter [to Governor Wallace]. Fort Walla Walla, W.T. June 8, 1863.

1 p. 28½ cm.

On the verso: "Sent this to Gov. Wallace."

Dr. Watkins came to Oregon in 1852. In 1861 he offered his services to the government and was appointed surgeon, with the rank of major, with the 1st Oregon Cavalry. In the summer of 1863 he was stationed at Fort Walla Walla.

The letter urged the Governor to come to Walla Walla to strengthen the Union cause as the local political situation was precarious.

[Miller Collection.]

516 WEBBER, JOHN, 1752–1793

View of Nootka Sound. Signed, J. Webber, pinx, 1783[?]

Painting in oil. 3'2" x 4'1".

John Webber, landscape painter of Swiss extraction, exhibited at the Royal Academy in London in 1776 and later. He was draftsman on Captain Cook's third voyage, 1776–1780, was employed by the Admiralty to superintend the engravings of the prints from his drawings, and later published colored etchings of places visited on that voyage.

This is the first known original view of the Northwest Coast. It was evidently painted from his original sketches after his return to London.

It is reproduced in the *Yale University Library Gazette*, 1948, XXIII, 46. A slightly different view is reproduced from an oil painting done on copper by Webber and entitled on the back "View of Nootka Sound, America, J. Webber, pinxt, 1786," as the frontispiece in John R. Jewitt, *A Journal Kept at Nootka Sound*. Reprinted from the original edition of 1807, Boston, 1931.

[Coe No. II, 274.]

517 WEED, L. N.

Narrative of a journey to California in 1849, by steamer to Galveston, Texas, and overland to Los Angeles and the mines by the southern route,

March 8 to October 26; a brief account of his stay at the mines, with a journal of the weather in California, November 1, 1849 to September 30, 1850; and his return to New York by Nicaragua and Havana, September 29 to December 30, 1850.

115 pp. 19½ cm. Original binding.

This narrative was written in 1857 with daily entries from his journal and is signed at the end of the journal of the weather [p. 115]: "Transferred to this book from my journal Dec. 21st. 1859."

The party left New York March 8, 1849 on the bark *Norumbega* and reached Galveston March 30. They proceeded to Houston by boat and set out on the overland journey April 7 following the southern route by Austin, Fredericksburg, Pecos River, Presidio del Norte, El Paso, Doña Ana, Cooke's and Graham's routes to Tucson, Pima, Gila River, Warner's Ranch and Los Angeles, and up the coast to Stockton and the mines, October 26, 1849. On September 11, 1850, he left the mines for the East, sailing from San Francisco on the 29th for Central America, crossed the Isthmus by Lake Nicaragua to San Juan, by boat to Chagres, and sailed on the *Pacific* December 12, transferring at Havana to the *Ohio*. After a very stormy voyage he landed, December 25, at Norfolk and finally reached New York December 31, 1850.

[Coe No. 193.]

518 WELSH, WILLIAM ERNEST, 1872–1932

A brief history of the military government of California. Submitted by Captain W. E. Welsh, 30th Infantry March 10, 1911, signed: "W. E. Welsh, Captain 30th Infantry."

Typewritten manuscript (carbon). 53 pp. 28 cm.

Colonel Welsh was graduated from West Point in 1894 and was still in active service at the time of his death in Washington, June 19, 1932.

The manuscript is divided into seven chapters covering conditions affecting the occupation of California, annexation of Texas, Oregon boundary dispute; preliminary orders and instructions, Frémont, Sloat, Slidell, Larkin and Kearny; end of Mexican rule, Frémont and the "Bear Flag Revolution"; first efforts in organizing a government; military government established, Kearny's proclamation of March 1, 1847, Frémont's actions and trial; military government as exercised during continuation of hostilities with Mexico, methods of administration, gold discovery, insurrection in Lower California; military government after the ratification of the treaty of peace; office of governor assumed by General Riley, end of military government.

The manuscript was sold at the Anderson Galleries, December 1923, sale No. 1781.

[Coe No. 194.]

519 WENTZEL, WILLARD FERDINAND, *ca.* 1777–1832

"Journal of a short trip to the Rocky Mountns. Summer 1807."

9 pp. 32½ cm. With typewritten transcript.

At beginning of text: "Journal of the Nahanny expedition intended as a continuation of the Journal of Winter 1807 to the embarkation. June 26th." Signed at the end by [Willard] Ferdd. Wentzel.

The manuscript has been folded and sealed and apparently sent to his employers of the North West Company as the address "Messrs. McKay Thomson & McKenzie" is written below the title on the last leaf and blotted out.

The journal covers the expedition from the departure from Fort Simpson June 26, up the Liard River to George Keith's Fort, across part of the Rockies in search of the Nahanies, to his return to Fort Simpson, July 30, 1807.

[Coe No. 195.]

520 WHITE, ELIJAH, 1806–1879

Quitclaim deed to Francis M. Warren, Charles E. Chapin, and Stephen W. Shelton for land in Pacific City [Oregon] signed April 20, 1850: "Elijah White. Witness A. A. Skinner."

Broadside. 22½ x 33 cm.

Document, printed for Elijah White, filled in by A. A. Skinner.

Endorsed: "Elijah White to F. M.

Warren & Co. Deed of quit claim. April 20/50."

[Coe No. III, 1771.]

521 WHITE, SAMUEL STEPHEN, 1821–1900

Report to Colonel Peter W. Conover on losses sustained by citizens of Pleasant Grove City, Utah County, as a result of the Indian difficulties of 1853 and 1854. Dated Pleasant Grove City, July 24, 1855.

3 pp. 32½ cm.

Endorsed: "Pleasant Grove Damage Report."

Samuel S. White came to Utah in 1848 with members of the Mormon Battalion, and settled in Pleasant Grove. He was a farmer and stock raiser, and served as constable and school trustee.

In 1853 Colonel Conover of the Utah Militia was sent to Utah County with 150 men to protect the smaller settlements from attacks by the Indians. This report from Major White lists 73 citizens of Pleasant Grove City and the losses they sustained during the years 1853 and 1854.

[Coe Collection.]

522 WHITMAN, ABIAL, d. 1850

Journal of an overland journey from Rochester, Wisconsin, to Georgetown, California, April 8 to September 12, 1850, and a brief stay in the mines to October 3, 1850.

2 vols. [i.e., 216 pp.] 15 and 12½ cm. Original bindings.

The journal describes the route in detail and conditions on the road. The route followed was by Iowa City, Canesville [sic] to the valley of the Platte and Fort Kearney, along the south bank of the Platte to the crossing south of Ash Hollow, Fort Laramie, the Sweetwater, South Pass, Fort Bridger and Great Salt Lake, the Mormon Route to the Humboldt and Carson Rivers, to Georgetown in the American River Valley. Whitman then visited Sacramento, Bear River Valley, and Marysville, and for a short time was mining on Pittsburg Bar. The diary breaks off October 3, 1850, when he was at Eliza City.

"Book A" contains the journal from April 8 to July 14, and "Book B" from July 14 to October 3, 1850. Many of the entries were originally in pencil and have been written over in ink. The first 29 pages of "Book B" contain the accounts of Whitman and other members of the California Company [later the Rochester California Company].

A note in another hand on the flyleaf of "Book B" reads: "We left San Francisco Oct. 29, 1850. Abial died Thursday Oct. 31 at four o'clock in the morning."

[Coe No. 196.]

523 WHITMAN, NARCISSA PRENTISS (MRS. MARCUS), 1808–1847

"Narcissa Prentiss Whitman's Diary." 1836.

Typewritten copy. 50 pp. 28 cm.

The transcript has headlines and captions, and an introductory note, dated January 8, 1931, saying that, through the courtesy of descendants of the Whitman family, it is being published serially in the *Chronicle Express* [Penn Yan, N.Y.].

The first instalment is a letter from Mrs. Whitman to her husband's half-brother, Oren, and half-sister, Nancy, from Vancouver, October 24, 1836; followed by a note to Mr. Whitman's mother, Mrs. Alice Loomis, October 13, 1836, transmitting a copy of the journal kept by Narcissa for her own mother. The diary covers the journey from Rendezvous to Vancouver, July 18–October 18, 1836.

The original diary sent to Mrs. Prentiss is now in the library of Whitman College.

The diary is published in Myron Eells, *Marcus Whitman*, Seattle, 1919, pp. 54–95; and, edited by T. C. Elliott, in the *Oregon Historical Quarterly*, 1936, XXXVII, 87–101, 171–191, 275–290.

The copy sent to Mrs. Loomis was, in 1937, in the possession of Miss Elona Underwood of Salt Lake City. It was printed in the *Transactions* of the Oregon Pioneer Association, 1891, from a poor transcript, and in the *Chronicle Express* of Penn Yan, N.Y., January 8, 1931. This copy and the Coe transcript break off in the midst of the entry for October 18, 1836, and vary slightly from the printed text of the original diary.

[Coe No. II, 289.]

524 WHITNEY, JOSIAH DWIGHT, 1819–1896

Letter to James Dwight Dana. San Francisco, January 24, 1862.

4 pp. 27 cm.

Josiah Dwight Whitney, after graduating from Yale College in 1839, studied under Dr. Hare in Philadelphia and at the École des Mines in Paris. In 1860 he was appointed state geologist of California and undertook a topographical, geological and natural history survey of the state.

The letter concerns his hopes and plans for publishing the results of the survey.

[In James Dwight Dana, Scientific Correspondence.]

525 WHYMPER, FREDERICK

Collection of original sepia and watercolor drawings by Frederick Whymper, artist of the Vancouver Island Exploring Expedition, 1864, under the command of Robert Brown.

23 views with 15 large and 20 smaller photographs. 11½ x 9 cm.–37½ x 20 cm.

The original drawings are numbered from 1 to 32, with nine missing, and all but 20 and 32 are signed: "F Whymper, delt."

The Vancouver Island Exploring Expedition was originated by Governor Kennedy to ascertain the resources of the colony. Robert Brown was appointed commander, with Peter Leech as lieutenant and astronomer, Frederick Whymper as artist, and John Buttle as assistant naturalist. The expedition left Victoria June 7, 1864 in H.M.S. *Grappler*, explored the coast and interior of the Island and returned to Victoria October 21.

Frederick Whymper was the artist also of the Western Union Telegraph Company's expedition to Alaska to survey a route for an overland telegraph line to Europe by Alaska and Siberia. In his *Travel and Adventure in the Territory of Alaska*, London, 1868, he includes a brief account of the expedition of 1864. This collection formerly belonged to Robert Brown, commander of the expedition, and was acquired from Professor Rudmore-Brown of Trinity College, Dublin.
[Coe No. III, 628.]

526 WILDMAN, AUGUSTUS and THOMAS GREGORY

The correspondence of Thomas and Augustus Wildman with members of their family, 1858–1865, the majority written from Denver City between June 1859 and June 1862; and letters to Thomas G. Wildman and Frederick S. Wildman, 1860–1881.

64 letters and one document. 220 pp. 19½–26½ cm. With typewritten transcripts.

Thomas and Augustus Wildman were the sons of Frederick S. Wildman of Danbury, Conn. Thomas, in 1858, was employed in St. Louis, and in 1859, after a visit to his home, set out for the Pikes Peak gold mines. He soon abandoned mining and moved to Denver, where he remained until 1865 when he and his wife and little daughter returned to the East. In 1860 he was joined in Denver by his brother Augustus, who had been in ill health. Augustus remained in Denver until 1866.

WILDMAN, AUGUSTUS. Eight letters to his mother. September 21, 1860–July 24, 1865. 28 pp.

—— Eight letters to his father. October 1, 1860–December 24, 1865. 29 pp.

—— Three letters to his sister, Mrs. Lucy Haskins. December 16, 1860–September 6, 1865. 12 pp.

—— Letter to his brother Horatio. May 29, 1861. 7 pp.

WILDMAN, THOMAS GREGORY. 18 letters to his mother. February 6, 1858–September 27, 1861. 57 pp.

—— Five letters to his brother Augustus. April 15, 1859–March 6, 1860. 17 pp.

—— Nine letters to his sister, Mrs. Lucy Haskins. April 25, 1859–May 17, 1860. 29 pp.

—— Three letters to his father, Frederick S. Wildman. October 17, 1859–September 8, 1862. 10 pp.

WILDMAN, MARY B. KEHLER (Mrs. Thomas G.). Two letters to Mrs. Frederick S. Wildman. October 24, 1860, January 23, 1863. 7 pp.

—— Four letters to Mrs. Lucy Haskins. December 12, 1860–June 11, 1862. 17 pp.

HARNEY, GEORGE. Letter to Thomas Wildman. November 14, 1864. 2 pp.

WHITSITT, RICHARD E. Letter to F. S. Wildman. October 15, 1866. 3 pp.

WILCOX, GURDON H. Letter to T. G. Wildman. January 12, 1881. 2 pp.

WHITE, ELI. Quitclaim to F. S. Wildman, Assignee of Sturdevant & Benedict, bankrupts, signed at Litchfield, Conn.,

September 29, 1870. Witnessed by George M. Woodruff, J.P., and George C. Woodruff. Recorded on Danbury Land Records, October 22, 1870. David B. Booth, town clerk. Printed form filled in by hand.

The letters describe the journey from Leavenworth to Denver City, conditions at the mines, the settlement and growth of Denver City, the Territory of Jefferson and the Provisional Government, life in Denver, duels, the Vigilance Committee, and the formation of Colorado Territory.

The first two letters of Thomas G. Wildman were added to the collection July 12, 1949, by gift of Edward Eberstadt.

[Coe No. 197.]

527 WILLIS, EDWARD J.

"Diary of Edward J. Willis, Giving account of travell from Independence Missouri to California in 1849, Across the Plains." May 1 to September 1.

62 pp. 18½ cm. Original binding. With typewritten transcript.

Willis was an attorney in Virginia before going to California in 1849. He settled in Sacramento and in 1850 was elected county judge. In 1854 he was ordained and became the first pastor of the First Baptist Church of Oakland.

The diary records in some detail the journey from the camp near Independence, starting May 3 on the Santa Fé road, across the Kansas River and the Blue to Fort Kearney and the Platte to South

Fork Crossing, Ash Hollow, Fort Laramie, South Pass, Sublette's Cut-off to Fort Hall, July 16, the California Trail by the Humboldt and Truckee Rivers to the mines on the north fork of Bear River, August 31. Soon after leaving Independence they joined an Indiana company and elected officers. On July 4 the company camped near the Charlestown [Va.] Company.

[Coe No. IV, 447.]

528 WILSON, JAMES S. R.

"Journal of a trip to the Yellowstone Park, July, Aug. and Sept 1875. By James S. R. Wilson."

56 pp. 21½ cm.

This journal has been written up after the events and has some corrections and alterations. It describes the preparations for the expedition, the trip from St. Paul to Bismarck, D.T., and Carroll, M.T., June 30–July 12, with some details not

included in the official report as printed; and the reconnaissance from Carroll to Camp Baker, Fort Ellis, Mammoth Springs and Yellowstone Park, July 13–August 13, which was commanded by Captain William Ludlow, Corps of Engineers.

The other members of the expedition were the captain's brother, Edwin Ludlow; W. H. Wood, assistant; George Bird Grinnell and Edward S. Dana, both of Yale College; Lieutenant R. E. Thompson, 6th Infantry, topographer and general assistant; Charles Reynolds, guide and hunter; Sergeants Becker and Wilson, and five men.

Sergeant Wilson in his journal describes his chief duty as plotting the course of the reconnaissance, for which he used a specially constructed, light, two-wheeled cart built to scale so that 400 revolutions of the wheels made exactly one mile.

Captain Ludlow's official report of the reconnaissance was published by the War Department in 1876: *U.S. War Dept. Report of a Reconnaissance from Carroll, Montana Territory, on the Upper Missouri, to the Yellowstone National Park, and Return, Made in the Summer of 1875,* by William Ludlow, Captain of Engineers, Brevet Lieutenant-Colonel, U.S. Army . . . Washington, 1876.

[Coe No. 198.]

529 WILSON, WILLIAM

"Wm. Wilson's Day Book, April 29, 1850. Vanburen Co. State of Iowa."

104 pp. 15 cm. Original binding.

The manuscript diary kept by William Wilson on his journey overland from Iowa to the gold mines of California from May 19, 1850, when he crossed the Missouri; during his stay in California until January 10, when he left the mines for San Francisco; during his passage on the bark *Philena*, January 17, 1851, to Panama and on the *North American* March 24 to New Orleans, and up the Mississippi to St. Louis, and home April 15, 1851.

Wilson again kept his journal from April 6, 1853, when he started for Oregon, over the Oregon Trail, reaching Albany September 21, and Marysville September 22, 1853. The entries are very brief, recording the weather, conditions of the roads and camps, distances, and graves passed. They are followed by brief notes, accounts, memoranda of mileage, and numbers of emigrants.

[Coe No. V, 51.]

530 WILSON, WILLIAM

Eight letters to his wife, Mrs. Lovina Wilson, at Business Corner, Van Buren County, Iowa, May 18 to November 24, 1850; and one letter to his father, December 26, 1850.

29 pp. 25 cm. With typewritten transcripts.

William Wilson was a man of little or no education, his letters are badly spelled and written, but he was observant, records conditions on the trail from Iowa to California, by the Platte River, Independence Rock, Fort Laramie, South Pass, Salt Lake City, and the Humboldt River to the mines in California.

The letters mention members of the party and other Iowans he meets.

[Coe No. V, 51.]

531 WINCHESTER, BENJAMIN

References to the Scriptures copied "from B. Winchester's Synopsis."

60 pp. 14½ cm. Original binding, stamped with Royal Arms and the words "Secretary's Book."

The manuscript is a copy in a very clear, unidentified hand of the references (omitting the quoted passages) and notes in Winchester's *Synopsis of the Holy Scriptures, and Concordance . . . Chiefly Designed to Illustrate the Doctrine of the Church of Jesus Christ of Latter-day Saints.* Philadelphia, 1842.

The manuscript forms a supplement to and is bound with the following pamphlet: Lorenzo D. Barnes, *Very Important References to Prove the Religion and Principles of the Latter-day Saints, to Be True.* Bradford, Yorkshire: Printed by B. Walker, Westgate, 1842.

[Coe No. I, 963.]

532 WISTAR, ISAAC JONES, 1827–1905

"Autobiography"

2 vols. [i.e., 670 pp.] 29 cm.

The manuscript is a carbon copy of the typewritten manuscript of the 1914 edition, prepared for the printer, with the location of illustrations indicated but without the Appendix.

Isaac Jones Wistar was born in Philadelphia in 1827. After attending Westtown, the Friends' Select School in Philadelphia, and Haverford, he was placed in a dry-goods store in Philadelphia but was not successful there or in other posts. In 1849 he set out for the West with Dr. William Gambel, assistant curator of the Philadelphia Academy of Natural Sciences. He became interested in the Wistar Museum in Philadelphia, named for his great uncle Caspar Wistar and later incorporated as the Wistar Institute of Anatomy and Biology.

The autobiography includes his diary of the journey from Independence to California; describes life at the mines and in California, trading with the miners, hunting and trapping in the Northwest, his return to the East, and service in the Civil War.

The autobiography was privately printed in 1914 by the Wistar Institute of Anatomy and Biology, in two volumes, and reprinted in 1937 in one volume with title: *Autobiography of Isaac Jones Wistar, 1827–1905. Half a Century in War and Peace.* Philadelphia, The Wistar Institute of Anatomy and Biology, 1937.

[Coe No. 199.]

533 WOLFE, JAMES, 1807–1848

"Journal of a Voyage on Discovery in the Pacific and Beering's Straits on board H.M.S. *Blossom*, Captn. F. W. Beechey, F.R.S. & Mem. Ast. Soc. 'Ours the wild life in tumult still to range.' By James Wolfe Mate." 1825–1828.

294 pp. 2 plans, 2 charts, illustrations, tables. 28 cm. Original binding, diced calf with metal clasp.

The charts and plans are: "Chart showing the Tracks of H.M.S. *Blossom* and *Hellespont* Brig round Cape Horn" [22½ x 16½ cm.]; Harbor of St. Peter and St. Paul, Awatska Bay. Sketch plan [4½ x 5½ cm.]; chart of the harbor of Port Lloyd, Peel's Island [20 x 15 cm.]; "Plan of the Harbour of Petropaulovski" [17 x 19½ cm.].

James Wolfe was born April 15, 1807, and died in 1848. He and two others served as Admiralty mates, and he took the observations and prepared the charts.

Captain Beechey was commanded to

proceed to Bering Sea to await the arrival of the expedition under Captain Parry that was searching for a Northwest Passage by way of Prince Regent's Inlet, and of that under Captain John Franklin exploring the north coast of Alaska; and on the way to survey and explore such parts of the Pacific as were within reach.

On May 19, 1825, H.M.S. *Blossom* sailed from Spithead for Cape Horn and Chile, reaching Valparaiso October 27. From Valparaiso they went to the Society Islands, Sandwich Islands, Kamchatka, Bering Sea, July 1826; California, January 1827, Sandwich Islands, the Philippines and China, May 1827, Awats Bay, Bering Strait, San Francisco, November 1827, Mexico, Chile, around Cape Horn to Brazil, the Azores, and Spithead October 12, 1828.

The journal, written in a small, copperplate hand and illustrated with pen and ink and wash drawings and charts, was prepared "to render more lasting the incidents of a voyage which for diversity of scenery has perhaps not been parallelled since the time of the immortal Cook, and intended solely for private perusal." Some pages have been left blank, possibly for further remarks or drawings, and in some spaces faint pencil sketches indicate what was intended. The journal breaks off on the homeward voyage at Coquimbo [*ca.* June 3, 1828].

The journal is followed by four appendices: Passages made in H.M.S. *Blossom;* Vocabulary of the Esquimaux language obtained from the natives at Kotzebue Sound; Distances of a comet from the fixed stars, October 1825; Meteorological journal. 70 pp.

The manuscript formerly belonged to W. H. V. Bythway, Esq., and was sold at Sotheby's in London, June 6, 1950.

Captain Beechey's report of the expedition was published under the title: *Narrative of a Voyage to the Pacific and Beering's Strait, to Co-operate with the Polar Expeditions: Performed in His Majesty's Ship Blossom, under Command of Captain F. W. Beechey, R.N. . . . in the Years 1825, 26, 27, 28.* London 1831. 2 vols. Wolfe's Journal follows the same general outline as the *Narrative* but differs widely in the details. The *Narrative* includes in its Appendix a "Vocabulary of Words of the Western Esquimaux" more extensive than that in the manuscript, and "Meteorological Observations."

[Coe Collection.]

534 YANKTON, D. T. CITY CLERK (E. L. WHITE)

Certificate of election, Andrew J. Faulk, on the 6th day of April, A.D. 1874, was elected alderman of the second ward. Signed by E. L. White, City Clerk, with seal, April 13, 1874, Yankton, Dakota Territory.

Broadside. Printed form filled in by hand. 21½ x 18½ cm.

(*See also* the Faulk papers, No. 195). [Coe No. III, 909.]

535 YOUNG, BRIGHAM, 1801-1877

Letters to William H. Hooper, second territorial delegate from Utah to Congress, at Washington, D.C. Great Salt Lake City, November 1, 1859 to May 11, 1861; May 30, 1862; December 5, 1865 to July 5, 1866; January 30, 1869.

60 letters. 253 pp. 20½–26½. With typewritten summary and transcripts.

The letters detail events and conditions in Salt Lake City, discuss U.S. troops in Utah, national affairs and attitude toward Utah, the overland mail, pony express and telegraph, gold discoveries, the Indians, family and church news; and instruct Hooper on appointments and legislation desired for Utah, and its admission as a state, recommending him to seek the advice of Colonel Kane.

[Coe No. 204.]

536 YOUNG, BRIGHAM, 1801–1877

Letter to his nephew, Colonel James A. Little. Great Salt Lake City, January 23, 1854. Signature only.

2 pp. 25 cm.

The letter informs Colonel Little that he has been selected to accompany Brother Franklin D. Richards on a mission to England, and tells him to come to Salt Lake City at once, so that they can start with the 1st of March mail.

[Coe Collection.]

537 YOUNG, BRIGHAM, 1801–1877

Letter to the officer commanding the forces now invading Utah Territory [Colonel Albert S. Johnston]. Governor's Office, Utah Territory, Great Salt Lake City, September 29, 1857. Signature only.

1 p. 26½ cm.

This letter was forwarded through General Wells to be delivered by General Robison, with the following letter:

WELLS, DANIEL HANMER. Letter to [Colonel Johnston]. Fort Bridger, September 30, 1857. Signature only. 1 p.

Governor Young's letter directed that Colonel Johnston and his troops retire forthwith from the Territory; or, if he prefers to remain until spring near his camp, that all arms and ammunition be deposited with Lewis Robison, Quartermaster of the Territory.

These letters were published in the *Report of the Secretary of War* (35th Congress, 1st Session, House Ex. Doc. No. 2, pp. 31–32, 1857).

[Coe Collection.]

538 YOUNG, BRIGHAM, 1801–1877

Letter to President Daniel H. Wells. President's Office, Gt. Salt Lake City, June 27, 1866. Signature only.

2 pp. 25 cm.

A brief account of local news for President Wells, who was in San Pete Valley urging forward the fortification of the settlements against attacks by the Indians.

[Coe No. 207.]

539 YOUNG, BRIGHAM, 1801–1877

"The word and the will of the Lord concerning the camp of Israel in their journeyings to the West." Winter Quarters Camp of Israel, January 14, 1847.

4 pp. 31½ cm.

Endorsed: "The word and will of the Lord given at the Winter Quarters of the Camp of Israel. Jany 14, 1847 No 5 /Copy /."

The Council meetings at Winter Quarters in 1846 were devoted largely to discussing plans for the exodus from the United States and finally, on January 14, 1847, Brigham Young announced "The Word and Will of the Lord" upon the march.

This is printed in full, with the exception of the paragraph naming specific saints to organize companies, in B. H. Roberts, *A Comprehensive History of the Church of Jesus Christ of Latter-day Saints*, 1930, III, 155–157.

[Coe Collection.]

540 YOUNG, BRIGHAM, 1801–1877

[Paper money] "G. S. L. City Jan. 20, 1849. No   1.00 d. Good to N K Whitney, or bearer one Dollar on demand. 1.00 d." Signed by Brigham Young, H. C. Kimball, Thos. Bullock, clerk.

Printed form, names filled in by hand. 9¾ x 5 cm. Mounted with an unsigned $2 bill.

The "Valley currency" was first issued January 1, 1849, signed by Brigham Young, Heber C. Kimball, and Thomas Bullock. It consisted of bills in amounts of $2, $1, and 50 cents. The type was set on January 22 and the bills run off for general use. This was the first type set and printing done in the valley.

[Coe No. I, 1261.]

541 YOUNG, JOSEPH WATSON

Three letters to his cousin, Joseph A. Young. Wyoming [N.T.], June 30 to July 8, 1864.

6 pp. 24½ cm. With typewritten transcripts.

Joseph Watson Young was the son of Brigham Young's brother Lorenzo Dow Young and in 1864 was in Wyoming, Neb. Ter., fitting out the emigrant parties arriving from the East for their journey across the Plains. William C. Staines was at that time the Church's emigration agent in New York and Joseph A. Young was assisting. The letters mention the parties arriving and leaving, among them John Murdock, Preston, Mathew White, Rollins, and Warren; Staines, and Schuttler who was to provide the wagons.

The third letter is not in Joseph Young's hand and is signed "per J.C.G."

[Coe No. 136.]

542 ZACHARY, JOHN

Letter to the Rev. H. H. Spalding. Linn County, Oregon, February 1868. Signature only.

3 pp. 25 cm.

Alexander and John Zachary were in the emigration of 1843 led by Elijah White and accompanied by Whitman on his return journey from the East.

The letter is about Whitman's aid to the emigrants of 1843, and the influence his reports had in inducing Zachary's father to join the emigration with his family.

[Miller Collection.]

INDEX

[Arabic numbers in the index refer to entries in the Catalogue; roman numbers refer to pages in the Introduction. Titles of persons are generally omitted except where the first name has not been determined.]

Bullock, Isaac, 1825–1891, 357, 535
Bullock, Thomas, 1816–1885, 156, 219, 540
Bulman, John, 195
Bulwer, William Henry Lytton Earle, baron Dalling and Bulwer, 1801–1872, 3
Bundy, O. C., 454
Burbank, John, 312, 313
Burbank, John A., 1827–, 195
Burbee, Jonathan, 289
Burch, John Chilton, 1826–1885, 55
Burche, B. Franklin, 50, 361
Burd, Julian F., 1853–1907, 454
Burdett, Samuel Swinfin, 1836–1914, 399
Bureau of Municipal Research, 56, 57
Burges, Anthony, 202
Burgess, J. H., 454
Burgess, R., 212
Burke, T. H., 131
Burke, Mrs. Walter, 454
Burleigh, Andrew F., 195
Burleigh, Caroline Faulk (Mrs. Walter A.), 195
Burleigh, Timothy B., 195
Burleigh, Walter Alwood, 1820–1896, 195
Burleigh, Walter Alwood, Jr., 195
Burlingham, Jannette, 447
Burnes, James N., 1827–1889, 352
Burnett, G. P., 454
Burnett, Peter Hardeman, 1807–1895, 173
Burnett, William C., 454
Burns, Captain of *Wilson G. Hunt*, 494
Burns, Mathew P., 332
Burr, David H., 279, 535
Burr, Dixie, 454
Burr, Frederick H., 172, 449, 451, 454
Burrell, Cuthbert, 1824–, 58
Burrell, Edward, 58
Burrell, Louisa Hannibal (Mrs. Edward), 58
Burrell, Mary (Mrs. George), 58
Burrell, Mary (afterward Mrs. Wesley Tonner), 1835–, 58
Burroughs, Mr., 361
Burt, Andrew Sheridan, 410
Burt, Hachaliah, 243, 305

Burt, James H., 389
Burton, Hiram, 99
Burton, R. P., 125
Burton, Robert Taylor, 1821–1907, 160, 279, 535
Burton, Z. T., 454
Busby, Houston, 131
Bush, Asahel, 1824–1913, 173
Bushman, Martin, 1802–1870, 383
Bustamante y Guerra, José, 402, 464
Butler, Charles William, 414
Butler, David, 1829–1891, 195, 212
Butler, James, 131
Butler, James M., 432
Butler, John M., 1829–1870, 99
Butler, Mann, 399, 432
Butler, Pierce Mason, 1798–1847, 202
Butler, William, 454
Butsch, Valentine, 242
Butt, William, 195
Butte Miner, 454
Butterfield, David A., 99
Butterfield, Philetta, 1793–, 447
Butterfield, Zimri, 1780?–, 447
Butterworth, Eb, 386
Buttre, John Chester, 1821–1893, 366
Buttrick, L., of Denver, 138
Byers, D. C., 454
Byers, William Newton, 1831–1903, 99, 215
Byles, C. N., 195
Bynum, Stephen, 454
Byrnes, M. F., 454

Cabanis, Lew G., 201, 336
Cabler, John, 454
Cache La Poudre Creek, 4
Cadle, Joseph, *d.* 1835, 202
Cady, C. C., 399
Cady, Edwin, 522
Cahoon, Thomas, 447
Cahuenga capitulation, 1847, 205
Cain, Andrew Jackson, *d.* 1879, 187, 509
Cain, John, 1805–1867, 59, 420
Caine, John Thomas, 1829–, 80, 279, 535
Calbreath, D., 454
Calder, David O., 1823–1884, 279, 535

Caldwell, A., 212
Caldwell, Richard S., 201, 336
Caldwell, William S., 173
Calhoon, Andrew, 447
Calhoun, James, d. 1876, 128
Calhoun, John, 1806–1859, 212, 352
Calhoun, John Caldwell, 1782–1850, 345
Calhoun, William Barron, 1795–1865, 334
California, 4, 9, 19, 20, 22, 30, 33, 47, 50, 55, 83, 93, 96, 103, 104, 115, 136, 139, 144, 161, 166, 199, 205, 218, 222, 225, 240, 286, 318, 350, 355, 471, 518, 532; see also Cattle industry; Indians; Mines; Missions; and names of cities
California and Oregon United States Mail Line, 60
California and Salt Lake Mail Line, 160
California Infantry, 201
California mint, 83
California Trail (Fort Hall to the Humboldt), 19, 30, 50, 81, 136, 142, 214, 255, 266, 307, 309, 473, 474, 527
"Californian's Address, The," 61
Calkins, A. B., 447
Callan, John F., 195
Callister, Thomas, 1821–1880, 219, 357
Calohan, William S., 212
Calvo, marquis de Casa; see Casa Calvo, Sebastian Calvo de la Puerta y O'Farrell, marquis de
Calypso, steamboat, 125
Camacho y Brenes, José, 12
Cambria, steamer, 359
Cameron, Hugh, 454
Cameron, J. G., 399
Cameron, James Donald, 1833–1918, 195
Cameron, William D., 454
Camp, Elisha Ely, d. 1867, 201
Camp, John B., 352
Camp Douglas, Utah, 410
Camp Floyd, Utah, 2, 535
Campa Cos, Fray Miguel de la, 52, 53, 379, 418
Campbell, Albert H., 361
Campbell, Archibald, 230
Campbell, C. C., 453

Campbell, C. T., 195
Campbell, J. W., 124
Campbell, James, 1812–1893, 212
Campbell, John, 372
Campbell, Orson, 447
Campbell, Robert, of St. Louis, 453
Campbell, Robert, of Salt Lake City, 279
Campbell, Robert, 1804–1879, 84
Campbell, William C., 335
Canadian River, 164, 165, 225, 455
Canby, Edward Richard Sprigg, 1817–1873, 6, 337
Canfield, I. A., 279
Canney, Claurisa (Mrs. James), 447
Canney, James, 447
Canning, George, 1770–1827, 268
Canning, Stratford, 1st Viscount Stratford de Redcliffe, 1786–1880, 268
Cannon, Forbis &; see Forbis & Cannon
Cannon, Frank, 466
Cannon, George Quayle, 1827–1901, 158, 279, 357, 381, 489, 535
Canton, Frank M., 1854–, 454
Cantonment Loring, 50, 369
Cantrell, William, 454
Capen, James W., 19
Caples, Luther W., 352
Caples, William G., 352
Capps, William, 336
Capron, Thaddeus Hurlbut, d. 1890, 377
Card, Benjamin C., 352, 482
Carder, Thomas R., 99
Cardwell, William B., 337
Carey, Stephen V., 283
Carey & Hart, 414
Caris, Peter W., 337
Carleton, James Henry, d. 1873, 148, 219
Carlin, William Passmore, 62, 126, 239
Carlisle, McCormick &; see McCormick & Carlisle
Carlisle, Robert S., 131
Carlton, Charles, 326
Carlton, Jack, 326
Carmicael, C., 228
Carn, R. B., 454
Carney, Thomas, 1824–1888, 352
Caroline, brig, 90

Cook, Reverend Mr., 447

Cook, C. E., 99, 138

Cook, Charles, 195

Cook, Charles A., 99, 138

Cook, Charles W., 1839–, 454

Cook, Charlotte Everett, 107, 108

Cook, Frederick, 158

Cook, George, 1858–, 454

Cook, George W., 1853–, 454

Cook, James, 1728–1779, 139, 516

Cook, Jehiel S., 124

Cook, John, 195

Cook, Joseph, 212

Cook, Joseph Witherspoon, 1836–, 107, 108, 398

Cook, Walter H., 42, 63

Cook, William A., 212

Cooke, J. B., 399

Cooke, John Rogers, d. 1891, 148

Cooke, Philip St. George, 1809–1895, 125, 148, 212, 219, 352

Cooke, Richard E., 99

Cooley, D., 447

Cooley, Dennis N., 125, 195, 483, 535

Cooley, Duane B., 195

Cooley, Mary E., 161

Coon, Homer, 109, 110

Cooney, J., 144

Cooper, Francis H., 482

Cooper, Frank, 447

Cooper, George E., d. 1881, 148

Cooper, Henry C., 399

Cooper, James, 359

Cooper, James, Master of the *Mary Dare*, 504

Cooper, James Graham, 1830–1902, 111, 217, 219, 361, 461

Cooper, Samuel, 1798–1876, 148, 443, 455, 481

Cooper, Stephen Stanley, 1826–1892, 352

Cooper, William, 454

Copeland, Reuben, 447

Copely, A. M., 201

Copely, Jessie Sinclair (Mrs. Alexander Wilton), 1844–, 112

Copley, Josiah, 195

Coppinger, John Joseph, 201

Cora, steamer, 388

Corbett, H. W., & Co., 60

Corbett, Henry Winslow, 1827–1903, 173, 336, 337, 366

Corbin, John B., 459

Corbin, Louis, 459

Corley, John, 212

Corn, Charles, Sioux Indian, 470

Cornelius, Thomas R., 1827–1899, 201, 336, 339

Cornell, of Tumwater, 317

Cornell, George, 113

Cornell, John, 1839–, 108

Cornell, Margaret Harris (Mrs. George), 113

Cornich, B., 144

Cornoyer, Narcisse A., 1820–1909, 337, 339

Cornwall, D., Master of brig *Genius*, 91

Corrill, John, 1794–, 364

Corwin, Thomas, 1794–1865, 3

Cos, Fray Miguel de Campa: *see* Campa Cos, Fray Miguel de la

Cothron, Gibson, 84, 388

Cotton, Captain, 454

Countryman, Henry, 454

Courtland, steamer, 423

Couthouy, Joseph Pitty, 166

Cowan, Frank, 195

Cowan, John E., 399

Cowden, John, 114

Cowdery, Oliver, 1806–1850, 79, 219, 447

Cowdry, O. L., 144

Cowen, William, 318

Cowles, Austin, 447

Cowles, N. M. H., 195

Cowles, Warren, 195

Cowlitz, bark, 504

Cowlitz farm, 264

Cox, J. L., 454

Cox, J. M., 454

Cox, Jacob Dolson, 1828–1900, 337, 486

Coyle, John, 212

Crackman, Charles, 213

Cradlebaugh, John, 219, 279, 318, 535

Craig, Henry Knox, d. 1869, 212

Craig, William, 1810–1869, 289, 339

Craighead, James Geddes, 1823–1895, 173

Crain, Jeremiah V., 83

Dawson County, Mont., Commissioners, 454

Day, Edward Henry, d. 1860, 201

Day, Elizabeth Little (Mrs. Frank), 454

Day, Frank, 1836–, 454

Day, George E., 447

Day, J. S., 454

Day, John, ca. 1770–1820, 457, 458

Dayton, A. O., 162, 166, 168

Deady, Matthew Paul, 1824–1893, 172–174, 388

Dear, L. C., 454

Dearborn, Greenleaf, d. 1846, 345

Dearing, St. Clair, 201

Deas, George, d. 1870, 148, 212

Deascey, W., 99

Dease, John Warren, 1783–1829, 245

Decatur, U.S. Sloop, 469

Decker, Charles Franklin, 1824–1901, 357, 535

Decker, F. B., 338

Deer Lodge County, Mont., 349

DeGray, Charles, 195

Degres, Charles, 125

DeHass, Wills, 195

De Haven, Edwin Jesse, 1816–1865, 166

Deitzler, George Washington, 1826–1884, 352

DeKay, Drake, 195

De Lacy, Walter Washington, 1819–1892, 442, 443, 454

Delahay, Mark William, d. 1879, 212, 352

Delano, Alonzo, 1806–1874, 136

Delano, Columbus, 1809–1896, 195, 337, 399

Delano, John S., 399

DeLano, Milton, 1844–, 340

De Lassus de Luzière, Charles de Hault; see Lassus de Luzière, Charles Dehault de

Delaware, U.S. Ship, 162

Dellenbaugh, Frederick Samuel, 1853–1935, 137, 216

Del Mar, Alexander, 1836–1926, 195

Delong, G. R., 19

Demary, Mary, 447

Dement, P. B., 399

Dement, Richard S., 399

Demers, Modeste, 1808–1877, 173

Demers, T. John, 454

DeMeurons, The, 396

DeMott, Martha, 454

De Mun, Julius, d. 1843, 399

Denman, Hampton B., 1829?–1906, 195, 352

Dennis, Ayrault W., 72

Dennis, Fountain M., 1836–, 454

Dennison, John, 447

Densmore, James, 447

Dent, Frederick Tracy, 1821–1892, 201, 219

Denver, James William, 1817–1892, 115, 318, 337, 352

Denver, Col., 99, 123, 410, 526; People's Government, 138, 526

Denver Town Company, 526

Derbigny, Pierre Auguste Charles Bourguignon, 1767–1829, 41

Derr, William, 279

Derrough, A., 447

DeRudio, Charles Camilus, d. 1910, 401

De Saussure, William Davie, 148, 455

"Descripcion geographico historica," 139

Descubierta, ship, 402, 464

DeSelding, Charles, 212

Deseret; see Utah

Deshler, James, d. 1863, 481

Des Moines, Iowa, 45

Des Moines River, 122

De Trobriand, Philip Regis, 1816–1897, 195, 486

De Ville, John Felix, 426

Devine, Alexander, 454

Dewey, S. P., 212

Dewey, William P., 195

Dewitt & Bach, 454

DeWolfe, Charles Henry, 119

DeWolfe, Eliza A. Hurd, 119

DeWolfe, Ezekiel, 212

Dexter, Benjamin, 454

Dibble, Charles Elias, 410

Dick, John T., 212

Dickerson, John H., d. 1872, 219, 361

Dickerson, Mahlon, 1770–1853, 162, 168

Dickey, Milton C., 479

Frields, Dr., of Fort McLeod, 454
Friend, J. O., 399
Fritz, Jacob, 1828–1898, 201
Frost, Burr, 1816–1878, 156
Frost, John, 173
Frost, T. J., 454
Frost, Mrs. T. J., 454
Fruit, James H., 321
Frush, John H., 206
Frush, William H., 206
Fuenclara, condé de; *see* Cebrián y
  Agustín, Pedro, condé de Fuenclara
Fuller, Alpheus G., 195
Fuller, George N., 447
Fuller, Perry, 195, 212, 413
Fullmer, Almon Linus, 1816–, 357
Fullmer, John S., 447
Fulton, J. Alexander, 195
Fulton, S. G., 1851–, 454
Fulton, T. M., 399
Fulton Company, 409
Fur trade, 13, 14, 76, 90, 92, 207, 261,
  263, 271, 308, 345, 356, 363, 382, 408,
  411, 457, 458, 467; *see also* American
  Fur Company, Hudson's Bay Com-
  pany, Missouri Fur Company, North
  West Company, Pacific Fur Com-
  pany, Russian–American Company
Furcey, William, 212
Furgerson, Samuel, 207
Furste, Edward, 332

Gagnier, Jean Baptiste, 359
Gaines, Archibald Kinkead, 1823–, 208
Gaines, John Pollard, 1795–1857, 208,
  209, 366
Gale, John, *d.* 1830, 15
Gale, R. Elizabeth, 119
Gale, Samuel, 396
Gale, Thomas, 447
Gallagher, George, 212
Gallagher, Henry, 507
Gallagher, J. E., 399
Gallatin, Albert, 1761–1849, 13
Gallatin, E. L., & Co., 454
Galloway, James, 309
Galvéz, José de, 1720–, 418
Gambel, William, 1821–1849, 532

Gamble, Hamilton Rowen, 1798–1864,
  399
Gamble, Henry, *d.* 1849, 309
Gamble, John Rankin, 1848–1891, 195
Gamble, Robert Jackson, 1851–1924,
  195
Gambrel, William, 301
Gamer, Fred, 1844–1911, 454
Gans & Klein, 454
Gardepie, François, 396
Gardner, Brainerd, & Co.; *see* Brainerd,
  Gardner & Co.
Gardner, Charles Kitchel, 1787–1869,
  217
Gardner, George, 40
Gardner, Ir[a?] H., 78
Gardner, W. H., 454
Gardner, William P., 119, 210
Garfielde, Selucius, *d.* 1889, 173, 265
Garland, John, *d.* 1861, 148, 219, 388
Garnett, Robert Selden, 1819–1861,
  201, 211, 219
Garnier, Louis C., 84
Garnsey, C. A., 399
Garnsey, Daniel Greene, 1779–1851,
  399
Garretson, Theodore, 114
Garrett, George W[?]., 144
Garrett, R., 212
Garrett, Samuel, 83
Garrett Society, 168
Garrison, William, 517
Garvey, Edward C. K., 212, 352
Garvey, John, 242
Garvin, Samuel, 454
Gaskell, G. A., 454
Gasmann, John G., 243, 305
Gasteiger, Rev. José, S.J., 429
Gaston, William H., 399
Gates, Jacob, 1811–1892, 535
Gates, John, 302
Gates, Mrs. Louise W., 212
Gaw, William B., 269
Gear, Mrs. Frances Sage, 414
Gear, Jerusha Sage (Mrs. Hiram),
  1806–, 414
Geary, Edward R., 1811–1886, 212,
  368
Geary, Edward R., II, 212
Geary, John, 212

Geary, John White, 1819–1873, vii, 212, 352, 406, 413

Gee, Perry, 213

Gee, Sarah Ann (Mrs. Perry), 213

Geiger, Vincent Eply, 1823?–1869, 214

Geiger, William, 1816–1901, 217, 503

Gelshaüsser, John, 258

Généreux, ship, 293

Genius, brig, 91

—, George, 215

George, George W., 212

George, Joseph, 447

George Emery, ship, 343

George Law, ship, 144

Georgiana, sloop, 179

Gerard, John B., 195

Gerrish, John H., 138

Getty, Thomas Murray, d. 1867, 239, 361

Ghent, William James, 1866–, 216, 401

Gholson, Richard Dickerson, 1802–1861; *see* Washington Territory, Governor

Gibbon, John, 1827–1896, 171, 204, 230, 401

Gibbons, Andrew Smith, 1825–1886, 156

Gibbs, Alfred, d. 1868, 148

Gibbs, Daniel S., 447

Gibbs, George, 1776–1833, 221

Gibbs, George, 1815–1873, 1, 217, 332, 442, 443, 461, 475

Gibbs, John Pemberton, 1825–1869, 409

Gibbs, Mary Ann Rothwell (Mrs. J. Pemberton), 1829–, 409

Gibbs, Mason, 1801–, 399

Gibbs, Wolcott, 1822–1908, 461

Gibson, Francis Marion, 401

Gibson, George, 1783–1861, 84, 345

Gibson, Henry, 1840–, 99

Gibson, Jacob, 447

Gibson, Robert Stewart, 202

Gibson, Thomas, 1819–, 99

Gibson, Walter Murray, 1823–1888, 535

Gibson, William Ruff, d. 1899, 148, 201

Gibson, William W., 202

Giddings, Ammi, 262

Giddings, Edward, 1822–1876, 172, 264, 475

Gifford, Oscar Sherman, 1842–1913, 195

Gigedo, Juan Vicente Güémez Pacheco de Padilla Horcasitas y Aguayo, condé de Revilla Gigedo; *see* Revilla Gigedo

Gihon, James L., 212

Gihon, John H., 212

Gihon, John L., 212

Gila Expedition, 148

Gila River, 131, 225, 517

Gilbert, Charles Champion, d. 1903, 64

Gilbert, F. W., 454

Gilbert, George, 318

Gilbert, George S., 318

Gilbert, John W., 454

Gilbert, Lyman D., 401

Gilchrist, Edward, 166

Giles, Frye Williams, 1819–1898, 479

Gill, A. J., 99

Gill, William H., 212

Gill & Steel, Portland, 337

Gillespie, Archibald H., 518

Gillespie, John, 45

Gillett, M. M., 447

Gillette, Henry C., 454

Gillette, Warren C., 249, 486

Gilliam, Cornelius, 1798–1848, 322

Gillingham, Edward[?] N., 337

Gilliss, James, d. 1898, 201

Gilliss, James Melville, 1811–1865, 168

Gillmer [or Gilmore] of New Albany, Ind., 423

Gilman, Charles, 212

Gilman, Daniel S., 218

Gilman, Moses D., 218

Gilman, Moses D., Jr., 218

Gilman, Patience (Mrs. Moses D.), 218

Gilmer, Thomas Walker, 1802–1844, 399

Gilpin, William, 1813–1894, 388, 526

Gilson, Horace C., 23

Ginn, John I., 219

Girard, Frederic F., 1829–, 401

Gish, John, 220

Gish, Mary (Mrs. John), 220

Gist, George W., 1795–1854, 352

Gist, John C., 352

Glafcke, Herman, d. 1912, 399

Glasgow, Thomas W., 1816?–, 431, 477

McCook, Alexander McDowell, 1831–1903, 148

McCook, Edwin Stanton, *d.* 1873, 195

McCorkle, W. M., 337

McCormick, Linas, 454

McCormick, Paul, 1845–, 454

McCormick, Richard Cunningham, 1832–1901, 195

McCormick, Washington J., 1835–1889, 454

McCormick & Carlisle, 454

McCotter, D. G., 417

McCowan, Ike, 409

McCoy, A. A., 195

McCoy, John, 503

McCrea, Cole, 352

McCubbin, Joseph L., 212

McCulloch, Ben, 1811–1862, 148, 219, 279

McCulloch, Hezekiah D., 447

McCulloh, R. L., 454

McCulloh, Broadwater, & Co.: *see* Broadwater, McCulloh, & Co.

McCune, John, 1830–, 454

McCurdy, Samuel M., 1805–1865, 443

McCurdy, Solomon P., 535

McCutcheon, Isaac D., 1840–, 454

McCutcheon, J. C., 253

McDermont, C., 399

McDevitt, James, 1849–, 454

McDonald, Alexander Findlay, 1825–, 357

McDonald, Angus, *d.* 1861, 217, 263

McDonald, Archibald, 1790–1853, 264, 501, 503

Macdonald, James, 99

McDonald, Jane Klyne (Mrs. Archibald), 1810–1879, 503

Macdonald, Ranald, 1824–1894, 6

McDonald, W., 399

McDonell, Alexander, 396

McDonell, William, 399

McDonough, Walter, 399

McDougal, George, 420

McDougall, Charles, *d.* 1885, 336

McDougall, Duncan, 13

McDougall, F. D., 201

McDougall, George, 396

McDougall, Thomas Mower, 128, 401

McDowell, Irvin, 1818–1885, 148, 276, 481

McDowell, James L., 352

McDowell, Robert, 318

McDowell, William C., *ca.* 1828–1867, 352

McDuff, Peter, 352

McElroy, James, 454

McFadden, Obadiah B., 1817–1875, 190, 317, 443, 506

McFadin, Andrew H., 212

McFarland, D. L., 454

McFarland, Noah C., 399

McFarlane, Parlan, 158

McFarren, Samuel, 212

Macfeely, Robert, *d.* 1901, 201

McGee, E. M., 212

McGill, Henry M., 190, 390, 510

McGillivray, William, 1764–1825, 13

McGinness, John Randolph, 336

McGinniss, James Thomson, *d.* 1891, 486

McGirl, Hoskins &; *see* Hoskins & McGirl

McGregor, Captain, 454

McGuire, Thomas, 131

McGulpin, William, 460

McGunnegle, James, *d.* 1822, 345

McGunnegle, Wilson, 345

McHatten, Green, 144

McHatten, James G., 144

McIntire, Timothy, 479

Mackall, William Whann, *d.* 1891, 443

McKay, Alexander, *d.* 1811, 273, 519

McKay, H., 423

McKay, Thomas, 1797–1850, 166, 421, 503

McKay, William Cameron, 1824–, 6, 337

McKeage, Barnett, 22

McKean, Theodore, 1829–1879, 158, 535

McKee, Samuel, 195

McKee, William, 1815–1879, 399

McKeeby, Caroline Augusta Sampson (Mrs. Lemuel C.), 318

McKeeby, Charles Beard, 1858–, 318

McKeeby, Lemuel Clarke, 1825–1915, **318**

McKenney, Thomas J., 337

McKenny, Thomas Irving, 1830–1899, 124

McKenzie, Aimée Gilbert Leffingwell (Mrs. Kenneth), 299

McKenzie, Alexander, 519

Mackenzie, Alexander Slidell, 1803–1848, 162

McKenzie, David, 1833–1912, 279, 357, 535

Mackenzie, Donald, 1783–1851, 245, 396

McKenzie, Kenneth, 1797–1861, 263

McKenzie, Owen, 1826–1863, 246

McKibben, David B., 190, 443

McKinlay, Archibald, 1811–1891, 11, 153, 173, 188, 265, 331, 435, 477, 501–503

McKinlay, Sarah Julia (Mrs. Archibald), 502

McKinney, Samuel T., 84

McKinnon, John F., d. 1854, 291

McKinstry, Justus, d. 1897, 148, 309

McKissack, William M. D., d. 1849, 84

McKnight, hotel keeper, 19

McKowen, Samuel, 212

McLane, George Washington, d. 1880, 352

McLane, Louis, Jr., 205

McLaren, Robert Neill, d. 1886, 483

McLean, Donald, 501, 503

McLean, Hector H., 219

McLean, Mrs. Hector H., 219

McLean, S. A., 501

McLean, Captain W. H., 124

McLeod, John, 442

McLeod, Norman, 535

Maclin, Sackfield, 352

McLoughlin, John, 1784–1857, 6, 166, 173, 260, 263, 319–321, 331, 389, 501–503

McLure, C. C., 212

McMaster, James B., 1839–, 454

McMennomy, James B., 466

MacMillan, James, 268

McMillan, John H., 84

McMillen, James H., 1823–, 322

McMullin, Fayette, d. 1880, 190, 332

McNally, Christopher Hely, d. 1889, 148

McNamara, Broadwater, & Co.; see Broadwater, McNamara, & Co.

McNamara, Thomas, 212

McNamara, Thomas M., d. 1834, 202

McNassar, James, 99

McNeil, William, 136

McNeill, Henry C., 148

McNeill, William Henry, 478

McNutt, Elizabeth; see Strang, Elizabeth McNutt (Mrs. James Jesse)

McNutt, James Oscar, 447

McNutt, Lena, 447

Macomber, Clara Elizabeth Robison (Mrs. Frank G.), 1858–, 399

Macomber, Frank Gair, 399

McPherson, John, 501, 503

McPherson, Murdock, 356

McQuaide, James G., 212

McQuestion, V. B., 1829–, 454

McQuiston, David, 7

McRae, Alexander, 1807–1891, 279

McRae, Alexander, d. 1862, 148

McRae, John, 279

McRae, Joseph, 279

McRae, Kenneth, 279

McSorley, Edward, 1830–, 454

Mactavish, Dugald, 1817–1871, 172, 263, 443, 501, 504

Madison, James, 1750/51–1836, 13, 323

Magee, Matthew J., d. 1824, 15

Maginnis, Martin, 1841–1919, 454, 486

Maginnis Mining Co., 454

Magoffin, James Wiley, 1799–1868, 131, 148

Magone, Joseph, 337

Magraw, Samuel M., 361

Magraw, William M. F., 219, 279, 361, 535

Magruder, George A., 166

Maguire, Edward, d. 1892, 401

Maguire, Thomas A., 212

Maiben, Henry, 279

Maillet, Louis R., 1834–1906, 449, 453, 454

Mailliard, J. Ward, Jr., 54

Main [?], Frank P., 399

Purse, William A., 212
Purviance, Eliza (Mrs. John S.), 391
Purviance, M. C., 391
Purviance, Marsh J., 391
Purviance, Marth, 391
Putnam, Haldimand Sumner, *d.* 1863, 428
Pyle, James M., 116

Quadra, Juan Francisco Bodega y; *see* Bodega y Quadra, Juan Francisco
Quaife, Milo Milton, 1880–, 447
Quallawowt, Snoqualmie Indian, 289, 477
Quantrill, William Clarke, 1837–1865, 352
Quarles, William, 202
Quartz Miners' Convention, 87
Queen Charlotte Islands, 261, 271, 497
Quesnelle, J. B., 454
Quiemuth, Nisqually chief, 224
Quimper, Manuel, 402
Quinlan, John J., 454
Quinn, James H., 84
Quinton, Amelia Stone (Mrs. Richard), 243
Quiros y Miranda, Fernando Bernardo, 12
Quivey, Addison M., 454

Rabbeson, Antonio B., 1824–, 431
Race, Ira, 466
Ractier, Eli, 459
Rader, C. T., 454
Raffety, Dr. C. H., 337
Ragan, Abraham B., 201
Railey, M. H., 138
Railroads, Washington, 344, 507
Rainey, William, 212
Rainier, Peter, 1741 ?–1808, 392
Rains, Gabriel Jones, 1803–1881, 201, 332
Raipe, William W., 454
Raleigh, Alonzo Hazeltine, 1818–1901, 78, 157, 357
Raleigh & Clarke, 454

Ralston, J. R., 321
Rambo, Leander, 529, 530
Ramsey, Alexander, 1815–1903, 173, 454
Rand, William M., 336
Randall, George Maxwell, 1810–1873, 108, 373
Randall, M. P., 212
Randall, William M., 175
Randle, C., 144
Randolph, John Field, *d.* 1880, 201
Randolph, Murray W., 201
Ranken, William B., 175
Rankins, Anthony, 202
Ransom, E. D., 447
Ransom, William, 213
Rathbun, Dan, 336
Raunseiler [?], William, 447
Rawn, Charles Cotesworth, *d.* 1887, 171
Rawson, Thomas, 466
Ray, Alexander, 212
Ray, Charles A., 195
Ray, James M., 399
Raymond, John Baldwin, 1844–1886, 195
Rayner, Kenneth, 1808–1884, 195
Raynolds, William Franklin, 1820–1894, 393
Raynor, James O., 173, 394
Razee, Lewis, 447
Read, Mrs. Eleanor, 411
Reading, Pierson Barton, 1816–1868, 205, 309
Reams, John T., 399
Rector, Volney, 1836–, 395
Rector, William Henry, *ca.* 1806–, 395
Red Cloud, 1822–1909, 32, 63, 377, 483
Red Elk, Snake Indian, 341
Red River emigration, 503
Red River of the North, 241, 363, 396, 408
Redden, Return Jackson, 1817–1891, 156
Reddick, Captain, 131
Redfield, Alexander H., 397
Redfield, William C., 1789–1857, 132
Redington, Murray, 359
Reed, Major A. S., 454
Reed, Belle; *see* Robison, Belle Reed (Mrs. Joseph)

Designed by Carl Purington Rollins.

Set in Original Old Style.

Printed by Vail-Ballou Press, Inc.